ALWAYS LEARNING

Compiled by Darryl Smith • Clare Chua, Ph.D.

Business Statistics
Volume 2

Fourteenth Custom Edition for Ryerson University
Ted Rogers School of Management

Taken from:
Business Statistics, Seventh Edition
by David M. Levine, Kathryn A. Szabat, and David F. Stephan

Pearson Education, Inc., 330 Hudson Street, New York, New York 10013
A Pearson Education Company
www.pearsoned.com

Printed in the United States of America

1 2 3 4 5 6 7 8 9 10 XXXX 21 20 19 18

000200010272098797
000200010272161418

EEB/KS

ISBN 10: 1-323-91208-8
ISBN 13: 978-1-323-91208-9

Brief Contents

10 Confidence Interval Estimation 1

11 Fundamentals of Hypothesis Testing: One-Sample Tests 41

12 Hypothesis Testing: Two-Sample Tests 99

13 One-Way ANOVA 177

14 Chi-Square Tests 221

15 Simple Linear Regression 263

16 Multiple Regression 331

Appendices A–C 401

Self-Test Solutions and Answers to Selected Problems 431

Contents

10 Confidence Interval Estimation   1

USING STATISTICS: **Getting Estimates at Ricknel Home Centers** 1

10.1 Confidence Interval Estimate for the Mean (σ Known) 2
     Can You Ever Know the Population Standard Deviation? 9

10.2 Confidence Interval Estimate for the Mean (σ Unknown) 9
     Student's t Distribution 9
     Properties of the t Distribution 10
     The Concept of Degrees of Freedom 12
     The Confidence Interval Statement 12

10.3 Confidence Interval Estimate for the Proportion 16
     How to Find 90% Confidence Interval Estimate for the Population Proportion Using the Calculator 19

10.4 Determining Sample Size 20
     Sample Size Determination for the Mean 20
     Sample Size Determination for the Proportion 22

10.5 Confidence Interval Estimation and Ethical Issues 24

10.6 Bootstrapping 24

USING STATISTICS: **Getting Estimates at Ricknel Home Centers, Revisited** 25

SUMMARY 25
REFERENCES 25
KEY EQUATIONS 26
KEY TERMS 26
CHECKING YOUR UNDERSTANDING 26
PROBLEMS 28

CASES FOR CHAPTER 10   35
     Managing Ashland MultiComm Services 35
     Digital Case 36
     Sure Value Convenience Stores 36
     CardioGood Fitness 37
     More Descriptive Choices Follow-Up 37
     Clear Mountain State Student Surveys 37
CHAPTER 10 CASIO CALCULATOR GUIDE 38
     Calculator Lesson 8 38

11 Fundamentals of Hypothesis Testing: One-Sample Tests   41

USING STATISTICS: **Significant Testing at Oxford Cereals** 41

11.1 Fundamentals of Hypothesis-Testing Methodology 42
     The Null and Alternative Hypotheses 42
     The Critical Value of the Test Statistic 43

Regions of Rejection and Nonrejection 44
     Risks in Decision Making Using Hypothesis Testing 45
     Z Test for the Mean (σ Known) 48
     Hypothesis Testing Using the Critical Value Approach 49
     How to Find Z_{STAT} and Z Critical Value Using the Calculator? 52
     Hypothesis Testing Using the p-Value Approach 53
     How to Find p-value with the Calculator? 57
     A Connection Between Confidence Interval Estimation and Hypothesis Testing 58

11.2 t Test of Hypothesis for the Mean (σ Unknown) 59
     The Critical Value Approach 59
     The p-Value Approach 62
     Checking the Normality Assumption 63

11.3 One-Tail Tests 64
     The Critical Value Approach 64
     The p-Value Approach 67
     To Find t Critical Value Using the Calculator 70

11.4 Z Test of Hypothesis for the Proportion 71
     The Critical Value Approach 71
     To Find z Critical Value Using the Calculator 73
     The p-Value Approach 73
     Determining the p-Value for a One-tail Test Using the Calculator 74
     To Find z Critical Value Using the Calculator 76

11.5 Potential Hypothesis-Testing Pitfalls and Ethical Issues 77
     Statistical Significance Versus Practical Significance 77
     Statistical *Insignificance* Versus Importance 78
     Reporting of Findings 78
     Ethical Issues 78

USING STATISTICS: **Significant Testing at Oxford Cereals, Revisited** 78

SUMMARY 79
REFERENCES 79
KEY EQUATIONS 79
KEY TERMS 80
CHECKING YOUR UNDERSTANDING 80
PROBLEMS 80

CASES FOR CHAPTER 11   87
     Managing Ashland MultiComm Services 87
     Digital Case 87
     Sure Value Convenience Stores 87
CHAPTER 11 CASIO CALCULATOR GUIDE 88
     Calculator Lesson 9A 88
     Calculator Lesson 9B 90
     Calculator Lesson 10A 93
     Calculator Lesson 10B 94
     Calculator Lesson 11A 96
     Calculator Lesson 11B 97

12 Hypothesis Testing: Two-Sample Tests   99

USING STATISTICS: **For North Fork, Are There Different Means to the Ends?** 99

12.1 Comparing the Means of Two Independent Populations 101
- Pooled-Variance t Test for the Difference Between Two Means 101
- How to Run the Pooled-variance t Test with a FX-9750GI Calculator 108
- Confidence Interval Estimate for the Difference Between Two Means 109
- t Test for the Difference Between Two Means, Assuming Unequal Variances 110

12.2 Comparing the Means of Two Related Populations 119
- Paired t Test 121
- How to Run the "Paired" t Test with a FX-9750GII Calculator 124
- How to Find t Critical Value Using Calculator? 125
- How to Run the "Paired" t Test with a FX-9750GII Calculator 128
- How to Find t Critical Value Using a Calculator? 129
- Confidence Interval Estimate for the Mean Difference 129
- How to Run a Paired-samples t-test with SPSS Version 25 130

12.3 Comparing the Proportions of Two Independent Populations 135
- Z Test for the Difference Between Two Proportions 135
- How to Run a z Test for Two Proportions with a FX-9750GII Calculator 139
- Confidence Interval Estimate for the Difference Between Two Proportions 141

12.4 F Test for the Ratio of Two Variances 141
- How to Run the F Test with a FX-9750GII Calculator 147
- How to Find F Critical Value Using a Calculator 147

USING STATISTICS: **For North Fork, Are There Different Means to the Ends? Revisited** 148

SUMMARY 148
REFERENCES 150
KEY EQUATIONS 150
KEY TERMS 150
CHECKING YOUR UNDERSTANDING 151
PROBLEMS 151

CASES FOR CHAPTER 12 156
- Managing Ashland MultiComm Services 156
- Digital Case 157
- Sure Value Convenience Stores 158
- CardioGood Fitness 158
- More Descriptive Choices Follow-Up 158
- Clear Mountain State Student Surveys 159
CHAPTER 12 CASIO CALCULATOR GUIDE 160
- Calculator Lesson 12A 160
- Calculator Lesson 12B 162
- Calculator Lesson 13A 165
- Calculator Lesson 13B 167
- Calculator Lesson 14A 169
- Calculator Lesson 14B 169
APPENDIX 12.1 SPSS—VERSION 15 LESSON 3 171

13 One-Way ANOVA   177

13.1 One-Way ANOVA 178
- F Test for Differences Among More Than Two Means 180
- How to Run the One-way ANOVA With a FX-9750GII Calculator 183
- How to Find F Critical Value Using Calculator 185
- One-Way ANOVA F Test Assumptions 186
- Levene Test for Homogeneity of Variance 187
- Multiple Comparisons: The Tukey-Kramer Procedure with SPSS 191
- How to Run the Tukey-Kramer Procedure with SPSS 193
- SPSS GUIDE– VERSION 21 – ANOVA 195

13.2 Effect Size 202
SUMMARY 202
REFERENCES 203
KEY EQUATIONS 204
KEY TERMS 204
CHECKING YOUR UNDERSTANDING 204
PROBLEMS 204

CASES FOR CHAPTER 13 209
- Managing Ashland MultiComm Services 209
- Digital Case 210
- Sure Value Convenience Stores 210
- CardioGood Fitness 211
- More Descriptive Choices Follow-Up 211
- Clear Mountain State Student Surveys 211
CHAPTER 13 CASIO CALCULATOR GUIDE 212
- Calculator Lesson 15A 212
- Calculator Lesson 15B 213
SPSS—VERSION 16—ANOVA 214

14 Chi-Square Tests   221

USING STATISTICS: **Avoiding Guesswork About Resort Guests** 221

14.1 Chi-Square Test for the Difference Between Two Proportions 222
- How to Calculate the Expected Frequency by Hand 225
- How to Find χ^2 Critical Value Using Calculator 227
- How to Run the Chi-Square Test with a FX-9750GII Calculator 229

14.2 Chi-Square Test for Differences Among More Than Two Proportions 231
- How to Find χ^2_{STAT} Test Statistic Using Calculator 235
- How to Find χ^2 Critical Value Using Calculator 237

14.3 Chi-Square Test of Independence 238
- How to Find χ^2_{STAT} Test Statistic Using Calculator 242
- How to Find χ^2 Critical Value Using Calculator 244

USING STATISTICS: **Avoiding Guesswork About Resort Guests, Revisited** 245

SUMMARY 246

REFERENCES 246

KEY EQUATIONS 247

KEY TERMS 247

CHECKING YOUR UNDERSTANDING 247

PROBLEMS 247

CASES FOR CHAPTER 14 252

    Managing Ashland MultiComm Services 252

    Digital Case 253

    CardioGood Fitness 253

    Clear Mountain State Student Surveys 254

CHAPTER 14 CASIO CALCULATOR GUIDE 255

    Calculator Lesson 16A 255

    Calculator Lesson 16B 257

    Calculator Lesson 17A 259

    Calculator Lesson 17B 261

15 Simple Linear Regression   263

USING STATISTICS: **Knowing Customers at Sunflowers Apparel** 263

15.1 Types of Regression Models 264

    Simple Linear Regression Models 265

15.2 Determining the Simple Linear Regression Equation 266

    How to Create a Scatter Plot Using Casio Calculator FX-9750GII 267

    The Least-Squares Method 268

    Predictions in Regression Analysis: Interpolation Versus Extrapolation 270

    How to Find Prediction Value Using the Calculator 271

    Computing the Y Intercept, b_0, and the Slope, b_1 272

    How to Compute the Y Intercept, b_0 and the Slope, b_1, for the Sunflowers Apparel data 274

15.3 Measures of Variation 276

    Computing the Sum of Squares 277

    The Coefficient of Determination 278

    Standard Error of the Estimate 280

15.4 Assumptions of Regression 282

15.5 Residual Analysis 282

    Evaluating the Assumptions 283

15.6 Measuring Autocorrelation: The Durbin-Watson Statistic 285

    Residual Plots to Detect Autocorrelation 285

    The Durbin-Watson Statistic 287

15.7 Inferences About the Slope and Correlation Coefficient 289

    t Test for the Slope 289

    How to Find t Critical Value Using Calculator 291

    F Test for the Slope 291

    How to Find F Critical Value Using Calculator 293

    Confidence Interval Estimate for the Slope 293

    t Test for the Correlation Coefficient 294

    How to Run t-test For the Slope with the Casio Calculator 296

15.8 Estimation of Mean Values and Prediction of Individual Values 297

    The Confidence Interval Estimate for the Mean Response 297

    The Prediction Interval for an Individual Response 299

15.9 Potential Pitfalls in Regression 300

USING STATISTICS: **Knowing Customers at Sunflowers Apparel, Revisited** 303

SUMMARY 303

REFERENCES 304

KEY EQUATIONS 305

KEY TERMS 306

CHECKING YOUR UNDERSTANDING 306

PROBLEMS 306

CASES FOR CHAPTER 15 317

    Managing Ashland MultiComm Services 317

    Digital Case 317

    Brynne Packaging 317

CHAPTER 15 CASIO CALCULATOR GUIDE 319

    Calculator Lesson 18A 319

    Calculator Lesson 18B 322

CHAPTER 15 SPSS GUIDE 326

16 Multiple Regression   331

USING STATISTICS: **The Multiple Effects of OmniPower Bars** 331

16.1 Developing a Multiple Regression Model 332

    Interpreting the Regression Coefficients 333

    Predicting the Dependent Variable Y 335

16.2 r^2, Adjusted r^2, and the Overall F Test 336

    Coefficient of Multiple Determination 336

    Adjusted r^2 337

    Test for the Significance of the Overall Multiple Regression Model 338

    How to Find F Critical Value Using the Calculator 339

16.3 Residual Analysis for the Multiple Regression Model 340

16.4 Inferences Concerning the Population Regression Coefficients 347

    Tests of Hypothesis 347

    How to Find t Critical Value Using Calculator 348

    Confidence Interval Estimation 350

16.5 Using Dummy Variables and Interaction Terms in Regression Models 351

    Dummy Variables 351

    Interactions 353

MULTIPLE REGRESSION PRACTICE QUESTIONS 355

USING STATISTICS: **The Multiple Effects of OmniPower Bars, Revisited** 381

SUMMARY 381

REFERENCES 381

KEY EQUATIONS 383

KEY TERMS 383

CHECKING YOUR UNDERSTANDING 383

PROBLEMS 383

CASES FOR CHAPTER 16 392
      Managing Ashland MultiComm Services 392
      Digital Case 392
CHAPTER 16 SPSS GUIDE 393

Appendices 401

A. Basic Math Concepts and Symbols 402
    A.1   Rules for Arithmetic Operations 402
    A.2   Rules for Algebra: Exponents and
          Square Roots 402
    A.3   Rules for Logarithms 403
    A.4   Summation Notation 404
    A.5   Statistical Symbols 407
    A.6   Greek Alphabet 407
B. Online Resources 409
    B.1   About the Online Resources for This Book 409
    B.2   Accessing the Online Resources 409

B.3   Details of Downloadable Files 409
B.4   PHStat 414
C. Tables 415
    C.1   Table of Random Numbers 415
    C.2   The Cumulative Standardized Normal
          Distribution 417
    C.3   Critical Values of t 419
    C.4   Critical Values of χ^2 421
    C.5   Critical Values of F 422
    C.6   Critical Values of the Studentized Range, Q 426
    C.7   Critical Values, d_L and d_U, of the Durbin-Watson
          Statistic, D (Critical Values Are One-Sided) 428
    C.8   Control Chart Factors 429
    C.9   The Standardized Normal Distribution 430

Self-Test Solutions and Answers to Selected Problems 431

Confidence Interval Estimation

CONTENTS

10.1 Confidence Interval Estimate for the Mean (σ Known)

10.2 Confidence Interval Estimate for the Mean (σ Unknown)

10.3 Confidence Interval Estimate for the Proportion

10.4 Determining Sample Size

10.5 Confidence Interval Estimation and Ethical Issues

10.6 Bootstrapping (*online*)

USING STATISTICS: Getting Estimates at Ricknel Home Centers, Revisited

CHAPTER 10 CASIO CALCULATOR GUIDE

OBJECTIVES

Construct and interpret confidence interval estimates for the mean and the proportion

Determine the sample size necessary to develop a confidence interval estimate for the mean or proportion

USING STATISTICS

Getting Estimates at Ricknel Home Centers

As a member of the AIS team at Ricknel Home Centers (see Chapter 6), you have already examined the probability of discovering questionable, or "tagged," invoices. Now you have been assigned the task of auditing the accuracy of the integrated inventory management and point of sale component of the firm's retail management system.

You could review the contents of each and every inventory and transactional record to check the accuracy of this system, but such a detailed review would be time-consuming and costly. Could you use statistical inference techniques to reach conclusions about the population of all records from a relatively small sample collected during an audit? At the end of each month, you could select a sample of the sales invoices to estimate population parameters such as

- The mean dollar amount listed on the sales invoices for the month
- The proportion of invoices that contain errors that violate the internal control policy of the warehouse

If you used a sampling technique, how accurate would the results from the sample be? How would you use the results you generate? How could you be certain that the sample size is large enough to give you the information you need?

Mangostock/Shutterstock

I n Section 8.4, you used the Central Limit Theorem and knowledge of the population distribution to determine the percentage of sample means that are within certain distances of the population mean. For instance, in the cereal-filling example used throughout Chapter 8, you can conclude that 95% of all sample means are between 362.12 and 373.88 grams. This is an example of *deductive* reasoning because the conclusion is based on taking something that is true in general (for the population) and applying it to something specific (the sample means).

Getting the results that Ricknel Home Centers needs requires *inductive* reasoning. Inductive reasoning lets you use some specifics to make broader generalizations. You cannot guarantee that the broader generalizations are absolutely correct, but with a careful choice of the specifics and a rigorous methodology, you can reach useful conclusions. As a Ricknel accountant, you need to use inferential statistics, which uses sample results (the "some specifics") to *estimate* (the making of "broader generalizations") unknown population parameters such as a population mean or a population proportion. Note that statisticians use the word *estimate* in the same sense of the everyday usage: something you are reasonably certain about but cannot flatly say is absolutely correct.

You estimate population parameters by using either point estimates or interval estimates. A **point estimate** is the value of a single sample statistic, such as a sample mean. A **confidence interval estimate** is a range of numbers, called an *interval*, constructed around the point estimate. The confidence interval is constructed such that the probability that the interval includes the population parameter is known.

Suppose you want to estimate the mean GPA of all the students at your university. The mean GPA for all the students is an unknown population mean, denoted by μ. You select a sample of students and compute the sample mean, denoted by $\overline{X}$, to be 2.80. As a *point estimate* of the population mean, μ, you ask how accurate is the 2.80 value as an estimate of the population mean, μ? By taking into account the variability from sample to sample (see Section 7.2, concerning the sampling distribution of the mean), you can construct a confidence interval estimate for the population mean to answer this question.

When you construct a confidence interval estimate, you indicate the confidence of correctly estimating the value of the population parameter, μ. This allows you to say that there is a specified confidence that μ is somewhere in the range of numbers defined by the interval.

After studying this chapter, you might find that a 95% confidence interval for the mean GPA at your university is $2.75 \leq \mu \leq 2.85$. You can interpret this interval estimate by stating that you are 95% confident that the mean GPA at your university is between 2.75 and 2.85.

In this chapter, you learn to construct a confidence interval for both the population mean and population proportion. You also learn how to determine the sample size that is necessary to construct a confidence interval of a desired width.

10.1 Confidence Interval Estimate for the Mean (σ Known)

In Section 8.4, you used the Central Limit Theorem and knowledge of the population distribution to determine the percentage of sample means that are within certain distances of the population mean. Suppose that in the cereal-filling example you wished to estimate the population mean, using the information from a single sample. Thus, rather than taking $\mu \pm (1.96)(\sigma/\sqrt{n})$ to find the upper and lower limits around μ, as in Section 7.2, you substitute the sample mean, $\overline{X}$, for the unknown μ and use $\overline{X} \pm (1.96)(\sigma/\sqrt{n})$ as an interval to estimate the unknown μ. Although in practice you select a single sample of n values and compute the mean, $\overline{X}$, in order to understand the full meaning of the interval estimate, you need to examine a hypothetical set of all possible samples of n values.

> **Student Tip**
> Remember, the confidence interval is for the population mean not the sample mean.

Suppose that a sample of $n = 25$ cereal boxes has a mean of 362.3 grams and a standard deviation of 15 grams. The interval developed to estimate μ is $362.3 \pm (1.96)(15)/(\sqrt{25})$, or 362.3 ± 5.88. The estimate of μ is

$$356.42 \leq \mu \leq 368.18$$

Because the population mean, μ (equal to 368), is included within the interval, this sample results in a correct statement about μ (see Figure 10.1).

FIGURE 10.1

Confidence interval estimates for five different samples of $n = 25$ taken from a population where $\mu = 368$ and $\sigma = 15$

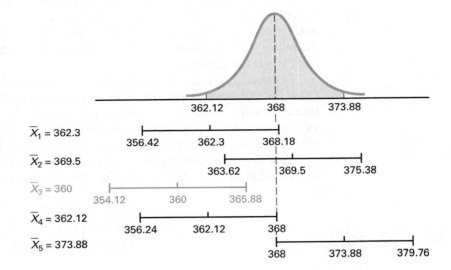

To continue this hypothetical example, suppose that for a different sample of $n = 25$ boxes, the mean is 369.5. The interval developed from this sample is

$$369.5 \pm (1.96)(15)/(\sqrt{25})$$

or 369.5 ± 5.88. The estimate is

$$363.62 \le \mu \le 375.38$$

Because the population mean, μ (equal to 368), is also included within this interval, this statement about μ is correct.

Now, before you begin to think that correct statements about μ are always made by developing a confidence interval estimate, suppose a third hypothetical sample of $n = 25$ boxes is selected and the sample mean is equal to 360 grams. The interval developed here is $360 \pm (1.96)(15)/(\sqrt{25})$, or 360 ± 5.88. In this case, the estimate of μ is

$$354.12 \le \mu \le 365.88$$

This estimate is *not* a correct statement because the population mean, μ, is not included in the interval developed from this sample (see Figure 10.1). Thus, for some samples, the interval estimate for μ is correct, but for others it is incorrect. In practice, only one sample is selected, and because the population mean is unknown, you cannot determine whether the interval estimate is correct. To resolve this, you need to determine the proportion of samples producing intervals that result in correct statements about the population mean, μ. To do this, consider two other hypothetical samples: the case in which $\overline{X} = 362.12$ grams and the case in which $\overline{X} = 373.88$ grams. If $\overline{X} = 362.12$, the interval is $362.12 \pm (1.96)(15)/(\sqrt{25})$, or 362.12 ± 5.88. This leads to the following interval:

$$356.24 \le \mu \le 368.00$$

Because the population mean of 368 is at the upper limit of the interval, the statement is correct (see Figure 10.1).

When $\overline{X} = 373.88$, the interval is $373.88 \pm (1.96)(15)/(\sqrt{25})$, or 373.88 ± 5.88. The interval estimate for the mean is

$$368.00 \le \mu \le 379.76$$

In this case, because the population mean of 368 is included at the lower limit of the interval, the statement is correct.

In Figure 10.1, you see that when the sample mean falls somewhere between 362.12 and 373.88 grams, the population mean is included *somewhere* within the interval. In Example 8.4 in Chapter 8, you found that 95% of the sample means are between 362.12 and 373.88 grams. Therefore, 95% of all samples of $n = 25$ boxes have sample means that will result in intervals that include the population mean.

Because, in practice, you select only one sample of size n, and μ is unknown, you never know for sure whether your specific interval includes the population mean. However, if you take all possible samples of n and compute their 95% confidence intervals, 95% of the intervals will include the population mean, and only 5% of them will not. In other words, you have 95% confidence that the population mean is somewhere in your interval.

Consider once again the first sample discussed in this section. A sample of $n = 25$ boxes had a sample mean of 362.3 grams. The interval constructed to estimate μ is

$$362.3 \pm (1.96)(15)/(\sqrt{25})$$
$$362.3 \pm 5.88$$
$$356.42 \leq \mu \leq 368.18$$

The interval from 356.42 to 368.18 is referred to as a *95% confidence interval*. The following contains an interpretation of the interval that most business professionals will understand. (For a technical discussion of different ways to interpret confidence intervals, see reference 4.)

"I am 95% confident that the mean amount of cereal in the population of boxes is somewhere between 356.42 and 368.18 grams."

To help you understand the meaning of the confidence interval, consider the order-filling process at a website. Filling orders consists of several steps, including receiving an order, picking the parts of the order, checking the order, packing, and shipping the order. The file **Order** contains the time, in minutes, to fill orders for a population of $N = 200$ orders on a recent day. Although in practice the population characteristics are rarely known, for this population of orders, the mean, μ, is known to be equal to 69.637 minutes; the standard deviation, σ, is known to be equal to 10.411 minutes; and the population is normally distributed. To illustrate how the sample mean and sample standard deviation can vary from one sample to another, 20 different samples of $n = 10$ were selected from the population of 200 orders, and the sample mean and sample standard deviation (and other statistics) were calculated for each sample. Figure 10.2 shows these results.

FIGURE 10.2

Sample statistics and 95% confidence intervals for 20 samples of $n = 10$ randomly selected from the population of $N = 200$ orders

Sample	n	Mean	Std Dev	Minimum	Median	Maximum	Range	95% Conf. Int.
S01	10	74.15	13.39	56.10	76.85	97.70	41.60	(67.70, 80.60)
S02	10	61.10	10.60	46.80	61.35	79.50	32.70	(54.65, 67.55)
S03	10	74.36	6.50	62.50	74.50	84.00	21.50	(67.91, 80.81)
S04	10	70.40	12.80	47.20	70.95	84.00	36.80	(63.95, 76.85)
S05	10	62.18	10.85	47.10	59.70	84.00	36.90	(55.73, 68.63)
S06	10	67.03	9.68	51.10	69.60	83.30	32.20	(60.58, 73.48)
S07	10	69.03	8.81	56.60	68.85	83.70	27.10	(62.58, 75.48)
S08	10	72.30	11.52	54.20	71.35	87.00	32.80	(65.85, 78.75)
S09	10	68.18	14.10	50.10	69.95	86.20	36.10	(61.73, 74.63)
S10	10	66.67	9.08	57.10	64.65	86.10	29.00	(60.22, 73.12)
S11	10	72.42	9.76	59.60	74.65	86.10	26.50	(65.97, 78.87)
S12	10	76.26	11.69	50.10	80.60	87.00	36.90	(69.81, 82.71)
S13	10	65.74	12.11	47.10	62.15	86.10	39.00	(59.29, 72.19)
S14	10	69.99	10.97	51.00	73.40	84.60	33.60	(63.54, 76.44)
S15	10	75.76	8.60	61.10	75.05	87.80	26.70	(69.31, 82.21)
S16	10	67.94	9.19	56.70	67.70	87.80	31.10	(61.49, 74.39)
S17	10	71.05	10.48	50.10	71.15	86.20	36.10	(64.60, 77.50)
S18	10	71.68	7.96	55.60	72.35	82.60	27.00	(65.23, 78.13)
S19	10	70.97	9.83	54.40	70.05	84.00	30.20	(64.52, 77.42)
S20	10	74.48	8.80	62.00	76.25	85.70	23.70	(68.03, 80.93)

From Figure 10.2, you can see the following:

- The sample statistics differ from sample to sample. The sample means vary from 61.10 to 76.26 minutes, the sample standard deviations vary from 6.50 to 14.10 minutes, the sample medians vary from 59.70 to 80.60 minutes, and the sample ranges vary from 21.50 to 41.60 minutes.
- Some of the sample means are greater than the population mean of 69.637 minutes, and some of the sample means are less than the population mean.
- Some of the sample standard deviations are greater than the population standard deviation of 10.411 minutes, and some of the sample standard deviations are less than the population standard deviation.
- The variation in the sample ranges is much more than the variation in the sample standard deviations.

The variation of sample statistics from sample to sample is called *sampling error*. **Sampling error** is the variation that occurs due to selecting a single sample from the population. The size of the sampling error is primarily based on the amount of variation in the population and on the sample size. Large samples have less sampling error than small samples, but large samples cost more to select.

The last column of Figure 10.2 contains 95% confidence interval estimates of the population mean order-filling time, based on the results of those 20 samples of $n = 10$. Begin by examining the first sample selected. The sample mean is 74.15 minutes, and the interval estimate for the population mean is 67.70 to 80.60 minutes. In a typical study, you would not know for sure whether this interval estimate is correct because you rarely know the value of the population mean. However, for this example *concerning the order-filling times*, the population mean is known to be 69.637 minutes. If you examine the interval 67.70 to 80.60 minutes, you see that the population mean of 69.637 minutes is located *between* these lower and upper limits. Thus, the first sample provides a correct estimate of the population mean in the form of an interval estimate. Looking over the other 19 samples, you see that similar results occur for all the other samples *except* for samples 2, 5, and 12. For each of the intervals generated (other than samples 2, 5, and 12), the population mean of 69.637 minutes is located *somewhere* within the interval.

For sample 2, the sample mean is 61.10 minutes, and the interval is 54.65 to 67.55 minutes; for sample 5, the sample mean is 62.18, and the interval is between 55.73 and 68.63; for sample 12, the sample mean is 76.26, and the interval is between 69.81 and 82.71 minutes. The population mean of 69.637 minutes is *not* located within any of these intervals, and the estimate of the population mean made using these intervals is incorrect. Although 3 of the 20 intervals did not include the population mean, if you had selected all the possible samples of $n = 10$ from a population of $N = 200$, 95% of the intervals would include the population mean.

In some situations, you might want a higher degree of confidence of including the population mean within the interval (such as 99%). In other cases, you might accept less confidence (such as 90%) of correctly estimating the population mean. In general, the **level of confidence** is symbolized by $(1 - \alpha) \times 100\%$, where α is the proportion in the tails of the distribution that is outside the confidence interval. The proportion in the upper tail of the distribution is $\alpha/2$, and the proportion in the lower tail of the distribution is $\alpha/2$. You use Equation (10.1) to construct a $(1 - \alpha) \times 100\%$ confidence interval estimate for the mean with σ known.

CONFIDENCE INTERVAL FOR THE MEAN (σ KNOWN)

$$\overline{X} \pm Z_{\alpha/2} \frac{\sigma}{\sqrt{n}}$$

or

$$\overline{X} - Z_{\alpha/2} \frac{\sigma}{\sqrt{n}} \leq \mu \leq \overline{X} + Z_{\alpha/2} \frac{\sigma}{\sqrt{n}} \tag{10.1}$$

where

$Z_{\alpha/2}$ is the value corresponding to an upper-tail probability of $\alpha/2$ from the standardized normal distribution (i.e., a cumulative area of $1 - \alpha/2$).

The value of $Z_{\alpha/2}$ needed for constructing a confidence interval is called the **critical value** for the distribution. 95% confidence corresponds to an α value of 0.05. The critical Z value corresponding to a cumulative area of 0.975 is 1.96 because there is 0.025 in the upper tail of the distribution, and the cumulative area less than $Z = 1.96$ is 0.975.

There is a different critical value for each level of confidence, $1 - \alpha$. A level of confidence of 95% leads to a Z value of 1.96 (see Figure 10.3). 99% confidence corresponds to an α value of 0.01. The Z value is approximately 2.58 because the upper-tail area is 0.005 and the cumulative area less than $Z = 2.58$ is 0.995 (see Figure 10.4).

FIGURE 10.3

Normal curve for determining the Z value needed for 95% confidence

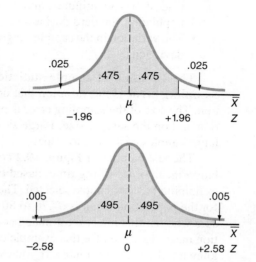

FIGURE 10.4

Normal curve for determining the Z value needed for 99% confidence

Now that various levels of confidence have been considered, why not make the confidence level as close to 100% as possible? Before doing so, you need to realize that any increase in the level of confidence is achieved only by widening (and making less precise) the confidence interval. There is no "free lunch" here. You would have more confidence that the population mean is within a broader range of values; however, this might make the interpretation of the confidence interval less useful. The trade-off between the width of the confidence interval and the level of confidence is discussed in greater depth in the context of determining the sample size in Section 10.4. Example 10.1 illustrates the application of the confidence interval estimate.

FIGURE 10.5

Using Casio Calculator to Determine the Z-Value for 99% Confidence

To find the Z-value associated with 99% confidence (i.e., probability = 0.99), mean = 0, and standard deviation = 1, follow these calculator steps:

Select **STAT F5**(DIST) **F1**(NORM) **F3**(InvN) **F2**(Var). Then select the following options.

Inverse Normal
Data   : **Variable**
Tail   : **CNTR (F3)**
Area   : **0.99**
σ : 1
μ : 0
Save Res : **None**
Execute
Now press **EXE** or **F1**(CALC).

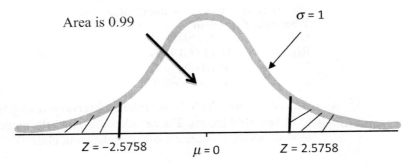

Area is 0.99

$\sigma = 1$

$Z = -2.5758$ $\mu = 0$ $Z = 2.5758$

The calculator will show the results:

Inverse Normal

X1Inv $= -2.5758293$

X2Inv $= 2.5758293$

EXAMPLE 10.1

Estimating the Mean Paper Length with 95% Confidence

A paper manufacturer has a production process that operates continuously throughout an entire production shift. The paper is expected to have a mean length of 11 inches, and the standard deviation of the length is 0.02 inch. At periodic intervals, a sample is selected to determine whether the mean paper length is still equal to 11 inches or whether something has gone wrong in the production process to change the length of the paper produced. You select a random sample of 100 sheets, and the mean paper length is 10.998 inches. Construct a 95% confidence interval estimate for the population mean paper length.

SOLUTION Using Equation (10.1) on page 5, with $Z_{\alpha/2} = 1.96$ for 95% confidence,

$$\overline{X} \pm Z_{\alpha/2}\frac{\sigma}{\sqrt{n}} = 10.998 \pm (1.96)\frac{0.02}{\sqrt{100}}$$

$$= 10.998 \pm 0.0039$$

$$10.9941 \leq \mu \leq 11.0019$$

Thus, with 95% confidence, you conclude that the population mean is between 10.9941 and 11.0019 inches. Because the interval includes 11, the value indicating that the production process is working properly, you have no reason to believe that anything is wrong with the production process.

FIGURE 10.6

Casio Calculator Instruction

Refer to Example 10.1: Construct a 95% confidence interval estimate for the population mean paper length. Use $\overline{X} = 10.998$, $\sigma = 0.02$, and $n = 100$.

To find the confidence interval for the population mean associated with a known population standard deviation, follow these calculator steps:

Select **STAT F4**(INTR) **F1**(Z) **F1**(1-S). Then select the following options.

(Note: Use the **EXE** key only after a new data entry. Otherwise, use the cursor ▼ arrow. If you accidentally hit the wrong key, use **AC/ON** or **EXIT** to go back.)

1-Sample zInterval

Data	: **F2(Var)**	▼
C-Level	: **0.95**	**EXE**
σ	: **0.02**	**EXE**
$\overline{x}$	: **10.998**	**EXE**
n	: **100**	**EXE**
Save Res	: None	

Now press **EXE** or **F1**(Calc).

The calculator will show the results:
1-Sample ZInterval
Left	= 10.9940801
Right	= 11.0019199
$\bar{x}$	= 10.998
n	= 100

As you can see, the 95% confidence interval estimate for the population mean is 10.9940801 to 11.0019199 inches. The calculator displays the numerical result only; you must remember to write up the complete answer as shown in class.

Example 10.2 illustrates the effect of using a 99% confidence interval. A 99 percent confidence interval would be wider than a 95 percent confidence interval.

EXAMPLE 10.2

Estimating the Mean Paper Length with 99% Confidence

Construct a 99% confidence interval estimate for the population mean paper length.

SOLUTION Using Equation (10.1) on page 5, with $Z_{\alpha/2} = 2.58$ for 99% confidence,

$$\bar{X} \pm Z_{\alpha/2}\frac{\sigma}{\sqrt{n}} = 10.998 \pm (2.58)\frac{0.02}{\sqrt{100}}$$

$$= 10.998 \pm 0.00516$$

$$10.9928 \leq \mu \leq 11.0032$$

Once again, because 11 is included within this wider interval, you have no reason to believe that anything is wrong with the production process.

FIGURE 10.7

Casio Calculator Instruction

Refer to Example 10.2: Construct a 99% confidence interval estimate for the population mean paper length. Use $\bar{X} = 10.998$, $\sigma = 0.02$, and $n = 100$.

To find the confidence interval for the population mean associated with a known population standard deviation, follow these calculator steps:

Select **STAT F4**(INTR) **F1**(Z) **F1**(1-S). Then select the following options.

(Note: Use the **EXE** key only after a new data entry. Otherwise, use the cursor ▼ arrow. If you accidentally hit the wrong key, use **AC/ON** or **EXIT** to go back.)

1-Sample zInterval
Data	: F2(Var)	▼
C-Level	: 0.99	EXE
σ	: 0.02	EXE
$\bar{x}$	: 10.998	EXE
n	: 100	EXE
Save Res	: None	

Now press **EXE** or **F1**(Calc).

The calculator will show the results:

1-Sample zInterval
Left	= 10.9928483
Right	= 11.0031517
$\bar{x}$	= 10.998
n	= 100

As you can see, the 99% confidence interval estimate for the population mean is 10.9928483 to 11.0031517 inches. The calculator displays the numerical result only; you must remember to write up the complete answer as shown in class.

As discussed in Section 8.2, the sampling distribution of the sample mean, $\overline{X}$, is normally distributed if the population for your characteristic of interest, X, follows a normal distribution. And if the population of X does not follow a normal distribution, the Central Limit Theorem almost always ensures that $\overline{X}$ is approximately normally distributed when n is large. However, when dealing with a small sample size and a population that does not follow a normal distribution, the sampling distribution of $\overline{X}$ is not normally distributed, and therefore the confidence interval discussed in this section is inappropriate. In practice, however, as long as the sample size is large enough and the population is not very skewed, you can use the confidence interval defined in Equation (10.1) to estimate the population mean when σ is known. To assess the assumption of normality, you can evaluate the shape of the sample data by constructing a histogram, stem-and-leaf display, boxplot, or normal probability plot.

Can You Ever Know the Population Standard Deviation?

Student Tip
Because understanding the confidence interval concept is very important when reading the rest of this book, review this section carefully to understand the underlying concept—even if you never have a practical reason to use the confidence interval estimate of the mean (σ known) method.

To solve Equation (10.1), you must know the value for σ, the population standard deviation. To know σ implies that you know all the values in the entire population. (How else would you know the value of this population parameter?) If you knew all the values in the entire population, you could directly compute the population mean. There would be no need to use the *inductive* reasoning of inferential statistics to *estimate* the population mean. In other words, if you know σ, you really do not have a need to use Equation (10.1) to construct a confidence interval estimate of the mean (σ known).

More significantly, in virtually all real-world business situations, you would never know the standard deviation of the population. In business situations, populations are often too large to examine all the values. So why study the confidence interval estimate of the mean (σ known) at all? This method serves as an important introduction to the concept of a confidence interval because it uses the normal distribution, which has already been thoroughly discussed in Chapters 7 and 8. In the next section, you will see that constructing a confidence interval estimate when σ is not known requires another distribution (the t distribution) not previously mentioned in this book.

10.2 Confidence Interval Estimate for the Mean (σ Unknown)

In the previous section, you learned that in most business situations, you do not know σ, the population standard deviation. This section discusses a method of constructing a confidence interval estimate of μ that uses the sample statistic S as an estimate of the population parameter σ.

Student's t Distribution

At the start of the twentieth century, William S. Gosset was working at Guinness in Ireland, trying to help brew better beer less expensively (see reference 5). As he had only small samples to study, he needed to find a way to make inferences about means without having to know σ. Writing under the pen name "Student,"[1] Gosset solved this problem by developing what today is known as the **Student's t distribution**, or the t distribution.

If the variable X is normally distributed, then the following statistic:

[1]Guinness considered all research conducted to be proprietary and a trade secret. The firm prohibited its employees from publishing their results. Gosset circumvented this ban by using the pen name "Student" to publish his findings.

$$t = \frac{\overline{X} - \mu}{\dfrac{S}{\sqrt{n}}}$$

has a t distribution with $n - 1$ **degrees of freedom**. This expression has the same form as the Z statistic in Equation (8.4) on Chapter 8, except that S is used to estimate the unknown σ.

Properties of the *t* Distribution

The *t* distribution is very similar in appearance to the standardized normal distribution. Both distributions are symmetrical and bell-shaped, with the mean and the median equal to zero. However, because *S* is used to estimate the unknown σ, the values of *t* are more variable than those for *Z*. Therefore, the *t* distribution has more area in the tails and less in the center than does the standardized normal distribution (see Figure 10.8).

FIGURE 10.8

Standardized normal distribution and *t* distribution for 5 degrees of freedom

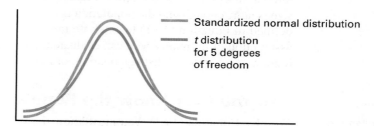

Standardized normal distribution

t distribution for 5 degrees of freedom

The degrees of freedom, $n - 1$, are directly related to the sample size, *n*. The concept of *degrees of freedom* is discussed further on page 12. As the sample size and degrees of freedom increase, *S* becomes a better estimate of σ, and the *t* distribution gradually approaches the standardized normal distribution, until the two are virtually identical. With a sample size of about 120 or more, *S* estimates σ closely enough so that there is little difference between the *t* and *Z* distributions.

As stated earlier, the *t* distribution assumes that the variable *X* is normally distributed. In practice, however, when the sample size is large enough and the population is not very skewed, in most cases you can use the *t* distribution to estimate the population mean when σ is unknown. When dealing with a small sample size and a skewed population distribution, the confidence interval estimate may not provide a valid estimate of the population mean. To assess the assumption of normality, you can evaluate the shape of the sample data by constructing a histogram, stem-and-leaf display, boxplot, or normal probability plot. However, the ability of any of these graphs to help you evaluate normality is limited when you have a small sample size.

You find the critical values of *t* for the appropriate degrees of freedom from the table of the *t* distribution (see Table E.3). The columns of the table present the most commonly used cumulative probabilities and corresponding upper-tail areas. The rows of the table represent the degrees of freedom. The critical *t* values are found in the cells of the table. For example, with 99 degrees of freedom, if you want 95% confidence, you find the appropriate value of *t*, as shown in Table 10.1. The 95% confidence level means that 2.5% of the values (an area of

TABLE 10.1

Determining the Critical Value from the *t* Table for an Area of 0.025 in Each Tail with 99 Degrees of Freedom

	Cumulative Probabilities					
	.75	.90	.95	.975	.99	.995
	Upper-Tail Areas					
Degrees of Freedom	.25	.10	.05	.025	.01	.005
1	1.0000	3.0777	6.3138	12.7062	31.8207	63.6574
2	0.8165	1.8856	2.9200	4.3027	6.9646	9.9248
3	0.7649	1.6377	2.3534	3.1824	4.5407	5.8409
4	0.7407	1.5332	2.1318	2.7764	3.7469	4.6041
5	0.7267	1.4759	2.0150	2.5706	3.3649	4.0322
⋮	⋮	⋮	⋮	⋮	⋮	⋮
96	0.6771	1.2904	1.6609	1.9850	2.3658	2.6280
97	0.6770	1.2903	1.6607	1.9847	2.3654	2.6275
98	0.6770	1.2902	1.6606	1.9845	2.3650	2.6269
99	0.6770	1.2902	1.6604	1.9842	2.3646	2.6264
100	0.6770	1.2901	1.6602	1.9840	2.3642	2.6259

Source: Extracted from Table E.3.

0.025) are in each tail of the distribution. Looking in the column for a cumulative probability of 0.975 and an upper-tail area of 0.025 in the row corresponding to 99 degrees of freedom gives you a critical value for t of 1.9842 (see Figure 10.9). Because t is a symmetrical distribution with a mean of 0, if the upper-tail value is +1.9842, the value for the lower-tail area (lower 0.025) is −1.9842. A t value of −1.9842 means that the probability that t is less than −1.9842 is 0.025, or 2.5%.

FIGURE 10.9

t distribution with 99 degrees of freedom

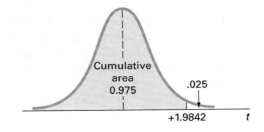

Note that for a 95% confidence interval, you will always have a cumulative probability of 0.975 and an upper-tail area of 0.025. Similarly, for a 99% confidence interval, you will have 0.995 and 0.005, and for a 90% confidence interval you will have 0.95 and 0.05.

FIGURE 10.10

Casio Calculator Model fx-9750GII Instruction

Question: Determine the t critical value using the calculator for an area of 0.025 in each tail with 99 degrees of freedom (df = 99).

To determine the t critical value(s), follow these calculator steps:

Select **STAT F5**(DIST) **F2**(t) **F3**(Invt) **F2**(Var). Then select the following options.

Inverse Normal
Data   : **Variable**
Area   : **0.025**
df   : **99**
Save Res : **None**
Execute

Now press **EXE** or **F1**(CALC).

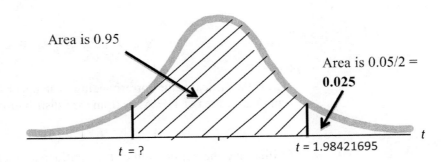

The calculator will show the result:

Inverse Normal
XInv = 1.98421695

The calculator gives you an upper-tail value of 1.98421695. The value for the lower-tail area (lower 0.025) is −1.98421695 because the t-distribution is symmetrical.

Answer: The critical values for a 95% confidence interval with df = 99 are −1.98421695 and 1.98421695.

The Concept of Degrees of Freedom

In Chapter 4, you learned that the numerator of the sample variance, S^2 requires the computation of the sum of squares around the sample mean:

$$\sum_{i=1}^{n}(X_i - \overline{X})^2$$

In order to compute S^2, you first need to know $\overline{X}$. Therefore, only $n - 1$ of the sample values are free to vary. This means that you have $n - 1$ degrees of freedom. For example, suppose a sample of five values has a mean of 20. How many values do you need to know before you can determine the remainder of the values? The fact that $n = 5$ and $\overline{X} = 20$ also tells you that

$$\sum_{i=1}^{n}X_i = 100$$

because

$$\frac{\sum_{i=1}^{n}X_i}{n} = \overline{X}$$

Thus, when you know four of the values, the fifth one is *not* free to vary because the sum must be 100. For example, if four of the values are 18, 24, 19, and 16, the fifth value must be 23, so that the sum is 100.

The Confidence Interval Statement

Equation (10.2) defines the $(1 - \alpha) \times 100\%$ confidence interval estimate for the mean with σ unknown.

CONFIDENCE INTERVAL FOR THE MEAN (σ UNKNOWN)

$$\overline{X} \pm t_{\alpha/2}\frac{S}{\sqrt{n}}$$

or

$$\overline{X} - t_{\alpha/2}\frac{S}{\sqrt{n}} \le \mu \le \overline{X} + t_{\alpha/2}\frac{S}{\sqrt{n}} \tag{10.2}$$

where

$t_{\alpha/2}$ is the critical value corresponding to an upper-tail probability of $\alpha/2$ (i.e., a cumulative area of $1 - \alpha/2$) from the t distribution with $n - 1$ degrees of freedom.

To illustrate the application of the confidence interval estimate for the mean when the standard deviation is unknown, recall the Ricknel Home Centers scenario presented on page 1. Using the DCOVA steps first discussed on Getting Started, you define the variable of interest as the dollar amount listed on the sales invoices for the month. Your business objective is to estimate the mean dollar amount. Then you collect the data by selecting a sample of 100 sales invoices from the population of sales invoices during the month. Once you have collected the data, you organize the data in a worksheet. You can construct various graphs (not shown here) to better visualize the distribution of the dollar amounts. To analyze the data, you compute the sample mean of the 100 sales invoices to be equal to $110.27 and the sample standard deviation to be equal to $28.95. For 95% confidence, the critical value from the t distribution (as shown in Table 10.1 on page 10) is 1.9842. Using Equation (10.2),

$$\overline{X} \pm t_{\alpha/2}\frac{S}{\sqrt{n}}$$

$$= 110.27 \pm (1.9842)\frac{28.95}{\sqrt{100}}$$

$$= 110.27 \pm 5.74$$

$$104.53 \le \mu \le 116.01$$

Figure 10.11 presents this confidence interval estimate of the mean dollar amount as computed by CASIO Calculator.

FIGURE 10.11

Calculator input and results for the confidence interval estimate for the mean sales invoice amount worksheet for the Ricknel Home Centers example

From the **Main Menu**, select the following:

STAT F4(INTR) **F2**(t) **F1**(1-S). Then enter the following items:

1-Sample tInterval
Data	: F2(Var)	▼
C-Level	: 0.95	EXE
$\overline{x}$	: 110.27	EXE
sx	: 28.95	EXE
n	: 100	EXE
Save Res	: None	

Now press **EXE** or **F1**(Calc).

The calculator will show the results:

1-Sample tInterval
Left	= 104.525692
Right	= 116.014308
$\overline{x}$	= 110.27
sx	= 28.95
n	= 100

The 95% confidence interval is $104.525692 \le \mu \le 116.014308$

Thus, with 95% confidence, you conclude that the mean amount of all the sales invoices is between \$104.53 and \$116.01. The 95% confidence level indicates that if you selected all possible samples of 100 (something that is never done in practice), 95% of the intervals developed would include the population mean somewhere within the interval. The validity of this confidence interval estimate depends on the assumption of normality for the distribution of the amount of the sales invoices. With a sample of 100, the normality assumption is not overly restrictive, and the use of the t distribution is likely appropriate. Example 10.3 further illustrates how you construct the confidence interval for a mean when the population standard deviation is unknown.

EXAMPLE 10.3

Estimating the Mean Processing Time of Life Insurance Applications

An insurance company has the business objective of reducing the amount of time it takes to approve applications for life insurance. The approval process consists of underwriting, which includes a review of the application, a medical information bureau check, possible requests for additional medical information and medical exams, and a policy compilation stage in which the policy pages are generated and sent for delivery. Using the DCOVA steps, you define the variable of interest as the total processing time in days. You collect the data by selecting a random sample of 27 approved policies during a period of one month. You organize the data collected in a worksheet. Table 10.2 lists the total processing time, in days, which are stored in Insurance . To analyze the data, you need to construct a 95% confidence interval estimate for the population mean processing time.

(continued)

TABLE 10.2													
Processing Time for Life Insurance Applications	73	19	16	64	28	28	31	90	60	56	31	56	22	18
	45	48	17	17	17	91	92	63	50	51	69	16	17

SOLUTION To visualize the data, you construct a boxplot of the processing time, as displayed in Figure 10.12, and a normal probability plot, as shown in Figure 10.13. To analyze the data, you construct the confidence interval estimate shown in Figure 10.14.

FIGURE 10.12

Excel and Minitab boxplots for the processing time for life insurance applications

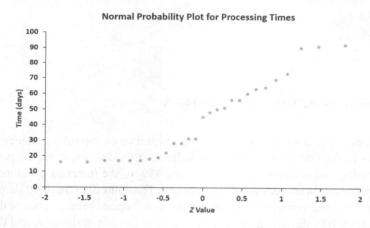
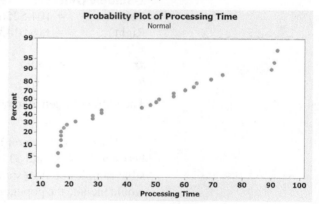

FIGURE 10.13

Excel and Minitab normal probability plots for the processing time for life insurance applications

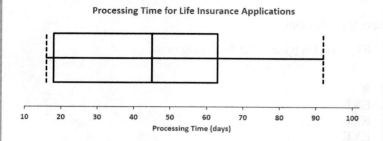
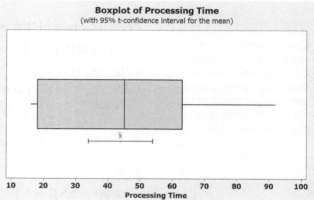

FIGURE 10.14

Using Casio Calculator to find the confidence interval estimates for the mean processing time worksheet for life insurance applications

To find the confidence interval for population mean, associated with unknown population standard deviation, follow these calculator steps:

From the **Main Menu** select **STAT**

Enter the data given on page 14 into **List 1**

Now, from the **STAT mode** select:

F4(INTR) **F2**(t) **F1**(1-S) then enter the following items:

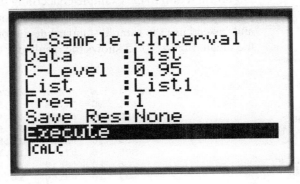

Now press **EXE** or **F1**(Calc)

The calculator will now show the results:

The calculator result shows the 95% confidence interval estimate for the population mean as between 33.8870613 (Left) and 53.8907165 (Right) days. The calculator shows the numerical result only. You must remember to write up the complete answer as shown in class.

Figure 10.14 shows that the sample mean is $\overline{X} = 43.89$ days and the sample standard deviation is $S = 25.28$ days. Using Equation (10.2) on page 12 to construct the confidence interval, you need to determine the critical value from the t table, using the row for 26 degrees of freedom. For 95% confidence, you use the column corresponding to an upper-tail area of 0.025 and a cumulative probability of 0.975. From Table E.3, you see that $t_{\alpha/2} = 2.0555$. Thus, using $\overline{X} = 43.89$, $S = 25.28$, $n = 27$, and $t_{\alpha/2} = 2.0555$,

$$\overline{X} \pm t_{\alpha/2}\frac{S}{\sqrt{n}}$$

$$= 43.89 \pm (2.0555)\frac{25.28}{\sqrt{27}}$$

$$= 43.89 \pm 10.00$$

$$33.89 \le \mu \le 53.89$$

You conclude with 95% confidence that the mean processing time for the population of life insurance applications is between 33.89 and 53.89 days. The validity of this confidence interval estimate depends on the assumption that the processing time is normally distributed. From the boxplot displayed in Figure 10.12 and the normal probability plot shown in Figure 10.13, the processing time appears right-skewed. Thus, although the sample size is close to 30, you would have some concern about the validity of this confidence interval in estimating the population mean processing time. The concern is that a 95% confidence interval based on a small sample from a skewed distribution will contain the population mean less than 95% of the time in repeated sampling. In the case of small sample sizes and skewed distributions, you might consider the sample median as an estimate of central tendency and construct a confidence interval for the population median (see reference 2).

The interpretation of the confidence interval when σ is unknown is the same as when σ is known. To illustrate the fact that the confidence interval for the mean varies more when σ is unknown, return to the example concerning the order-filling times discussed in Section 10.1 on pages 4 and 5. Suppose that, in this case, you do *not* know the population standard deviation and instead use the sample standard deviation to construct the confidence interval estimate of the mean. Figure 10.15 shows the results for each of 20 samples of $n = 10$ orders.

FIGURE 10.15

Confidence interval estimates of the mean for 20 samples of $n = 10$ randomly selected from the population of $N = 200$ orders with σ unknown

Sample	N	Mean	Std Dev	SE Mean	95% Conf. Int.
S01	10	71.64	7.58	2.40	(66.22, 77.06)
S02	10	67.22	10.95	3.46	(59.39, 75.05)
S03	10	67.97	14.83	4.69	(57.36, 78.58)
S04	10	73.90	10.59	3.35	(66.33, 81.47)
S05	10	67.11	11.12	3.52	(59.15, 75.07)
S06	10	68.12	10.83	3.43	(60.37, 75.87)
S07	10	65.80	10.85	3.43	(58.03, 73.57)
S08	10	77.58	11.04	3.49	(69.68, 85.48)
S09	10	66.69	11.45	3.62	(58.50, 74.88)
S10	10	62.55	8.58	2.71	(56.41, 68.69)
S11	10	71.12	12.82	4.05	(61.95, 80.29)
S12	10	70.55	10.52	3.33	(63.02, 78.08)
S13	10	65.51	8.16	2.58	(59.67, 71.35)
S14	10	64.90	7.55	2.39	(59.50, 70.30)
S15	10	66.22	11.21	3.54	(58.20, 74.24)
S16	10	70.43	10.21	3.23	(63.12, 77.74)
S17	10	72.04	6.25	1.96	(67.57, 76.51)
S18	10	73.91	11.29	3.57	(65.83, 81.99)
S19	10	71.49	9.76	3.09	(64.51, 78.47)
S20	10	70.15	10.84	3.43	(62.39, 77.91)

In Figure 10.15, observe that the standard deviation of the samples varies from 6.25 (sample 17) to 14.83 (sample 3). Thus, the width of the confidence interval developed varies from 8.94 in sample 17 to 21.22 in sample 3. Because you know that the population mean order time $\mu = 69.637$ minutes, you can see that the interval for sample 8 ($69.68 - 85.48$) and the interval for sample 10 ($56.41 - 68.69$) do not correctly estimate the population mean. All the other intervals correctly estimate the population mean. Once again, remember that in practice you select only one sample, and you are unable to know for sure whether your one sample provides a confidence interval that includes the population mean.

10.3 Confidence Interval Estimate for the Proportion

Student Tip

As noted in Chapter 8, do not confuse this use of the Greek letter pi, π, to represent the population proportion with the mathematical constant pi.

The concept of a confidence interval also applies to categorical data. With categorical data, you want to estimate the proportion of items in a population having a certain characteristic of interest. The unknown population proportion is represented by the Greek letter π. The point estimate for π is the sample proportion, $p = X/n$, where n is the sample size and X is the number of items in the sample having the characteristic of interest. Equation (10.3) defines the confidence interval estimate for the population proportion.

CONFIDENCE INTERVAL ESTIMATE FOR THE PROPORTION

$$p \pm Z_{\alpha/2}\sqrt{\frac{p(1-p)}{n}}$$

or

$$p - Z_{\alpha/2}\sqrt{\frac{p(1-p)}{n}} \le \pi \le p + Z_{\alpha/2}\sqrt{\frac{p(1-p)}{n}} \qquad \textbf{(10.3)}$$

where

$$p = \text{sample proportion} = \frac{X}{n} = \frac{\text{Number of items having the characteristic}}{\text{sample size}}$$

π = population proportion

$Z_{\alpha/2}$ = critical value from the standardized normal distribution

n = sample size

Note: To use this equation for the confidence interval, the sample size n must be large enough to ensure that both X and $n - X$ are greater than 5.

You can use the confidence interval estimate for the proportion defined in Equation (10.3) to estimate the proportion of sales invoices that contain errors (see the Ricknel Home Centers scenario on page 1). Using the DCOVA steps, you define the variable of interest as whether the invoice contains errors (yes or no). Then, you collect the data from a sample of 100 sales invoices. The results, which you organize and store in a worksheet, show that 10 invoices contain errors. To analyze the data, you compute, for these data, $p = X/n = 10/100 = 0.10$. Since both $X = 10$ and $n - X = 100 - 10 = 90$ are > 5, using Equation (10.3) and $Z_{\alpha/2} = 1.96$, for 95% confidence,

$$p \pm Z_{\alpha/2}\sqrt{\frac{p(1 - p)}{n}}$$

$$= 0.10 \pm (1.96)\sqrt{\frac{(0.10)(0.90)}{100}}$$

$$= 0.10 \pm (1.96)(0.03)$$

$$= 0.10 \pm 0.0588$$

$$0.0412 \leq \pi \leq 0.1588$$

Therefore, you have 95% confidence that the population proportion of all sales invoices containing errors is between 0.0412 and 0.1588. This means that you estimate that between 4.12% and 15.88% of all the sales invoices contain errors. Figure 10.16 shows a confidence interval estimate for this example by Casio Calculator.

FIGURE 10.16

Using the Casio Calculator to find the confidence interval estimates for the proportion of sales invoices that contain errors worksheet

To find the confidence interval for population proportion of in-error sales invoice, follow these calculator steps.

From the **Main Menu** select:

STAT F4(INTR) **F1**(z) **F3**(1-p) then enter the following items:

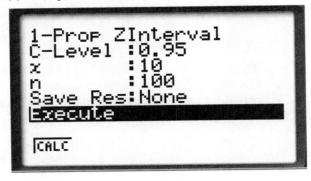

Now press **EXE** or **F1**(Calc)

The calculator will now show the results:

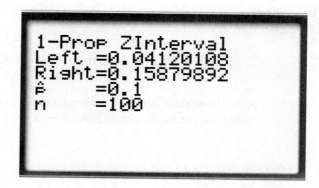

The 95% confidence interval is $0.04120108 \leq \pi \leq 0.15879892$.

Example 10.4 illustrates another application of a confidence interval estimate for the proportion.

EXAMPLE 10.4

Estimating the Proportion of Nonconforming Newspapers Printed

The operations manager at a large newspaper wants to estimate the proportion of newspapers printed that have a nonconforming attribute. Using the DCOVA steps, you define the variable of interest as whether the newspaper has excessive rub-off, improper page setup, missing pages, or duplicate pages. You collect the data by selecting a random sample of $n = 200$ newspapers from all the newspapers printed during a single day. You organize the results in a worksheet, which shows that 35 newspapers contain some type of nonconformance. To analyze the data, you need to construct and interpret a 90% confidence interval estimate for the proportion of newspapers printed during the day that have a nonconforming attribute.

SOLUTION Using Equation (10.3),

$$p = \frac{X}{n} = \frac{35}{200} = 0.175, \text{ and with a 90\% level of confidence } Z_{\alpha/2} = 1.645$$

$$p \pm Z_{\alpha/2}\sqrt{\frac{p(1-p)}{n}}$$

$$= 0.175 \pm (1.645)\sqrt{\frac{(0.175)(0.825)}{200}}$$

$$= 0.175 \pm (1.645)(0.0269)$$

$$= 0.175 \pm 0.0442$$

$$0.1308 \leq \pi \leq 0.2192$$

You conclude with 90% confidence that the population proportion of all newspapers printed that day with nonconformities is between 0.1308 and 0.2192. This means you estimate that between 13.08% and 21.92% of the newspapers printed on that day have some type of nonconformance.

How to Find 90% Confidence Interval Estimate for the Population Proportion Using the Calculator

Refer to Example 9.4, construct a 90% confidence interval estimate for the population proportion of newspapers printed during the day that have a nonconforming attribute.

To find the confidence interval for population proportion with a 90% level of confidence, follow these calculator steps:

STAT F4(INTR) **F1**(Z) **F3**(1-P) then enter the following items:

```
1-Prop ZInterval
C-Level :0.9
x       :35
n       :200
Save Res:None
Execute

CALC
```

Now key **EXE** or **F1**(Calc)

The calculator will now show the results:

```
1-Prop ZInterval
Left =0.13080651
Right=0.21919348
p̂    =0.175
n    =200
```

This shows that the 90% confidence interval estimate for the population proportion is 0.13080651 to 0.21919348. The calculator shows the numerical result only. You must remember to write up the complete answer as shown in class.

Equation (10.3) contains a Z statistic because you can use the normal distribution to approximate the binomial distribution when the sample size is sufficiently large. In Example 10.4, the confidence interval using Z provides an excellent approximation for the population proportion because both X and $n - X$ are greater than 5. However, if you do not have a sufficiently large sample size, you should use the binomial distribution rather than Equation (10.3) (see references 1, 3, and 9). The exact confidence intervals for various sample sizes and proportions of items of interest have been tabulated by Fisher and Yates (reference 3).

10.4 Determining Sample Size

In each confidence interval developed so far in this chapter, the sample size was reported along with the results, with little discussion of the width of the resulting confidence interval. In the business world, sample sizes are determined prior to data collection to ensure that the confidence interval is narrow enough to be useful in making decisions. Determining the proper sample size is a complicated procedure, subject to the constraints of budget, time, and the amount of acceptable sampling error. In the Ricknel Home Centers scenario, if you want to estimate the mean dollar amount of the sales invoices, you must determine in advance how large a sampling error to allow in estimating the population mean. You must also determine, in advance, the level of confidence (i.e., 90%, 95%, or 99%) to use in estimating the population parameter.

Sample Size Determination for the Mean

To develop an equation for determining the appropriate sample size needed when constructing a confidence interval estimate for the mean, recall Equation (10.1) on page 5:

$$\overline{X} \pm Z_{\alpha/2} \frac{\sigma}{\sqrt{n}}$$

The amount added to or subtracted from $\overline{X}$ is equal to half the width of the interval. This quantity represents the amount of imprecision in the estimate that results from sampling error.[2] The sampling error, e, is defined as

[2]In this context, some statisticians refer to e as the **margin of error**.

$$e = Z_{\alpha/2} \frac{\sigma}{\sqrt{n}}$$

Solving for n gives the sample size needed to construct the appropriate confidence interval estimate for the mean. "Appropriate" means that the resulting interval will have an acceptable amount of sampling error.

SAMPLE SIZE DETERMINATION FOR THE MEAN

The sample size, n, is equal to the product of the $Z_{\alpha/2}$ value squared and the standard deviation, σ, squared, divided by the square of the sampling error, e.

$$n = \frac{Z_{\alpha/2}^2 \sigma^2}{e^2} \qquad\qquad (10.4)$$

To compute the sample size, you must know three quantities:

[3]You use Z instead of t because, to determine the critical value of t, you need to know the sample size, but you do not know it yet. For most studies, the sample size needed is large enough that the standardized normal distribution is a good approximation of the t distribution.

- The desired confidence level, which determines the value of $Z_{\alpha/2}$, the critical value from the standardized normal distribution[3]
- The acceptable sampling error, e
- The standard deviation, σ

In some business-to-business relationships that require estimation of important parameters, legal contracts specify acceptable levels of sampling error and the confidence level required. For companies in the food and drug sectors, government regulations often specify sampling errors and confidence levels. In general, however, it is usually not easy to specify the three quantities needed to determine the sample size. How can you determine the level of confidence and sampling error? Typically, these questions are answered only by a subject matter expert (i.e., an individual very familiar with the variables under study). Although 95% is the most common confidence level used, if more confidence is desired, then 99% might be more appropriate; if less confidence is deemed acceptable, then 90% might be used. For the sampling error, you should think not of how much sampling error you would like to have (you really do not want any error) but of how much you can tolerate when reaching conclusions from the confidence interval.

In addition to specifying the confidence level and the sampling error, you need an estimate of the standard deviation. Unfortunately, you rarely know the population standard deviation, σ. In some instances, you can estimate the standard deviation from past data. In other situations, you can make an educated guess by taking into account the range and distribution of the variable. For example, if you assume a normal distribution, the range is approximately equal to 6σ (i.e., $\pm 3\sigma$ around the mean) so that you estimate σ as the range divided by 6. If you cannot estimate σ in this way, you can conduct a small-scale study and estimate the standard deviation from the resulting data.

To explore how to determine the sample size needed for estimating the population mean, consider again the audit at Ricknel Home Centers. In Section 10.2, you selected a sample of 100 sales invoices and constructed a 95% confidence interval estimate for the population mean sales invoice amount. How was this sample size determined? Should you have selected a different sample size?

Suppose that, after consulting with company officials, you determine that a sampling error of no more than $\pm\$5$ is desired, along with 95% confidence. Past data indicate that the standard deviation of the sales amount is approximately $25. Thus, $e = \$5, \sigma = \$25$, and $Z_{\alpha/2} = 1.96$ (for 95% confidence). Using Equation (10.4),

$$n = \frac{Z_{\alpha/2}^2 \sigma^2}{e^2} = \frac{(1.96)^2(25)^2}{(5)^2}$$
$$= 96.04$$

Because the general rule is to slightly oversatisfy the criteria by rounding the sample size up to the next whole integer, you should select a sample of size 97. Thus, the sample of size $n = 100$ used on page 12 is slightly more than what is necessary to satisfy the needs of the company, based on the estimated standard deviation, desired confidence level, and sampling error. Because the calculated sample standard deviation is slightly higher than expected, $28.95 compared to $25.00, the confidence interval is slightly wider than desired. Figure 10.17 shows a worksheet for determining the sample size.

FIGURE 10.17

Excel worksheet for determining the sample size for estimating the mean sales invoice amount for the Ricknel Home Centers example

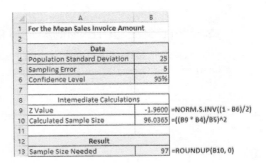

Example 10.5 illustrates another application of determining the sample size needed to develop a confidence interval estimate for the mean.

EXAMPLE 10.5

Determining the Sample Size for the Mean

Returning to Example 10.3 on page 13, suppose you want to estimate, with 95% confidence, the population mean processing time to within ± 4 days. On the basis of a study conducted the previous year, you believe that the standard deviation is 25 days. Determine the sample size needed.

SOLUTION Using Equation (10.4) on page 20 and $e = 4$, $\sigma = 25$, and $Z_{\alpha/2} = 1.96$ for 95% confidence,

$$n = \frac{Z_{\alpha/2}^2 \sigma^2}{e^2} = \frac{(1.96)^2 (25)^2}{(4)^2}$$
$$= 150.06$$

Therefore, you should select a sample of 151 applications because the general rule for determining sample size is to always round up to the next integer value in order to slightly oversatisfy the criteria desired. An actual sampling error slightly larger than 4 will result if the sample standard deviation calculated in this sample of 151 is greater than 25 and slightly smaller if the sample standard deviation is less than 25.

Sample Size Determination for the Proportion

So far in this section, you have learned how to determine the sample size needed for estimating the population mean. Now suppose that you want to determine the sample size necessary for estimating a population proportion.

To determine the sample size needed to estimate a population proportion, π, you use a method similar to the method for a population mean. Recall that in developing the sample size for a confidence interval for the mean, the sampling error is defined by

$$e = Z_{\alpha/2} \frac{\sigma}{\sqrt{n}}$$

When estimating a proportion, you replace σ with $\sqrt{\pi(1 - \pi)}$. Thus, the sampling error is

$$e = Z_{\alpha/2} \sqrt{\frac{\pi(1 - \pi)}{n}}$$

Solving for n, you have the sample size necessary to develop a confidence interval estimate for a proportion.

SAMPLE SIZE DETERMINATION FOR THE PROPORTION

The sample size n is equal to the product of $Z_{\alpha/2}$ squared, the population proportion, π, and 1 minus the population proportion, π, divided by the square of the sampling error, e.

$$n = \frac{Z_{\alpha/2}^2 \pi(1 - \pi)}{e^2} \tag{10.5}$$

To determine the sample size, you must know three quantities:

- The desired confidence level, which determines the value of $Z_{\alpha/2}$, the critical value from the standardized normal distribution
- The acceptable sampling error (or margin of error), e
- The population proportion, π

In practice, selecting these quantities requires some planning. Once you determine the desired level of confidence, you can find the appropriate $Z_{\alpha/2}$ value from the standardized normal distribution. The sampling error, e, indicates the amount of error that you are willing to tolerate in estimating the population proportion. The third quantity, π, is actually the population parameter that you want to estimate! Thus, how do you state a value for what you are trying to determine?

Here you have two alternatives. In many situations, you may have past information or relevant experience that provides an educated estimate of π. If you do not have past information or relevant experience, you can try to provide a value for π that would never *underestimate* the sample size needed. Referring to Equation (10.5), you can see that the quantity $\pi(1 - \pi)$ appears in the numerator. Thus, you need to determine the value of π that will make the quantity $\pi(1 - \pi)$ as large as possible. When $\pi = 0.5$, the product $\pi(1 - \pi)$ achieves its maximum value. To show this result, consider the following values of π, along with the accompanying products of $\pi(1 - \pi)$:

When $\pi = 0.9$, then $\pi(1 - \pi) = (0.9)(0.1) = 0.09$.

When $\pi = 0.7$, then $\pi(1 - \pi) = (0.7)(0.3) = 0.21$.

When $\pi = 0.5$, then $\pi(1 - \pi) = (0.5)(0.5) = 0.25$.

When $\pi = 0.3$, then $\pi(1 - \pi) = (0.3)(0.7) = 0.21$.

When $\pi = 0.1$, then $\pi(1 - \pi) = (0.1)(0.9) = 0.09$.

Therefore, when you have no prior knowledge or estimate for the population proportion, π, you should use $\pi = 0.5$ for determining the sample size. Using $\pi = 0.5$ produces the largest possible sample size and results in the narrowest and most precise confidence interval. This increased precision comes at the cost of spending more time and money for an increased sample size. Also, note that if you use $\pi = 0.5$ and the proportion is different from 0.5, you will overestimate the sample size needed, because you will get a confidence interval narrower than originally intended.

Returning to the Ricknel Home Centers scenario on page 1, suppose that the auditing procedures require you to have 95% confidence in estimating the population proportion of sales invoices with errors to within ± 0.07. The results from past months indicate that the largest proportion has been no more than 0.15. Thus, using Equation (10.5) with $e = 0.07$, $\pi = 0.15$, and $Z_{\alpha/2} = 1.96$ for 95% confidence,

$$n = \frac{Z_{\alpha/2}^2 \pi(1 - \pi)}{e^2}$$

$$= \frac{(1.96)^2(0.15)(0.85)}{(0.07)^2}$$

$$= 99.96$$

Because the general rule is to round the sample size up to the next whole integer to slightly oversatisfy the criteria, a sample size of 100 is needed. Thus, the sample size needed to satisfy the requirements of the company, based on the estimated proportion, desired confidence level, and sampling error, is equal to the sample size taken on page 16. The actual confidence interval is narrower than required because the sample proportion is 0.10, whereas 0.15 was used for π in Equation (10.5). Figure 10.18 shows a worksheet for determining the sample size.

FIGURE 10.18

Excel worksheet for determining sample size for estimating the proportion of in-error sales invoices for Ricknel Home Centers

	A	B	
1	For the Proportion of In-Error Sales Invoices		
2			
3	Data		
4	Estimate of True Proportion	0.15	
5	Sampling Error	0.07	
6	Confidence Level	95%	
7			
8	Intermediate Calculations		
9	Z Value	-1.9600	=NORM.S.INV((1 - B6) / 2)
10	Calculated Sample Size	99.9563	=(B9^2 * B4 * (1 - B4)) / B5^2
11			
12	Result		
13	Sample Size Needed	100	=ROUNDUP(B10, 0)

Example 10.6 provides another application of determining the sample size for estimating the population proportion.

EXAMPLE 10.6

Determining the Sample Size for the Population Proportion

You want to have 90% confidence of estimating the proportion of office workers who respond to email within an hour to within ±0.05. Because you have not previously undertaken such a study, there is no information available from past data. Determine the sample size needed.

SOLUTION Because no information is available from past data, assume that $\pi = 0.50$. Using Equation (10.5) on page 22 and $e = 0.05$, $\pi = 0.50$, and $Z_{a/2} = 1.645$ for 90% confidence,

$$n = \frac{Z_{\alpha/2}^2 \pi(1 - \pi)}{e^2}$$

$$= \frac{(1.645)^2(0.50)(0.50)}{(0.05)^2}$$

$$= 270.6$$

Therefore, you need a sample of 271 office workers to estimate the population proportion to within ±0.05 with 90% confidence.

10.5 Confidence Interval Estimation and Ethical Issues

The selection of samples and the inferences that accompany them raise several ethical issues. The major ethical issue concerns whether confidence interval estimates accompany point estimates. Failure to include a confidence interval estimate might mislead the user of the results into thinking that the point estimate is all that is needed to predict the population characteristic with certainty. Confidence interval limits (typically set at 95%), the sample size used, and an interpretation of the meaning of the confidence interval in terms that a person untrained in statistics can understand should always accompany point estimates.

When media outlets publicize the results of a political poll, they often overlook including this type of information. Sometimes, the results of a poll include the sampling error, but the sampling error is often presented in fine print or as an afterthought to the story being reported. A fully ethical presentation of poll results would give equal prominence to the confidence levels, sample size, sampling error, and confidence limits of the poll.

When you prepare your own point estimates, always state the interval estimate in a *prominent* place and include a brief explanation of the meaning of the confidence interval. In addition, make sure you highlight the sample size and sampling error.

10.6 Bootstrapping

The confidence interval estimation procedures discussed in this chapter make assumptions that are often not valid, especially for small samples. Bootstrapping, the selection of an initial sample and repeated sampling from that initial sample, provides an alternative approach that does not rely on those assumptions. The **Section 8.6 online topic** explains this alternative technique.

USING STATISTICS

Getting Estimates at Ricknel Home Centers, Revisited

Mangostock/Shutterstock

In the Ricknel Home Centers scenario, you were an accountant for a distributor of home improvement supplies in the northeastern United States. You were responsible for the accuracy of the integrated inventory management and sales information system. You used confidence interval estimation techniques to draw conclusions about the population of all records from a relatively small sample collected during an audit.

At the end of the month, you collected a random sample of 100 sales invoices and made the following inferences:

- With 95% confidence, you concluded that the mean amount of all the sales invoices is between $104.53 and $116.01.

- With 95% confidence, you concluded that between 4.12% and 15.88% of all the sales invoices contain errors.

These estimates provide an interval of values that you believe contain the true population parameters. If these intervals are too wide (i.e., the sampling error is too large) for the types of decisions Ricknel Home Centers needs to make, you will need to take a larger sample. You can use the sample size formulas in Section 10.4 to determine the number of sales invoices to sample to ensure that the size of the sampling error is acceptable.

SUMMARY

This chapter discusses confidence intervals for estimating the characteristics of a population, along with how you can determine the necessary sample size. You learned how to apply these methods to numerical and categorical data. Table 10.3 provides a list of topics covered in this chapter.

To determine what equation to use for a particular situation, you need to answer these questions:

- Are you constructing a confidence interval, or are you determining sample size?
- Do you have a numerical variable, or do you have a categorical variable?

The next three chapters develop a hypothesis-testing approach to making decisions about population parameters.

TABLE 10.3

Summary of Topics in Chapter 10

	TYPE OF DATA	
TYPE OF ANALYSIS	**Numerical**	**Categorical**
Confidence interval for a population parameter	Confidence interval estimate for the mean (Sections 10.1 and 10.2)	Confidence interval estimate for the proportion (Section 10.3)
Determining sample size	Sample size determination for the mean (Section 10.4)	Sample size determination for the proportion (Section 10.4)

REFERENCES

1. Cochran, W. G. *Sampling Techniques*, 3rd ed. New York: Wiley, 1977.
2. Daniel, W. W. *Applied Nonparametric Statistics*, 2nd ed. Boston: PWS Kent, 1990.
3. Fisher, R. A., and F. Yates. *Statistical Tables for Biological, Agricultural and Medical Research*, 5th ed. Edinburgh: Oliver & Boyd, 1957.
4. Hahn, G., and W. Meeker. *Statistical Intervals: A Guide for Practitioners*. New York: John Wiley and Sons, Inc., 1991.
5. Kirk, R. E., ed. *Statistical Issues: A Reader for the Behavioral Sciences*. Belmont, CA: Wadsworth, 1972.
6. Larsen, R. L., and M. L. Marx. *An Introduction to Mathematical Statistics and Its Applications*, 5th ed. Upper Saddle River, NJ: Prentice Hall, 2012.
7. *Microsoft Excel 2013*. Redmond, WA: Microsoft Corp., 2012.
8. *Minitab Release 16*. State College, PA: Minitab, Inc., 2010.
9. Snedecor, G. W., and W. G. Cochran. *Statistical Methods*, 7th ed. Ames, IA: Iowa State University Press, 1980.

KEY EQUATIONS

Confidence Interval for the Mean (σ Known)

$$\overline{X} \pm Z_{\alpha/2}\frac{\sigma}{\sqrt{n}}$$

or

$$\overline{X} - Z_{\alpha/2}\frac{\sigma}{\sqrt{n}} \leq \mu \leq \overline{X} + Z_{\alpha/2}\frac{\sigma}{\sqrt{n}} \qquad \textbf{(10.1)}$$

Confidence Interval for the Mean (σ Unknown)

$$\overline{X} \pm t_{\alpha/2}\frac{S}{\sqrt{n}}$$

or

$$\overline{X} - t_{\alpha/2}\frac{S}{\sqrt{n}} \leq \mu \leq \overline{X} + t_{\alpha/2}\frac{S}{\sqrt{n}} \qquad \textbf{(10.2)}$$

Confidence Interval Estimate for the Proportion

$$p \pm Z_{\alpha/2}\sqrt{\frac{p(1-p)}{n}}$$

or

$$p - Z_{\alpha/2}\sqrt{\frac{p(1-p)}{n}} \leq \pi \leq p + Z_{\alpha/2}\sqrt{\frac{p(1-p)}{n}} \quad \textbf{(10.3)}$$

Sample Size Determination for the Mean

$$n = \frac{Z_{\alpha/2}^2\, \sigma^2}{e^2} \qquad \textbf{(10.4)}$$

Sample Size Determination for the Proportion

$$n = \frac{Z_{\alpha/2}^2\, \pi(1-\pi)}{e^2} \qquad \textbf{(10.5)}$$

KEY TERMS

confidence interval estimate 2
critical value 6
degrees of freedom 9

level of confidence 5
margin of error 20
point estimate 2

sampling error 5
Student's t distribution 9

CHECKING YOUR UNDERSTANDING

10.1 Why can you never really have 100% confidence of correctly estimating the population characteristic of interest?

10.2 When should you use the t distribution to develop the confidence interval estimate for the mean?

10.3 Why is it true that for a given sample size, n, an increase in confidence is achieved by widening (and making less precise) the confidence interval?

10.4 Why is the sample size needed to determine the proportion smaller when the population proportion is 0.20 than when the population proportion is 0.50?

FLOWCHART FOR CONFIDENCE INTERVAL ESTIMATE

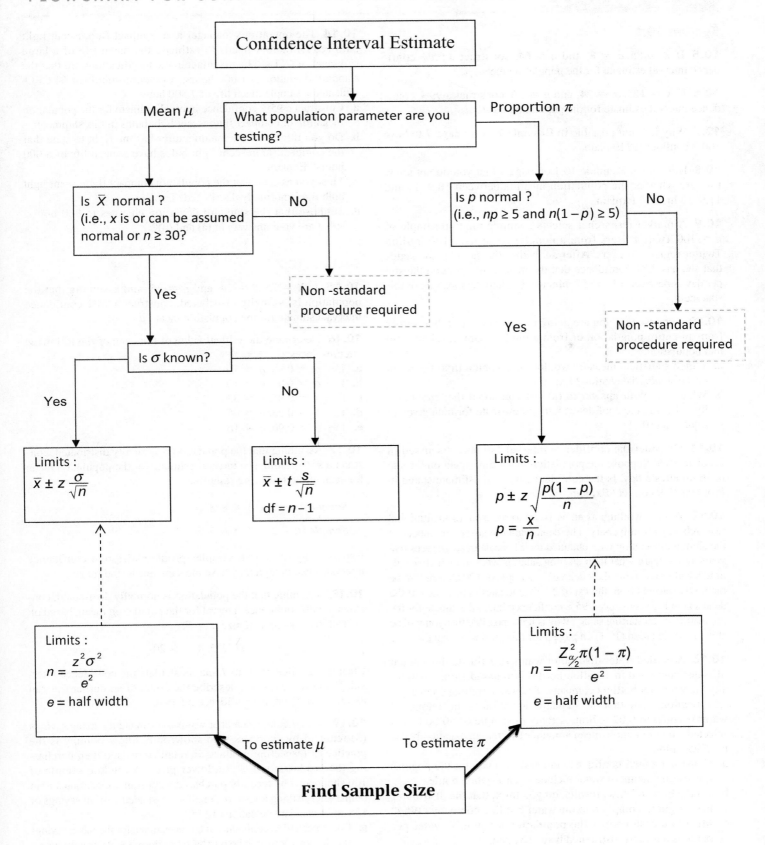

PROBLEMS

Section 10.1

10.5 If $\bar{X} = 85$, $\sigma = 8$, and $n = 64$, construct a 95% confidence interval estimate for the population mean, μ.

10.6 If $\bar{X} = 125$, $\sigma = 24$, and $n = 36$, construct a 99% confidence interval estimate for the population mean, μ.

10.7 Why is it not possible in Example 10.1 on page 7 to have 100% confidence? Explain.

10.8 Is it true in Example 10.1 on page 7 that you do not know for sure whether the population mean is between 10.9941 and 11.0019 inches? Explain.

10.9 A market researcher selects a simple random sample of $n = 100$ Twitter users from a population of over 100 million Twitter registered users. After analyzing the sample, she states that she has 95% confidence that the mean time spent on the site per day is between 15 and 57 minutes. Explain the meaning of this statement.

10.10 Suppose that you are going to collect a set of data, either from an entire population or from a random sample taken from that population.
a. Which statistical measure would you compute first: the mean or the standard deviation? Explain.
b. What does your answer to (a) tell you about the "practicality" of using the confidence interval estimate formula given in Equation (10.1)?

10.11 Consider the confidence interval estimate discussed in Problem 10.9. Suppose the population mean time spent on the site is 36 minutes a day. Is the confidence interval estimate stated in Problem 10.9 correct? Explain.

10.12 You are working as an assistant to the dean of institutional research at your university. The dean wants to survey members of the alumni association who obtained their baccalaureate degrees five years ago to learn what their starting salaries were in their first full-time job after receiving their degrees. A sample of 100 alumni is to be randomly selected from the list of 2,500 graduates in that class. If the dean's goal is to construct a 95% confidence interval estimate for the population mean starting salary, why is it not possible that you will be able to use Equation (10.1) on page 5 for this purpose? Explain.

10.13 A bottled water distributor wants to estimate the amount of water contained in 1-gallon bottles purchased from a nationally known water bottling company. The water bottling company's specifications state that the standard deviation of the amount of water is equal to 0.02 gallon. A random sample of 50 bottles is selected, and the sample mean amount of water per 1-gallon bottle is 0.995 gallon.
a. Construct a 99% confidence interval estimate for the population mean amount of water included in a 1-gallon bottle.
b. On the basis of these results, do you think that the distributor has a right to complain to the water bottling company? Why?
c. Must you assume that the population amount of water per bottle is normally distributed here? Explain.
d. Construct a 95% confidence interval estimate. How does this change your answer to (b)?

10.14 The operations manager at a compact fluorescent light bulb (CFL) factory needs to estimate the mean life of a large shipment of CFLs. The manufacturer's specifications are that the standard deviation is 1,000 hours. A random sample of 64 CFLs indicated a sample mean life of 7,500 hours.
a. Construct a 95% confidence interval estimate for the population mean life of compact fluorescent light bulbs in this shipment.
b. Do you think that the manufacturer has the right to state that the compact fluorescent light bulbs have a mean life of 8,000 hours? Explain.
c. Must you assume that the population compact fluorescent light bulb life is normally distributed? Explain.
d. Suppose that the standard deviation changes to 800 hours. What are your answers in (a) and (b)?

Section 10.2

10.15 If $\bar{X} = 75$, $S = 24$, and $n = 36$, and assuming that the population is normally distributed, construct a 95% confidence interval estimate for the population mean, μ.

10.16 Determine the critical value of t in each of the following circumstances:
a. $1 - \alpha = 0.95$, $n = 10$
b. $1 - \alpha = 0.99$, $n = 10$
c. $1 - \alpha = 0.95$, $n = 32$
d. $1 - \alpha = 0.95$, $n = 65$
e. $1 - \alpha = 0.90$, $n = 16$

10.17 Assuming that the population is normally distributed, construct a 95% confidence interval estimate for the population mean for each of the following samples:

    Sample A: 1 1 1 1 8 8 8 8

    Sample B: 1 2 3 4 5 6 7 8

Explain why these two samples produce different confidence intervals even though they have the same mean and range.

10.18 Assuming that the population is normally distributed, construct a 95% confidence interval for the population mean, based on the following sample of size $n = 7$:

    1 2 3 4 5 6 20

Change the value of 20 to 7 and recalculate the confidence interval. Using these results, describe the effect of an outlier (i.e., an extreme value) on the confidence interval.

10.19 A marketing researcher wants to estimate the mean savings ($) realized by shoppers who showroom. Showrooming is the practice of inspecting products in retail stores and then purchasing the products online at a lower price. A random sample of 100 shoppers who recently purchased a consumer electronics item online after making a visit to a retail store yielded a mean savings of $58 and a standard deviation of $55.
a. Construct a 95% confidence interval estimate for the mean savings for all showroomers who purchased a consumer electronics item.
b. Suppose the owners of a consumer electronics retailer wants to estimate the total value of lost sales attributed to the next

1,000 showroomers that enter their retail store. How are the results in (a) useful in assisting the consumer electronics retailer in their estimation?

10.20 A survey of nonprofit organizations showed that online fundraising has increased in the past year. Based on a random sample of 55 nonprofits, the mean one-time gift donation in the past year was $75, with a standard deviation of $9.
a. Construct a 95% confidence interval estimate for the population mean one-time gift donation.
b. Interpret the interval constructed in (a).

10.21 The U.S. Department of Transportation requires tire manufacturers to provide tire performance information on the sidewall of a tire to better inform prospective customers as they make purchasing decisions. One very important measure of tire performance is the tread wear index, which indicates the tire's resistance to tread wear compared with a tire graded with a base of 100. A tire with a grade of 200 should last twice as long, on average, as a tire graded with a base of 100. A consumer organization wants to estimate the actual tread wear index of a brand name of tires that claims "graded 200" on the sidewall of the tire. A random sample of $n = 18$ indicates a sample mean tread wear index of 195.3 and a sample standard deviation of 21.4.
a. Assuming that the population of tread wear indexes is normally distributed, construct a 95% confidence interval estimate for the population mean tread wear index for tires produced by this manufacturer under this brand name.
b. Do you think that the consumer organization should accuse the manufacturer of producing tires that do not meet the performance information provided on the sidewall of the tire? Explain.
c. Explain why an observed tread wear index of 210 for a particular tire is not unusual, even though it is outside the confidence interval developed in (a).

10.22 The file **FastFood** contains the amount that a sample of 15 customers spent for lunch ($) at a fast-food restaurant:

> 7.42 6.29 5.83 6.50 8.34 9.51 7.10 6.80 5.90
> 4.89 6.50 5.52 7.90 8.30 9.60

a. Construct a 95% confidence interval estimate for the population mean amount spent for lunch ($) at a fast-food restaurant, assuming a normal distribution.
b. Interpret the interval constructed in (a).

10.23 The file **Sedans** contains the overall miles per gallon (MPG) of 2014 midsized sedans:

> 38 26 30 26 25 27 24 22 27 32 39
> 26 24 24 23 24 25 31 26 37 22 33

Source: Data extracted from "Which Car Is Right for You," *Consumer Reports,* April 2014, pp. 40–41.

a. Construct a 95% confidence interval estimate for the population mean MPG of 2014 midsized sedans, assuming a normal distribution.
b. Interpret the interval constructed in (a).
c. Compare the results in (a) to those in Problem 10.24(a).

10.24 The file **SUV** contains the overall MPG of 2014 small SUVs:

> 26 22 23 21 25 24 22 26 25 22
> 21 21 22 22 23 24 23 22 21 22

Source: Data extracted from "Which Car Is Right for You," *Consumer Reports,* April 2014, pp. 60–61.

a. Construct a 95% confidence interval estimate for the population mean MPG of 2014 small SUVs, assuming a normal distribution.
b. Interpret the interval constructed in (a).
c. Compare the results in (a) to those in Problem 10.23(a).

10.25 Is there a difference in the yields of different types of investments? The file **CDRate** contains the yields for a one-year certificate of deposit (CD) and a five-year CD for 22 banks in the United States as of March 12, 2014. (Data extracted from **www.Bankrate.com**, March 12, 2014.)
a. Construct a 95% confidence interval estimate for the mean yield of one-year CDs.
b. Construct a 95% confidence interval estimate for the mean yield of five-year CDs.
c. Compare the results of (a) and (b).

10.26 One of the major measures of the quality of service provided by any organization is the speed with which the organization responds to customer complaints. A large family-held department store selling furniture and flooring, including carpet, had undergone a major expansion in the past several years. In particular, the flooring department had expanded from 2 installation crews to an installation supervisor, a measurer, and 15 installation crews. The store had the business objective of improving its response to complaints. The variable of interest was defined as the number of days between when the complaint was made and when it was resolved. Data were collected from 50 complaints that were made in the past year. The data, stored in **Furniture**, are as follows:

> 54 5 35 137 31 27 152   2 123 81 74 27
> 11 19 126 110 110 29 61 35 94 31 26 5
> 12 4 165 32 29 28 29 26 25 1 14 13
> 13 10   5 27   4 52 30 22 36 26 20 23
> 33 68

a. Construct a 95% confidence interval estimate for the population mean number of days between the receipt of a complaint and the resolution of the complaint.
b. What assumption must you make about the population distribution in order to construct the confidence interval estimate in (a)?
c. Do you think that the assumption needed in order to construct the confidence interval estimate in (a) is valid? Explain.
d. What effect might your conclusion in (c) have on the validity of the results in (a)?

10.27 A manufacturing company produces electric insulators. You define the variable of interest as the strength of the insulators. If the insulators break when in use, a short circuit is likely. To test the strength of the insulators, you carry out destructive testing to determine how much force is required to break the insulators. You measure force by observing how many pounds are applied to the insulator before it breaks. You collect the force data for 30 insulators selected for the experiment and organize and store these data in **Force**:

> 1,870 1,728 1,656 1,610 1,634 1,784 1,522 1,696
> 1,592 1,662 1,866 1,764 1,734 1,662 1,734 1,774
> 1,550 1,756 1,762 1,866 1,820 1,744 1,788 1,688
> 1,810 1,752 1,680 1,810 1,652 1,736

a. Construct a 95% confidence interval estimate for the population mean force.

b. What assumption must you make about the population distribution in order to construct the confidence interval estimate in (a)?

c. Do you think that the assumption needed in order to construct the confidence interval estimate in (a) is valid? Explain.

10.28 The file **Market Penetration** contains Facebook penetration values (the percentage of the country population that are Facebook users) for 22 of the world's largest economies:

> 56 57 43 55 42 35   7 25 42 17 43
>
>   6 31 28 59 20 27 36 45 80 57 56

Source: Data extracted from **slidesha.re/ODv6vG**.

a. Construct a 95% confidence interval estimate for the population mean Facebook penetration.

b. What assumption do you need to make about the population to construct the interval in (a)?

c. Given the data presented, do you think the assumption needed in (a) is valid? Explain.

10.29 One operation of a mill is to cut pieces of steel into parts that are used in the frame for front seats in an automobile. The steel is cut with a diamond saw, and the resulting parts must be cut to be within ± 0.005 inch of the length specified by the automobile company. The measurement reported from a sample of 100 steel parts (stored in **Steel**) is the difference, in inches, between the actual length of the steel part, as measured by a laser measurement device, and the specified length of the steel part. For example, the first observation, -0.002, represents a steel part that is 0.002 inch shorter than the specified length.

a. Construct a 95% confidence interval estimate for the population mean difference between the actual length of the steel part and the specified length of the steel part.

b. What assumption must you make about the population distribution in order to construct the confidence interval estimate in (a)?

c. Do you think that the assumption needed in order to construct the confidence interval estimate in (a) is valid? Explain.

d. Compare the conclusions reached in (a).

Section 10.3

10.30 If $n = 200$ and $X = 50$, construct a 95% confidence interval estimate for the population proportion.

10.31 If $n = 400$ and $X = 25$, construct a 99% confidence interval estimate for the population proportion.

10.32 A cellphone provider has the business objective of wanting to estimate the proportion of subscribers who would upgrade to a new cellphone with improved features if it were made available at a substantially reduced cost. Data are collected from a random sample of 500 subscribers. The results indicate that 135 of the subscribers would upgrade to a new cellphone at a reduced cost.

a. Construct a 99% confidence interval estimate for the population proportion of subscribers that would upgrade to a new cellphone at a reduced cost.

b. How would the manager in charge of promotional programs use the results in (a)?

10.33 In a survey of 529 travelers, 386 said that location was very important and 323 said that room quality was very important in choosing a hotel. (Source: C. Jones, "Top Reason for Picking a Hotel? It's Where It's At," *USA Today*, April 28, 2014, p. 3B.)

a. Construct a 95% confidence interval estimate for the population proportion of travelers who said that location was very important for choosing a hotel.

b. Construct a 95% confidence interval estimate for the population proportion of travelers who said that room quality was very important in choosing a hotel.

c. Write a short summary of the information derived from (a) and (b).

10.34 Are you likely to purchase an item promoted by a celebrity on a social media site? According to a Brand Republic survey, 26% of social media users have made such a purchase (Source: "Celebrity endorsement on social media," **bit.ly/1o4yNHa**.)

a. Suppose that the survey had a sample size of $n = 1,000$. Construct a 95% confidence interval estimate for the population proportion of social media users that have purchased an item promoted by a celebrity on a social media site.

b. Based on (a), can you claim that more than a quarter of all social media users have purchased an item promoted by a celebrity on a social media site?

c. Repeat parts (a) and (b), assuming that the survey had a sample size of $n = 10,000$.

d. Discuss the effect of sample size on confidence interval estimation.

10.35 In a survey of 239 organizations, 75 responded that "the need for collaboration among increasing number of locations" is a business driver that led them to implement cloud solutions. Cloud solutions enable more effective employee communication and higher decision maker visibility into real-time data. (Source: *The Benefits of Cloud ERP: It's About Transforming Your Business,* Aberdeen Group, available at **bit.ly/1meEC3D**.)

Construct a 95% confidence interval estimate for the population proportion of organizations that indicated "the need for collaboration among increasing number of locations" as a business driver for cloud solution implementation.

10.36 In a Pew Research Center survey of 960 Facebook users, 452 cited "seeing photos or videos" as a major reason why they use Facebook, while 298 cited "keeping up with news and current events" as a major reason why they use Facebook. (Source: "6 new facts about Facebook," **bit.ly/1lAmkv5**.)

a. Construct a 95% confidence interval estimate for the population proportion of Facebook users who cite "seeing photos or videos" as a major reason for why they use Facebook.

b. Construct a 95% confidence interval estimate for the population proportion of Facebook users who cite "keeping up with news and current events" as a major reason why they use Facebook.

c. Compare the results of (a) and (b).

10.37 What are the global trends that technology CEOs believe will transform their business? According to a PwC white paper, 105 of 117 technology CEOs from around the world responded that technological advances will transform their business and 42 responded that resource scarcity and climate change will transform their business. (Source: *Fit for the Future: 17th Annual Global CEO Survey,* available at **pwc.to/PRQZYr**.)

a. Construct a 95% confidence interval estimate for the population proportion of tech CEOs who indicate technological advances as one of the global trends that will transform their business.

b. Construct a 95% confidence interval estimate for the population proportion of tech CEOs who indicate resource scarcity and climate change as one of the global trends that will transform their business.

c. Interpret the intervals in (a) and (b).

Section 10.4

10.38 If you want to be 95% confident of estimating the population mean to within a sampling error of ± 5 and the standard deviation is assumed to be 15, what sample size is required?

10.39 If you want to be 99% confident of estimating the population mean to within a sampling error of ± 20 and the standard deviation is assumed to be 100, what sample size is required?

10.40 If you want to be 99% confident of estimating the population proportion to within a sampling error of ± 0.04, what sample size is needed?

10.41 If you want to be 95% confident of estimating the population proportion to within a sampling error of ± 0.02 and there is historical evidence that the population proportion is approximately 0.40, what sample size is needed?

10.42 A survey is planned to determine the mean annual family medical expenses of employees of a large company. The management of the company wishes to be 95% confident that the sample mean is correct to within $\pm \$50$ of the population mean annual family medical expenses. A previous study indicates that the standard deviation is approximately $400.
a. How large a sample is necessary?
b. If management wants to be correct to within $\pm \$25$, how many employees need to be selected?

10.43 If the manager of a bottled water distributor wants to estimate, with 95% confidence, the mean amount of water in a 1-gallon bottle to within ± 0.004 gallon and also assumes that the standard deviation is 0.02 gallon, what sample size is needed?

10.44 If a light bulb manufacturing company wants to estimate, with 95% confidence, the mean life of compact fluorescent light bulbs to within ± 200 hours and also assumes that the population standard deviation is 1,000 hours, how many compact fluorescent light bulbs need to be selected?

10.45 If the inspection division of a county weights and measures department wants to estimate the mean amount of soft-drink fill in 2-liter bottles to within ± 0.01 liter with 95% confidence and also assumes that the standard deviation is 0.05 liter, what sample size is needed?

10.46 An advertising executive wants to estimate the mean weekly amount of time consumers spend watching traditional television daily. Based on previous studies, the standard deviation is assumed to be 20 minutes. The executive wants to estimate, with 99% confidence, the mean weekly amount of time to within ± 5 minutes.
a. What sample size is needed?
b. If 95% confidence is desired, how many consumers need to be selected?

10.47 An advertising executive wants to estimate the mean amount of time that consumers spend with digital media daily. From past studies, the standard deviation is estimated as 45 minutes.
a. What sample size is needed if the executive wants to be 90% confident of being correct to within ± 5 minutes?
b. If 99% confidence is desired, how many consumers need to be selected?

10.48 A growing niche in the restaurant business is gourmet-casual breakfast, lunch, and brunch. Chains in this group include EggSpectation and Panera Bread. Suppose that the mean per-person check for breakfast at EggSpectation is approximately $14.50.

a. Assuming a standard deviation of $2.00, what sample size is needed to estimate, with 95% confidence, the mean per-person check for EggSpectation to within $\pm \$0.25$?
b. Assuming a standard deviation of $2.50, what sample size is needed to estimate, with 95% confidence, the mean per-person check for EggSpectation to within $\pm \$0.25$?
c. Assuming a standard deviation of $3.00, what sample size is needed to estimate, with 95% confidence, the mean per-person check for EggSpectation to within $\pm \$0.25$?
d. Discuss the effect of variation on the sample size needed.

10.49 What advertising medium gives a brand the most credibility in influencing brand decisions? According to an Adroit Digital survey, 35% of Millennials point to TV. (Source: "U.S. Millennials: TV is Most Influential Advertising Medium," *MC Marketing Charts*, March 20, 2014.)
a. To conduct a follow-up study that would provide 95% confidence that the point estimate is correct to within ± 0.04 of the population proportion, how large a sample size is required?
b. To conduct a follow-up study that would provide 99% confidence that the point estimate is correct to within ± 0.04 of the population proportion, how many people need to be sampled?
c. To conduct a follow-up study that would provide 95% confidence that the point estimate is correct to within ± 0.02 of the population proportion, how large a sample size is required?
d. To conduct a follow-up study that would provide 99% confidence that the point estimate is correct to within ± 0.02 of the population proportion, how many people need to be sampled?
e. Discuss the effects on sample size requirements of changing the desired confidence level and the acceptable sampling error.

10.50 A Nielsen Mobile Shopping Report looks at how consumers are using mobile devices throughout their purchase journey. In response to a survey question about shopping, 27% of tablet owners said they use mobile devices for payment, 21% said they use such devices to make social media comments about their purchases, and 10% said they use such devices to retrieve mobile coupons. (Source: "Mobile Ticks All the Shopping Boxes," **bit.ly/1hfKC8K**.)

Suppose the results are based on a survey of 300 tablet owners. Construct a 95% confidence interval estimate of the population proportion of tablet owners who said they use their mobile device while shopping
a. for payment.
b. to make social media comments about their purchases.
c. to retrieve mobile coupons.
d. You have been asked to update the results of this study. Determine the sample size necessary to estimate, with 95% confidence, the population proportions in (a) through (c) to within ± 0.02.

10.51 In a study of 413 nonprofits nationwide, 83 indicated that turnover has been the biggest employment challenge at their organization. (Source: Nonprofit HR, *2014 Nonprofit Employment Practices Survey*, available at **bit.ly/1mfy2tJ**.)
a. Construct a 95% confidence interval for the population proportion of nonprofits that indicate turnover as the biggest employment challenge at their organization.
b. Interpret the interval constructed in (a).
c. If you wanted to conduct a follow-up study to estimate the population proportion of nonprofits that indicate turnover as the biggest employment challenge at their organization to within ± 0.01 with 95% confidence, how many nonprofits would you survey?

10.52 According to a study released by The Financial Brand, an online publication focusing on branding issues and advice affecting retail banks and credit unions, 68% of financial institutions use churn rate (attrition) to gauge the effectiveness of their marketing efforts. (Source: "2014 State of Bank & Credit Union Marketing," **bit.ly/1np8FVx.**)

a. If you conduct a follow-up study to estimate the population proportion of financial institutions that use churn rate to gauge the effectiveness of their marketing efforts, would you use a π of 0.68 or 0.50 in the sample size formula?

b. Using your answer in (a), find the sample size necessary to estimate, with 95% confidence, the population proportion to within ± 0.03.

10.53 What prevents consumers from sharing data with retailers? A recent ClickFox Consumer Behavior Survey (**bit.ly/1fAfJAI**) found that 32% of consumers responded "breaches of consumer data."

a. To conduct a follow-up study that would provide 99% confidence that the point estimate is correct to within ±0.03 of the population proportion, how many consumers need to be sampled?

b. To conduct a follow-up study that would provide 99% confidence that the point estimate is correct to within ±0.05 of the population proportion, how many consumers need to be sampled?

c. Compare the results of (a) and (b).

Review

10.54 The Pew Internet Project survey of 1,006 American adults found the following:

    906 have a cell phone
    584 have a smartphone
    322 have an ebook reader
    423 have a tablet computer

Source: "Device Ownership Over Time," **bit.ly/1fvWYrL.**

a. Construct 95% confidence interval estimates for the population proportion of the electronic devices adults own.

b. What conclusions can you reach concerning what electronic devices adults have?

10.55 What proposals for dealing with energy and the environment do Americans favor? Gallup conducted a survey of 1,048 adults, ages 18+ in all 50 U.S. states and the District of Columbia and found the following:

    Spending more government money on developing solar and wind power: 702
    Setting higher emissions and pollutions standards for business and industry: 681
    Setting stricter standards on the use of techniques to extract natural gas from the earth: 608
    Expanding the use of nuclear power: 493

Source: "Americans Still Favor Energy Conservation Over Production," **bit.ly/1iLhkn2.**

a. Construct a 95% confidence interval estimate for the population proportion of each proposal Americans favor for dealing with energy and the environment.

b. What conclusions can you reach concerning proposals Americans favor for dealing with energy and the environment?

10.56 A market researcher for a consumer electronics company wants to study the media viewing behavior of residents of a particular

area. A random sample of 40 respondents is selected, and each respondent is instructed to keep a detailed record of time spent engaged viewing content across all screens (traditional TV, DVD/Blu-ray, game console, Internet on a computer, video on a computer, video on a mobile phone) in a particular week. The results are as follows:

- Content viewing time per week: $\overline{X} = 41$ hours, $S = 3.5$ hours.
- 30 respondents have high definition (HD) on at least one television set.

a. Construct a 95% confidence interval estimate for the mean content viewing time per week in this area.

b. Construct a 95% confidence interval estimate for the population proportion of residents who have HD on at least one television set.

Suppose that the market researcher wants to take another survey in a different location. Answer these questions:

c. What sample size is required to be 95% confident of estimating the population mean content viewing time to within ± 2 hours assuming that the population standard deviation is equal to 5 hours?

d. How many respondents need to be selected to be 95% confident of being within ± 0.06 of the population proportion who have HD on at least one television set if no previous estimate is available?

e. Based on (c) and (d), how many respondents should the market researcher select if a single survey is being conducted?

10.57 An information technology (IT) consulting firm specializing in health care solutions wants to study communication deficiencies in the health care industry. A random sample of 70 health care clinicians reveals the following:

- Time wasted in a day due to outdated communication technologies: $\overline{X} = 45$ minutes, $S = 10$ minutes.
- Thirty-six health care clinicians cite inefficiency of pagers as the reason for the wasted time.

a. Construct a 99% confidence interval estimate for the population mean time wasted in a day due to outdated communication technologies.

b. Construct a 95% confidence interval estimate for the population proportion of health care clinicians who cite inefficiency of pagers as the reason for the wasted time.

10.58 The human resource (HR) director of a large corporation wishes to study absenteeism among its mid-level managers at its central office during the year. A random sample of 25 mid-level managers reveals the following:

- Absenteeism: $\overline{X} = 6.2$ days, $S = 7.3$ days.
- 13 mid-level managers cite stress as a cause of absence.

a. Construct a 95% confidence interval estimate for the mean number of absences for mid-level managers during the year.

b. Construct a 95% confidence interval estimate for the population proportion of mid-level managers who cite stress as a cause of absence.

Suppose that the HR director wishes to administer a survey in one of its regional offices. Answer these questions:

c. What sample size is needed to have 95% confidence in estimating the population mean absenteeism to within ± 1.5 days if the population standard deviation is estimated to be 8 days?

d. How many mid-level managers need to be selected to have 90% confidence in estimating the population proportion of mid-level managers who cite stress as a cause of absence to within ± 0.075 if no previous estimate is available?

e. Based on (c) and (d), what sample size is needed if a single survey is being conducted?

10.59 A national association devoted to HR and workplace programs, practices, and training wants to study HR department practices and employee turnover of its member organizations. HR professionals and organization executives focus on turnover not only because it has significant cost implications but also because it affects overall business performance. A survey is designed to estimate the proportion of member organizations that have both talent and development programs in place to drive human-capital management as well as the member organizations' mean annual employee turnover rate (the ratio of the number of employees that left an organization in a given time period to the average number of employees in the organization during the given time period). A random sample of 100 member organizations reveals the following:

- Annual turnover rate: $\overline{X} = 8.1\%$, $S = 1.5\%$.
- Thirty member organizations have both talent and development programs in place to drive human-capital management.

a. Construct a 95% confidence interval estimate for the population mean annual turnover rate of member organizations.

b. Construct a 95% confidence interval estimate for the population proportion of member organizations that have both talent and development programs in place to drive human-capital management.

c. What sample size is needed to have 99% confidence of estimating the population mean annual employee turnover rate to within ± 1.5%?

d. How many member organizations need to be selected to have 90% confidence of estimating the population proportion of organizations that have both talent and development programs in place to drive human-capital management to within ± 0.045?

10.60 The financial impact of IT systems downtime is a concern of plant operations management today. A survey of manufacturers examined the satisfaction level with the reliability and availability of their manufacturing IT applications. The variables of focus are whether the manufacturer experienced downtime in the past year that affected one or more manufacturing IT applications, the number of downtime incidents that occurred in the past year, and the approximate cost of a typical downtime incident. The results from a sample of 200 manufacturers are as follows:

- Sixty-two experienced downtime this year that affected one or more manufacturing applications.
- Number of downtime incidents: $\overline{X} = 3.5$, $S = 2.0$
- Cost of downtime incidents: $\overline{X} = \$18,000$, $S = \$3,000$.

a. Construct a 90% confidence interval estimate for the population proportion of manufacturers who experienced downtime in the past year that affected one or more manufacturing IT applications.

b. Construct a 95% confidence interval estimate for the population mean number of downtime incidents experienced by manufacturers in the past year.

c. Construct a 95% confidence interval estimate for the population mean cost of downtime incidents.

10.61 The branch manager of an outlet (Store 1) of a nationwide chain of pet supply stores wants to study characteristics of her customers. In particular, she decides to focus on two variables: the amount of money spent by customers and whether the customers own only one dog, only one cat, or more than one dog and/or cat. The results from a sample of 70 customers are as follows:

- Amount of money spent: $\overline{X} = \$21.34$, $S = \$9.22$.
- Thirty-seven customers own only a dog.
- Twenty-six customers own only a cat.
- Seven customers own more than one dog and/or cat.

a. Construct a 95% confidence interval estimate for the population mean amount spent in the pet supply store.

b. Construct a 90% confidence interval estimate for the population proportion of customers who own only a cat.

The branch manager of another outlet (Store 2) wishes to conduct a similar survey in his store. The manager does not have access to the information generated by the manager of Store 1. Answer the following questions:

c. What sample size is needed to have 95% confidence of estimating the population mean amount spent in this store to within ± \$1.50 if the standard deviation is estimated to be \$10?

d. How many customers need to be selected to have 90% confidence of estimating the population proportion of customers who own only a cat to within ± 0.045?

e. Based on your answers to (c) and (d), how large a sample should the manager take?

10.62 Scarlett and Heather, the owners of an upscale restaurant in Dayton, Ohio, want to study the dining characteristics of their customers. They decide to focus on two variables: the amount of money spent by customers and whether customers order dessert. The results from a sample of 60 customers are as follows:

- Amount spent: $\overline{X} = \$38.54$, $S = \$7.26$.
- Eighteen customers purchased dessert.

a. Construct a 95% confidence interval estimate for the population mean amount spent per customer in the restaurant.

b. Construct a 90% confidence interval estimate for the population proportion of customers who purchase dessert.

Jeanine, the owner of a competing restaurant, wants to conduct a similar survey in her restaurant. Jeanine does not have access to the information that Scarlett and Heather have obtained from the survey they conducted. Answer the following questions:

c. What sample size is needed to have 95% confidence of estimating the population mean amount spent in her restaurant to within ± \$1.50, assuming that the standard deviation is estimated to be \$8?

d. How many customers need to be selected to have 90% confidence of estimating the population proportion of customers who purchase dessert to within ± 0.04?

e. Based on your answers to (c) and (d), how large a sample should Jeanine take?

10.63 The manufacturer of Ice Melt claims that its product will melt snow and ice at temperatures as low as 0° Fahrenheit. A representative for a large chain of hardware stores is interested in testing this claim. The chain purchases a large shipment of 5-pound bags for distribution. The representative wants to know, with 95% confidence and within ± 0.05, what proportion of bags of Ice Melt perform the job as claimed by the manufacturer.

a. How many bags does the representative need to test? What assumption should be made concerning the population proportion? (This is called *destructive testing*; i.e., the product being tested is destroyed by the test and is then unavailable to be sold.)

b. Suppose that the representative tests 50 bags, and 42 of them do the job as claimed. Construct a 95% confidence interval estimate for the population proportion that will do the job as claimed.

c. How can the representative use the results of (b) to determine whether to sell the Ice Melt product?

10.64 Claims fraud (illegitimate claims) and buildup (exaggerated loss amounts) continue to be major issues of concern among automobile insurance companies. Fraud is defined as specific material misrepresentation of the facts of a loss; buildup is defined as the inflation of an otherwise legitimate claim. A recent study examined auto injury claims closed with payment under private passenger coverages. Detailed data on injury, medical treatment, claimed losses, and total payments, as well as claim-handling techniques, were collected. In addition, auditors were asked to review the claim files to indicate whether specific elements of fraud or buildup appeared in the claim and, in the case of buildup, to specify the amount of excess payment. The file InsuranceClaims contains data for 90 randomly selected auto injury claims. The following variables are included: CLAIM—Claim ID; BUILDUP—1 if buildup indicated, 0 if not; and EXCESSPAYMENT—excess payment amount, in dollars.
a. Construct a 95% confidence interval for the population proportion of all auto injury files that have exaggerated loss amounts.
b. Construct a 95% confidence interval for the population mean dollar excess payment amount.

10.65 A quality characteristic of interest for a tea-bag-filling process is the weight of the tea in the individual bags. In this example, the label weight on the package indicates that the mean amount is 5.5 grams of tea in a bag. If the bags are underfilled, two problems arise. First, customers may not be able to brew the tea to be as strong as they wish. Second, the company may be in violation of the truth-in-labeling laws. On the other hand, if the mean amount of tea in a bag exceeds the label weight, the company is giving away product. Getting an exact amount of tea in a bag is problematic because of variation in the temperature and humidity inside the factory, differences in the density of the tea, and the extremely fast filling operation of the machine (approximately 170 bags per minute). The following data (stored in Teabags) are the weights, in grams, of a sample of 50 tea bags produced in one hour by a single machine:

5.65	5.44	5.42	5.40	5.53	5.34	5.54	5.45	5.52	5.41
5.57	5.40	5.53	5.54	5.55	5.62	5.56	5.46	5.44	5.51
5.47	5.40	5.47	5.61	5.53	5.32	5.67	5.29	5.49	5.55
5.77	5.57	5.42	5.58	5.58	5.50	5.32	5.50	5.53	5.58
5.61	5.45	5.44	5.25	5.56	5.63	5.50	5.57	5.67	5.36

a. Construct a 99% confidence interval estimate for the population mean weight of the tea bags.
b. Is the company meeting the requirement set forth on the label that the mean amount of tea in a bag is 5.5 grams?
c. Do you think the assumption needed to construct the confidence interval estimate in (a) is valid?

10.66 A manufacturing company produces steel housings for electrical equipment. The main component part of the housing is a steel trough that is made from a 14-gauge steel coil. It is produced using a 250-ton progressive punch press with a wipe-down operation that puts two 90-degree forms in the flat steel to make the trough. The distance from one side of the form to the other is critical because of weatherproofing in outdoor applications. The widths (in inches), shown below and stored in Trough , are from a sample of 49 troughs:

8.312	8.343	8.317	8.383	8.348	8.410	8.351	8.373	8.481
8.422	8.476	8.382	8.484	8.403	8.414	8.419	8.385	8.465
8.498	8.447	8.436	8.413	8.489	8.414	8.481	8.415	8.479
8.429	8.458	8.462	8.460	8.444	8.429	8.460	8.412	8.420
8.410	8.405	8.323	8.420	8.396	8.447	8.405	8.439	8.411
8.427	8.420	8.498	8.409					

a. Construct a 95% confidence interval estimate for the mean width of the troughs.
b. Interpret the interval developed in (a).
c. Do you think the assumption needed to construct the confidence interval estimate in (a) is valid?

10.67 The manufacturer of Boston and Vermont asphalt shingles knows that product weight is a major factor in a customer's perception of quality. The last stage of the assembly line packages the shingles before they are placed on wooden pallets. Once a pallet is full (a pallet for most brands holds 16 squares of shingles), it is weighed, and the measurement is recorded. The file Pallet contains the weight (in pounds) from a sample of 368 pallets of Boston shingles and 330 pallets of Vermont shingles.
a. For the Boston shingles, construct a 95% confidence interval estimate for the mean weight.
b. For the Vermont shingles, construct a 95% confidence interval estimate for the mean weight.
c. Do you think the assumption needed to construct the confidence interval estimates in (a) and (b) is valid?
d. Based on the results of (a) and (b), what conclusions can you reach concerning the mean weight of the Boston and Vermont shingles?

10.68 The manufacturer of Boston and Vermont asphalt shingles provides its customers with a 20-year warranty on most of its products. To determine whether a shingle will last the entire warranty period, accelerated-life testing is conducted at the manufacturing plant. Accelerated-life testing exposes the shingle to the stresses it would be subject to in a lifetime of normal use via a laboratory experiment that takes only a few minutes to conduct. In this test, a shingle is repeatedly scraped with a brush for a short period of time, and the shingle granules removed by the brushing are weighed (in grams). Shingles that experience low amounts of granule loss are expected to last longer in normal use than shingles that experience high amounts of granule loss. In this situation, a shingle should experience no more than 0.8 grams of granule loss if it is expected to last the length of the warranty period. The file Granule contains a sample of 170 measurements made on the company's Boston shingles and 140 measurements made on Vermont shingles.
a. For the Boston shingles, construct a 95% confidence interval estimate for the mean granule loss.
b. For the Vermont shingles, construct a 95% confidence interval estimate for the mean granule loss.
c. Do you think the assumption needed to construct the confidence interval estimates in (a) and (b) is valid?
d. Based on the results of (a) and (b), what conclusions can you reach concerning the mean granule loss of the Boston and Vermont shingles?

REPORT WRITING EXERCISE

10.69 Referring to the results in Problem 10.66 concerning the width of a steel trough, write a report that summarizes your conclusions.

CASES FOR CHAPTER 10

Managing Ashland MultiComm Services

The marketing department has been considering ways to increase the number of new subscriptions to the *3-For-All* cable/phone/Internet service. Following the suggestion of Assistant Manager Lauren Adler, the department staff designed a survey to help determine various characteristics of households who subscribe to cable television service from Ashland. The survey consists of the following 10 questions:

1. Does your household subscribe to telephone service from Ashland?
   (1) Yes   (2) No

2. Does your household subscribe to Internet service from Ashland?
   (1) Yes   (2) No

3. What type of cable television service do you have?
   (1) Basic   (2) Enhanced
   (If Basic, skip to question 5.)

4. How often do you watch the cable television stations that are only available with enhanced service?
   (1) Every day   (2) Most days
   (3) Occasionally or never

5. How often do you watch premium or on-demand services that require an extra fee?
   (1) Almost every day   (2) Several times a week
   (3) Rarely   (4) Never

6. Which method did you use to obtain your current AMS subscription?
   (1) AMS toll-free phone number
   (2) AMS website
   (3) Direct mail reply card
   (4) Good Tunes & More promotion
   (5) Other

7. Would you consider subscribing to the *3-For-All* cable/phone/Internet service for a trial period if a discount were offered?
   (1) Yes   (2) No
   (If no, skip to question 9.)

8. If purchased separately, cable, Internet, and phone services would currently cost $24.99 per week. How much would you be willing to pay per week for the *3-For-All* cable/phone/Internet service?

9. Does your household use another provider of telephone service?
   (1) Yes   (2) No

10. AMS may distribute Ashland Gold Cards that would provide discounts at selected Ashland-area restaurants for subscribers who agree to a two-year subscription contract to the *3-For-All* service. Would being eligible to receive a Gold Card cause you to agree to the two-year term?
    (1) Yes   (2) No

Of the 500 households selected that subscribe to cable television service from Ashland, 82 households either refused to participate, could not be contacted after repeated attempts, or had telephone numbers that were not in service. The summary results for the 418 households that were contacted are as follows:

Household Has AMS Telephone Service	Frequency
Yes	83
No	335

Household Has AMS Internet Service	Frequency
Yes	262
No	156

Type of Cable Service	Frequency
Basic	164
Enhanced	254

Watches Enhanced Programming	Frequency
Every day	50
Most days	144
Occasionally or never	60

Watches Premium or On-Demand Services	Frequency
Almost every day	14
Several times a week	35
Almost never	313
Never	56

Method Used to Obtain Current AMS Subscription	Frequency
Toll-free phone number	230
AMS website	106
Direct mail	46
Good Tunes & More	10
Other	26

Would Consider Discounted Trial Offer	Frequency
Yes	40
No	378

Trial Weekly Rate ($) Willing to Pay (stored in `AMS10`)

23.00 20.00 22.75 20.00 20.00 24.50 17.50 22.25 18.00 21.00
18.25 21.00 18.50 20.75 21.25 22.25 22.75 21.75 19.50 20.75
16.75 19.00 22.25 21.00 16.75 19.00 22.25 21.00 19.50 22.75
23.50 19.50 21.75 22.00 24.00 23.25 19.50 20.75 18.25 21.50

Uses Another Phone Service Provider	Frequency
Yes	354
No	64

Gold Card Leads to Two-Year Agreement	Frequency
Yes	38
No	380

Analyze the results of the survey of Ashland households that receive AMS cable television service. Write a report that discusses the marketing implications of the survey results for Ashland MultiComm Services.

Digital Case

Apply your knowledge about confidence interval estimation in this Digital Case, which extends the MyTVLab Digital Case from Chapter 7.

Among its other features, the MyTVLab website allows customers to purchase MyTVLab LifeStyles merchandise online. To handle payment processing, the management of MyTVLab has contracted with the following firms:

- **PayAFriend (PAF)**—This is an online payment system with which customers and businesses such as MyTVLab register in order to exchange payments in a secure and convenient manner, without the need for a credit card.

- **Continental Banking Company (Conbanco)**—This processing services provider allows MyTVLab customers to pay for merchandise using nationally recognized credit cards issued by a financial institution.

To reduce costs, management is considering eliminating one of these two payment systems. However, Lorraine Hildick of the sales department suspects that customers use the two forms of payment in unequal numbers and that customers display different buying behaviors when using the two forms of payment. Therefore, she would like to first determine the following:

- The proportion of customers using PAF and the proportion of customers using a credit card to pay for their purchases.

- The mean purchase amount when using PAF and the mean purchase amount when using a credit card.

Assist Ms. Hildick by preparing an appropriate analysis. Open **PaymentsSample.pdf**, read Ms. Hildick's comments, and use her random sample of 50 transactions as the basis for your analysis. Summarize your findings to determine whether Ms. Hildick's conjectures about MyTVLab LifeStyle customer purchasing behaviors are correct. If you want the sampling error to be no more than $3 when estimating the mean purchase amount, is Ms. Hildick's sample large enough to perform a valid analysis?

Sure Value Convenience Stores

You work in the corporate office for a nationwide convenience store franchise that operates nearly 10,000 stores. The per-store daily customer count has been steady, at 900, for some time (i.e., the mean number of customers in a store in one day is 900). To increase the customer count, the franchise is considering cutting coffee prices. The 12-ounce size will now be $0.59 instead of $0.99, and the 16-ounce size will be $0.69 instead of $1.19. Even with this reduction in price, the franchise will have a 40% gross margin on coffee. To test the new initiative, the franchise has reduced coffee prices in a sample of 34 stores, where customer counts have been running almost exactly at the national average of 900. After four weeks, the sample stores stabilize at a mean customer count of 974 and a standard deviation of 96. This increase seems like a substantial amount to you, but it also seems like a pretty small sample. Is there some way to get a feel for what the mean per-store count in all the stores will be if you cut coffee prices nationwide? Do you think reducing coffee prices is a good strategy for increasing the mean customer count?

CardioGood Fitness

Return to the CardioGood Fitness case first presented in Chapter 1. Using the data stored in `CardioGood Fitness`:

1. Construct 95% confidence interval estimates to create a customer profile for each CardioGood Fitness treadmill product line.

2. Write a report to be presented to the management of CardioGood Fitness detailing your findings.

More Descriptive Choices Follow-Up

Follow up the More Descriptive Choices, Revisited Using Statistics scenario in Chapter 4 by constructing 95% confidence intervals estimates of the three-year return percentages, five-year return percentages, and ten-year return percentages for the sample of growth and value funds and for the small, mid-cap, and large market cap funds (stored in `Retirement Funds`). In your analysis, examine differences between the growth and value funds as well as the differences among the small, mid-cap, and large market cap funds.

Clear Mountain State Student Surveys

1. The Student News Service at Clear Mountain State University (CMSU) has decided to gather data about the undergraduate students that attend CMSU. They create and distribute a survey of 14 questions and receive responses from 62 undergraduates (stored in `UndergradSurvey`). For each variable included in the survey, construct a 95% confidence interval estimate for the population characteristic and write a report summarizing your conclusions.

2. The Dean of Students at CMSU has learned about the undergraduate survey and has decided to undertake a similar survey for graduate students at CMSU. She creates and distributes a survey of 14 questions and receives responses from 44 graduate students (stored in `GradSurvey`). For each variable included in the survey, construct a 95% confidence interval estimate for the population characteristic and write a report summarizing your conclusions.

CHAPTER 10 CASIO CALCULATOR GUIDE

CALCULATOR LESSON 8

CASIO FX-9750GII CALCULATOR

Lesson 8—Confidence Interval

EXAMPLE 10.7

1-Sample Z Interval (Using sample statistics)

A certain population is known to have a standard deviation of 4.0. A sample of 40 has been chosen and the mean is 9.7. Construct a 95% confidence interval estimate for the mean.

Solution: From the **Main Menu** select the following:

STAT F4(INTR) **F1**(Z) **F1**(1-S). Then enter the following items:

(Note: Use the **EXE** key only after a new data entry. Otherwise, use the cursor ▼ arrow. If you accidentally hit the wrong key, use **AC/ON** or **EXIT** to go back.)

1-Sample ZInterval

Data	: **F2**(Var)	▼
C-Level	: **.95**	**EXE**
σ	: **4**	**EXE**
$\bar{x}$	: **9.7**	**EXE**
n	: **40**	**EXE**
Save Res	: None(press **F1**)	

Now press **EXE** or **F1**(Calc).

The calculator will show the results:

1-Sample ZInterval

Left	=8.46040994
Right	=10.9395901
$\bar{x}$	=9.7
n	=40

As you can see, the 95% confidence interval estimate for the population mean is 8.46 to 10.94. The calculator will display the numerical result only; you must remember to write up the complete answer as shown in class.

EXAMPLE 10.8

1-Sample Z Interval (Using raw data)

A random survey of eight dry-cleaning outlets indicated that the amounts of GST collected from the outlets on the previous day were $70, $65, $76, $53, $75, $71, $59, and $67. Use this information to estimate the mean daily amount of GST collected by all dry-cleaning outlets if the amounts are known to be normally distributed, with a standard deviation of $5. Determine the 90% confidence interval estimate.

Solution:

First enter the data into **List 1**.

Now, from the **Main Menu** select the following:

STAT F4(INTR) **F1**(Z) **F1**(1-S). Then enter the following items:

1-Sample ZInterval

Data	: **F1**(List)	▼
C-Level	: **.90**	**EXE**
σ	: **5**	**EXE**

List	: List1	EXE (Press F1 and answer the question.)
Freq	: 1 (F1)	EXE Note: If the data given are a weighted data, then enter the weight values in a list–in that case, you would select list (F2).

Save Res   : None

Now press **EXE** or **F1**(Calc).

The calculator will show the results:

1-Sample ZInterval

Left	=64.0922821
Right	=69.9077179
$\bar{x}$	=67
sx	=9.13392421
n	=8

As you can see, the 90% confidence interval estimate for the population mean is $64.09 to $69.91. The calculator will display the numerical result only; you must remember to write up the complete answer as shown in class.

EXAMPLE 10.9

1-Sample t Interval (Using sample statistics)

Management at a bank wishes to estimate the mean amount of time customers spend at the automated teller machine (ATM). It believes the times to be normally distributed. A random sample of 20 customers has been selected and the sample mean time was 255 seconds, with a standard deviation of 33 seconds. Construct a 95% confidence interval estimate for the mean time at the ATM machine per customer.

Solution: From the **Main Menu** select the following:

STAT   F4(INTR)   **F2**(t)   **F1**(1-S). Then enter the following items:

(Note: Use the **EXE** key only after a new data entry. Otherwise, use the cursor ▼ arrow. If you accidentally hit the wrong key, use **AC/ON** or **EXIT** to go back.)

1-Sample tInterval

Data	: F2(Var) ▼	
C-Level	: **0.95**	EXE
$\bar{x}$	: **255**	EXE
sx	: **33**	EXE
n	: **20**	EXE
Save Res	: None	

Now press **EXE** or **F1**(Calc).

The calculator will show the results:

1-Sample tInterval

Left	=239.555525
Right	=270.444475
$\bar{x}$	=255
sx	=33
n	=20

As you can see, the 95% confidence interval estimate for the population mean is 240 to 270 seconds. The calculator will display the numerical result only; you must remember to write up the complete answer as shown in class.

EXAMPLE 10.10

1-Sample t Interval (Using raw data)

A random survey of eight dry-cleaning outlets indicated that the amounts of GST collected from the outlets on the previous day were $70, $65, $76, $53, $75, $71, $59, and $67. Use this information to estimate the mean daily amount of GST collected by all dry-cleaning outlets if the amounts are known to be normally distributed. Determine the 90% confidence interval estimate.

Solution:

First enter the data into **List 1**.

Now, from the **Main Menu** select the following:

STAT   F4(INTR)   **F2**(t)   **F1**(1-S). Then enter the following items:

1-Sample tInterval
Data	: **F1**(List)	▼
C-Level	: **0.90**	**EXE**
List	: **List1**	▼
Freq	: **1**	**EXE**
Save Res	: None	

Now press **EXE** or **F1**(Calc).

The calculator will show the results:

1-Sample tInterval
Left	=61.7257164
Right	=72.2742836
$\bar{x}$	=67
sx	=9.13392421
n	=8

As you can see, the 90% confidence interval estimate for the population mean is $60.88 to $73.12. The calculator will display the numerical result only; you must remember to write up the complete answer as shown in class.

EXAMPLE 10.11

1-Proportion Z Interval

A bank manager wants to estimate the proportion of all the bank's customers who use the ATM to pay bills. A random sample of 80 customers has been selected and it was found that 43 of those customers use the ATM to pay bills. Determine the 99% confidence interval estimate for the proportion of all the bank's customers who use the ATM to pay bills.

Solution: From the **Main Menu** select:

STAT   F4(INTR)   **F1**(Z)   **F3**(1-P). Then enter the following items:

1-Prop ZInterval
C-Level	: **0.99**	**EXE**
x	: **43**	**EXE**
n	: **80**	**EXE**
Save Res	: None	

Now press **EXE** or **F1**(Calc).

The calculator will show the results:

1-Prop ZInterval
Left	=0.39391231
Right	=0.68108768
$\hat{p}$	=0.5375
n	=80

As you can see, the 99% confidence interval estimate for the population proportion is 0.394 to 0.681. The calculator will display the numerical result only; you must remember to write up the complete answer as shown in class.

Fundamentals of Hypothesis Testing: One-Sample Tests

CONTENTS

11.1 Fundamentals of Hypothesis-Testing Methodology

Z Test of Hypothesis for the Mean (σ is known)

Can You Ever Know the Population Standard Deviation?

11.2 t Test of Hypothesis for the Mean (σ Unknown)

11.3 One-Tail Tests

11.4 Z Test of Hypothesis for the Proportion

11.5 Potential Hypothesis-Testing Pitfalls and Ethical Issues

USING STATISTICS: Significant Testing at Oxford Cereals, Revisited

CHAPTER 11 CASIO CALCULATOR GUIDE

OBJECTIVES

Learn the basic principles of hypothesis testing

How to use hypothesis testing to test a mean or proportion

Identify the assumptions of each hypothesis-testing procedure, how to evaluate them, and the consequences if they are seriously violated

Become aware of the pitfalls and ethical issues involved in hypothesis testing

How to avoid the pitfalls involved in hypothesis testing

Significant Testing at Oxford Cereals

You find yourself as plant operations manager for Oxford Cereals. Among other responsibilities, you are responsible for monitoring the amount in each cereal box filled. Company specifications require a mean weight of 368 grams per box. You must adjust the cereal-filling process when the mean fill-weight in the population of boxes differs from 368 grams. Adjusting the process requires shutting down the cereal production line temporarily, so you do not want to make unnecessary adjustments.

What decision-making method can you use to decide if the cereal-filling process needs to be adjusted? You decide to begin by selecting a random sample of 25 cereal boxes and weighing each box. From the weights collected, you compute a sample mean. How could that sample mean be used to help decide whether adjustment is necessary?

Peter Close/Shutterstock

I n this Oxford Cereals scenario, you seek to use a sample mean to validate a claim about the population mean, a somewhat different problem. For this type of situation, you use the inferential method known as **hypothesis testing**. Hypothesis testing requires that you state a claim unambiguously. In this scenario, the claim is that the population mean is 368 grams. You examine a sample statistic to see if it better supports the stated claim, called the *null hypothesis*, or the mutually exclusive alternative hypothesis (for this scenario, that the population mean is not 368 grams).

In this chapter, you will learn several applications of hypothesis testing. You will learn how to make inferences about a population parameter by *analyzing differences* between the results observed, the sample statistic, and the results you would expect to get if an underlying hypothesis were actually true. For the Oxford Cereals scenario, hypothesis testing allows you to infer one of the following:

- The mean weight of the cereal boxes in the sample is a value consistent with what you would expect if the mean of the entire population of cereal boxes were 368 grams.
- The population mean is not equal to 368 grams because the sample mean is significantly different from 368 grams.

11.1 Fundamentals of Hypothesis-Testing Methodology

Hypothesis testing typically begins with a theory, a claim, or an assertion about a particular parameter of a population. For example, your initial hypothesis in the cereal example is that the process is working properly, so the mean fill is 368 grams, and no corrective action is needed.

The Null and Alternative Hypotheses

The hypothesis that the population parameter is equal to the company specification is referred to as the null hypothesis. A **null hypothesis** is often one of status quo and is identified by the symbol H_0. Here the null hypothesis is that the filling process is working properly, and therefore the mean fill is the 368-gram specification provided by Oxford Cereals. This is stated as

$$H_0 : \mu = 368$$

Student Tip

Remember, hypothesis testing reaches conclusions about parameters, not statistics.

Even though information is available only from the sample, the null hypothesis is stated in terms of the population parameter because your focus is on the population of all cereal boxes. You use the sample statistic to make inferences about the entire filling process. One inference may be that the results observed from the sample data indicate that the null hypothesis is false. If the null hypothesis is considered false, something else must be true.

Whenever a null hypothesis is specified, an alternative hypothesis is also specified, and it must be true if the null hypothesis is false. The **alternative hypothesis**, H_1, is the opposite of the null hypothesis, H_0. This is stated in the cereal example as

$$H_1 : \mu \neq 368$$

The alternative hypothesis represents the conclusion reached by rejecting the null hypothesis. In many research situations, the alternative hypothesis serves as the hypothesis that is the focus of the research being conducted. The null hypothesis is rejected when there is sufficient evidence from the sample data that the null hypothesis is false. In the cereal example, if the weights of the sampled boxes are sufficiently above or below the expected 368-gram mean specified by Oxford Cereals, you reject the null hypothesis in favor of the alternative hypothesis that the mean fill is different from 368 grams. You stop production and take whatever action is necessary to correct the problem. If the null hypothesis is not rejected, you should continue to believe that the process is working correctly and that no corrective action is necessary. In this second circumstance, you have not proven that the process is working correctly.

Rather, you have failed to prove that it is working incorrectly, and therefore you continue your belief (although unproven) in the null hypothesis.

In hypothesis testing, you reject the null hypothesis when the sample evidence suggests that it is far more likely that the alternative hypothesis is true. However, failure to reject the null hypothesis is not proof that it is true. You can never prove that the null hypothesis is correct because the decision is based only on the sample information, not on the entire population. Therefore, if you fail to reject the null hypothesis, you can only conclude that there is insufficient evidence to warrant its rejection. The following key points summarize the null and alternative hypotheses:

- The null hypothesis, H_0, represents the current belief in a situation.
- The alternative hypothesis, H_1, is the opposite of the null hypothesis and represents a research claim or specific inference you would like to prove.
- If you reject the null hypothesis, you have statistical proof that the alternative hypothesis is correct.
- If you do not reject the null hypothesis, you have failed to prove the alternative hypothesis. The failure to prove the alternative hypothesis, however, does not mean that you have proven the null hypothesis.
- The null hypothesis, H_0, always refers to a specified value of the population parameter (such as μ), not a sample statistic (such as $\overline{X}$).
- The statement of the null hypothesis always contains an equal sign regarding the specified value of the population parameter (e.g., $H_0 : \mu = 368$ grams).
- The statement of the alternative hypothesis never contains an equal sign regarding the specified value of the population parameter (e.g., $H_1 : \mu \neq 368$ grams).

EXAMPLE 11.1

The Null and Alternative Hypotheses

You are the manager of a fast-food restaurant. You want to determine whether the waiting time to place an order has changed in the past month from its previous population mean value of 4.5 minutes. State the null and alternative hypotheses.

SOLUTION The null hypothesis is that the population mean has not changed from its previous value of 4.5 minutes. This is stated as

$$H_0 : \mu = 4.5$$

The alternative hypothesis is the opposite of the null hypothesis. Because the null hypothesis is that the population mean is 4.5 minutes, the alternative hypothesis is that the population mean is not 4.5 minutes. This is stated as

$$H_1 : \mu \neq 4.5$$

The Critical Value of the Test Statistic

Hypothesis testing uses sample data to determine how likely it is that the null hypothesis is true. In the Oxford Cereal Company scenario, the null hypothesis is that the mean amount of cereal per box in the entire filling process is 368 grams (the population parameter specified by the company). You select a sample of boxes from the filling process, weigh each box, and compute the sample mean $\overline{X}$. This sample statistic is an estimate of the corresponding parameter, the population mean, μ. Even if the null hypothesis is true, the sample statistic $\overline{X}$ is likely to differ from the value of the parameter (the population mean, μ) because of variation due to sampling.

You do expect the sample statistic to be close to the population parameter if the null hypothesis is true. If the sample statistic is close to the population parameter, you have insufficient evidence to reject the null hypothesis. For example, if the sample mean is 367.9 grams, you might conclude that the population mean has not changed (i.e., $\mu = 368$) because a sample mean of 367.9 grams is very close to the hypothesized value of 368 grams. Intuitively, you think that it is likely that you could get a sample mean of 367.9 grams from a population whose mean is 368.

However, if there is a large difference between the value of the sample statistic and the hypothesized value of the population parameter, you might conclude that the null hypothesis is false. For example, if the sample mean is 320 grams, you might conclude that the population mean is not 368 grams (i.e., $\mu \neq 368$) because the sample mean is very far from the hypothesized value of 368 grams. In such a case, you might conclude that it is very unlikely to get a sample mean of 320 grams if the population mean is really 368 grams. Therefore, it is more logical to conclude that the population mean is not equal to 368 grams. Here you reject the null hypothesis.

However, the decision-making process is not always so clear-cut. Determining what is "very close" and what is "very different" is arbitrary without clear definitions. Hypothesis-testing methodology provides clear definitions for evaluating differences. Furthermore, it enables you to quantify the decision-making process by computing the probability of getting a certain sample result if the null hypothesis is true. You calculate this probability by determining the sampling distribution for the sample statistic of interest (e.g., the sample mean) and then computing the particular **test statistic** based on the given sample result. Because the sampling distribution for the test statistic often follows a well-known statistical distribution, such as the standardized normal distribution or t distribution, you can use these distributions to help determine whether the null hypothesis is true.

Regions of Rejection and Nonrejection

The sampling distribution of the test statistic is divided into two regions, a **region of rejection** (sometimes called the critical region) and a **region of nonrejection** (see Figure 11.1). If the test statistic falls into the region of nonrejection, you do not reject the null hypothesis. In the Oxford Cereals scenario, you conclude that there is insufficient evidence that the population mean fill is different from 368 grams. If the test statistic falls into the rejection region, you reject the null hypothesis. In this case, you conclude that the population mean is not 368 grams.

FIGURE 11.1

Regions of rejection and nonrejection in hypothesis testing

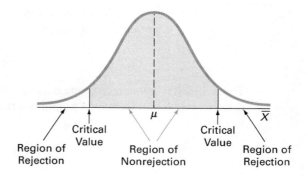

The region of rejection consists of the values of the test statistic that are unlikely to occur if the null hypothesis is true. These values are much more likely to occur if the null hypothesis is false. Therefore, if a value of the test statistic falls into this rejection region, you reject the null hypothesis because that value is unlikely if the null hypothesis is true.

To make a decision concerning the null hypothesis, you first determine the **critical value** of the test statistic. The critical value divides the nonrejection region from the rejection region. Determining the critical value depends on the size of the rejection region. The size of the rejection region is directly related to the risks involved in using only sample evidence to make decisions about a population parameter.

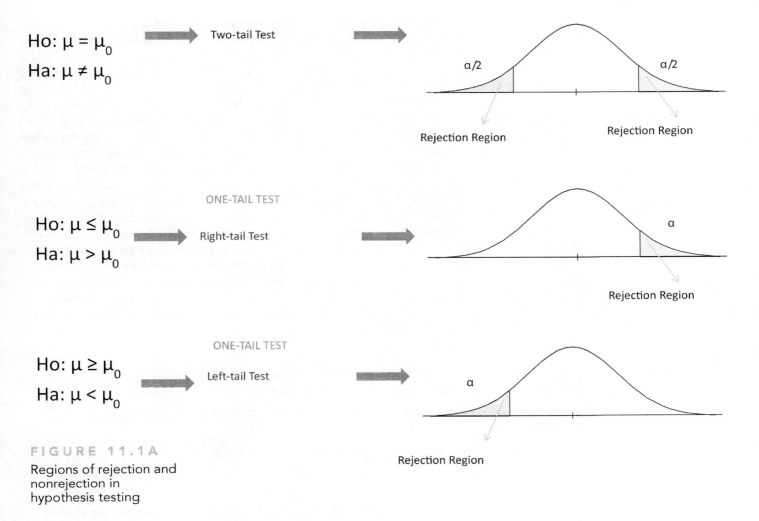

$Ho: \mu = \mu_0$
$Ha: \mu \neq \mu_0$

Two-tail Test

$\alpha/2$ $\alpha/2$

Rejection Region   Rejection Region

ONE-TAIL TEST

$Ho: \mu \leq \mu_0$
$Ha: \mu > \mu_0$

Right-tail Test

α

Rejection Region

ONE-TAIL TEST

$Ho: \mu \geq \mu_0$
$Ha: \mu < \mu_0$

Left-tail Test

α

Rejection Region

FIGURE 11.1A
Regions of rejection and nonrejection in hypothesis testing

Risks in Decision Making Using Hypothesis Testing

Using hypothesis testing involves the risk of reaching an incorrect conclusion. You might wrongly reject a true null hypothesis, H_0, or, conversely, you might wrongly *not* reject a false null hypothesis, H_0. These types of risk are called Type I and Type II errors.

TYPE I AND TYPE II ERRORS

A **Type I error** occurs if you reject the null hypothesis, H_0, when it is true and should not be rejected. A Type I error is a "false alarm." The probability of a Type I error occurring is α.

A **Type II error** occurs if you do not reject the null hypothesis, H_0, when it is false and should be rejected. A Type II error represents a "missed opportunity" to take some corrective action. The probability of a Type II error occurring is β.

In the Oxford Cereals scenario, you would make a Type I error if you concluded that the population mean fill is *not* 368 grams when it *is* 368 grams. This error causes you to needlessly adjust the filling process (the "false alarm") even though the process is working properly. In the same scenario, you would make a Type II error if you concluded that the population mean fill *is* 368 grams when it is *not* 368 grams. In this case, you would allow the process to continue without adjustment, even though an adjustment is needed (the "missed opportunity").

Traditionally, you control the Type I error by determining the risk level, α (the lowercase Greek letter *alpha*), that you are willing to have of rejecting the null hypothesis when it is true. This risk, or probability, of committing a Type I error is called the *level of significance* (α). Because you specify the level of significance before you perform the hypothesis test, you directly control the risk of committing a Type I error. Traditionally, you select a level of 0.01, 0.05, or 0.10. The choice of a particular risk level for making a Type I error depends on the cost of making a Type I error. After you specify the value for α, you can then determine the critical values that divide the rejection and nonrejection regions. You know the size of the rejection region because α is the probability of rejection when the null hypothesis is true. From this, you can then determine the critical value or values that divide the rejection and nonrejection regions.

The probability of committing a Type II error is called the β *risk*. Unlike the Type I error, which you control through the selection of α, the probability of making a Type II error depends on the difference between the hypothesized and actual values of the population parameter. Because large differences are easier to find than small ones, if the difference between the hypothesized and actual values of the population parameter is large, β is small. For example, if the population mean is 330 grams, there is a small chance (β) that you will conclude that the mean has not changed from 368 grams. However, if the difference between the hypothesized and actual values of the parameter is small, β is large. For example, if the population mean is actually 367 grams, there is a large chance (β) that you will conclude that the mean is still 368 grams.

PROBABILITY OF TYPE I AND TYPE II ERRORS

The **level of significance** ($\boldsymbol{\alpha}$) of a statistical test is the probability of committing a Type I error.

The $\boldsymbol{\beta}$ **risk** is the probability of committing a Type II error.

The complement of the probability of a Type I error, $(1 - \alpha)$, is called the *confidence coefficient*. The confidence coefficient is the probability that you will not reject the null hypothesis, H_0, when it is true and should not be rejected. In the Oxford Cereals scenario, the confidence coefficient measures the probability of concluding that the population mean fill is 368 grams when it is actually 368 grams.

The complement of the probability of a Type II error, $(1 - \beta)$, is called the *power of a statistical test*. The power of a statistical test is the probability that you will reject the null hypothesis when it is false and should be rejected. In the Oxford Cereals scenario, the power of the test is the probability that you will correctly conclude that the mean fill amount is not 368 grams when it actually is not 368 grams.

COMPLEMENTS OF TYPE I AND TYPE II ERRORS

The **confidence coefficient**, $(1 - \alpha)$, is the probability that you will not reject the null hypothesis, H_0, when it is true and should not be rejected.

The **power of a statistical test**, $(1 - \beta)$, is the probability that you will reject the null hypothesis when it is false and should be rejected.

Table 11.1 illustrates the results of the two possible decisions (do not reject H_0 or reject H_0) that you can make in any hypothesis test. You can make a correct decision or make one of two types of errors.

TABLE 11.1

Hypothesis Testing and Decision Making

	ACTUAL SITUATION	
STATISTICAL DECISION	H_0 **True**	H_0 **False**
Do not reject H_0	Correct decision Confidence $= (1 - \alpha)$	Type II error $P(\text{Type II error}) = \beta$
Reject H_0	Type I error $P(\text{Type I error}) = \alpha$	Correct decision Power $= (1 - \beta)$

One way to reduce the probability of making a Type II error is by increasing the sample size. Large samples generally permit you to detect even very small differences between the hypothesized values and the actual population parameters. For a given level of α, increasing the sample size decreases β and therefore increases the power of the statistical test to detect that the null hypothesis, H_0, is false.

However, there is always a limit to your resources, and this affects the decision of how large a sample you can select. For any given sample size, you must consider the trade-offs between the two possible types of errors. Because you can directly control the risk of a Type I error, you can reduce this risk by selecting a smaller value for α. For example, if the negative consequences associated with making a Type I error are substantial, you could select $\alpha = 0.01$ instead of 0.05. However, when you decrease α, you increase β, so reducing the risk of a Type I error results in an increased risk of a Type II error. However, to reduce β, you could select a larger value for α. Therefore, if it is important to try to avoid a Type II error, you can select α of 0.05 or 0.10 instead of 0.01.

In the Oxford Cereals scenario, the risk of a Type I error occurring involves concluding that the mean fill amount has changed from the hypothesized 368 grams when it actually has not changed. The risk of a Type II error occurring involves concluding that the mean fill amount has not changed from the hypothesized 368 grams when it actually has changed. The choice of reasonable values for α and β depends on the costs inherent in each type of error. For example, if it is very costly to change the cereal-filling process, you would want to be very confident that a change is needed before making any changes. In this case, the risk of a Type I error occurring is more important, and you would choose a small α. However, if you want to be very certain of detecting changes from a mean of 368 grams, the risk of a Type II error occurring is more important, and you would choose a higher level of α.

Now that you have been introduced to hypothesis testing, recall that in the Oxford Cereals scenario on page 41, the business problem facing Oxford Cereals is to determine if the mean fill-weight in the population of boxes in the cereal-filling process differs from 368 grams. To make this determination, you select a random sample of 25 boxes, weigh each box, compute the sample mean, $\overline{X}$, and then evaluate the difference between this sample statistic and the hypothesized population parameter by comparing the sample mean weight (in grams) to the expected population mean of 368 grams specified by the company. The null and alternative hypotheses are:

$$H_0 : \mu = 368$$
$$H_1 : \mu \neq 368$$

Flow chart for hypothesis test of one population parameter

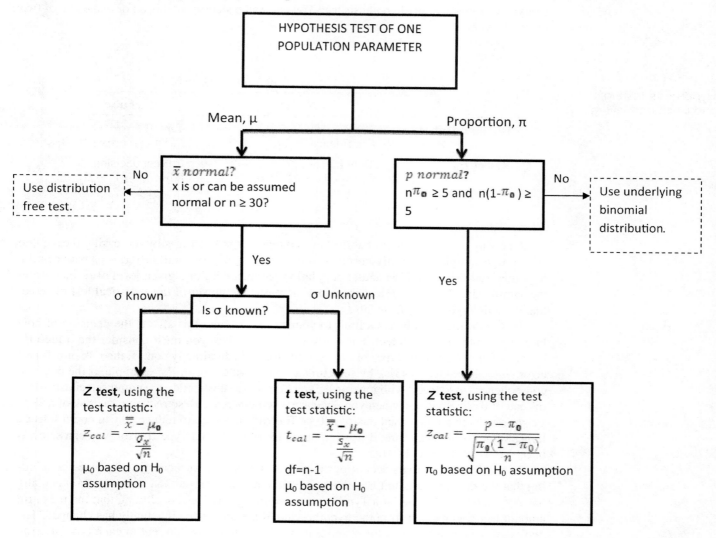

Z Test for the Mean (σ Known)

When the standard deviation, σ, is known (which rarely occurs), you use the **Z test for the mean** if the population is normally distributed. If the population is not normally distributed, you can still use the Z test if the sample size is large enough for the Central Limit Theorem to take effect (see Section 8.2). Equation (11.1) defines the Z_{STAT} test statistic for determining the difference between the sample mean, $\overline{X}$, and the population mean, μ, when the standard deviation, σ, is known.

Z TEST FOR THE MEAN (σ KNOWN)

$$Z_{STAT} = \frac{\overline{X} - \mu}{\dfrac{\sigma}{\sqrt{n}}}$$

(11.1)

In Equation (11.1), the numerator measures the difference between the observed sample mean, $\overline{X}$, and the hypothesized mean, μ. The denominator is the standard error of the mean, so Z_{STAT} represents the difference between $\overline{X}$ and μ in standard error units.

Hypothesis Testing Using the Critical Value Approach

The critical value approach compares the value of the computed Z_{STAT} test statistic from Equation (11.1) to critical values that divide the normal distribution into regions of rejection and nonrejection. The critical values are expressed as standardized Z values that are determined by the level of significance.

For example, if you use a level of significance of 0.05, the size of the rejection region is 0.05. Because the null hypothesis contains an equal sign and the alternative hypothesis contains a not equal sign, you have a **two-tail test** in which the rejection region is divided into the two tails of the distribution, with two equal parts of 0.025 in each tail. For this two-tail test, a rejection region of 0.025 in each tail of the normal distribution results in a cumulative area of 0.025 below the lower critical value and a cumulative area of 0.975 $(1 - 0.025)$ below the upper critical value (which leaves an area of 0.025 in the upper tail). According to the cumulative standardized normal distribution table (Table E.2), the critical values that divide the rejection and nonrejection regions are -1.96 and $+1.96$. Figure 11.2 illustrates that if the mean is actually 368 grams, as H_0 claims, the values of the Z_{STAT} test statistic have a standardized normal distribution centered at $Z = 0$ (which corresponds to an $\overline{X}$ value of 368 grams). Values of Z_{STAT} greater than $+1.96$ and less than -1.96 indicate that $\overline{X}$ is sufficiently different from the hypothesized $\mu = 368$ that it is unlikely that such an $\overline{X}$ value would occur if H_0 were true.

FIGURE 11.2

Testing a hypothesis about the mean (σ known) at the 0.05 level of significance

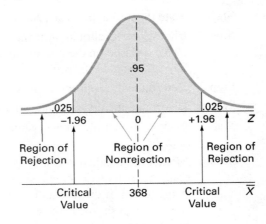

Therefore, the decision rule is

$$\text{Reject } H_0 \text{ if } Z_{STAT} > +1.96$$
$$\text{or if } Z_{STAT} < -1.96;$$
$$\text{otherwise, do not reject } H_0.$$

Suppose that the sample of 25 cereal boxes indicates a sample mean, $\overline{X}$, of 372.5 grams, and the population standard deviation, σ, is 15 grams. Using Equation (11.1) on page 48,

$$Z_{STAT} = \frac{\overline{X} - \mu}{\dfrac{\sigma}{\sqrt{n}}} = \frac{372.5 - 368}{\dfrac{15}{\sqrt{25}}} = +1.50$$

Because $Z_{STAT} = +1.50$ is greater than -1.96 and less than $+1.96$, you do not reject H_0 (see Figure 11.3).

You continue to believe that the mean fill amount is 368 grams. To take into account the possibility of a Type II error, you state the conclusion as "there is insufficient evidence that the mean fill is different from 368 grams."

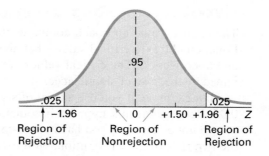

FIGURE 11.3

Testing a hypothesis about the mean cereal weight (σ known) at the 0.05 level of significance

Exhibit 11.1 summarizes the critical value approach to hypothesis testing. Steps 1 and 2 are part of the Define task, step 5 combines the Collect and Organize tasks, and steps 3, 4, and 6 involve the Visualize and Analyze tasks of the DCOVA framework first introduced on page 2. Examples 11.2 and 11.3 apply the critical value approach to hypothesis testing to Oxford Cereals and to a fast-food restaurant.

EXHIBIT 11.1

The Critical Value Approach to Hypothesis Testing

Step 1 State the null hypothesis, H_0, and the alternative hypothesis, H_1.

Step 2 Choose the level of significance, α, and the sample size, n. The level of significance is based on the relative importance of the risks of committing Type I and Type II errors in the problem.

Step 3 Determine the appropriate test statistic and sampling distribution.

Step 4 Determine the critical values that divide the rejection and nonrejection regions.

Step 5 Collect the sample data, organize the results, and compute the value of the test statistic.

Step 6 Make the statistical decision, determine whether the assumptions are valid, and state the managerial conclusion in the context of the theory, claim, or assertion being tested. If the test statistic falls into the nonrejection region, you do not reject the null hypothesis. If the test statistic falls into the rejection region, you reject the null hypothesis.

EXAMPLE 11.2

Applying the Critical Value Approach to Hypothesis Testing at Oxford Cereals

State the critical value approach to hypothesis testing at Oxford Cereals.

SOLUTION

Step 1 State the null and alternative hypotheses. The null hypothesis, H_0, is always stated as a mathematical expression, using population parameters. In testing whether the mean fill is 368 grams, the null hypothesis states that μ equals 368. The alternative hypothesis, H_1, is also stated as a mathematical expression, using population parameters. Therefore, the alternative hypothesis states that μ is not equal to 368 grams.

Step 2 Choose the level of significance and the sample size. You choose the level of significance, α, according to the relative importance of the risks of committing Type I and Type II errors in the problem. The smaller the value of α, the less risk there is of making a Type I error. In this example, making a Type I error means that you conclude that the population mean is not 368 grams when it is 368 grams. Thus, you will take corrective action on the filling process even though the process is working properly. Here, $\alpha = 0.05$ is selected. The sample size, n, is 25.

Step 3 Select the appropriate test statistic. Because σ is known from information about the filling process, you use the normal distribution and the Z_{STAT} test statistic.

Step 4 Determine the rejection region. Critical values for the appropriate test statistic are selected so that the rejection region contains a total area of α when H_0 is true and the nonrejection region contains a total area of $1 - \alpha$ when H_0 is true. Because $\alpha = 0.05$ in the cereal example, the critical values of the Z_{STAT} test statistic are -1.96 and $+1.96$. The rejection region is therefore $Z_{STAT} < -1.96$ or $Z_{STAT} > +1.96$. The nonrejection region is $-1.96 \leq Z_{STAT} \leq +1.96$.

Step 5 Collect the sample data and compute the value of the test statistic. In the cereal example, $\overline{X} = 372.5$, and the value of the test statistic is $Z_{STAT} = +1.50$.

Step 6 State the statistical decision and the managerial conclusion. First, determine whether the test statistic has fallen into the rejection region or the nonrejection region. For the cereal example, $Z_{STAT} = +1.50$ is in the region of nonrejection because $-1.96 \leq Z_{STAT} = +1.50 \leq +1.96$. Because the test statistic falls into the nonrejection region, the statistical decision is to not reject the null hypothesis, H_0. The managerial conclusion is that insufficient evidence exists to prove that the mean fill is different from 368 grams. No corrective action on the filling process is needed.

EXAMPLE 11.3

Testing and Rejecting a Null Hypothesis

You are the manager of a fast-food restaurant. The business problem is to determine whether the population mean waiting time to place an order has changed in the past month from its previous population mean value of 4.5 minutes. From past experience, you can assume that the population is normally distributed, with a population standard deviation of 1.2 minutes. You select a sample of 25 orders during a one-hour period. The sample mean is 5.1 minutes. Use the six-step approach listed in Exhibit 11.1 on page 50 to determine whether there is evidence at the 0.05 level of significance that the population mean waiting time to place an order has changed in the past month from its previous population mean value of 4.5 minutes.

SOLUTION

Step 1 The null hypothesis is that the population mean has not changed from its previous value of 4.5 minutes:

$$H_0 : \mu = 4.5$$

The alternative hypothesis is the opposite of the null hypothesis. Because the null hypothesis is that the population mean is 4.5 minutes, the alternative hypothesis is that the population mean is not 4.5 minutes:

$$H_1 : \mu \neq 4.5$$

Step 2 You have selected a sample of $n = 25$. The level of significance is 0.05 (i.e., $\alpha = 0.05$).

Step 3 Because σ is assumed to be known, you use the normal distribution and the Z_{STAT} test statistic.

Step 4 Because $\alpha = 0.05$, the critical values of the Z_{STAT} test statistic are -1.96 and $+1.96$. The rejection region is $Z_{STAT} < -1.96$ or $Z_{STAT} > +1.96$. The nonrejection region is $-1.96 \leq Z_{STAT} \leq +1.96$.

Step 5   You collect the sample data and compute $\overline{X} = 5.1$. Using Equation (11.1) on page 48, you compute the test statistic:

$$Z_{STAT} = \frac{\overline{X} - \mu}{\frac{\sigma}{\sqrt{n}}} = \frac{5.1 - 4.5}{\frac{1.2}{\sqrt{25}}} = +2.50$$

Step 6   Because $Z_{STAT} = +2.50 > +1.96$, you reject the null hypothesis. You conclude that there is evidence that the population mean waiting time to place an order has changed from its previous value of 4.5 minutes. The mean waiting time for customers is longer now than it was last month. As the manager, you would now want to determine how waiting time could be reduced to improve service.

How to Find Z$_{STAT}$ and Z Critical Value using the Calculator?

You can use the calculator to find the **z critical value** in **Step 4**

Perform the following calculator instructions to obtain z critical value.

From the **Main Menu** select:

   STAT   **F5** (DIST)   **F1** (NORM)   **F3**(InvN)   then enter the following items:

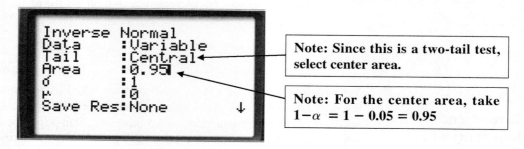

Now press **EXE** or **F1**(CALC)

The calculator will now show the results:

You can use the calculator to find the **test statistic, Z$_{STAT}$** in **Step 5**

Perform the following calculator instructions to obtain **Z$_{STAT}$**

From the **Main Menu** select:

STAT   **F3**(TEST)   **F1**(Z)   **F1**(1–S)   then enter the following items:

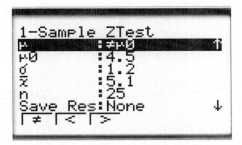

Now press **EXE** or **F1**(CALC)
The calculator will now show the results:

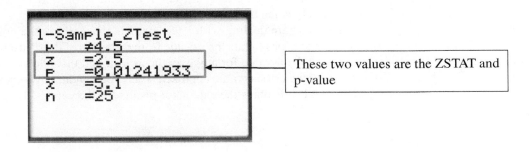

These two values are the ZSTAT and p-value

Hypothesis Testing Using the *p*-Value Approach

The ***p*-value** is the probability of getting a test statistic equal to or more extreme than the sample result, given that the null hypothesis, H_0, is true. The *p*-value is also known as the *observed level of significance*. Using the *p*-value to determine rejection and nonrejection is another approach to hypothesis testing.

The decision rules for rejecting H_0 in the *p*-value approach are

- If the *p*-value is greater than or equal to α, do not reject the null hypothesis.
- If the *p*-value is less than α, reject the null hypothesis.

Many people confuse these rules, mistakenly believing that a high *p*-value is reason for rejection. You can avoid this confusion by remembering the following:

If the *p*-value is low, then H_0 must go.

To understand the *p*-value approach, consider the Oxford Cereals scenario. You tested whether the mean fill was equal to 368 grams. The test statistic resulted in a Z_{STAT} value of $+1.50$ and you did not reject the null hypothesis because $+1.50$ was less than the upper critical value of $+1.96$ and greater than the lower critical value of -1.96.

To use the *p*-value approach for the *two-tail test*, you find the probability that the test statistic Z_{STAT} is equal to or *more extreme than* 1.50 standard error units from the center of a standardized normal distribution. In other words, you need to compute the probability that the Z_{STAT} value is greater than $+1.50$ along with the probability that the Z_{STAT} value is less than -1.50. Table E.2 shows that the probability of a Z_{STAT} value below -1.50 is 0.0668. The probability of a value below $+1.50$ is 0.9332, and the probability of a value above $+1.50$ is $1 - 0.9332 = 0.0668$. Therefore, the *p*-value for this two-tail test is $0.0668 + 0.0668 = 0.1336$ (see Figure 11.4). Thus, the probability of a test statistic equal to or more extreme than the sample result is 0.1336. Because 0.1336 is greater than $\alpha = 0.05$, you do not reject the null hypothesis.

FIGURE 11.4

Finding a *p*-value for a two-tail test

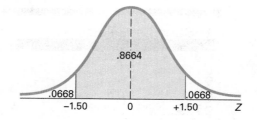

In this example, the observed sample mean is 372.5 grams, 4.5 grams above the hypothesized value, and the *p*-value is 0.1336. Thus, if the population mean is 368 grams, there is a 13.36% chance that the sample mean differs from 368 grams by at least 4.5 grams (i.e., is $\geq$ 372.5 grams or $\leq$ 363.5 grams). Therefore, even though 372.5 grams is above the hypothesized value of 368 grams, a result as extreme as or more extreme than 372.5 grams is not highly unlikely when the population mean is 368 grams.

Unless you are dealing with a test statistic that follows the normal distribution, you will only be able to approximate the *p*-value from the tables of the distribution. However, a calculator can compute the *p*-value for any hypothesis test, and this allows you to substitute the *p*-value approach for the critical value approach when you conduct hypothesis testing.

Figure 11.5 displays the calculator results for the cereal-filling example discussed beginning on page 54.

FIGURE 11.5

Calculator result for Z-test for the mean (σ known) for the cereal-filling example

Perform the following calculator instructions to obtain Z_{STAT}.

From the **Main Menu** select:
STAT F3(TEST) **F1**(Z) **F1**(1–S)   then enter the following items:

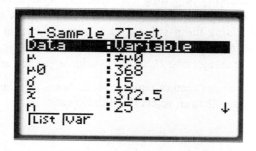

Now press **EXE** or **F1**(CALC) or **F6** (DRAW)
If you select **F6** (DRAW), you will see a normal distribution.
If you select either **EXE** or **F1**(Calc), the calculator will now show the results:

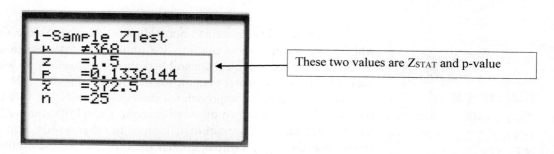

These two values are Z_{STAT} and p-value

Perform the following calculator instructions to obtain Z critical values.

From the **Main Menu** select:

STAT **F5**(DIST) **F1**(NORM) **F3**(InvN)   then enter the following items:

The critical values are:

```
Inverse Normal
x1Inv=-1.959964
x2Inv=1.95996398
```

Exhibit 11.2 summarizes the *p*-value approach to hypothesis testing. Example 11.4 applies the *p*-value approach to the fast-food restaurant example.

EXHIBIT 11.2

The *p*-Value Approach to Hypothesis Testing

Step 1 State the null hypothesis, H_0, and the alternative hypothesis, H_1.

Step 2 Choose the level of significance, α, and the sample size, n. The level of significance is based on the relative importance of the risks of committing Type I and Type II errors in the problem.

Step 3 Determine the appropriate test statistic and the sampling distribution.

Step 4 Collect the sample data, compute the value of the test statistic, and compute the *p*-value.

Step 5 Make the statistical decision and state the managerial conclusion in the context of the theory, claim, or assertion being tested. If the *p*-value is greater than or equal to α, do not reject the null hypothesis. If the *p*-value is less than α, reject the null hypothesis.

EXAMPLE 11.4

Testing and Rejecting a Null Hypothesis Using the *p*-Value Approach

You are the manager of a fast-food restaurant. The business problem is to determine whether the population mean waiting time to place an order has changed in the past month from its previous value of 4.5 minutes. From past experience, you can assume that the population standard deviation is 1.2 minutes and the population waiting time is normally distributed. You select a sample of 25 orders during a one-hour period. The sample mean is 5.1 minutes. Use the five-step *p*-value approach of Exhibit 11.2 to determine whether there is evidence that the population mean waiting time to place an order has changed in the past month from its previous population mean value of 4.5 minutes.

SOLUTION

Step 1 The null hypothesis is that the population mean has not changed from its previous value of 4.5 minutes:

$$H_0 : \mu = 4.5$$

The alternative hypothesis is the opposite of the null hypothesis. Because the null hypothesis is that the population mean is 4.5 minutes, the alternative hypothesis is that the population mean is not 4.5 minutes:

$$H_1 : \mu \neq 4.5$$

Step 2 You have selected a sample of $n = 25$ and you have chosen a 0.05 level of significance (i.e., $\alpha = 0.05$).

Step 3 Select the appropriate test statistic. Because σ is assumed known, you use the normal distribution and the Z_{STAT} test statistic.

Step 4 You collect the sample data and compute $\overline{X} = 5.1$. Using Equation (11.1) on page 48, you compute the test statistic as follows:

$$Z_{STAT} = \frac{\overline{X} - \mu}{\dfrac{\sigma}{\sqrt{n}}} = \frac{5.1 - 4.5}{\dfrac{1.2}{\sqrt{25}}} = +2.50$$

To find the probability of getting a Z_{STAT} test statistic that is equal to or more extreme than 2.50 standard error units from the center of a standardized normal distribution, you compute the probability of a Z_{STAT} value greater than $+2.50$ along with the probability of a Z_{STAT} value less than -2.50. From Table E.2, the probability of a Z_{STAT} value below -2.50 is 0.0062. The probability of a value below $+2.50$ is 0.9938. Therefore, the probability of a value above $+2.50$ is $1 - 0.9938 = 0.0062$. Thus, the p-value for this two-tail test is $0.0062 + 0.0062 = 0.0124$.

Step 5 Because the p-value $= 0.0124 < \alpha = 0.05$, you reject the null hypothesis. You conclude that there is evidence that the population mean waiting time to place an order has changed from its previous population mean value of 4.5 minutes. The mean waiting time for customers is longer now than it was last month.

EXAMPLE 11.4A

Using the Calculator to Perform Z-test for Mean

You can use the calculator to find the **test statistic, Z_{STAT}** in **Step 4**
Perform the following calculator instructions to obtain Z_{STAT}

From the **Main Menu** select:

STAT F3(TEST) **F1**(Z) **F1**(1–S)   then enter the following items:

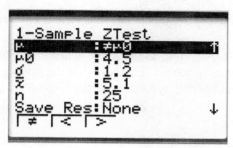

Now press **EXE** or **F1**(CALC) or **F6** (DRAW)
If you select **F6** (DRAW), you will see a normal distribution.
If you select either **EXE** or **F1**(Calc), the calculator will now show the results:

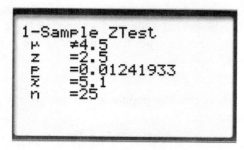

Statistical Decision: Using the *p*-value approach, we compare the p-value with α (level of significance). Since p-value is less $\alpha = 0.05$ than we reject the null hypothesis.

How to Find *p*-value with the Calculator?

You can find the *p*-value without running the Z test as shown above. You can only do this if you are given the Z stat value.

To find *p*-value with $Z_{STAT} = 2.5$, follow the following instructions

From the **Main Menu** select:

STAT F5(DIST) **F1**(NORM) **F2**(Ncd)   then enter the following items:

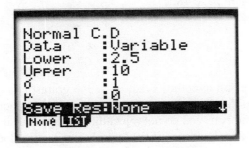

Now press **EXE** or **F1**(CALC)

The calculator will now show the results:

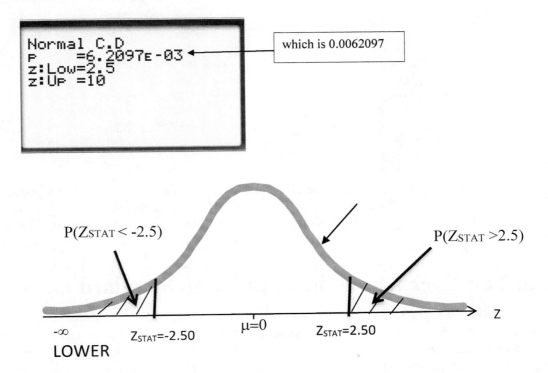

The p-value for this two tailed test is 0.0062097 + 0.0062097 = 0.0124194. The p-value is the same as above when you run the z-test.

A Connection Between Confidence Interval Estimation and Hypothesis Testing

This chapter and Chapter 10 discuss confidence interval estimation and hypothesis testing, the two major elements of statistical inference. Although confidence interval estimation and hypothesis testing share the same conceptual foundation, they are used for different purposes. In Chapter 10, confidence intervals estimated parameters. In this chapter, hypothesis testing makes decisions about specified values of population parameters. Hypothesis tests are used when trying to determine whether a parameter is less than, more than, or not equal to a specified value. Proper interpretation of a confidence interval, however, can also indicate whether a parameter is less than, more than, or not equal to a specified value. For example, in this section, you tested whether the population mean fill amount was different from 368 grams by using Equation (11.1) on page 48:

$$Z_{STAT} = \frac{\overline{X} - \mu}{\dfrac{\sigma}{\sqrt{n}}}$$

Instead of testing the null hypothesis that $\mu = 368$ grams, you can reach the same conclusion by constructing a confidence interval estimate of μ. If the hypothesized value of $\mu = 368$ is contained within the interval, you do not reject the null hypothesis because 368 would not be considered an unusual value. However, if the hypothesized value does not fall into the interval, you reject the null hypothesis because $\mu = 368$ grams is then considered an unusual value. Using Equation (10.1) on page 5 and the following results:

$$n = 25, \overline{X} = 372.5 \text{ grams}, \sigma = 15 \text{ grams}$$

for a confidence level of 95% (i.e., $\alpha = 0.05$),

$$\overline{X} \pm Z_{\alpha/2} \frac{\sigma}{\sqrt{n}}$$

$$372.5 \pm (1.96) \frac{15}{\sqrt{25}}$$

$$372.5 \pm 5.88$$

so that

$$366.62 \le \mu \le 378.38$$

Because the interval includes the hypothesized value of 368 grams, you do not reject the null hypothesis. There is insufficient evidence that the mean fill amount for the entire filling process is not 368 grams. You reached the same decision by using a two-tail hypothesis test.

Can You Ever Know the Population Standard Deviation?

The end of Section 10.1 on page 2 discussed how learning a confidence interval estimation method that required knowing σ, the population standard deviation, served as an effective introduction to the concept of a confidence interval. That section then revealed that you would be unlikely to use that procedure for most practical applications for several reasons.

Likewise, for most practical applications, you are unlikely to use a hypothesis-testing method that requires knowing σ. If you knew the population standard deviation, you would also know the population mean and would not need to form a hypothesis about the mean

and then test that hypothesis. So why study a hypothesis test of the mean, which requires that σ is known? Using such a test makes it much easier to explain the fundamentals of hypothesis testing. With a known population standard deviation, you can use the normal distribution and compute p-values using the tables of the normal distribution.

Because it is important that you understand the concept of hypothesis testing when reading the rest of this book, review this section carefully—even if you anticipate never having a practical reason to use the test represented in Equation (11.1).

11.2 *t* Test of Hypothesis for the Mean (σ Unknown)

In virtually all hypothesis-testing situations concerning the population mean, μ, you do not know the population standard deviation, σ. However, you will always be able to know the sample standard deviation, S. If you assume that the population is normally distributed, then the sampling distribution of the mean will follow a *t* distribution with $n - 1$ degrees of freedom and you can use the **t test for the mean**. If the population is not normally distributed, you can still use the *t* test if the population is not too skewed and the sample size is not too small. Equation (11.2) defines the test statistic for determining the difference between the sample mean, $\overline{X}$, and the population mean, μ, when using the sample standard deviation, S.

t TEST FOR THE MEAN (σ UNKNOWN)

$$t_{STAT} = \frac{\overline{X} - \mu}{\dfrac{S}{\sqrt{n}}} \tag{11.2}$$

where the t_{STAT} test statistic follows a *t* distribution having $n - 1$ degrees of freedom.

To illustrate the use of the *t* test for the mean, return to the Chapter 10 Ricknel Home Centers scenario on page 1. The business objective is to determine whether the mean amount per sales invoice is unchanged from the $120 of the past five years. As an accountant for the company, you need to determine whether this amount has changed. In other words, the hypothesis test is used to try to determine whether the mean amount per sales invoice is increasing or decreasing.

The Critical Value Approach

To perform this two-tail hypothesis test, you use the six-step method listed in Exhibit 11.1 on page 50.

Step 1 You define the following hypotheses:

$$H_0 : \mu = 120$$
$$H_1 : \mu \neq 120$$

> **Student Tip**
> Remember, the null hypothesis uses an equal sign and the alternative hypothesis *never* uses an equal sign.

The alternative hypothesis contains the statement you are trying to prove. If the null hypothesis is rejected, then there is statistical evidence that the population mean amount per sales invoice is no longer $120. If the statistical conclusion is "do not reject H_0," then you will conclude that there is insufficient evidence to prove that the mean amount differs from the long-term mean of $120.

Step 2 You collect the data from a sample of $n = 12$ sales invoices. You decide to use $\alpha = 0.05$.

Step 3 Because σ is unknown, you use the *t* distribution and the t_{STAT} test statistic. You must assume that the population of sales invoices is approximately normally distributed in order to use the *t* distribution because the sample size is only 12. This assumption is discussed on page 63.

TABLE 11.2

Determining the Critical Value from the *t* Table for an Area of 0.025 in Each Tail, with 11 Degrees of Freedom

	Cumulative Probabilities					
	.75	.90	.95	.975	.99	.995
Degrees of Freedom	Upper-Tail Areas					
	.25	.10	.05	.025	.01	.005
1	1.0000	3.0777	6.3138	12.7062	31.8207	63.6574
2	0.8165	1.8856	2.9200	4.3027	6.9646	9.9248
3	0.7649	1.6377	2.3534	3.1824	4.5407	5.8409
4	0.7407	1.5332	2.1318	2.7764	3.7469	4.6041
5	0.7267	1.4759	2.0150	2.5706	3.3649	4.0322
6	0.7176	1.4398	1.9432	2.4469	3.1427	3.7074
7	0.7111	1.4149	1.8946	2.3646	2.9980	3.4995
8	0.7064	1.3968	1.8595	2.3060	2.8965	3.3554
9	0.7027	1.3830	1.8331	2.2622	2.8214	3.2498
10	0.6998	1.3722	1.8125	2.2281	2.7638	3.1693
11	0.6974	1.3634	1.7959	2.2010	2.7181	3.1058

Source: Extracted from Table E.3.

TABLE 11.2A

Determining the *t* critical value for α=0.05 using the calculator

Find *t* critical value using the calculator

Instead of using the *t* table (i.e. Table E.3.) to find the *t* critical value, it is better to use the calculator to find the *t*-critical value. The disadvantage of using the Table E.3. is that the critical values are limited to the level of significance provided in the Table E.3.

To find the t critical value for $\alpha = 0.05$ with 11 degree of freedom, follow the following calculator instructions:

From the **Main Menu** select:

STAT   F6(DIST)   **F2**(t)   **F3**(Invt)   then enter the following items:

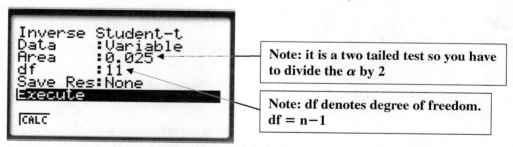

Note: it is a two tailed test so you have to divide the α by 2

Note: df denotes degree of freedom. df = n−1

The calculator will now show the results:

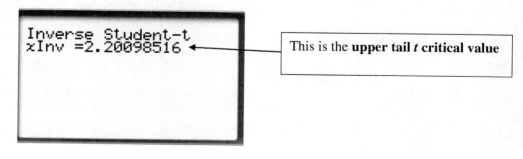

This is the **upper tail *t* critical value**

The answer given is for the upper tail *t* critical value. For the lower tail *t* critical value you insert the minus sign to the value. Thus, the lower tail critical value is −2.2010 because the *t* distribution is symmetric.

FIGURE 11.6

Testing a hypothesis about the mean (σ unknown) at the 0.05 level of significance with 11 degrees of freedom

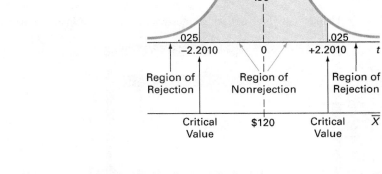

Student Tip

Since this is a two-tail test, the level of significance, $\alpha = 0.05$, is divided into two equal 0.025 parts, in each of the two tails of the distribution.

Step 4 For a given sample size, *n*, the test statistic t_{STAT} follows a *t* distribution with $n - 1$ degrees of freedom. The critical values of the *t* distribution with $12 - 1 = 11$ degrees of freedom are found in Table E.3, as illustrated in Table 11.2 and Figure 11.6. The alternative hypothesis, $H_1 : \mu \neq 120$, has two tails. The area in the rejection region of the *t* distribution's left (lower) tail is 0.025, and the area in the rejection region of the *t* distribution's right (upper) tail is also 0.025.

From the *t* table as given in Table E.3, a portion of which is shown in Table 11.2, the critical values are ±2.2010. The decision rule is

$$\text{Reject } H_0 \text{ if } t_{STAT} < -2.2010$$
$$\text{or if } t_{STAT} > +2.2010;$$
$$\text{otherwise, do not reject } H_0.$$

Step 5 You organize and store the data from a random sample of 12 sales invoices in **Invoices**:

| 108.98 | 152.22 | 111.45 | 110.59 | 127.46 | 107.26 |
| 93.32 | 91.97 | 111.56 | 75.71 | 128.58 | 135.11 |

Using Equations (4.1) and (4.5) in Chapter 4,

$$\overline{X} = \$112.85 \text{ and } S = \$20.80$$

From Equation (11.2) on page 59,

$$t_{STAT} = \frac{\overline{X} - \mu}{\dfrac{S}{\sqrt{n}}} = \frac{112.85 - 120}{\dfrac{20.80}{\sqrt{12}}} = -1.1908$$

Step 6 Because $-2.2010 < t_{STAT} = -1.1908 < 2.2010$, you do not reject H_0. You have insufficient evidence to conclude that the mean amount per sales invoice differs from $120. The audit suggests that the mean amount per invoice has not changed.

Figure 11.7 shows the results for this test of hypothesis, as computed by a calculator.

FIGURE 11.7

Calculator *t*-test of sales invoices

Perform *t*-test of hypothesis for the mean using the calculator. You can use the calculator to find the test static, t_{STAT} in Step 5. Follow the following calculator instructions:

From the **Main Menu** select:

STAT   F3(TEST)   **F2**(t)   **F1**(1-S)   then enter the following items:

Using "Variable" option to enter your data and the instructions would be:

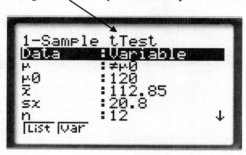

or you could use "List" option to enter your data: Before you run the *t*-test, you must input the data in a list. Enter the data given on page 61 into **List 1**

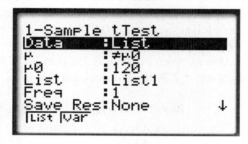

Note: Both options of entering your data (either as variable or a list) will provide the same results as shown below:

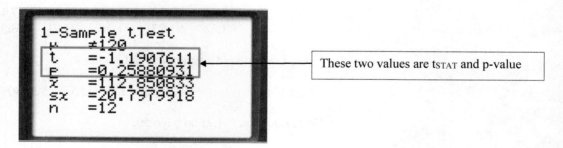

These two values are t_{STAT} and p-value

Statistical Decision: Do not reject the null hypothesis.

The *p*-Value Approach

To perform this two-tail hypothesis test, you use the five-step method listed in Exhibit 11.2 on page 55.

Step 1–3   These steps are the same as in the critical value approach discussed on page 50.

Step 4   From the Figure 11.7 results, $t_{STAT} = -1.19$ and the *p*-value $= 0.2588$

Step 5   The Casio calculator results give the *p*-value for this two-tail test as 0.259. Because the *p*-value of 0.259 is greater than $\alpha = 0.05$, you do not reject H_0. The data provide insufficient evidence to conclude that the mean amount per sales invoice differs from $120. You should inform the finance department that the audit suggests that the mean amount per invoice has not changed. The *p*-value indicates that if the null hypothesis is true, the probability that a sample of 12 invoices could have a sample mean that differs by $7.15 or more from the stated $120 is 0.259. In other words, if the mean amount per sales invoice is truly $120, then there is a 25.9% chance of observing a sample mean below $112.85 or above $127.15.

Step 6   Because the *p*-value of 0.2588 is greater than $\alpha = 0.05$, you do not reject H_0. The data provide insufficient evidence to conclude that the mean amount per sales invoice differs from $120. The audit suggests that the mean amount per invoice has not changed. The *p*-value indicates that if the null hypothesis is true, the probability that a sample of 12 invoices could have a sample mean that differs by $7.15 or more from the stated $120 is 0.2588. In other words, if the mean amount per sales invoice is truly $120, then there is a 25.88% chance of observing a sample mean below $112.85 or above $127.15.

In the preceding example, it is incorrect to state that there is a 25.88% chance that the null hypothesis is true. Remember that the *p*-value is a conditional probability, calculated by *assuming* that the null hypothesis is true. In general, it is proper to state the following:

If the null hypothesis is true, there is a (*p*-value) × 100% chance of observing a test statistic at least as contradictory to the null hypothesis as the sample result.

Checking the Normality Assumption

You use the *t* test when the population standard deviation, σ, is not known and is estimated using the sample standard deviation, *S*. To use the *t* test, you assume that the data represent a random sample from a population that is normally distributed. In practice, as long as the sample size is not very small and the population is not very skewed, the *t* distribution provides a good approximation of the sampling distribution of the mean when σ is unknown.

There are several ways to evaluate the normality assumption necessary for using the *t* test. You can examine how closely the sample statistics match the normal distribution's theoretical properties. You can also construct a histogram, stem-and-leaf display, boxplot, or normal probability plot to visualize the distribution of the sales invoice amounts. For details on evaluating normality, see Section 7.3.

Figures 11.8 and 11.9 show the descriptive statistics, boxplot, and normal probability plot for the sales invoice data.

The mean is very close to the median, and the points on the normal probability plot appear to be increasing approximately in a straight line. The boxplot appears to be approximately symmetrical. Thus, you can assume that the population of sales invoices is approximately normally distributed. The normality assumption is valid, and therefore the auditor's results are valid.

FIGURE 11.8

Descriptive statistics and boxplots for the sales invoice data

	Invoice Amount
Mean	112.8508
Median	111.02
Mode	#N/A
Minimum	75.71
Maximum	152.22
Range	76.51
Variance	432.5565
Standard Deviation	20.7980
Coeff. of Variation	18.43%
Skewness	0.1336
Kurtosis	0.1727
Count	12
Standard Error	6.0039

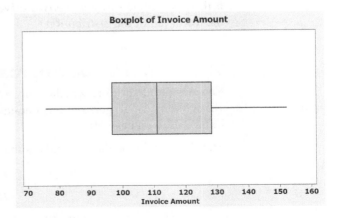

FIGURE 11.9
Normal probability plots for the sales invoice data

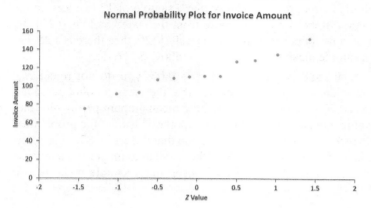

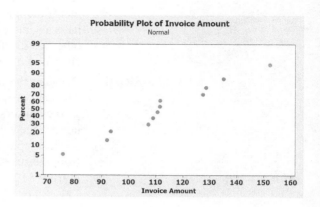

The t test is a **robust** test. A robust test does not lose power if the shape of the population departs somewhat from a normal distribution, particularly when the sample size is large enough to enable the test statistic t to follow the t distribution. However, you can reach erroneous conclusions and can lose statistical power if you use the t test incorrectly. If the sample size, n, is small (i.e., less than 30) and you cannot easily make the assumption that the underlying population is at least approximately normally distributed, then *nonparametric* testing procedures are more appropriate (see references 2 and 3).

11.3 One-Tail Tests

The examples of hypothesis testing in Sections 11.1 and 11.2 are called two-tail tests because the rejection region is divided into the two tails of the sampling distribution of the mean. In contrast, some hypothesis tests are one-tail tests because they require an alternative hypothesis that focuses on a *particular direction*.

One example of a one-tail hypothesis test would test whether the population mean is *less than* a specified value. One such situation involves the business problem concerning the service time at the drive-through window of a fast-food restaurant. According to *QSR* magazine, the speed with which customers are served is of critical importance to the success of the service (see **bit.ly/WoJpTT**). In one past study, an audit of McDonald's drive-throughs had a mean service time of 188.83 seconds, which was slower than the drive-throughs of several other fast-food chains. Suppose that McDonald's began a quality improvement effort to reduce the service time by deploying an improved drive-through service process in a sample of 25 stores. Because McDonald's would want to institute the new process in all of its stores only if the test sample saw a *decreased* drive-through time, the entire rejection region is located in the lower tail of the distribution.

The Critical Value Approach

You wish to determine whether the new drive-through process has a mean that is less than 188.83 seconds. To perform this one-tail hypothesis test, you use the six-step method listed in Exhibit 11.1 on page 50:

Step 1   You define the null and alternative hypotheses:

$$H_0 : \mu \geq 188.83$$

$$H_1 : \mu < 188.83$$

The alternative hypothesis contains the statement for which you are trying to find evidence. If the conclusion of the test is "reject H_0," there is statistical evidence that

Student Tip

The rejection region matches the direction of the alternative hypothesis. If the alternative hypothesis contains a $<$ sign, the rejection region is in the lower tail. If the alternative hypothesis contains a $>$ sign, the rejection region is in the upper tail.

the mean drive-through time is less than the drive-through time in the old process. This would be reason to change the drive-through process for the entire population of stores. If the conclusion of the test is "do not reject H_0," then there is insufficient evidence that the mean drive-through time in the new process is significantly less than the drive-through time in the old process. If this occurs, there would be insufficient reason to institute the new drive-through process in the population of stores.

Step 2   You collect the data by selecting a sample of $n = 25$ stores. You decide to use $\alpha = 0.05$.

Step 3   Because σ is unknown, you use the t distribution and the t_{STAT} test statistic. You need to assume that the drive-through time is normally distributed because a sample of only 25 drive-through times is selected.

Step 4   The rejection region is entirely contained in the lower tail of the sampling distribution of the mean because you want to reject H_0 only when the sample mean is significantly less than 188.83 seconds. When the entire rejection region is contained in one tail of the sampling distribution of the test statistic, the test is called a **one-tail test**, or **directional test**. If the alternative hypothesis includes the *less than* sign, the critical value of t is negative. As shown in Table 11.3 and Figure 11.10, because the entire rejection region is in the lower tail of the t distribution and contains an area of 0.05, due to the symmetry of the t distribution, the critical value of the t test statistic with $25 - 1 = 24$ degrees of freedom is -1.7109.

The decision rule is

$$\text{Reject } H_0 \text{ if } t_{STAT} < -1.7109;$$

$$\text{otherwise, do not reject } H_0.$$

Step 5   From the sample of 25 stores you selected, you find that the sample mean service time at the drive-through equals 170.8 seconds and the sample standard deviation equals 21.3 seconds. Using $n = 25$, $\overline{X} = 170.8$, $S = 21.3$, and Equation (11.2) on page 59,

$$t_{STAT} = \frac{\overline{X} - \mu}{\dfrac{S}{\sqrt{n}}} = \frac{170.8 - 188.83}{\dfrac{21.3}{\sqrt{25}}} = -4.2324$$

Step 6   Because $t_{STAT} = -4.2324 < -1.7109$, you reject the null hypothesis (see Figure 11.10). You conclude that the mean service time at the drive-through is less than 188.83 seconds. There is sufficient evidence to change the drive-through process for the entire population of stores.

TABLE 11.3

Determining the Critical Value from the t Table for an Area of 0.05 in the Lower Tail, with 24 Degrees of Freedom

			Cumulative Probabilities			
	.75	.90	.95	.975	.99	.995
Degrees of Freedom			Upper-Tail Areas			
	.25	.10	.05	.025	.01	.005
1	1.0000	3.0777	6.3138	12.7062	31.8207	63.6574
2	0.8165	1.8856	2.9200	4.3027	6.9646	9.9248
3	0.7649	1.6377	2.3534	3.1824	4.5407	5.8409
⋮	⋮	⋮	⋮	⋮	⋮	⋮
23	0.6853	1.3195	1.7139	2.0687	2.4999	2.8073
24	0.6848	1.3178	1.7109	2.0639	2.4922	2.7969
25	0.6844	1.3163	1.7081	2.0595	2.4851	2.7874

Source: Extracted from Table E.3.

TABLE 11.3A

Determining the
t critical Value for
$\alpha=0.05$ in the lower
tail with 24 degree
of freedom using the
calculator

To find *t* critical value (in Step 4) using the calculator

Instead of using the *t* table (i.e. Table E.3.) to find the *t* critical value, it is better to use the calculator to find the *t*-critical value. The disadvantage of using the Table E.3. is that the critical values are limited to the level of significance provided in the Table E.3.

Follow these instructions to find *t*-critical value:

From the **Main Menu** select:

STAT   F6(DIST)   **F2**(t)   **F3**(Invt)   then enter the following items:

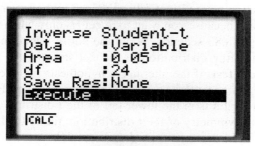

Now press **EXE** or **F1**(CALC)
The calculator will now show the results:

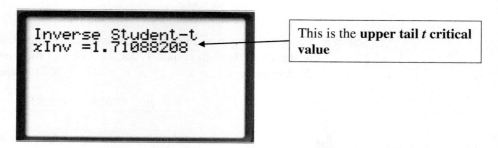

This is the **upper tail *t* critical value**

The answer given is for the upper tail *t* critical value. For the lower tail *t* critical value you insert the minus sign to the value. Thus, the lower tail critical value is -1.7109 because the *t* distribution is symmetric.

Alternatively, you can enter 0.95 for the area, which represents the upper tail area.

Recalculate the lower tail *t* critical value as follows:

STAT   F6(DIST)   **F2**(t)   **F3**(Invt)   then enter the following items:

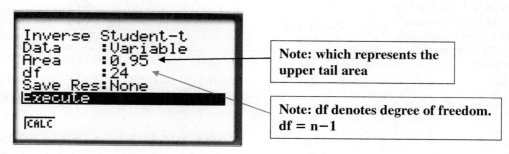

Note: which represents the upper tail area

Note: df denotes degree of freedom. df = n−1

Now key **EXE** or **F1**(CALC)

The calculator will now show the results:

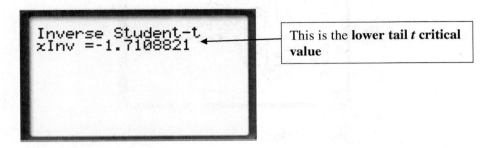

Inverse Student-t
xInv =-1.7108821

This is the **lower tail *t* critical value**

FIGURE 11.10

One-tail test of hypothesis for a mean (σ unknown) at the 0.05 level of significance

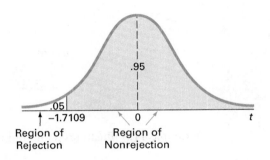

.95

.05
−1.7109   0   *t*

Region of   Region of
Rejection   Nonrejection

The *p*-Value Approach

Use the five steps listed in Exhibit 11.2 on page 55 to illustrate the *t* test for the drive-through time study using the *p*-value approach:

Step 1–3   These steps are the same as was used in the critical value approach on page 71.

Step 4 $t_{STAT} = -4.2324$ (see step 5 of the critical value approach). Because the alternative hypothesis indicates a rejection region entirely in the lower tail of the sampling distribution, to compute the *p*-value, you need to find the probability that the t_{STAT} test statistic will be less than −4.2324. Figure 11.11 shows that the *p*-value is 0.0001.

Step 5   The *p*-value of 0.0001 is less than $\alpha = 0.05$ (see Figure 11.12). You reject H_0 and conclude that the mean service time at the drive-through is less than 188.83 seconds. There is sufficient evidence to change the drive-through process for the entire population of stores.

FIGURE 11.11

Calculator *t* Test Result for the Drive-through Time Study

Perform *t*-test to obtain t_{STAT} and *p*-value in Steps 4 and 5 by following these instructions using the calculator:

From the **Main Menu** select:

STAT   F3(TEST)   **F2**(t)   **F1**(1-S)   then enter the following items:

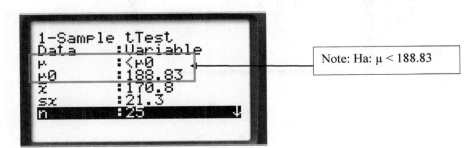

1-Sample tTest
Data   :Variable
μ   :<μ0
μ0   :188.83
x̄   :170.8
sx   :21.3
n   :25

Note: Ha: μ < 188.83

If you select either **EXE** or **F1**(Calc), the calculator will now show the results:

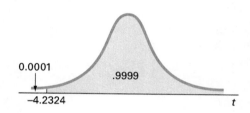

Statistical Decision: Reject the null hypothesis.

FIGURE 11.12

Determining the
p-value for a one-tail
test with calculator

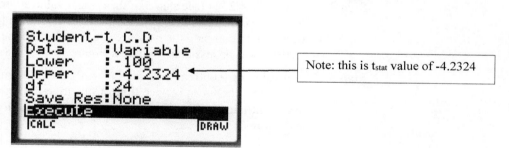

Example 11.5 illustrates a one-tail test in which the rejection region is in the lower tail.

FIGURE 11.12A

Determining the
p-value for a one-
tail test using the
calculator

Perform the following calculator instructions to obtain p-value in Step 4.

From the **Main Menu** select:

STAT F5(DIST) **F2**(t) **F2**(tcd)   then enter the following items:

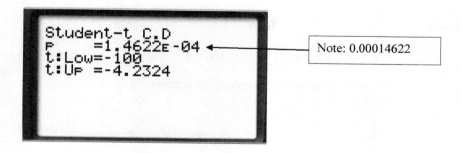

The calculator will now show the results:

EXAMPLE 11.5

A One-Tail Test for the Mean

A company that manufactures chocolate bars is particularly concerned that the mean weight of a chocolate bar is not greater than 6.03 ounces. A sample of 50 chocolate bars is selected; the sample mean is 6.034 ounces, and the sample standard deviation is 0.02 ounce. Using the $\alpha = 0.01$ level of significance, is there evidence that the population mean weight of the chocolate bars is greater than 6.03 ounces?

SOLUTION Using the critical value approach, listed in Exhibit 11.1 on page 50,

Step 1 First, you define the null and alternative hypotheses:

$$H_0 : \mu \leq 6.03$$

$$H_1 : \mu > 6.03$$

Step 2 You collect the data from a sample of $n = 50$. You decide to use $\alpha = 0.01$.

Step 3 Because σ is unknown, you use the t distribution and the t_{STAT} test statistic.

Step 4 The rejection region is entirely contained in the upper tail of the sampling distribution of the mean because you want to reject H_0 only when the sample mean is significantly greater than 6.03 ounces. Because the entire rejection region is in the upper tail of the t distribution and contains an area of 0.01, the critical value of the t distribution with $50 - 1 = 49$ degrees of freedom is 2.4049 (see Table E.3).

The decision rule is

Reject H_0 if $t_{STAT} > 2.4049$;

otherwise, do not reject H_0.

Step 5 From your sample of 50 chocolate bars, you find that the sample mean weight is 6.034 ounces, and the sample standard deviation is 0.02 ounces. Using $n = 50, \overline{X} = 6.034, S = 0.02$, and Equation (11.2) on page 59,

$$t_{STAT} = \frac{\overline{X} - \mu}{\dfrac{S}{\sqrt{n}}} = \frac{6.034 - 6.03}{\dfrac{0.02}{\sqrt{50}}} = 1.414$$

Step 6 Because $t_{STAT} = 1.414 < 2.4049$ or the p-value (from Excel) is $0.0818 > 0.01$, you do not reject the null hypothesis. There is insufficient evidence to conclude that the population mean weight is greater than 6.03 ounces.

EXAMPLE 11.5A

A One-Tail Test for the Mean – using the calculator to obtain the t_STAT and p-value

Refer to Example 11.5: At the 0.01 level of significance, is there evidence that the population mean weight of the chocolate bars is greater than 6.03 ounces?

Perform the following calculator instructions to obtain t_{STAT} in Step 5.

From the **Main Menu** select:

STAT   F3(TEST)   **F2**(t)   **F1**(1-S)   then enter the following items:

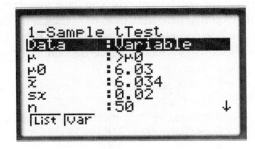

Now press **EXE** or **F1**(CALC) or **F6** (DRAW)

If you select **F6** (DRAW), you will see a *t* distribution.

If you select either **EXE** or **F1**(CALC), the calculator will now show the results:

```
1-Sample tTest
 μ    >6.03
 t    =1.41421356
 p    =0.081811
 x̄    =6.034
 sx   =0.02
 n    =50
```

Statistical Decision: Do not reject the null hypothesis because p-value (0.0818) is greater than α (0.01) or t_{STAT} (1.414) is less than t critical value (2.4049).

To Find *t* Critical Value using the Calculator.

To find the t critical value using the Casio Calculator fx-9750GII, follow the following calculator steps:

From the **Main Menu** select:

STAT F5(DIST) **F2**(t) **F3**(Invt)   then enter the following items:

Inverse Student-t
Data   : **F2**(Var) ▼
Area   : **0.01**
df   : **50-1**   **EXE**
Save Res   : None

Now key **EXE** or **F1**(CALC)

The calculator will now show the results:
Inverse Student-t
x-Inv = 2.40489176

To perform one-tail tests of hypotheses, you must properly formulate H_0 and H_1. A summary of the null and alternative hypotheses for one-tail tests is as follows:

- The null hypothesis, H_0, represents the status quo or the current belief in a situation.
- The alternative hypothesis, H_1, is the opposite of the null hypothesis and represents a research claim or specific inference you would like to prove.
- If you reject the null hypothesis, you have statistical proof that the alternative hypothesis is correct.
- If you do not reject the null hypothesis, you have failed to prove the alternative hypothesis. The failure to prove the alternative hypothesis, however, does not mean that you have proven the null hypothesis.
- The null hypothesis always refers to a specified value of the *population parameter* (such as μ), not to a *sample statistic* (such as $\overline{X}$).
- The statement of the null hypothesis *always* contains an equal sign regarding the specified value of the parameter (e.g., $H_0 : \mu \geq 188.83$).
- The statement of the alternative hypothesis *never* contains an equal sign regarding the specified value of the parameter (e.g., $H_1 : \mu < 188.83$).

11.4 Z Test of Hypothesis for the Proportion

In some situations, you want to test a hypothesis about the proportion of events of interest in the population, π, rather than test the population mean. To begin, you select a random sample and compute the **sample proportion**, $p = X/n$. You then compare the value of this statistic to the hypothesized value of the parameter, π, in order to decide whether to reject the null hypothesis.

If the number of events of interest (X) and the number of events that are not of interest $(n - X)$ are each at least five, the sampling distribution of a proportion approximately follows a normal distribution, and you can use the **Z test for the proportion**. Equation (11.3) defines this hypothesis test for the difference between the sample proportion, p, and the hypothesized population proportion, π.

Z TEST FOR THE PROPORTION

$$Z_{STAT} = \frac{p - \pi}{\sqrt{\dfrac{\pi(1 - \pi)}{n}}} \tag{11.3}$$

where

$$p = \text{sample proportion} = \frac{X}{n} = \frac{\text{number of events of interest in the sample}}{\text{sample size}}$$

$$\pi = \text{hypothesized proportion of events of interest in the population}$$

The Z_{STAT} test statistic approximately follows a standardized normal distribution when X and $(n - X)$ are each at least 5.

Alternatively, by multiplying the numerator and denominator by n, you can write the Z_{STAT} test statistic in terms of the number of events of interest, X, as shown in Equation (11.4).

Z TEST FOR THE PROPORTION IN TERMS OF THE NUMBER OF EVENTS OF INTEREST

$$Z_{STAT} = \frac{X - n\pi}{\sqrt{n\pi(1 - \pi)}} \tag{11.4}$$

The Critical Value Approach

In a survey of 792 Internet users, 681 said that they had taken steps to remove or mask their digital footprints. (Source: E. Dwoskin, "Give Me Back My Privacy," *The Wall Street Journal*, March 24, 2014, p. R2.) Suppose that a survey conducted in the previous year indicated that 80% of Internet users said that they had taken steps to remove or mask their digital footprints. Is there evidence that the proportion of Internet users who said that they had taken steps to remove or mask their digital footprints has changed from the previous year? To investigate this question, the null and alternative hypotheses are as follows:

$H_0 : \pi = 0.80$ (i.e., the proportion of Internet users who said that they had taken steps to remove or mask their digital footprints has not changed from the previous year)

$H_1 : \pi \neq 0.80$ (i.e., the proportion of Internet users who said that they had taken steps to remove or mask their digital footprints has changed from the previous year)

FIGURE 11.13
Two-tail test of
hypothesis for the
proportion at the 0.05
level of significance

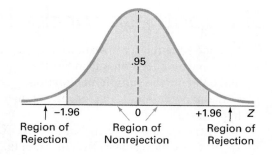

Because you are interested in determining whether the population proportion of Internet users who said that they had taken steps to remove or mask their digital footprints has changed from 0.80 in the previous year, you use a two-tail test. If you select the $\alpha = 0.05$ level of significance, the rejection and nonrejection regions are set up as in Figure 11.13, and the decision rule is

$$\text{Reject } H_0 \text{ if } Z_{STAT} < -1.96 \text{ or if } Z_{STAT} > +1.96;$$
$$\text{otherwise, do not reject } H_0.$$

Because 681 of the 792 Internet users said that they had taken steps to remove or mask their digital footprints,

$$p = \frac{681}{792} = 0.8598$$

Since $X = 681$ and $n - X = 111$, each > 5, using Equation (11.3),

$$Z_{STAT} = \frac{p - \pi}{\sqrt{\dfrac{\pi(1 - \pi)}{n}}} = \frac{0.8598 - 0.80}{\sqrt{\dfrac{0.80(1 - 0.80)}{792}}} = \frac{0.0598}{0.0142} = 4.2107$$

or, using Equation (11.4),

$$Z_{STAT} = \frac{X - n\pi}{\sqrt{n\pi(1 - \pi)}} = \frac{681 - (792)(0.80)}{\sqrt{792(0.80)(0.20)}} = \frac{47.4}{11.257} = 4.2107$$

Because $Z_{STAT} = 4.2107 > 1.96$, you reject H_0. There is evidence that the population proportion of all Internet users who said that they had taken steps to remove or mask their digital footprints has changed from 0.80 in the previous year. Figure 11.14 presents the calculator results for these data.

FIGURE 11.14

Casio Calculator
FX-9750GII results for
the Z test for whether
the proportion of
internet users who said
that they had taken steps
to remove or mask their
digital footprints has
changed from 0.80 in the
previous year

Perform z-test with the following calculator instructions to obtain Z_{STAT}

From the **Main Menu** select:

STAT   F3(TEST)   **F1**(Z)   **F3**(1-p)   then enter the following items:

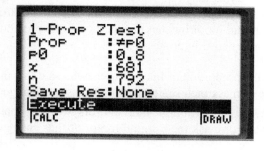

Now press **EXE** or **F1**(CALC) or **F6** (DRAW)

If you select **F6** (DRAW), you will see a normal distribution.

If you select either **EXE** or **F1**(Calc), the calculator will now show the results:

```
1-Prop ZTest
 Prop≠0.8
  z   =4.21071415
  p   =2.5456ε-05
  p̂   =0.85984848
  n   =792
```

Statistical Decision: Reject the null hypothesis.

To Find z Critical Value using the Calculator:

From the **Main Menu** select:

STAT   F5(DIST)   **F1**(NORM)   **F3**(InvN)   then enter the following items:

```
Inverse Normal
Data    :Variable
Tail    :Central
Area    :0.95
σ       :1
μ       :0
Save Res:None        ↓
[None LIST]
```

The calculator will now show the results:

```
Inverse Normal
x1Inv=-1.959964
x2Inv=1.95996398
```

The p-Value Approach

As an alternative to the critical value approach, you can compute the p-value. For this two-tail test in which the rejection region is located in the lower tail and the upper tail, you need to find the area below a Z value of -4.2107 and above a Z value of $+4.2107$. Figure 11.14 reports a p-value of 0.0000. Because this value is less than the selected level of significance ($\alpha = 0.05$), you reject the null hypothesis.

Example 11.6 illustrates a one-tail test for a proportion.

Determining the *p*-value for a One-tail Test Using the Calculator.

You can compute the p-value using the calculator. For the two-tail test in which the rejection region is located in the lower tail and upper tail, you need to find the area below a Z-value of -4.2107 and above a z value of $+4.2107$ as shown below.

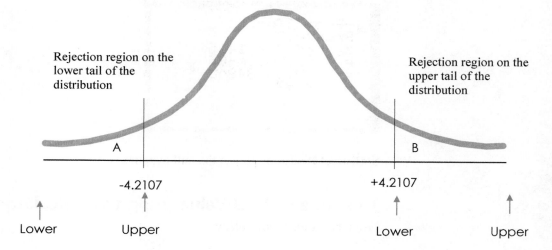

Find area A which is the p-value on the lower tail of the distribution, using the calculator.

From the **Main Menu** select:

STAT F5(DIST) **F1**(NORM) **F2**(Ncd)   then enter the following items:

Now press **EXE** or **F1**(CALC) or **F6** (DRAW)

If you select **F6** (DRAW), you will see a normal distribution.

If you select either **EXE** or **F1**(CALC), the calculator will now show the results:

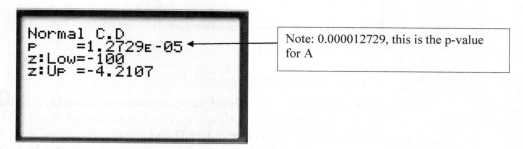

Note: 0.000012729, this is the p-value for A

Find area B which is the p-value on the upper tail of the distribution, using the calculator.

From the **Main Menu** select:

STAT F5(DIST) **F1**(NORM) **F2**(Ncd)   then enter the following items:

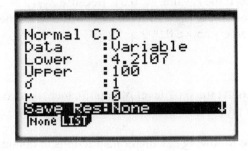

Now press **EXE** or **F1**(CALC)   or **F6** (DRAW)

If you select **F6** (DRAW), you will see a normal distribution.

If you select either **EXE** or **F1**(CALC), the calculator will now show the results:

```
Normal C.D
P     =1.2729E-05   ◄────
z:Low=4.2107
z:Up =100
```

Note: 0.000012729, this is the p-value for B

For a two-tail test, multiply p-value of 0.000012729 by 2 = 0.000025458.

EXAMPLE 11.6

Testing a
Hypothesis for
a Proportion

In addition to the business problem of the speed of service at the drive-through, fast-food chains want to fill orders correctly. The same audit that reported that McDonald's had a drive-through service time of 188.83 seconds also reported that McDonald's filled 90.9% of its drive-through orders correctly. Suppose that McDonald's begins a quality improvement effort to ensure that orders at the drive-through are filled correctly. The business problem is defined as determining whether the new process can increase the percentage of orders filled correctly. Data are collected from a sample of 400 orders using the new process. The results indicate that 378 orders were filled correctly. At the 0.01 level of significance, can you conclude that the new process has increased the proportion of orders filled correctly?

SOLUTION The null and alternative hypotheses are

$H_0 : \pi \leq 0.909$ (i.e., the population proportion of orders filled correctly using the new process is less than or equal to 0.909)

$H_1 : \pi > 0.909$ (i.e., the population proportion of orders filled correctly using the new process is greater than 0.909)

Since $X = 378$ and $n - X = 22$, both > 5, using Equation (11.3) on page 71,

$$p = \frac{X}{n} = \frac{378}{400} = 0.945$$

$$Z_{STAT} = \frac{p - \pi}{\sqrt{\dfrac{\pi(1 - \pi)}{n}}} = \frac{0.945 - 0.909}{\sqrt{\dfrac{0.909(1 - 0.909)}{400}}} = \frac{0.036}{0.0144} = 2.5034$$

The p-value for $Z_{STAT} > 2.5034$ is 0.0062.

Using the critical value approach, you reject H_0 if $Z_{STAT} > 2.33$. Using the p-value approach, you reject H_0 if the p-value < 0.01. Because $Z_{STAT} = 2.5034 > 2.33$ or the p-value $= 0.0062 < 0.01$, you reject H_0. You have evidence that the new process has increased the proportion of correct orders above 0.909 or 90.9%.

EXAMPLE 11.6A

Casio Calculator FX-9750GII Results for the *Z* Test of Hypothesis for a Proportion

Refer to Example 11.6. At the 0.01 level of significance, can you conclude that the new process has increased the proportion of orders filled correctly?

Perform z-test with the following calculator instructions to obtain Z_{STAT}

From the **Main Menu** select:

STAT   F3(TEST)   **F1**(Z)   **F3**(1-p)   then enter the following items:

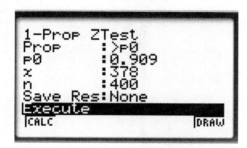

Now press **EXE** or **F1**(CALC) or **F6** (DRAW)
If you select **F6** (DRAW), you will see a normal distribution. If you select either **EXE** or **F1**(CALC), the calculator will now show the results:

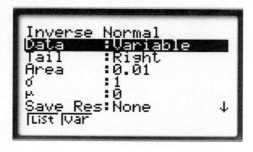

Statistical Decision: Reject the null hypothesis.

To Find *z* Critical Value Using the Calculator:

From the **Main Menu** select:

STAT   F5(DIST)   **F1**(NORM)   **F3**(InvN)   then enter the following items:

The calculator will now show the results:

11.5 Potential Hypothesis-Testing Pitfalls and Ethical Issues

To this point, you have studied the fundamental concepts of hypothesis testing. You have used hypothesis testing to analyze differences between sample statistics and hypothesized population parameters in order to make business decisions concerning the underlying population characteristics. You have also learned how to evaluate the risks involved in making these decisions.

When planning to carry out a hypothesis test based on a survey, research study, or designed experiment, you must ask several questions to ensure that you use proper methodology. You need to raise and answer questions such as the following in the planning stage:

- What is the goal of the survey, study, or experiment? How can you translate the goal into a null hypothesis and an alternative hypothesis?
- Is the hypothesis test a two-tail test or one-tail test?
- Can you select a random sample from the underlying population of interest?
- What types of data will you collect in the sample? Are the variables numerical or categorical?
- At what level of significance should you conduct the hypothesis test?
- Is the intended sample size large enough to achieve the desired power of the test for the level of significance chosen?
- What statistical test procedure should you use and why?
- What conclusions and interpretations can you reach from the results of the hypothesis test?

Failing to consider these questions early in the planning process can lead to biased or incomplete results. Proper planning can help ensure that the statistical study will provide objective information needed to make good business decisions.

Statistical Significance Versus Practical Significance

You need to make a distinction between the existence of a statistically significant result and its practical significance in a field of application. Sometimes, due to a very large sample size, you may get a result that is statistically significant but has little practical significance. For example, suppose that prior to a national marketing campaign focusing on a series of expensive television commercials, you believe that the proportion of people who recognize your brand is 0.30. At the completion of the campaign, a survey of 20,000 people indicates that 6,168 recognized your brand. A one-tail test trying to prove that the proportion is now greater than 0.30 results in a p-value of 0.0047, and the correct statistical conclusion is that the proportion of consumers recognizing your brand name has now increased. Was the campaign successful? The result of the hypothesis test indicates a statistically significant increase in brand awareness, but is this increase practically important? The population proportion is now estimated at $6,168/20,000 = 0.3084 = 0.3084$ or 30.84%. This increase is less than 1% more than the hypothesized value of 30%. Did the large expenses associated with the marketing campaign produce a result with a meaningful increase in brand awareness? Because of the minimal real-world impact that an increase of less than 1% has on the overall marketing strategy and the huge expenses associated with the marketing campaign, you should conclude that the campaign was not successful. On the other hand, if the campaign increased brand awareness from 30% to 50%, you would be inclined to conclude that the campaign was successful.

Statistical *Insignificance* Versus Importance

In contrast to the issue of the practical significance of a statistically significant result is the situation in which an important result may not be statistically significant. In a recent case (see reference 1), the U.S. Supreme Court ruled that companies cannot rely solely on whether the result of a study is significant when determining what they communicate to investors. In some situations (see reference 6), the lack of a large enough sample size may result in a nonsignificant result when in fact an important difference does exist. A study that compared male and female entrepreneurship rates globally and within Massachusetts found a significant difference globally but not within Massachusetts, even though the entrepreneurship rates for females and for males in the two geographic areas were similar (8.8% for males in Massachusetts as compared to 8.4% globally; 5% for females in both geographic areas). The difference was due to the fact that the global sample size was 20 times larger than the Massachusetts sample size.

Reporting of Findings

In conducting research, you should document both good and bad results. You should not just report the results of hypothesis tests that show statistical significance but omit those for which there is insufficient evidence in the findings. In instances in which there is insufficient evidence to reject H_0, you must make it clear that this does not prove that the null hypothesis is true. What the result indicates is that with the sample size used, there is not enough information to *disprove* the null hypothesis.

Ethical Issues

You need to distinguish between poor research methodology and unethical behavior. Ethical considerations arise when the hypothesis-testing process is manipulated. Some of the areas where ethical issues can arise include the use of human subjects in experiments, the data collection method, the type of test (one-tail or two-tail test), the choice of the level of significance, the cleansing and discarding of data, and the failure to report pertinent findings.

USING STATISTICS

Significant Testing at Oxford Cereals, Revisited

As the plant operations manager for Oxford Cereals, you were responsible for the cereal-filling process. It was your responsibility to adjust the process when the mean fill-weight in the population of boxes deviated from the company specification of 368 grams. You chose to conduct a hypothesis test.

You determined that the null hypothesis should be that the population mean fill was 368 grams. If the mean weight of the sampled boxes was sufficiently above or below the expected 368-gram mean specified by Oxford Cereals, you would reject the null hypothesis in favor of the alternative hypothesis that the mean fill was different from 368 grams. If this happened, you would stop production and take whatever action was necessary to correct the problem. If the null hypothesis was not rejected, you would continue to believe in the status quo—that the process was working correctly—and therefore take no corrective action.

Shutterstock

Before proceeding, you considered the risks involved with hypothesis tests. If you rejected a true null hypothesis, you would make a Type I error and conclude that the population mean fill was not 368 when it actually was 368 grams. This error would result in adjusting the filling process even though the process was working properly. If you did not reject a false null hypothesis, you would make a Type II error and conclude that the population mean fill was 368 grams when it actually was not 368 grams. Here, you would allow the process to continue without adjustment even though the process was not working properly.

After collecting a random sample of 25 cereal boxes, you used either the six-step critical value approach or the five-step *p*-value approach to hypothesis testing. Because the test statistic fell into the nonrejection region, you did not reject the null hypothesis. You concluded that there was insufficient evidence to prove that the mean fill differed from 368 grams. No corrective action on the filling process was needed.

SUMMARY

This chapter presented the foundation of hypothesis testing. You learned how to perform tests on the population mean and on the population proportion. The chapter developed both the critical value approach and the *p*-value approach to hypothesis testing.

In deciding which test to use, you should ask the following question: Does the test involve a numerical variable or a categorical variable? If the test involves a numerical variable, you use the *t* test for the mean. If the test involves a categorical variable, you use the *Z* test for the proportion. Table 11.4 lists the hypothesis tests covered in the chapter.

TABLE 11.4

Summary of Topics in Chapter 11

| | | TYPE OF DATA | |
TYPE OF ANALYSIS		**Numerical**	**Categorical**
Hypothesis test concerning a single parameter		*Z* test of hypothesis for the mean (Section 11.1) *t* test of hypothesis for the mean (Section 11.2)	*Z* test of hypothesis for the proportion (Section 11.4)

REFERENCES

1. Bialik, C. "Making a Stat Less Significant." *The Wall Street Journal*, April 2, 2011, A5.
2. Bradley, J. V. *Distribution-Free Statistical Tests*. Upper Saddle River, NJ: Prentice Hall, 1968.
3. Daniel, W. *Applied Nonparametric Statistics*, 2nd ed. Boston: Houghton Mifflin, 1990.
4. *Microsoft Excel 2013*. Redmond, WA: Microsoft Corp., 2012.
5. *Minitab Release 16*. State College, PA: Minitab, Inc., 2010.
6. Seaman, J., and E. Allen. "Not Significant, But Important?" *Quality Progress*, August 2011, 57–59.

KEY EQUATIONS

Z Test for the Mean (σ Known)

$$Z_{STAT} = \frac{\bar{X} - \mu}{\dfrac{\sigma}{\sqrt{n}}} \tag{11.1}$$

t Test for the Mean (σ Unknown)

$$t_{STAT} = \frac{\bar{X} - \mu}{\dfrac{S}{\sqrt{n}}} \tag{11.2}$$

Z Test for the Proportion

$$Z_{STAT} = \frac{p - \pi}{\sqrt{\dfrac{\pi(1 - \pi)}{n}}} \tag{11.3}$$

Z Test for the Proportion in Terms of the Number of Events of Interest

$$Z_{STAT} = \frac{X - n\pi}{\sqrt{n\pi(1 - \pi)}} \tag{11.4}$$

KEY TERMS

alternative hypothesis (H_1) 42
β risk 46
confidence coefficient 46
critical value 44
directional test 65
hypothesis testing 42
level of significance (α) 46
null hypothesis (H_0) 42

one-tail test 65
p-value 53
power of a statistical test 46
region of nonrejection 44
region of rejection 44
robust 64
sample proportion 71
t test for the mean 59

test statistic 44
two-tail test 49
Type I error 45
Type II error 45
Z test for the mean 48
Z test for the proportion 71

CHECKING YOUR UNDERSTANDING

11.1 What is the difference between a null hypothesis, H_0, and an alternative hypothesis, H_1?

11.2 What is the difference between a Type I error and a Type II error?

11.3 What is meant by the power of a test?

11.4 What is the difference between a one-tail test and a two-tail test?

11.5 What is meant by a p-value?

11.6 How can a confidence interval estimate for the population mean provide conclusions for the corresponding two-tail hypothesis test for the population mean?

11.7 What is the six-step critical value approach to hypothesis testing?

11.8 What is the five-step p-value approach to hypothesis testing?

PROBLEMS

Section 11.1

11.9 If you use a 0.05 level of significance in a two-tail hypothesis test, what decision will you make if $Z_{STAT} = -0.76$?

11.10 If you use a 0.05 level of significance in a two-tail hypothesis test, what decision will you make if $Z_{STAT} = +2.21$?

11.11 If you use a 0.10 level of significance in a two-tail hypothesis test, what is your decision rule for rejecting a null hypothesis that the population mean equals 500 if you use the Z test?

11.12 If you use a 0.01 level of significance in a two-tail hypothesis test, what is your decision rule for rejecting $H_0 : \mu = 12.5$ if you use the Z test?

11.13 What is your decision in Problem 11.12 if $Z_{STAT} = -2.61$?

11.14 What is the p-value if, in a two-tail hypothesis test, $Z_{STAT} = +2.00$?

11.15 In Problem 11.14, what is your statistical decision if you test the null hypothesis at the 0.10 level of significance?

11.16 What is the p-value if, in a two-tail hypothesis test, $Z_{STAT} = -1.38$?

11.17 In the U.S. legal system, a defendant is presumed innocent until proven guilty. Consider a null hypothesis, H_0, that a defendant is innocent, and an alternative hypothesis, H_1, that the defendant is guilty. A jury has two possible decisions: Convict the defendant (i.e., reject the null hypothesis) or do not convict the defendant (i.e., do not reject the null hypothesis). Explain the meaning of the risks of committing either a Type I or Type II error in this example.

11.18 Suppose the defendant in Problem 11.17 is presumed guilty until proven innocent. How do the null and alternative hypotheses differ from those in Problem 11.17? What are the meanings of the risks of committing either a Type I or Type II error here?

11.19 Many consumer groups feel that the U.S. Food and Drug Administration (FDA) drug approval process is too easy and, as a result, too many drugs are approved that are later found to be unsafe. On the other hand, a number of industry lobbyists have pushed for a more lenient approval process so that pharmaceutical companies can get new drugs approved more easily and quickly. Consider a null hypothesis that a new, unapproved drug is unsafe and an alternative hypothesis that a new, unapproved drug is safe.
a. Explain the risks of committing a Type I or Type II error.
b. Which type of error are the consumer groups trying to avoid? Explain.
c. Which type of error are the industry lobbyists trying to avoid? Explain.
d. How would it be possible to lower the chances of both Type I and Type II errors?

11.20 As a result of complaints from both students and faculty about lateness, the registrar at a large university is ready to undertake a study to determine whether the scheduled break between classes should be changed. Until now, the registrar has believed that there should be 20 minutes between scheduled classes. State the null hypothesis, H_0, and the alternative hypothesis, H_1.

11.21 Do business seniors at your school prepare for class more than, less than, or about the same as business seniors at other schools? The National Survey of Student Engagement (NSSE) found that business seniors spent a mean of 14 hours per week preparing for class. (*Source: A Fresh Look at Student Engagement Annual Results 2013,* available at **bit.ly/1j3Ob7N**.)

a. State the null and alternative hypotheses to try to prove that the mean number of hours preparing for class by business seniors at your school is different from the 14-hour-per-week benchmark reported by the NSSE.

b. What is a Type I error for your test?

c. What is a Type II error for your test?

11.22 The quality-control manager at a compact fluorescent light bulb (CFL) factory needs to determine whether the mean life of a large shipment of CFLs is equal to 7,500 hours. The population standard deviation is 1,000 hours. A random sample of 64 CFLs indicates a sample mean life of 7,250 hours.

a. At the 0.05 level of significance, is there evidence that the mean life is different from 7,500 hours?

b. Compute the p-value and interpret its meaning.

c. Construct a 95% confidence interval estimate of the population mean life of the CFLs.

d. Compare the results of (a) and (c). What conclusions do you reach?

11.23 Suppose that in Problem 11.22, the standard deviation is 1,200 hours.

a. Repeat (a) through (d) of Problem 11.22, assuming a standard deviation of 1,200 hours.

b. Compare the results of (a) to those of Problem 11.22.

11.24 A bottled water distributor wants to determine whether the mean amount of water contained in 1-gallon bottles purchased from a nationally known water bottling company is actually 1 gallon. You know from the water bottling company specifications that the standard deviation of the amount of water per bottle is 0.02 gallon. You select a random sample of 50 bottles, and the mean amount of water per 1-gallon bottle is 0.995 gallon.

a. Is there evidence that the mean amount is different from 1.0 gallon? (Use $\alpha = 0.01$.)

b. Compute the p-value and interpret its meaning.

c. Construct a 99% confidence interval estimate of the population mean amount of water per bottle.

d. Compare the results of (a) and (c). What conclusions do you reach?

11.25 Suppose that in Problem 11.24, the standard deviation is 0.012 gallon.

a. Repeat (a) through (d) of Problem 11.24, assuming a standard deviation of 0.012 gallon.

b. Compare the results of (a) to those of Problem 11.24.

Section 11.2

11.26 If, in a sample of $n = 16$ selected from a normal population, $\overline{X} = 56$ and $S = 12$, what is the value of t_{STAT} if you are testing the null hypothesis $H_0: \mu = 50$?

11.27 In Problem 11.26, how many degrees of freedom does the t test have?

11.28 In Problems 11.26 and 11.27, what are the critical values of t if the level of significance, α, is 0.05 and the alternative hypothesis, H_1, is $\mu \neq 50$?

11.29 In Problems 11.26, 11.27, and 11.28, what is your statistical decision if the alternative hypothesis, H_1, is $\mu \neq 50$?

11.30 If, in a sample of $n = 16$ selected from a left-skewed population, $\overline{X} = 65$, and $S = 21$, would you use the t test to test the null hypothesis $H_0: \mu = 60$? Discuss.

11.31 If, in a sample of $n = 160$ selected from a left-skewed population, $\overline{X} = 65$, and $S = 21$, would you use the t test to test the null hypothesis $H_0: \mu = 60$? Discuss.

11.32 You are the manager of a restaurant for a fast-food franchise. Last month, the mean waiting time at the drive-through window for branches in your geographic region, as measured from the time a customer places an order until the time the customer receives the order, was 3.7 minutes. You select a random sample of 64 orders. The sample mean waiting time is 3.57 minutes, with a sample standard deviation of 0.8 minute.

a. At the 0.05 level of significance, is there evidence that the population mean waiting time is different from 3.7 minutes?

b. Because the sample size is 64, do you need to be concerned about the shape of the population distribution when conducting the t test in (a)? Explain.

11.33 A manufacturer of chocolate candies uses machines to package candies as they move along a filling line. Although the packages are labeled as 8 ounces, the company wants the packages to contain a mean of 8.17 ounces so that virtually none of the packages contain less than 8 ounces. A sample of 50 packages is selected periodically, and the packaging process is stopped if there is evidence that the mean amount packaged is different from 8.17 ounces. Suppose that in a particular sample of 50 packages, the mean amount dispensed is 8.159 ounces, with a sample standard deviation of 0.051 ounce.

a. Is there evidence that the population mean amount is different from 8.17 ounces? (Use a 0.05 level of significance.)

b. Determine the p-value and interpret its meaning.

11.34 A marketing researcher wants to estimate the mean savings ($) realized by shoppers who showroom. Showrooming is the practice of inspecting products in retail stores and then purchasing the products online at a lower price. A random sample of 100 shoppers who recently purchased a consumer electronics item online after making a visit to a retail store yielded a mean savings of $58 and a standard deviation of $55.

a. Is there evidence that the population mean savings for all showroomers who purchased a consumer electronics item is different from $50? (Use a 0.05 level of significance.)

b. Determine the p-value and interpret its meaning.

11.35 The U.S. Department of Transportation requires tire manufacturers to provide performance information on tire sidewalls to help prospective buyers make their purchasing decisions. One very important piece of information is the tread wear index, which indicates the tire's resistance to tread wear. A tire with a grade of 200 should last twice as long, on average, as a tire with a grade of 100.

A consumer organization wants to test the actual tread wear index of a brand name of tires that claims "graded 200" on the sidewall of the tire. A random sample of $n = 18$ indicates a sample mean tread wear index of 195.3 and a sample standard deviation of 21.4.

a. Is there evidence that the population mean tread wear index is different from 200? (Use a 0.05 level of significance.)

b. Determine the p-value and interpret its meaning.

11.36 The file FastFood contains the amount that a sample of fifteen customers spent for lunch ($) at a fast-food restaurant:

7.42 6.29 5.83 6.50 8.34 9.51 7.10 6.80 5.90
4.89 6.50 5.52 7.90 8.30 9.60

a. At the 0.05 level of significance, is there evidence that the mean amount spent for lunch is different from $6.50?
b. Determine the p-value in (a) and interpret its meaning.
c. What assumption must you make about the population distribution in order to conduct the t test in (a) and (b)?
d. Because the sample size is 15, do you need to be concerned about the shape of the population distribution when conducting the t test in (a)? Explain.

11.37 An insurance company has the business objective of reducing the amount of time it takes to approve applications for life insurance. The approval process consists of underwriting, which includes a review of the application, a medical information bureau check, possible requests for additional medical information and medical exams, and a policy compilation stage in which the policy pages are generated and sent for delivery. The ability to deliver approved policies to customers in a timely manner is critical to the profitability of this service. During a period of one month, you collect a random sample of 27 approved policies and the total processing time, in days, stored in Insurance, are:

73 19 16 64 28 28 31 90 60 56 31 56 22 18 45 48
17 17 17 91 92 63 50 51 69 16 17

a. In the past, the mean processing time was 45 days. At the 0.05 level of significance, is there evidence that the mean processing time has changed from 45 days?
b. What assumption about the population distribution is needed in order to conduct the t test in (a)?
c. Construct a boxplot or a normal probability plot to evaluate the assumption made in (b).
d. Do you think that the assumption needed in order to conduct the t test in (a) is valid? Explain.

11.38 The following data (in Drink) represent the amount of soft drink filled in a sample of 50 consecutive 2-liter bottles. The results, listed horizontally in the order of being filled, were:

2.109 2.086 2.066 2.075 2.065 2.057 2.052 2.044
2.036 2.038 2.031 2.029 2.025 2.029 2.023 2.020
2.015 2.014 2.013 2.014 2.012 2.012 2.012 2.010
2.005 2.003 1.999 1.996 1.997 1.992 1.994 1.986
1.984 1.981 1.973 1.975 1.971 1.969 1.966 1.967
1.963 1.957 1.951 1.951 1.947 1.941 1.941 1.938
1.908 1.894

a. At the 0.05 level of significance, is there evidence that the mean amount of soft drink filled is different from 2.0 liters?
b. Determine the p-value in (a) and interpret its meaning.
c. In (a), you assumed that the distribution of the amount of soft drink filled was normally distributed. Evaluate this assumption by constructing a boxplot or a normal probability plot.
d. Do you think that the assumption needed in order to conduct the t test in (a) is valid? Explain.
e. Examine the values of the 50 bottles in their sequential order, as given in the problem. Does there appear to be a pattern to the results? If so, what impact might this pattern have on the validity of the results in (a)?

11.39 One of the major measures of the quality of service provided by any organization is the speed with which it responds to customer complaints. A large family-held department store selling furniture and flooring, including carpet, had undergone a major expansion in the past several years. In particular, the flooring department had expanded from 2 installation crews to an installation supervisor, a measurer, and 15 installation crews. The store had the business objective of improving its response to complaints. The variable of interest was defined as the number of days between when the complaint was made and when it was resolved. Data were collected from 50 complaints that were made in the past year. These data, stored in Furniture, are:

54   5   35 137   31 27 152   2 123 81 74 27
11 19 126 110 110 29   61 35   94 31 26   5
12   4 165   32   29 28   29 26   25   1 14 13
13 10   5   27   4 52   30 22   36 26 20 23
33 68

a. The installation supervisor claims that the mean number of days between the receipt of a complaint and the resolution of the complaint is 20 days. At the 0.05 level of significance, is there evidence that the claim is not true (i.e., the mean number of days is different from 20)?
b. What assumption about the population distribution is needed in order to conduct the t test in (a)?
c. Construct a boxplot or a normal probability plot to evaluate the assumption made in (b).
d. Do you think that the assumption needed in order to conduct the t test in (a) is valid? Explain.

11.40 A manufacturing company produces steel housings for electrical equipment. The main component part of the housing is a steel trough that is made out of a 14-gauge steel coil. It is produced using a 250-ton progressive punch press with a wipe-down operation that puts two 90-degree forms in the flat steel to make the trough. The distance from one side of the form to the other is critical because of weatherproofing in outdoor applications. The company requires that the width of the trough be between 8.31 inches and 8.61 inches. The file Trough contains the widths of the troughs, in inches, for a sample of $n = 49$:

8.312 8.343 8.317 8.383 8.348 8.410 8.351 8.373 8.481 8.422
8.476 8.382 8.484 8.403 8.414 8.419 8.385 8.465 8.498 8.447
8.436 8.413 8.489 8.414 8.481 8.415 8.479 8.429 8.458 8.462
8.460 8.444 8.429 8.460 8.412 8.420 8.410 8.405 8.323 8.420
8.396 8.447 8.405 8.439 8.411 8.427 8.420 8.498 8.409

a. At the 0.05 level of significance, is there evidence that the mean width of the troughs is different from 8.46 inches?
b. What assumption about the population distribution is needed in order to conduct the t test in (a)?
c. Evaluate the assumption made in (b).
d. Do you think that the assumption needed in order to conduct the t test in (a) is valid? Explain.

11.41 One operation of a steel mill is to cut pieces of steel into parts that are used in the frame for front seats in an automobile. The steel is cut with a diamond saw and requires the resulting parts must be cut to be within ±0.005 inch of the length specified by the automobile company. The file Steel contains a sample of 100 steel parts. The measurement reported is the difference, in inches, between the actual length of the steel part, as measured by a laser measurement device, and the specified length of the steel part. For example, a value of -0.002 represents a steel part that is 0.002 inch shorter than the specified length.

a. At the 0.05 level of significance, is there evidence that the mean difference is different from 0.0 inches?
b. Construct a 95% confidence interval estimate of the population mean. Interpret this interval.
c. Compare the conclusions reached in (a) and (b).
d. Because $n = 100$, do you have to be concerned about the normality assumption needed for the t test and t interval?

11.42 In Problem 4.111 in Chapter 4, you were introduced to a tea-bag-filling operation. An important quality characteristic of interest for this process is the weight of the tea in the individual bags. The file Teabags contains an ordered array of the weight, in grams, of a sample of 50 tea bags produced during an 8-hour shift.

a. Is there evidence that the mean amount of tea per bag is different from 5.5 grams? (Use $\alpha = 0.01$.)
b. Construct a 99% confidence interval estimate of the population mean amount of tea per bag. Interpret this interval.
c. Compare the conclusions reached in (a) and (b).

11.43 Experian Marketing Services reported that the typical American spends a mean of 144 minutes (2.4 hours) per day accessing the Internet via a mobile device. (Source: *The 2014 Digital Marketer*, available at **ex.pn/1kXJjfX.**) In order to test the validity of this statement, you select a sample of 30 friends and family. The results for the time spent per day accessing the Internet via mobile device (in minutes) are stored in InternetMobileTime .

a. Is there evidence that the population mean time spent per day accessing the Internet via mobile device is different from 144 minutes? Use the p-value approach and a level of significance of 0.05.
b. What assumption about the population distribution is needed in order to conduct the t test in (a)?
c. Make a list of the various ways you could evaluate the assumption noted in (b).
d. Evaluate the assumption noted in (b) and determine whether the test in (a) is valid.

Section 11.3

11.44 In a one-tail hypothesis test where you reject H_0 only in the *upper* tail, what is the p-value if $Z_{STAT} = +2.00$?

11.45 In Problem 11.44, what is your statistical decision if you test the null hypothesis at the 0.05 level of significance?

11.46 In a one-tail hypothesis test where you reject H_0 only in the *lower* tail, what is the p-value if $Z_{STAT} = -1.38$?

11.47 In Problem 11.46, what is your statistical decision if you test the null hypothesis at the 0.01 level of significance?

11.48 In a one-tail hypothesis test where you reject H_0 only in the *lower* tail, what is the p-value if $Z_{STAT} = +1.38$?

11.49 In Problem 11.48, what is the statistical decision if you test the null hypothesis at the 0.01 level of significance?

11.50 In a one-tail hypothesis test where you reject H_0 only in the *upper* tail, what is the critical value of the t-test statistic with 10 degrees of freedom at the 0.01 level of significance?

11.51 In Problem 11.50, what is your statistical decision if $t_{STAT} = +2.39$?

11.52 In a one-tail hypothesis test where you reject H_0 only in the *lower* tail, what is the critical value of the t_{STAT} test statistic with 20 degrees of freedom at the 0.01 level of significance?

11.53 In Problem 11.52, what is your statistical decision if $t_{STAT} = -1.15$?

11.54 The Los Angeles County Metropolitan Transportation Authority has set a bus mechanical reliability goal of 3,900 bus miles. Bus mechanical reliability is measured specifically as the number of bus miles between mechanical road calls. Suppose a sample of 100 buses resulted in a sample mean of 3,975 bus miles and a sample standard deviation of 275 bus miles.

a. Is there evidence that the population mean bus miles is greater than 3,900 bus miles? (Use a 0.05 level of significance.)
b. Determine the p-value and interpret its meaning.

11.55 *CarMD* reports that the cost of repairing a hybrid vehicle is falling even while typical repairs on conventional vehicles are getting more expensive. The most common hybrid repair, replacing the hybrid inverter assembly, had a mean repair cost of $2,826 in 2013. (Data extracted from *2014 CarMD Vehicle Health Index*, available at **corp.carmd.com.**) Industry experts suspect that the cost will continue to decrease given the increase in the number of technicians who have gained expertise on fixing gas–electric engines in recent months. Suppose a sample of 100 hybrid inverter assembly repairs completed in the last month was selected. The sample mean repair cost was $2,700 with the sample standard deviation of $500.

a. Is there evidence that the population mean cost is less than $2,826? (Use a 0.05 level of significance.)
b. Determine the p-value and interpret its meaning.

11.56 A quality improvement project was conducted with the objective of improving the wait time in a county health department (CHD) Adult Primary Care Unit (APCU). The evaluation plan included *waiting room time* as one key waiting time process measure. Waiting room time was defined as the time elapsed between requesting that the patient be seated in the waiting room and the time he or she was called to be placed in an exam room. Suppose that, initially, a targeted wait time goal of 25 minutes was set. After implementing an improvement framework and process, the quality improvement team collected data on a sample of 355 patients. In this sample, the mean wait time was 23.05 minutes, with a standard deviation of 16.83 minutes. (Data extracted from M. Michael, S. D. Schaffer, P. L. Egan, B. B. Little, and P. S. Pritchard, "Improving Wait Times and Patient Satisfaction in Primary Care," *Journal for Healthcare Quality*, 2013, 35(2), pp. 50–60.)

a. If you test the null hypothesis at the 0.01 level of significance, is there evidence that the population mean wait time is less than 25 minutes?
b. Interpret the meaning of the p-value in this problem.

11.57 You are the manager of a restaurant that delivers pizza to college dormitory rooms. You have just changed your delivery process in an effort to reduce the mean time between the order and completion of delivery from the current 25 minutes. A sample of 36 orders using the new delivery process yields a sample mean of 22.4 minutes and a sample standard deviation of 6 minutes.

a. Using the six-step critical value approach, at the 0.05 level of significance, is there evidence that the population mean delivery time has been reduced below the previous population mean value of 25 minutes?

b. At the 0.05 level of significance, use the five-step *p*-value approach.

c. Interpret the meaning of the *p*-value in (b).

d. Compare your conclusions in (a) and (b).

11.58 A survey of nonprofit organizations showed that online fundraising has increased in the past year. Based on a random sample of 55 nonprofit organizations, the mean one-time gift donation in the past year was $75, with a standard deviation of $9.

a. If you test the null hypothesis at the 0.01 level of significance, is there evidence that the mean one-time gift donation is greater than $70?

b. Interpret the meaning of the *p*-value in this problem.

11.59 The population mean waiting time to check out of a supermarket has been 4 minutes. Recently, in an effort to reduce the waiting time, the supermarket has experimented with a system in which infrared cameras use body heat and in-store software to determine how many lanes should be opened. A sample of 100 customers was selected, and their mean waiting time to check out was 3.25 minutes, with a sample standard deviation of 2.7 minutes.

a. At the 0.05 level of significance, using the critical value approach to hypothesis testing, is there evidence that the population mean waiting time to check out is less than 4 minutes?

b. At the 0.05 level of significance, using the *p*-value approach to hypothesis testing, is there evidence that the population mean waiting time to check out is less than 4 minutes?

c. Interpret the meaning of the *p*-value in this problem.

d. Compare your conclusions in (a) and (b).

Section 11.4

11.60 If, in a random sample of 400 items, 88 are defective, what is the sample proportion of defective items?

11.61 In Problem 11.60, if the null hypothesis is that 20% of the items in the population are defective, what is the value of Z_{STAT}?

11.62 In Problems 11.60 and 11.61, suppose you are testing the null hypothesis $H_0 : \pi = 0.20$ against the two-tail alternative hypothesis $H_1 : \pi \neq 0.20$ and you choose the level of significance $\alpha = 0.05$. What is your statistical decision?

11.63 According to a recent National Association of Colleges and Employers (NACE) report, 48% of college student internships are unpaid. (Source: "Just 38 Percent of Unpaid Internships Were Subject to FLSA Guidelines," **bit.ly/Rx76M8**.) A recent survey of 60 college interns at a local university found that 30 had unpaid internships.

a. Use the five-step *p*-value approach to hypothesis testing and a 0.05 level of significance to determine whether the proportion of college interns that had unpaid internships is different from 0.48.

b. Assume that the study found that 37 of the 60 college interns had unpaid internships and repeat (a). Are the conclusions the same?

11.64 The worldwide market share for the Mozilla Firefox web browser was 17% in a recent month. (Data extracted from **netmarketshare.com**.) Suppose that you decide to select a sample of 100 students at your university and you find that 22 use the Mozilla Firefox web browser.

a. Use the five-step *p*-value approach to try to determine whether there is evidence that the market share for the Mozilla Firefox web browser at your university is greater than the worldwide market share of 17%. (Use the 0.05 level of significance.)

b. Suppose that the sample size is $n = 400$, and you find that 22% of the sample of students at your university (88 out of 400) use the Mozilla Firefox web browser. Use the five-step *p*-value approach to try to determine whether there is evidence that the market share for the Mozilla Firefox web browser at your university is greater than the worldwide market share of 17%. (Use the 0.05 level of significance.)

c. Discuss the effect that sample size has on hypothesis testing.

d. What do you think are your chances of rejecting any null hypothesis concerning a population proportion if a sample size of $n = 20$ is used?

11.65 One of the issues facing organizations is increasing diversity throughout an organization. One of the ways to evaluate an organization's success at increasing diversity is to compare the percentage of employees in the organization in a particular position with a specific background to the percentage in a particular position with that specific background in the general workforce. Recently, a large academic medical center determined that 9 of 17 employees in a particular position were female, whereas 55% of the employees for this position in the general workforce were female. At the 0.05 level of significance, is there evidence that the proportion of females in this position at this medical center is different from what would be expected in the general workforce?

11.66 How do professionals stay on top of their careers? Of 935 surveyed U.S. LinkedIn members, 543 reported that they engaged in professional networking within the last month. (Source: LinkedIn Talent Solutions, *Talent Trends 2014*, available at **linkd.in/Rx7o5T**.) At the 0.05 level of significance, is there evidence that the proportion of all LinkedIn members who engaged in professional networking within the last month is different from 52%?

11.67 A cellphone provider has the business objective of wanting to determine the proportion of subscribers who would upgrade to a new cellphone with improved features if it were made available at a substantially reduced cost. Data are collected from a random sample of 500 subscribers. The results indicate that 135 of the subscribers would upgrade to a new cellphone at a reduced cost.

a. At the 0.05 level of significance, is there evidence that more than 20% of the customers would upgrade to a new cellphone at a reduced cost?

b. How would the manager in charge of promotional programs concerning residential customers use the results in (a)?

11.68 Actuation Consulting and Enterprise Agility recently conducted a global survey of product teams with the goal of better understanding the dynamics of product team performance and uncovering the practices that make these teams successful. One of the survey findings was that 37% of organizations have a coherent business strategy that they stick to and effectively communicate. (Source: *The Study of Product Team Performance, 2013*, available at **bit.ly/1ja3ndA**.) Suppose another study is conducted to check the validity of this result, with the goal of proving that the percentage is less than 37%.

a. State the null and research hypotheses.

b. A sample of 100 organizations is selected, and results indicate that 34 organizations have a coherent business strategy that they stick to and effectively communicate. Use either the six-step critical value hypothesis testing approach or the five-step *p*-value approach to determine at the 0.05 level of significance whether there is evidence that the percentage is less than 37%.

Review

11.69 In hypothesis testing, the common level of significance is $\alpha = 0.05$. Some might argue for a level of significance greater than 0.05. Suppose that web designers tested the proportion of potential web page visitors with a preference for a new web design over the existing web design. The null hypothesis was that the population proportion of web page visitors preferring the new design was 0.50, and the alternative hypothesis was that it was not equal to 0.50. The p-value for the test was 0.20.

a. State, in statistical terms, the null and alternative hypotheses for this example.

b. Explain the risks associated with Type I and Type II errors in this case.

c. What would be the consequences if you rejected the null hypothesis for a p-value of 0.20?

d. What might be an argument for raising the value of α?

e. What would you do in this situation?

f. What is your answer in (e) if the p-value equals 0.12? What if it equals 0.06?

11.70 Financial institutions utilize prediction models to predict bankruptcy. One such model is the Altman Z-score model, which uses multiple corporate income and balance sheet values to measure the financial health of a company. If the model predicts a low Z-score value, the firm is in financial stress and is predicted to go bankrupt within the next two years. If the model predicts a moderate or high Z-score value, the firm is financially healthy and is predicted to be a non-bankrupt firm (see **pages.stern.nyu .edu/~ealtman/Zscores.pdf**). This decision-making procedure can be expressed in the hypothesis-testing framework. The null hypothesis is that a firm is predicted to be a non-bankrupt firm. The alternative hypothesis is that the firm is predicted to be a bankrupt firm.

a. Explain the risks associated with committing a Type I error in this case.

b. Explain the risks associated with committing a Type II error in this case.

c. Which type of error do you think executives want to avoid? Explain.

d. How would changes in the model affect the probabilities of committing Type I and Type II errors?

11.71 Salesforce ExactTarget Marketing Cloud conducted a study of U.S. consumers that included 205 tablet owners. The study found that 134 tablet owners use their tablet while watching TV at least once per day. (Source: "New Mobile Tracking & Survey Data: 2014 Mobile Behavior Report," **bit.ly/1odMZ3D**.) The authors of the report imply that the survey proves that more than half of all tablet owners use their tablet while watching TV at least once per day.

a. Use the five-step p-value approach to hypothesis testing and a 0.05 level of significance to try to prove that more than half of all tablet owners use their tablet while watching TV at least once per day.

b. Based on your result in (a), is the claim implied by the authors valid?

c. Suppose the study found that 105 tablet owners use their tablet while watching TV at least once per day. Repeat parts (a) and (b).

d. Compare the results of (b) and (c).

11.72 The owner of a specialty coffee shop wants to study coffee purchasing habits of customers at her shop. She selects a random sample of 60 customers during a certain week, with the following results:

- The amount spent was $\overline{X} = \$7.25$, $S = \$1.75$.
- Thirty-one customers say they "definitely will" recommend the specialty coffee shop to family and friends.

a. At the 0.05 level of significance, is there evidence that the population mean amount spent was different from $6.50?

b. Determine the p-value in (a).

c. At the 0.05 level of significance, is there evidence that more than 50% of all the customers say they "definitely will" recommend the specialty coffee shop to family and friends?

d. What is your answer to (a) if the sample mean equals $6.25?

e. What is your answer to (c) if 39 customers say they "definitely will" recommend the specialty coffee shop to family and friends?

11.73 An auditor for a government agency was assigned the task of evaluating reimbursement for office visits to physicians paid by Medicare. The audit was conducted on a sample of 75 reimbursements, with the following results:

- In 12 of the office visits, there was an incorrect amount of reimbursement.
- The amount of reimbursement was $\overline{X} = \$93.70$, $S = \$34.55$.

a. At the 0.05 level of significance, is there evidence that the population mean reimbursement was less than $100?

b. At the 0.05 level of significance, is there evidence that the proportion of incorrect reimbursements in the population was greater than 0.10?

c. Discuss the underlying assumptions of the test used in (a).

d. What is your answer to (a) if the sample mean equals $90?

e. What is your answer to (b) if 15 office visits had incorrect reimbursements?

11.74 A bank branch located in a commercial district of a city has the business objective of improving the process for serving customers during the noon-to-1:00 P.M. lunch period. The waiting time (defined as the time the customer enters the line until he or she reaches the teller window) of a random sample of 15 customers is collected, and the results are organized and stored in Bank1 . These data are:

4.21 5.55 3.02 5.13 4.77 2.34 3.54 3.20
4.50 6.10 0.38 5.12 6.46 6.19 3.79

a. At the 0.05 level of significance, is there evidence that the population mean waiting time is less than 5 minutes?

b. What assumption about the population distribution is needed in order to conduct the t test in (a)?

c. Construct a boxplot or a normal probability plot to evaluate the assumption made in (b).

d. Do you think that the assumption needed in order to conduct the t test in (a) is valid? Explain.

e. As a customer walks into the branch office during the lunch hour, she asks the branch manager how long she can expect to wait. The branch manager replies, "Almost certainly not longer than 5 minutes." On the basis of the results of (a), evaluate this statement.

11.75 A manufacturing company produces electrical insulators. If the insulators break when in use, a short circuit is likely to occur. To test the strength of the insulators, destructive testing is carried out to determine how much force is required to break the insulators. Force is measured by observing the number of pounds of force applied to the insulator before it breaks. The following data (stored in Force) are from 30 insulators subjected to this testing:

1,870 1,728 1,656 1,610 1,634 1,784 1,522 1,696 1,592 1,662
1,866 1,764 1,734 1,662 1,734 1,774 1,550 1,756 1,762 1,866
1,820 1,744 1,788 1,688 1,810 1,752 1,680 1,810 1,652 1,736

a. At the 0.05 level of significance, is there evidence that the population mean force required to break the insulator is greater than 1,500 pounds?
b. What assumption about the population distribution is needed in order to conduct the t test in (a)?
c. Construct a histogram, boxplot, or normal probability plot to evaluate the assumption made in (b).
d. Do you think that the assumption needed in order to conduct the t test in (a) is valid? Explain.

11.76 An important quality characteristic used by the manufacturer of Boston and Vermont asphalt shingles is the amount of moisture the shingles contain when they are packaged. Customers may feel that they have purchased a product lacking in quality if they find moisture and wet shingles inside the packaging. In some cases, excessive moisture can cause the granules attached to the shingles for texture and coloring purposes to fall off the shingles, resulting in appearance problems. To monitor the amount of moisture present, the company conducts moisture tests. A shingle is weighed and then dried. The shingle is then reweighed, and, based on the amount of moisture taken out of the product, the pounds of moisture per 100 square feet are calculated. The company would like to show that the mean moisture content is less than 0.35 pound per 100 square feet. The file Moisture includes 36 measurements (in pounds per 100 square feet) for Boston shingles and 31 for Vermont shingles.

a. For the Boston shingles, is there evidence at the 0.05 level of significance that the population mean moisture content is less than 0.35 pound per 100 square feet?
b. Interpret the meaning of the p-value in (a).
c. For the Vermont shingles, is there evidence at the 0.05 level of significance that the population mean moisture content is less than 0.35 pound per 100 square feet?
d. Interpret the meaning of the p-value in (c).
e. What assumption about the population distribution is needed in order to conduct the t tests in (a) and (c)?
f. Construct histograms, boxplots, or normal probability plots to evaluate the assumption made in (a) and (c).
g. Do you think that the assumption needed in order to conduct the t tests in (a) and (c) is valid? Explain.

11.77 Studies conducted by the manufacturer of Boston and Vermont asphalt shingles have shown product weight to be a ma-

jor factor in the customer's perception of quality. Moreover, the weight represents the amount of raw materials being used and is therefore very important to the company from a cost standpoint. The last stage of the assembly line packages the shingles before the packages are placed on wooden pallets. Once a pallet is full (a pallet for most brands holds 16 squares of shingles), it is weighed, and the measurement is recorded. The file Pallet contains the weight (in pounds) from a sample of 368 pallets of Boston shingles and 330 pallets of Vermont shingles.

a. For the Boston shingles, is there evidence at the 0.05 level of significance that the population mean weight is different from 3,150 pounds?
b. Interpret the meaning of the p-value in (a).
c. For the Vermont shingles, is there evidence at the 0.05 level of significance that the population mean weight is different from 3,700 pounds?
d. Interpret the meaning of the p-value in (c).
e. In (a) through (d), do you have to be concerned with the normality assumption? Explain.

11.78 The manufacturer of Boston and Vermont asphalt shingles provides its customers with a 20-year warranty on most of its products. To determine whether a shingle will last through the warranty period, accelerated-life testing is conducted at the manufacturing plant. Accelerated-life testing exposes the shingle to the stresses it would be subject to in a lifetime of normal use in a laboratory setting via an experiment that takes only a few minutes to conduct. In this test, a shingle is repeatedly scraped with a brush for a short period of time, and the shingle granules removed by the brushing are weighed (in grams). Shingles that experience low amounts of granule loss are expected to last longer in normal use than shingles that experience high amounts of granule loss. The file Granule contains a sample of 170 measurements made on the company's Boston shingles and 140 measurements made on Vermont shingles.

a. For the Boston shingles, is there evidence at the 0.05 level of significance that the population mean granule loss is different from 0.30 grams?
b. Interpret the meaning of the p-value in (a).
c. For the Vermont shingles, is there evidence at the 0.05 level of significance that the population mean granule loss is different from 0.30 grams?
d. Interpret the meaning of the p-value in (c).
e. In (a) through (d), do you have to be concerned with the normality assumption? Explain.

REPORT WRITING EXERCISE

11.79 Referring to the results of Problems 11.76 through 11.78 concerning Boston and Vermont shingles, write a report that evaluates the moisture level, weight, and granule loss of the two types of shingles.

CASES FOR CHAPTER 11

Managing Ashland MultiComm Services

The technical operations department wants to ensure that the mean target upload speed for all Internet service subscribers is at least 0.97 on a standard scale in which the target value is 1.0. Each day, upload speed was measured 50 times, with the following results (stored in **AMS11**).

0.854 1.023 1.005 1.030 1.219 0.977 1.044 0.778 1.122 1.114
1.091 1.086 1.141 0.931 0.723 0.934 1.060 1.047 0.800 0.889
1.012 0.695 0.869 0.734 1.131 0.993 0.762 0.814 1.108 0.805

1.223 1.024 0.884 0.799 0.870 0.898 0.621 0.818 1.113 1.286
1.052 0.678 1.162 0.808 1.012 0.859 0.951 1.112 1.003 0.972

1. Compute the sample statistics and determine whether there is evidence that the population mean upload speed is less than 0.97.

2. Write a memo to management that summarizes your conclusions.

Digital Case

Apply your knowledge about hypothesis testing in this Digital Case.

In response to the negative statements made by the Concerned Consumers About Cereal Cheaters (CCACC), Oxford Cereals recently conducted an experiment concerning cereal packaging. The company claims that the results of the experiment refute the CCACC allegations that Oxford Cereals has been cheating consumers by packaging cereals at less than labeled weights.

Open **OxfordCurrentNews.pdf**, a portfolio of current news releases from Oxford Cereals. Review the relevant press releases and supporting documents. Then answer the following questions:

1. Are the results of the experiment valid? Why or why not? If you were conducting the experiment, is there anything you would change?

2. Do the results support the claim that Oxford Cereals is not cheating its customers?

3. Is the claim of the Oxford Cereals CEO that many cereal boxes contain *more* than 368 grams surprising? Is it true?

4. Could there ever be a circumstance in which the results of the Oxford Cereals experiment *and* the CCACC's results are both correct? Explain.

Sure Value Convenience Stores

You work in the corporate office for a nationwide convenience store franchise that operates nearly 10,000 stores. The per-store daily customer count (i.e., the mean number of customers in a store in one day) has been steady, at 900, for some time. To increase the customer count, the chain is considering cutting prices for coffee beverages. The small size will now be $0.59 instead of $0.99, and the medium size will be $0.69 instead of $1.19. Even with this reduction in price, the chain will have a 40% gross margin on coffee.

To test the new initiative, the chain has reduced coffee prices in a sample of 34 stores, where customer counts have been running almost exactly at the national average of 900. After four weeks, the stores sampled stabilize at a mean customer count of 974 and a standard deviation of 96. This increase seems like a substantial amount to you, but it also seems like a pretty small sample. Is there statistical evidence that reducing coffee prices is a good strategy for increasing the mean customer count? Be prepared to explain your conclusion.

CHAPTER 11 CASIO CALCULATOR GUIDE

CALCULATOR LESSON 9A

**CFX-9850GB
CALCULATOR**

Lesson 9A—Z Test of a Single Mean

EXAMPLE 11.7

A company that makes batteries for computers needs to make sure that the voltage of these batteries is not too low or too high. The ideal voltage for the QMS model battery, which is used in many computers, is 5.60 volts. The process that is used to make these batteries is also used to make many other models of batteries with different voltages. It is known that the standard deviation of the process is 0.18 volts and that the voltages will fit a normal distribution. The process has just been set up to produce 1 million QMS batteries. Before too many are produced the batteries need to be checked to see if the average voltage is close to 5.60 volts. A sample of 25 QMS batteries is tested, and the average voltage is 5.65 volts. Should the process be allowed to continue production of the QMS battery, or should it be adjusted? Use a 5% level of significance.

Solution: From the **Main Menu** select

STAT   F3(TEST) **F1**(Z) **F1**(1-S), and then enter the following items.

(Note: Only use the **EXE** key after a new entry. Otherwise, use the cursor ▼ arrow. If you accidentally hit the wrong key, use **AC/**^{ON} or **EXIT** to go back.)

1-Sample ZTest

Data	: **F2**(Var) ▼	
μ	: **F1**($\neq\mu 0$) ▼	
$\mu 0$	: **5.60**	**EXE**
σ	: **.18**	**EXE**
$\bar{x}$	: **5.65**	**EXE**
n	: **25**	**EXE**

Now press **EXE** or **F1**(Calc).

The calculator will show the following results:

1-Sample ZTest

μ	$\neq 5.6$
z	$=1.3888$
p	$=0.16486$
x	$=5.65$
n	$=25$

Since the p-value > 0.05, the conclusion is to not reject the null hypothesis. In other words, the process does not need to be adjusted.

EXAMPLE 11.8

A company that sells a brand of soft drink with a label of 355 ml is suspected of cheating its purchasers. The consumers understand that it is not necessary that every can contain 355 ml, but the average should be at least 355 ml. They believe that the average amount in the cans is less than 355 ml. A group of concerned consumers has approached a consumer advocate who has found out that the bottling process that fills this type of can has a standard deviation of 2 ml and that the volume of soft drink in the cans will fit a normal distribution. To obtain evidence, a sample of 4 cases of 24 cans was measured carefully and the mean volume was found to be 354.5 ml. At the 5% level of significance, does this evidence support the claim of the consumers?

Solution: From the **Main Menu** select

STAT F3(TEST) **F1**(Z) **F1**(1-S), and then enter the following items.

1-Sample ZTest

Data	: F2(Var) ▼	
μ	: F2(<μ0) ▼	
μ0	: 355	EXE
σ	: 2	EXE
$\bar{x}$	: 354.5	EXE
n	: 96	EXE

Now press **EXE** or **F1**(Calc).

The calculator will show the following results:

1-Sample ZTest

μ <355

z = −2.4495

p =7.1529e-03 (=0.0071529)

$\bar{x}$ =354.5

n =96

Since the p-value < 0.05, the conclusion is to *reject* the null hypothesis. In other words the evidence supports the consumers' claim.

EXAMPLE 11.9

In the past an automobile manufacturer has been using seatbelts that could withstand a breaking force of 1000 kgs. New legislation has dictated that seatbelts should be able to withstand an average of at least 1500 kgs. One supplier has approached the manufacturer with a claim that its seatbelts have an average breaking strength that is significantly higher than 1500 kgs. The standard deviation of its process is known to be 48 kgs. In order to test the claim, the automobile manufacturer has purchased 60 of these seatbelts and has determined that their mean breaking strength is 1517 kgs. At the 1% level of significance, should the auto company accept the seatbelt manufacturer's claim?

Solution: From the **Main Menu** select

STAT F3(TEST) **F1**(Z) **F1**(1-S), and then enter the following items.

Data	: F2(Var) ▼	
μ	: F3(>μ0) ▼	
μ0	: 1500	EXE
σ	: 48	EXE
$\bar{x}$	: 1517	EXE
n	: 60	EXE

Now press **EXE** or **F1**(Calc).

The calculator will show the following results:

1-Sample ZTest

μ >1500

z =2.7434

p =3.0407e-03 (=.0030407)

$\bar{x}$ =1517

n =60

Since the p-value < 0.01, the conclusion is to *reject* the null hypothesis. In other words, the evidence supports the seatbelt manufacturer's claim.

EXAMPLE 11.10

A researcher is asked to test the hypothesis that the average price of a 2-star (CAA rating) motel room has decreased since last year. Last year a study showed that the prices of all rooms were normally distributed with an average of $89.50 and a standard deviation of $2.80. A random sample of twelve 2-star motels has yielded the following information on room prices: $85.00, 92.50, 87.50, 89.90, 90.00, 82.50, 87.50, 90.00, 85.00, 89.00, 91.50 and $87.50. If it is believed that the standard deviation of the population of room prices has not changed since last year and the prices are still normally distributed, at the 5% level of significance, what conclusion should the researcher make?

Solution:

First enter the data into **List 1.**

Now, from the **Main Menu** select

STAT F3(TEST) **F1**(Z) **F1**(1-S), and then enter the following items:

Data	: **F1**(List) ▼	
μ	: **F2**($<μ0$) ▼	
μ0	: **89.50**	EXE
σ	: **2.80**	EXE
List	: **List1**	EXE
Freq	: **1**	EXE

Now press **EXE** or **F1**(Calc).

The calculator will show the following results:

1-Sample ZTest

μ	<89.5
z	$= -1.6599$
p	$=0.048469$
$\bar{x}$	$=88.158$
xσn-1	$=2.9203$
n	$=12$

Since the *p*-value < 0.05, the conclusion is to *reject* the null hypothesis. In other words, the evidence indicates that the mean price of a 2-star motel room has decreased this year and is lower than last year's mean of $89.50.

CALCULATOR LESSON 9B

CASIO FX-9750GII CALCULATOR

Lesson 9B—Z Test of a Single Mean

EXAMPLE 11.11

A company that makes batteries for computers needs to make sure that the voltage of these batteries is not too low or too high. The ideal voltage for the QMS model battery, which is used in many computers, is 5.60 volts. The process that is used to make these batteries is also used to make many other models of batteries with different voltages. It is known that the standard deviation of the process is 0.18 volts and that the voltages will fit a normal distribution. The process has just been set up to produce 1 million QMS batteries. Before too many are produced the batteries need to be checked to see if the average voltage is close to 5.60 volts. A sample of 25 QMS batteries is tested, and the average voltage was 5.65 volts. Should the process be allowed to continue production of the QMS battery, or should it be adjusted? Use a 5% level of significance.

Solution: From the **Main Menu** select

STAT F3(TEST) **F1**(Z) **F1**(1-S), and then enter the following items.

(Note: Only use the **EXE** key after a new entry. Otherwise, use the cursor ▼ arrow. If you accidentally hit the wrong key, use **AC/^{ON}** or **EXIT** to go back.)

1-Sample ZTest

Data	: **F2**(Var)	▼
μ	: **F1**(≠μ0)	▼
μ0	: **5.60**	**EXE**
σ	: **0.18**	**EXE**
$\bar{x}$	: **5.65**	**EXE**
n	: **25**	**EXE**
Save Res	: None	

Now press **EXE** or **F1**(Calc) or **F6**(DRAW).

If you select **F6**(DRAW), you will see a normal distribution.

If you select either **EXE** or **F1**(Calc), the calculator will show the following results:

1-Sample ZTest

μ	5.6
z	$= 1.38888889$
p	$= 0.16486654$
$\bar{x}$	$= 5.65$
n	$= 25$

Since the p-value > 0.05, the conclusion is to *not reject* the null hypothesis. In other words, the process does not need to be adjusted.

EXAMPLE 11.12   A company that sells a brand of soft drink with a label of 355 ml is suspected of cheating its purchasers. The consumers understand that it is not necessary that every can contain 355 ml, but the average should be at least 355 ml. They believe that the average amount in the cans is less than 355 ml. A group of concerned consumers has approached a consumer advocate who has found out that the bottling process that fills this type of can has a standard deviation of 2 ml and that the volume of soft drink in the cans will fit a normal distribution. To obtain evidence, a sample of 4 cases of 24 cans was measured carefully and the mean volume was found to be 354.5 ml. At the 5% level of significance, does this evidence support the claim of the consumers?

Solution: From the **Main Menu** select

STAT   F3(TEST) **F1**(Z) **F1**(1-S), and then enter the following items:

1-Sample ZTest

Data	: **F2**(Var)	▼
μ	: **F2**(<μ0)	▼
μ0	: **355**	**EXE**
σ	: **2**	**EXE**
$\bar{x}$	: **354.5**	**EXE**
n	: **96**	**EXE**
Save Res	: None	

Now press **EXE** or **F1**(Calc) or **F6**(DRAW).

If you select **F6**(DRAW), you will see a normal distribution.

If you select either **EXE** or **F1**(Calc), the calculator will show the following results:

1-Sample ZTest

μ	< 355
z	$= -2.4494897$
p	$= 7.1529\text{E-}03 \ (= 0.0071529)$

$\bar{x}$ =354.5

n   =25

Since the *p*-value < 0.05, the conclusion is to *reject* the null hypothesis. In other words, the evidence supports the consumers claim.

EXAMPLE 11.13   In the past an automobile manufacturer has been using seatbelts that could withstand a breaking force of 1000 kgs. New legislation has dictated that seatbelts should be able to withstand an average of at least 1500 kgs. One supplier has approached the manufacturer with a claim that its seatbelts have an average breaking strength that is significantly higher than 1500 kgs. The standard deviation of its process is known to be 48 kgs. In order to test the claim, the automobile manufacturer has purchased 60 of these seatbelts and has determined that their mean breaking strength is 1517 kgs. At the 1% level of significance, should the auto company accept the seatbelt manufacturer's claim?

Solution: From the **Main Menu** select

STAT F3(TEST) **F1**(Z) **F1**(1-S), and then enter the following items:

Data	: **F2**(Var)	▼
μ	: **F3**(>μ0)	▼
μ0	: **1500**	**EXE**
σ	: **48**	**EXE**
$\bar{x}$	: **1517**	**EXE**
n	: **60**	**EXE**
Save Res	: None	

Now press **EXE** or **F1**(Calc) or **F6**(DRAW).

If you select **F6**(DRAW), you will see a normal distribution.

If you select either **EXE** or **F1**(Calc), the calculator will show the following results:

1-Sample ZTest

μ >1500

z   =2.7433632

p   =3.0406E-03 (=.0030406)

$\bar{x}$ =1517

n   =60

Since the *p*-value < 0.01, the conclusion is to *reject* the null hypothesis. In other words, the evidence supports the seatbelt manufacturer's claim.

EXAMPLE 11.14   A researcher is asked to test the hypothesis that the average price of a 2-star (CAA rating) motel room has decreased since last year. Last year a study showed that the prices were normally distributed with an average of $89.50 and a standard deviation of $2.80. A random sample of twelve 2-star motels has yielded the following information on room prices: $85.00, 92.50, 87.50, 89.90, 90.00, 82.50, 87.50, 90.00, 85.00, 89.00, 91.50 and $87.50. If it is believed that the standard deviation of room prices has not changed since last year and the prices are still normally distributed, at the 5% level of significance, what conclusion should the researcher make?

Solution:

First enter the data into **List 1**.

Now, from the **Main Menu** select

STAT F3(TEST) **F1**(Z) **F1**(1-S), and then enter the following items:

Data	: **F1**(List)	▼
μ	: **F2**(<μ0)	▼

$\mu 0$	: 89.50	EXE
σ	: 2.80	EXE
List	: List1	EXE
Freq	: 1	EXE
Save Res	: None	

Now press **EXE** or **F1**(Calc) or **F6**(DRAW).

If you select **F6**(DRAW), you will see a normal distribution.

If you select either **EXE** or **F1**(Calc), the calculator will show the following results:

1-Sample ZTest

μ	<89.5
z	= −1.659882
p	=0.04846909
$\bar{x}$	=88.1583333
sx	=2.92029212
n	=12

Since the *p*-value < 0.05, the conclusion is to *reject* the null hypothesis. In other words, the evidence indicates that the mean price of a 2-star motel room has decreased this year and is lower than last year's mean of $89.50.

CALCULATOR LESSON 10A

CFX-9850GB CALCULATOR

Lesson 10A—t Test of a Single Mean

EXAMPLE 11.15

A new winter ice-gripping tire has been developed. It will sell in a high price range, and it is hoped that the manufacturer can claim that it will last more than 80,000 km on average. The manufacturer is certain that the mileages will be normally distributed. A random sample of 50 tires has been tested, and they lasted an average of 81,200 km with a standard deviation of 5,400 km. Use a 5% level of significance.

Solution: From the **Main Menu** select

STAT   F3(TEST)   **F2**(t)   **F1**(1-S), and then enter the following items.

(Note: Only use the **EXE** key after a new data entry. Otherwise, use the cursor ▼ arrow. If you accidentally hit the wrong key, use **AC/^{ON}** or **EXIT** to go back.)

1-Sample tTest

Data	: F2(Var)	▼
μ	: F3(>)	▼
μ_0	: 80000	EXE
$\bar{x}$	: 81200	EXE
xσn-1	: 5400	EXE
n	: 50	EXE

Now press **EXE** or **F1**(Calc).

The calculator will show the following results:

1-Sample tTest

μ	>80000
t	=1.5713
p	=0.061269

$\bar{x}$	=81200
xσn-1	=5400
n	=50

Since the *p*-value > 0.05, the conclusion is to *not reject* the null hypothesis. In other words, there is insufficient evidence to indicate that the tires last more then 80,000 km on average.

EXAMPLE 11.16 A researcher is asked to test the hypothesis that the average price of a 2-star (CAA rating) motel room has decreased since last year. Last year a study showed that the prices were normally distributed with an average of $89.50. A random sample of twelve 2-star motels has yielded the following information on room prices: $85.00, 92.50, 87.50, 89.90, 90.00, 82.50, 87.50, 90.00, 85.00, 89.00, 91.50 and $87.50. If it is believed that the distribution of room prices is normal, at the 5% level of significance, what conclusion should the researcher make?

Solution:

First enter the data into **List 1.**

Now, from the **Main Menu** select

STAT   F3(TEST)   **F2**(t)   **F1**(1-S), and then enter the following items.

1-Sample tTest
Data	: **F1**(List) ▼
μ	: **F2**(<) ▼
μ_0	: **89.50 EXE**
List	: **List1** ▼
Freq	: **F1**(1) ▼

Now press **EXE** or **F1**(Calc).

The calculator will show the following results:

1-Sample tTest
μ	<89.5
t	= −1.5915
p	=0.069901
$\bar{x}$	=88.158
xσn-1	=2.9203
n	=12

Since the *p*-value > 0.05, the conclusion is to *not reject* the null hypothesis. In other words, the evidence does not indicate that the mean price of a 2-star motel room has decreased this year.

CALCULATOR LESSON 10B

CASIO FX-9750GII CALCULATOR

Lesson 10B—*t* Test of a Single Mean

EXAMPLE 11.17 A new winter ice-gripping tire has been developed. It will sell in a high price range, and the manufacturer hopes to claim that they will last more than 80,000 km on average. The manufacturer is certain that the mileages will be normally distributed. A random sample of 50 tires has been tested, and they lasted an average of 81,200 km with a standard deviation of 5,400 km. Use a 5% level of significance.

Solution: From the **Main Menu** select,

STAT   F3(TEST)   **F2**(t)   **F1**(1-S), and then enter the following items.

(Note: Only use the **EXE** key after a new data entry. Otherwise, use the cursor ▼ arrow. If you accidentally hit the wrong key, use **AC/ON** or **EXIT** to go back.)

1-Sample tTest

Data	: **F2**(Var)	▼
μ	: **F3**(>)	▼
μ_0	: **80000**	**EXE**
$\bar{x}$	: **81200**	**EXE**
sx	: **5400**	**EXE**
n	: **50**	**EXE**
Save Res	: None	▼

Now press **EXE** or **F1**(Calc) or **F6**(DRAW).

If you select **F6**(DRAW), you will see a normal distribution.

If you select either **EXE** or **F1**(Calc), the calculator will show the following results:

1-Sample tTest

μ	>80000
t	=1.5713484
p	=0.06126869
$\bar{x}$	=81200
Sx	=5400
n	=50

Since the *p*-value > 0.05, the conclusion is to *not reject* the null hypothesis. In other words, the tires do not average more than 80,000 km.

EXAMPLE 11.18   A researcher is asked to test the hypothesis that the average price of a 2-star (CAA rating) motel room has decreased since last year. Last year a study showed that the prices were normally distributed with an average of $89.50. A random sample of twelve 2-star motels has yielded the following information on room prices: $85.00, 92.50, 87.50, 89.90, 90.00, 82.50, 87.50, 90.00, 85.00, 89.00, 91.50 and $87.50. If it is believed that the distribution of room prices is normal, at the 5% level of significance, what conclusion should the researcher make?

Solution:

First enter the data into **List 1.**

Now, from the **Main Menu** select,

STAT   F3(TEST)   **F2**(t)   **F1**(1-S), and then enter the following items.

1-Sample tTest

Data	: **F1**(List)	▼
μ	: **F2**(<)	▼
μ_0	: **89.50**	**EXE**
List	: **List1**	(Press F1 to enter list number.)
Freq	: **1**	▼
Save Res	: None	

Now press **EXE** or **F1**(Calc) or **F6**(DRAW).

If you select **F6**(DRAW), you will see a normal distribution.

If you select either **EXE** or **F1**(Calc), the calculator will show the following results:

1-Sample tTest

μ	<89.5
t	$=-1.5915085$
p	$=0.06990119$
$\bar{x}$	$=88.1583333$
sx	$=2.92029212$
n	$=12$

Since the *p*-value > 0.05, the conclusion is to *not reject* the null hypothesis. In other words, the evidence does not indicate that the mean price of a 2-star motel room has decreased this year.

CALCULATOR LESSON 11A

CFX-9850GB CALCULATOR

EXAMPLE 11.19

Lesson 10A—*Z* Test of a Single Proportion

A bank manager wants to test the hypothesis that less than 60% of all the bank's customers use the ATM to pay some of their bills. A random sample of 80 customers was selected and it was found that 43 of those customers use the ATM to pay some bills. Use the 10% significance level.

Solution: From the **Main Menu** select

STAT   F3(test)   **F1**(Z)   **F3**(1-P), and then enter the following items:

(Note: Only use the **EXE** key after a new data entry. Otherwise, use the cursor ▼ arrow. If you accidentally hit the wrong key, use **AC/ON** or **EXIT** to go back.)

1-Prop ZTest

Prop	: **F2**(<)	▼
p0	: **0.6**	**EXE**
x	: **43**	**EXE**
n	: **80**	**EXE**

Now press **EXE** or **F1**(Calc).

The calculator will show the following results:

1-Prop ZTest

μ	<0.6
z	$=-1.141$
p	$=0.12692$
$\hat{p}$	$=0.5375$
n	$=80$

Since the *p*-value > 0.05, the conclusion is to *not reject* the null hypothesis. In other words, the bank manager cannot say that less than 60% of the bank's customers use the ATM to pay some bills.

CALCULATOR LESSON 11B

CASIO FX9750GII CALCULATOR

EXAMPLE 11.20

Lesson 11B—Z Test of a Single Proportion

A bank manager wants to test the hypothesis that less than 60% of all the bank's customers use the ATM to pay some of their bills. A random sample of 80 customers was selected and it was found that 43 of the customers use the ATM to pay some bills. Use the 10% significance level.

Solution: From the **Main Menu** select

STAT   F3(test)   **F1**(Z)   **F3**(1-P), and then enter the following items.

(Note: Only use the **EXE** key after a new data entry. Otherwise, use the cursor ▼ arrow. If you accidentally hit the wrong key, use **AC/ON** or **EXIT** to go back.)

1-Prop ZTest

Prop	: **F2**(<)	▼
p0	: **0.6**	**EXE**
x	: **43**	**EXE**
n	: **80**	**EXE**

Save Res   : None

Now press **EXE** or **F1**(Calc) or **F6**(DRAW).

If you select **F6**(DRAW), you will see a normal distribution.

If you select either **EXE** or **F1**(Calc), the calculator will show the following results:

1-Prop ZTest

μ	<0.6
z	= −1.1410887
p	=0.12691651
$\hat{p}$	=0.5375
n	=80

Since the *p*-value > 0.05, the conclusion is to *not reject* the null hypothesis. In other words, the bank manager cannot say that less than 60% of the bank's customers use the ATM to pay some bills.

Hypothesis Testing: Two-Sample Tests

CONTENTS

12.1 Comparing the Means of Two Independent Populations

Do People Really Do This?

12.2 Comparing the Means of Two Related Populations

12.3 Comparing the Proportions of Two Independent Populations

12.4 *F* Test for the Ratio of Two Variances

USING STATISTICS: For North Fork, Are There Different Means to the Ends? Revisited

CHAPTER 12 CASIO CALCULATOR GUIDE

Appendix 12.1

SPSS—Version 15 Lesson 3

OBJECTIVES

Compare the means of two independent populations

Compare the means of two related populations

Compare the proportions of two independent populations

Compare the variances of two independent populations

Compare the means of more than two populations

USING STATISTICS

For North Fork, Are There Different Means to the Ends?

To what extent does the location of products affect sales in a supermarket? As a North Fork Beverages sales manager, you are negotiating with the management of FoodPlace Supermarkets for the location of displays for the new HandMade Real Citrus Cola. FoodPlace Supermarkets has offered you two different end-aisle display areas to feature your new cola: one near the produce department and the other at the front of the aisle that contains other beverage products. These ends of aisle, or end-caps, have different costs, and you would like to compare the effectiveness of the produce end-cap to the beverage end-cap.

To test the comparative effectiveness of the two end-caps, FoodPlace agrees to a pilot study. You will be able to select 20 stores from the supermarket chain that experience similar storewide sales volumes. You then randomly assign 10 of the 20 stores to sample 1 and 10 other stores to sample 2. In the sample 1 stores, you will place the new cola in the beverage end-cap, while in the sample 2 stores you will place the new cola in the produce end-cap. At the end of one week, the sales of the new cola will be recorded. How can you determine whether the sales of the new cola using beverage end-caps are different from the sales of the new cola using produce end-caps? How can you decide if the variability in new cola sales from store to store is different for the two types of displays? How could you use the answers to these questions to improve sales of your new HandMade Real Citrus Cola?

Fotolia

I n Chapter 11, you learned several hypothesis-testing procedures commonly used to test a single sample of data selected from a single population. In this chapter, you learn how to extend hypothesis testing to **two-sample tests** that compare statistics from samples selected from *two* populations. In the North Fork Beverages scenario one such test would be "Are the mean weekly sales of the new cola when using the beverage end-cap location (one population) different from the mean weekly sales of the new cola when using the produce end-cap location (a second population)?"

The test for independent samples are summarized in the flowchart below.

Flow chart for hypothesis test of two population parameters

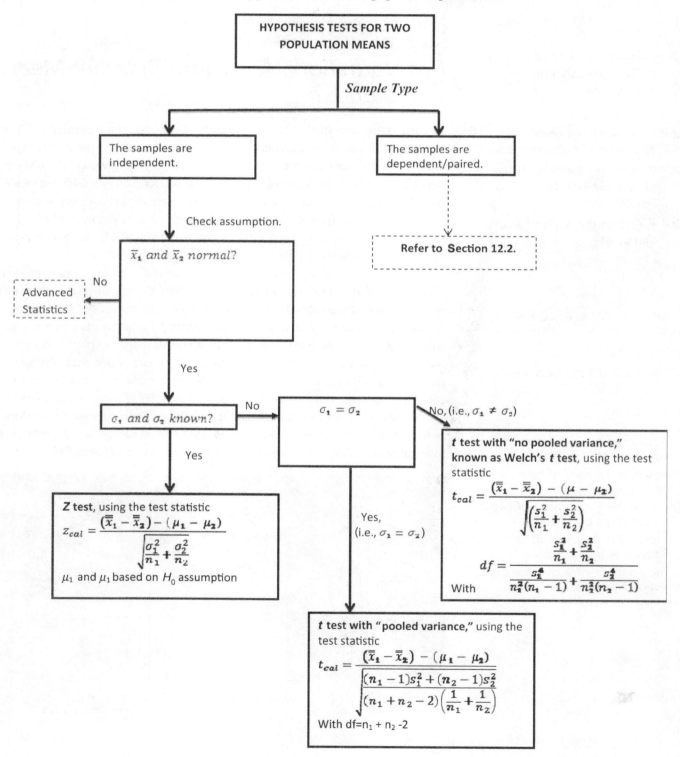

12.1 Comparing the Means of Two Independent Populations

In Sections 10.1 and 11.1, you learned that in almost all cases, you would not know the standard deviation of the population under study. Likewise, when you take a random sample from each of two independent populations, you almost always do not know the standard deviation of either population. In addition, when using a two-sample test that compares the means of samples selected from two populations, you must establish whether the assumption that the variances in the two populations are equal holds. The statistical method used to test whether the means of each population are different depends on whether the assumption holds or not.

Pooled-Variance t Test for the Difference Between Two Means

If you assume that the random samples are independently selected from two populations and that the populations are normally distributed and have equal variances, you can use a **pooled-variance t test** to determine whether there is a significant difference between the means. If the populations do not differ greatly from a normal distribution, you can still use the pooled-variance t test, especially if the sample sizes are large enough (typically ≥ 30 for each sample).

Using subscripts to distinguish between the population mean of the first population, μ_1, and the population mean of the second population, μ_2, the null hypothesis of no difference in the means of two independent populations can be stated as

$$H_0: \mu_1 = \mu_2 \quad \text{or} \quad \mu_1 - \mu_2 = 0$$

and the alternative hypothesis, that the means are different, can be stated as

$$H_1: \mu_1 \neq \mu_2 \quad \text{or} \quad \mu_1 - \mu_2 \neq 0$$

[1] When the two sample sizes are equal (i.e., $n_1 = n_2$), the equation for the pooled variance can be simplified to
$$S_p^2 = \frac{S_1^2 + S_2^2}{2}$$

To test the null hypothesis, you use the pooled-variance t test statistic t_{STAT} shown in Equation (12.1). The pooled-variance t test gets its name from the fact that the test statistic pools, or combines, the two sample variances S_1^2 and S_2^2 to compute S_p^2, the best estimate of the variance common to both populations, under the assumption that the two population variances are equal.[1]

POOLED-VARIANCE t TEST FOR THE DIFFERENCE BETWEEN TWO MEANS

$$t_{STAT} = \frac{(\overline{X}_1 - \overline{X}_2) - (\mu_1 - \mu_2)}{\sqrt{S_p^2 \left(\frac{1}{n_1} + \frac{1}{n_2} \right)}} \tag{12.1}$$

where

$$S_p^2 = \frac{(n_1 - 1)S_1^2 + (n_2 - 1)S_2^2}{(n_1 - 1) + (n_2 - 1)}$$

and S_p^2 = pooled variance

$\overline{X}_1$ = mean of the sample taken from population 1

S_1^2 = variance of the sample taken from population 1

n_1 = size of the sample taken from population 1

$\overline{X}_2$ = mean of the sample taken from population 2

S_2^2 = variance of the sample taken from population 2

n_2 = size of the sample taken from population 2

The t_{STAT} test statistic follows a t distribution with $n_1 + n_2 - 2$ degrees of freedom.

For a given level of significance, α, in a two-tail test, you reject the null hypothesis if the computed t_{STAT} test statistic is greater than the upper-tail critical value from the t distribution or if the computed t_{STAT} test statistic is less than the lower-tail critical value from the t distribution. Figure 12.1 displays the regions of rejection.

In a one-tail test in which the rejection region is in the lower tail, you reject the null hypothesis if the computed t_{STAT} test statistic is less than the lower-tail critical value from the t distribution. In a one-tail test in which the rejection region is in the upper tail, you reject the null hypothesis if the computed t_{STAT} test statistic is greater than the upper-tail critical value from the t distribution.

To demonstrate the pooled-variance t test, return to the North Fork Beverages scenario on page 99. Using the DCOVA problem-solving approach, you define the business objective as determining whether there is a difference in the mean weekly sales of the new cola when using the beverage end-cap location and when using the produce end-cap location. There are two populations of interest. The first population is the set of all possible weekly sales of the new cola if all the FoodPlace Supermarkets used the beverage end-cap location. The second population is the set of all possible weekly sales of the new cola if all the FoodPlace Supermarkets used the produce end-cap location. You collect the data from a sample of 10 FoodPlace Supermarkets that have been assigned a beverage end-cap location and another sample of 10 FoodPlace Supermarkets that have been assigned a produce end-cap location. You organize and store the results in Cola . Table 12.1 contains the new cola sales (in number of cases) for the two samples.

> **Student Tip**
>
> When *lower* or *less than* is used in an example, you have a lower-tail test. When *upper* or *more than* is used in an example, you have an upper-tail test. When *different* or *the same as* is used in an example, you have a two-tail test.

TABLE 12.1

Comparing New Cola Weekly Sales from Two Different End-Cap Locations (in number of cases)

DISPLAY LOCATION									
Beverage End-Cap					**Produce End-Cap**				
22	34	52	62	30	52	71	76	54	67
40	64	84	56	59	83	66	90	77	84

The null and alternative hypotheses are

$$H_0: \mu_1 = \mu_2 \quad \text{or} \quad \mu_1 - \mu_2 = 0$$

$$H_1: \mu_1 \neq \mu_2 \quad \text{or} \quad \mu_1 - \mu_2 \neq 0$$

Assuming that the samples are from normal populations having equal variances, you can use the pooled-variance t test. The t_{STAT} test statistic follows a t distribution with $10 + 10 - 2 = 18$ degrees of freedom. Using an $\alpha = 0.05$ level of significance, you divide the rejection region into the two tails for this two-tail test (i.e., two equal parts of 0.025 each). Table E.3 shows that the critical values for this two-tail test are $+2.1009$ and -2.1009. As shown in Figure 12.2, the decision rule is

$$\text{Reject } H_0 \text{ if } t_{STAT} > +2.1009$$

$$\text{or if } t_{STAT} < -2.1009;$$

$$\text{otherwise, do not reject } H_0.$$

FIGURE 12.2

Two-tail test of hypothesis for the difference between the means at the 0.05 level of significance with 18 degrees of freedom

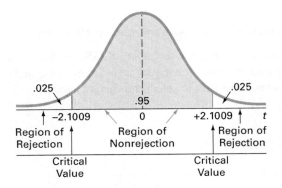

How to find *t* critical value using calculator?

Calculate the t critical value for $\alpha = 0.05$ with 18 degree of freedom, using the Casio Calculator fx-9750GII and follow the following calculator steps:

From the **Main Menu** select:

STAT F5 (DIST) **F2** (t) **F3**(Invt)   then enter the following items:

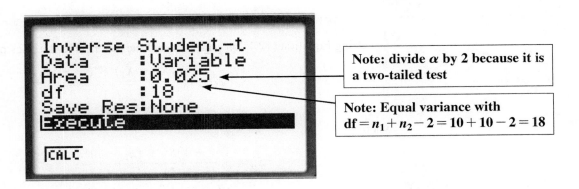

Now press **EXE** or **F1**(CALC)

The calculator will now show the results:

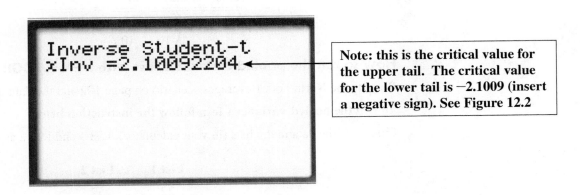

From Figure 12.3, the computed t_{STAT} test statistic for this test is -3.0446 and the *p*-value is 0.0070.

FIGURE 12.3
SPSS independent *t*-test results for the two-end cap locations data

Note: When you perform the independent *t*-test using SPSS, the SPSS output contains both the pooled-variance (i.e. equal variance assumed) and separate variance (i.e. equal variance not assumed) *t*-test results besides the Levene's test for equality of variance. Perform the Levene test first to select the correct t-test.

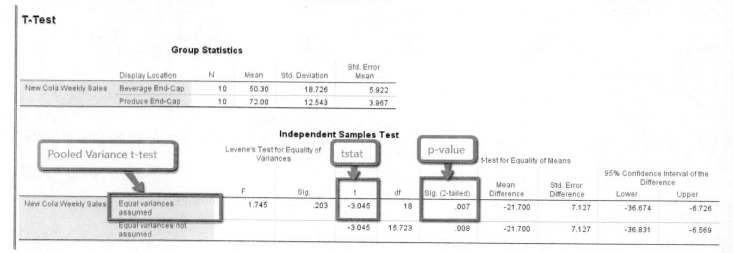

Using Equation (12.1) on page 101 and the descriptive statistics provided in Figure 12.3,

$$t_{STAT} = \frac{(\overline{X}_1 - \overline{X}_2) - (\mu_1 - \mu_2)}{\sqrt{S_p^2 \left(\frac{1}{n_1} + \frac{1}{n_2} \right)}}$$

where

$$S_p^2 = \frac{(n_1 - 1)S_1^2 + (n_2 - 1)S_2^2}{(n_1 - 1) + (n_2 - 1)}$$
$$= \frac{9(18.7264)^2 + 9(12.5433)^2}{9 + 9} = 254.0056$$

Therefore,

$$t_{STAT} = \frac{(50.3 - 72.0) - 0.0}{\sqrt{254.0056 \left(\frac{1}{10} + \frac{1}{10} \right)}} = \frac{-21.7}{\sqrt{50.801}} = -3.0446$$

How to run the pooled-variance *t* test with a FX-9750GII calculator?

Refer to the North Fork Beverages scenario on page 102 and the data in Table 12.1.

To run the pooled-variance t test, follow the instruction below.

First enter the data in the lists (in your calculator): List 1 and List 2 as shown below:

List 1	List 2
22	52
40	83
34	71
64	66
52	76
84	90
62	54
56	77
30	67
59	84

After you have entered the data, go to the **Main Menu** and select the following functions:

STAT F3(TEST) **F2**(t) **F2**(2-s)   then enter the following items:

2-Sample *t* Test

Data   : **List (F1-List)**   ▼

$\mu 1$: $\neq \mu 2$ **(F1)**   **EXE**   (**Note: Ha:** $\mu_1 \neq \mu_2$)

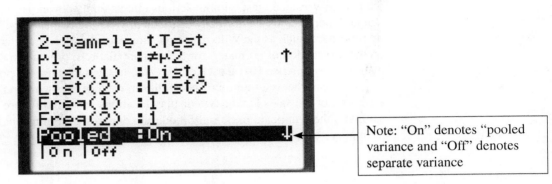

Note: "On" denotes "pooled variance and "Off" denotes separate variance

Save Res   : None

Execute

Now key **EXE** or **F1**(CALC) or **F6** (DRAW)

If you select **F6** (DRAW), you will see a *t* distribution.

If you select either **EXE** or **F1**(Calc), the calculator will now show the results:

```
2-Sample tTest
μ1      ≠μ2
t       =-3.0445501
p       =6.9749ε-03
df      =18
x̄1      =50.3
x̄2      =72             ↓
```

Scroll down for the rest of the result:

```
2-Sample tTest
x̄2      =72             ↑
sx1     =18.7263925
sx2     =12.5432585
sp      =15.9375517
n1      =10
n2      =10
```

Note: This is the pooled standard deviation

You reject the null hypothesis because $t_{STAT} = -3.0446 < -2.1009$ and the *p*-value is 0.0070. In other words, the probability that $t_{STAT} > 3.0446$ or $t_{STAT} < -3.0446$ is equal to 0.0070. This *p*-value indicates that if the population means are equal, the probability of observing a difference in the two sample means this large or larger is only 0.0070. Because the *p*-value is less than $\alpha = 0.05$, there is sufficient evidence to reject the null hypothesis. You can conclude that the mean sales are different for the beverage end-cap and produce end-cap locations. Because the t_{STAT} statistic is negative, you can conclude that the mean sales are lower for the beverage end-cap location (and, therefore, higher for the produce end-cap location).

In testing for the difference between the means, you assume that the populations are normally distributed, with equal variances. For situations in which the two populations have equal variances, the pooled-variance t test is **robust** (i.e., not sensitive) to moderate departures from the assumption of normality, provided that the sample sizes are large. In such situations, you can use the pooled-variance t test without serious effects on its power. However, if you cannot assume that both populations are normally distributed, you have two choices. You can use a nonparametric procedure, such as the Wilcoxon rank sum test (see references 1 and 2), that does not depend on the assumption of normality for the two populations, or you can use a normalizing transformation (see reference 10) on each of the outcomes and then use the pooled-variance t test.

To check the assumption of normality in each of the two populations, you can construct a boxplot of the sales for the two display locations shown in Figure 12.4. For these two small samples, there appears to be only moderate departure from normality, so the assumption of normality needed for the t test is not seriously violated.

FIGURE 12.4

Boxplots for beverage and produce end-cap sales

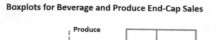

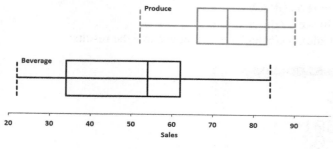

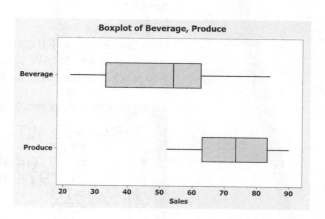

Example 12.1 provides another application of the pooled-variance t test.

EXAMPLE 12.1

Testing for the Difference in the Mean Delivery Times

You and some friends have decided to test the validity of an advertisement by a local pizza restaurant, which says it delivers to the dormitories faster than a local branch of a national chain. Both the local pizza restaurant and national chain are located across the street from your college campus. You define the variable of interest as the delivery time, in minutes, from the time the pizza is ordered to when it is delivered. You collect the data by ordering 10 pizzas from the local pizza restaurant and 10 pizzas from the national chain at different times. You organize and store the data in PizzaTime . Table 12.2 shows the delivery times.

TABLE 12.2

Delivery Times (in minutes) for a Local Pizza Restaurant and a National Pizza Chain

Local		Chain	
16.8	18.1	22.0	19.5
11.7	14.1	15.2	17.0
15.6	21.8	18.7	19.5
16.7	13.9	15.6	16.5
17.5	20.8	20.8	24.0

At the 0.05 level of significance, is there evidence that the mean delivery time for the local pizza restaurant is less than the mean delivery time for the national pizza chain?

SOLUTION Because you want to know whether the mean is *lower* for the local pizza restaurant than for the national pizza chain, you have a one-tail test with the following null and alternative hypotheses:

$H_0: \mu_1 \geq \mu_2$ (The mean delivery time for the local pizza restaurant is equal to or greater than the mean delivery time for the national pizza chain.)

$H_1: \mu_1 < \mu_2$ (The mean delivery time for the local pizza restaurant is less than the mean delivery time for the national pizza chain.)

Figure 12.5 displays the results for the pooled-variance t test for these data.

FIGURE 12.5

SPSS results of the pooled-variance t-test (i.e. equal variances assumed) for the pizza delivery times data

Group Statistics

Pizzarestaurant		N	Mean	Std. Deviation	Std. Error Mean
Delivery Time	Local Pizza restaurant	10	16.700	3.0955	.9789
	National Pizza Chain	10	18.880	2.8662	.9064

Independent Samples Test

		Levene's Test for Equality of Variances		t-test for Equality of Means					95% Confidence Interval of the Difference	
		F	Sig.	t	df	Sig. (2-tailed)	Mean Difference	Std. Error Difference	Lower	Upper
Delivery Time	equal variances assumed	.001	.980	-1.634	18	.120	-2.1800	1.3341	-4.9828	.6228
	Equal variances not assumed			-1.634	17.894	.120	-2.1800	1.3341	-4.9840	.6240

Note: By default, SPSS performs a two-tailed t-test. For a one-tailed t-test, you have to divide the p-value by 2. The p-value would be 0.06 (0.120 ÷ 2) to test the hypothesis.

To illustrate the computations, using Equation (12.1) on page 101,

$$t_{STAT} = \frac{(\bar{X}_1 - \bar{X}_2) - (\mu_1 - \mu_2)}{\sqrt{S_p^2\left(\frac{1}{n_1} + \frac{1}{n_2}\right)}}$$

where

$$S_p^2 = \frac{(n_1 - 1)S_1^2 + (n_2 - 1)S_2^2}{(n_1 - 1) + (n_2 - 1)}$$

$$= \frac{9(3.0955)^2 + 9(2.8662)^2}{9 + 9} = 8.8986$$

Therefore,

$$t_{STAT} = \frac{(16.7 - 18.88) - 0.0}{\sqrt{8.8986\left(\frac{1}{10} + \frac{1}{10}\right)}} = \frac{-2.18}{\sqrt{1.7797}} = -1.6341$$

(*continued*)

You do not reject the null hypothesis because $t_{STAT} = -1.6341 > -1.7341$. The p-value (as computed in Figure 12.5) is 0.0598. This p-value indicates that the probability that $t_{STAT} < -1.6341$ is equal to 0.0598. In other words, if the population means are equal, the probability that the sample mean delivery time for the local pizza restaurant is at least 2.18 minutes faster than the national chain is 0.0598. Because the p-value is greater than $\alpha = 0.05$, there is insufficient evidence to reject the null hypothesis. Based on these results, there is insufficient evidence for the local pizza restaurant to make the advertising claim that it has a faster delivery time.

How to Run the Pooled-variance *t* Test with a FX-9750GII Calculator

Refer to Example 12.1 on page 106 and the data in Table 12.2.

To run the pooled-variance *t* test, follow the instruction below.

First enter the data in the lists (in your calculator): List 1 and List 2 as shown below:

List 1	List 2
16.8	22.0
11.7	15.2
15.6	18.7
16.7	15.6
17.5	20.8
18.1	19.5
14.1	17.0
21.8	19.5
13.9	16.5
20.8	24.0

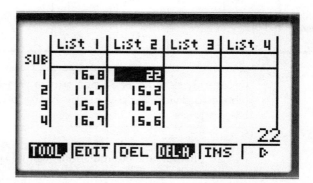

After you have entered the data, go to the **Main Menu** and select the following functions:

STAT   F3(test)   **F2**(t)   **F2**(2-s)   then enter the following items:

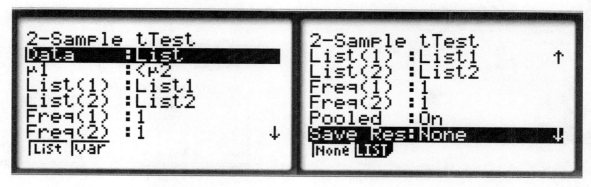

Pooled   : On (F1)   (Note: "On" denotes "pooled variance" and "Off" denotes separate variance.)

Now press **EXE** or **F1**(CALC) or **F6** (DRAW)

If you select **F6** (DRAW), you will see a t distribution.

If you select either **EXE** or **F1**(Calc), the calculator will now show the results:

```
2-Sample tTest        2-Sample tTest
μ1    <μ2              x̄2    =18.88        ↑
t     =-1.6341015      sx1   =3.09551647
p     =0.05980277      sx2   =2.86620151
df    =18              sp    =2.9830633
x̄1    =16.7            n1    =10
x̄2    =18.88        ↓  n2    =10
```

Confidence Interval Estimate for the Difference Between Two Means

Instead of, or in addition to, testing for the difference between the means of two independent populations, you can use Equation (12.2) to develop a confidence interval estimate of the difference in the means.

CONFIDENCE INTERVAL ESTIMATE FOR THE DIFFERENCE BETWEEN THE MEANS OF TWO INDEPENDENT POPULATIONS

$$(\overline{X}_1 - \overline{X}_2) \pm t_{\alpha/2}\sqrt{S_p^2\left(\frac{1}{n_1} + \frac{1}{n_2}\right)} \tag{12.2}$$

or

$$(\overline{X}_1 - \overline{X}_2) - t_{\alpha/2}\sqrt{S_p^2\left(\frac{1}{n_1} + \frac{1}{n_2}\right)} \leq \mu_1 - \mu_2 \leq (\overline{X}_1 - \overline{X}_2) + t_{\alpha/2}\sqrt{S_p^2\left(\frac{1}{n_1} + \frac{1}{n_2}\right)}$$

where $t_{\alpha/2}$ is the critical value of the t distribution, with $n_1 + n_2 - 2$ degrees of freedom, for an area of $\alpha/2$ in the upper tail.

For the sample statistics pertaining to the two end-cap locations reported in Figure 12.3 on page 104, using 95% confidence, and Equation (12.2),

$\overline{X}_1 = 50.3, n_1 = 10, \overline{X}_2 = 72.0, n_2 = 10, S_p^2 = 254.0056$, and with $10 + 10 - 2$
   $= 18$ degrees of freedom, $t_{0.025} = 2.1009$

$$(50.3 - 72.0) \pm (2.1009)\sqrt{254.0056\left(\frac{1}{10} + \frac{1}{10}\right)}$$

$$-21.7 \pm (2.1009)(7.1275)$$

$$-21.7 \pm 14.97$$

$$-36.67 \leq \mu_1 - \mu_2 \leq -6.73$$

Therefore, you are 95% confident that the difference in mean sales between the beverage and produce end-cap locations is between -36.67 cases of cola and -6.73 cases of cola. In other words, you can estimate, with 95% confidence, that the produce end-cap location sells, on average, 6.73 to 36.67 cases more than the beverage end-cap location. From a hypothesis-testing perspective, using a two-tail test at the 0.05 level of significance, because the interval does not include zero, you reject the null hypothesis of no difference between the means of the two populations.

t Test for the Difference Between Two Means, Assuming Unequal Variances

If you can assume that the two independent populations are normally distributed but cannot assume that they have equal variances, you cannot pool the two sample variances into the common estimate S_p^2 and therefore cannot use the pooled-variance *t* test. Instead, you use the **separate-variance *t* test** developed by Satterthwaite that uses the two separate sample variances (see reference 9).

Figure 12.6 displays the separate-variance *t* test results for the end-cap display location data. Observe that the test statistic $t_{STAT} = -3.0446$ and the *p*-value is $0.0082 < 0.05$. Thus, the results for the separate-variance *t* test are nearly the same as those of the pooled-variance *t* test.

FIGURE 12.6

SPSS results of the separate-variance (i.e. equal variances not assumed) *t*-test results for the sales data for the two end-caps.

Group Statistics

	Display	N	Mean	Std. Deviation	Std. Error Mean
Weekly Sales	Normal	10	50.30	18.726	5.922
	End-Aisle	10	72.00	12.543	3.967

Independent Samples Test

		Levene's Test for Equality of Variances		t-test for Equality of Means						
									95% Confidence Interval of the Difference	
		F	Sig.	t	df	Sig. (2-tailed)	Mean Difference	Std. Error Difference	Lower	Upper
Weekly Sales	Equal variances assumed	1.745	.203	-3.045	18	.007	-21.700	7.127	-36.674	-6.726
	Equal variances not assumed			-3.045	15.723	.008	-21.700	7.127	-36.831	-6.569

How to run the separate-variance *t* test with a FX-9750GII calculator?

Refer to the North Fork Beverages scenario on page 102 and the data in Table 12.1.

To run the separate-variance *t* test, follow the instruction below.

First enter the data in the lists (in your calculator): List 1 and List 2 as shown below:

List 1	List 2
22	52
40	83
34	71
64	66
52	76
84	90
62	54
56	77
30	67
59	84

After you have entered the data, go to the **Main Menu** and select the following functions:

STAT   F3(TEST)   **F2**(t)   **F2**(2-s)   then enter the following items:

Pooled   : Off (F2)   (Note: "On" denotes "pooled variance and "Off" denotes separate variance.)

Now key **EXE** or **F1**(CALC)   or **F6** (DRAW)

If you select **F6** (DRAW), you will see a *t* distribution.

If you select either **EXE** or **F1**(Calc), the calculator will now show the results:

Do People Really Do This?

Some question whether decision makers really use confirmatory methods, such as hypothesis testing, in this emerging era of big data. The following real case study, contributed by a former student of a colleague of the authors, reveals a role that confirmatory methods still play in business as well as answering another question: "Do businesses really monitor their customer service calls for quality assurance purposes as they sometime claim?"

In her first full-time job at a financial services company, a student was asked to improve a training program for new hires at a call center that handled customer questions about outstanding loans. For feedback and evaluation, she planned to randomly select phone calls received by each new employee and rate the employee on 10 aspects of the call, including whether the employee maintained a pleasant tone with the customer. When she presented her plan to her boss for approval, her boss wanted proof that her new training program would improve customer service. The boss, quoting a famous statistician, said "In God we trust; all others must bring data." Faced with this request, she called her business statistics professor. "Hello, Professor, you'll never believe why I called. I work for a large company, and in the project I am currently working on, I have to put some of the statistics you taught us to work! Can you help?" Together they formulated this test:

- Randomly assign the 60 most recent hires to two training programs. Assign half to the preexisting training program and the other half to the new training program.

- At the end of the first month, compare the mean score for the 30 employees in the new training program against the mean score for the 30 employees in the preexisting training program.

She listened as her professor explained, "What you are trying to show is that the mean score from the new training program is higher than the mean score from the current program. You can make the null hypothesis that the means are equal and see if you can reject it in favor of the alternative that the mean score from the new program is higher."

"Or, as you used to say, 'if the *p*-value is low, H_0 must go!'—yes, I do remember!" she replied. Her professor chuckled and added, "If you can reject H_0 you will have the evidence to present to your boss." She thanked him for his help and got back to work, with the newfound confidence that she would be able to successfully apply the *t* test that compares the means of two independent populations.

The assumption of equality of population variances had no appreciable effect on the results. Sometimes, however, the results from the pooled-variance and separate-variance *t* tests conflict because the assumption of equal variances is violated. Therefore, it is important that you evaluate the assumptions and use those results as a guide in selecting a test procedure. In Section 12.4, the *F* test for the ratio of two variances is used to determine whether there is evidence of a difference in the two population variances. The results of that test can help you decide which of the *t* tests—pooled-variance or separate-variance—is more appropriate.

How to run a two Independent Samples T-Test with SPSS version 25?

We will use the scenario, "Delivery Times for Local Pizza Restaurant and National Pizza Chain" on page 106 (Example 12.1), to demonstrate how to perform two independent samples T test using SPSS.

A local pizza restaurant located close to a college campus advertises that their delivery time to a college dormitory is less than for a local branch of a national pizza chain. In order to determine whether this advertisement is valid, you and some friends have decided to order 10 pizzas from the local pizza restaurant and 10 pizzas from the national chain, all at different times. The data is shown below:

Local	Chain
16.8	22.0
11.7	15.2
15.6	18.7
16.7	15.6
17.5	20.8
18.1	19.5
14.1	17.0
21.8	19.5
13.9	16.5
20.8	24.0

At the 0.05 level of significance, is there evidence that the mean delivery time is lower for the local pizza restaurant than for the national pizza chain?

Solution:
Performing an Independent-Samples T test on SPSS – Version 25
Step 1: Open a new spreadsheet called the "New Dataset".
Click "New Dataset"

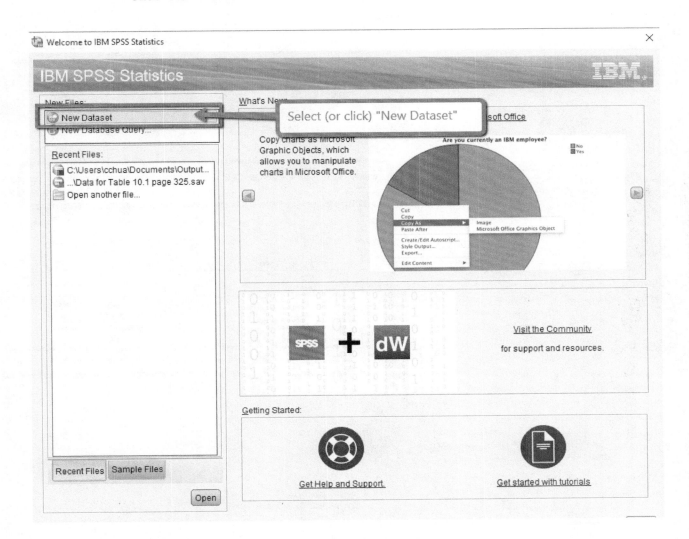

Step 2: Define the variables and give the variables a label.
Click "**Variable View**" (at the bottom of the window) to go to the variable view window to define the variables and fix the data at zero or one decimal places.

- Enter the first variable name -"Restaurant" and then click **values.** Key "**1**" in the value box and key "**Local Pizza Restaurant**" in the Label box, and then click **Add**. Similarly enter "**2**" for "**National Pizza Chain**".

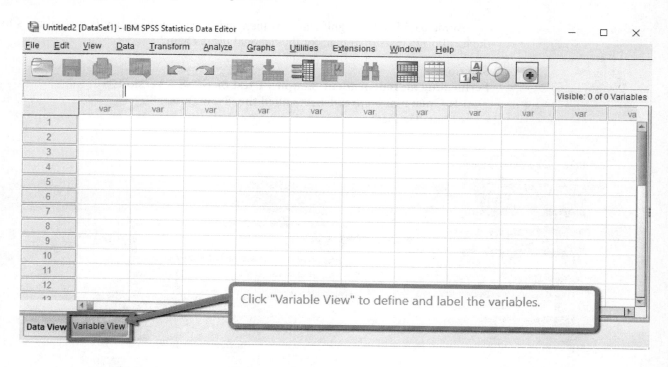

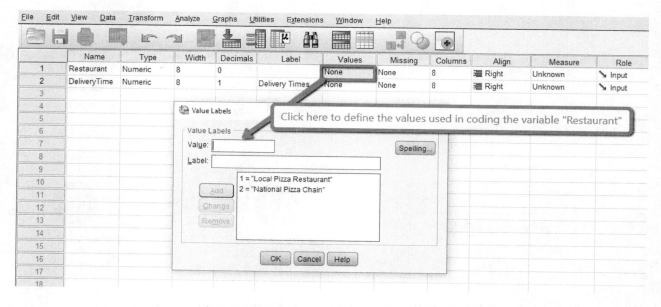

• Enter the second variable name – "Deliverytime" and label it as "Delivery Times".

Step 3: Create a SPSS data file.

Click "**Data View**" to return to the data view window. Now, enter the raw data (in Table 12.2) into the respective column of variables.

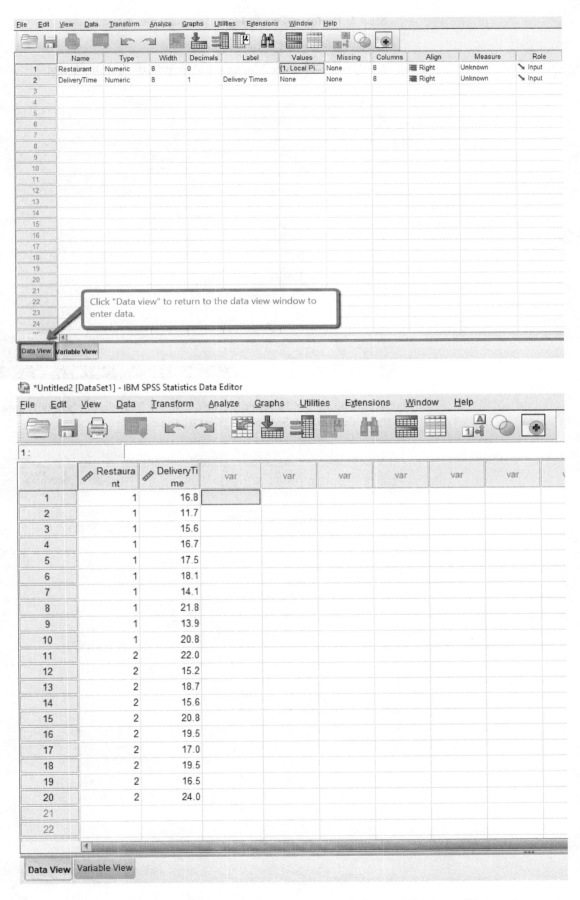

After you have entered all the data, save it as "twosampleTtest.sav" (or any filename).

Step 3: Perform Two independent samples t-test.

Make the following menu selections:

Analyze→Compare Means→Independent-Samples T test

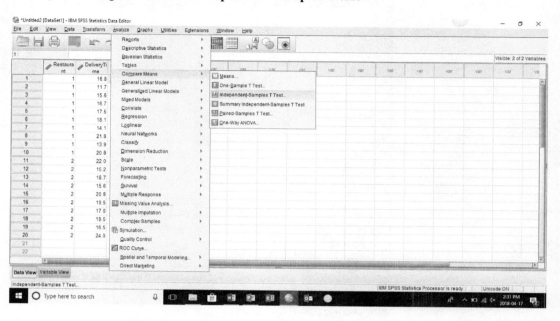

At this point, the **Independent Samples T Test** dialog box will appear. Make these entries in the **Independent-Samples T Test** dialog box:

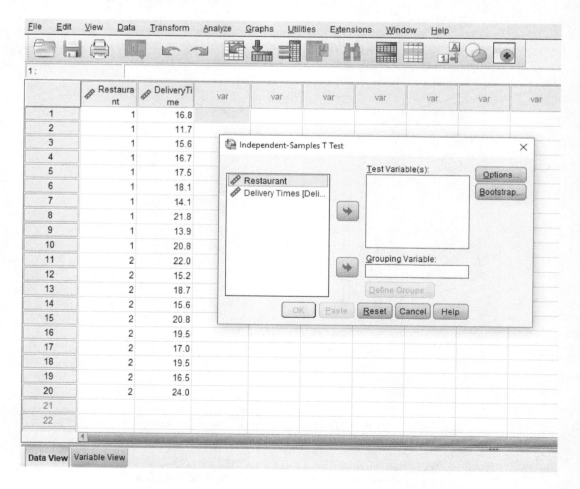

- Highlight on the "**Delivery Times**" variable and click on the arrow
- key (→). The variable will automatically fall into the **Test Variable(s)** box.
- Highlight on the "**Restaurant**" variable and click on the arrow key (→). The variable will automatically fall into the **Grouping Variable** box.

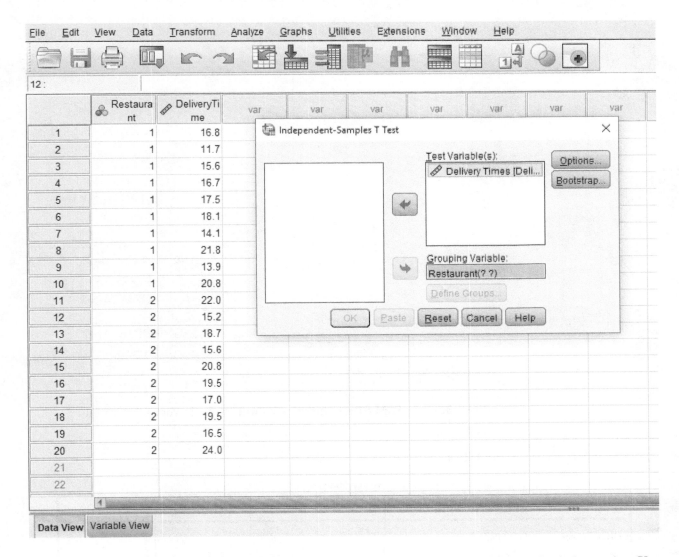

- Next, click on the **Define Groups** button. In the "Define Groups" window, select **Use specified values** by entering "1" for Group 1 and "2" for Group 2. The values of "1" and "2" depend on how you define the two groups at the beginning when you define the variables. Then click on **continue** button to return to the "Independent-Samples T Test" window.

- Click on the **Ok** button to obtain the SPSS results.

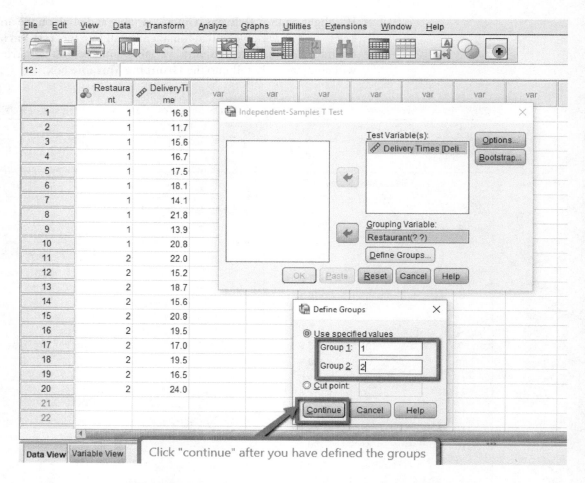

Click "continue" after you have defined the groups

Step 3: Go to **IBM SPSS Statistics Viewer** to obtain your SPSS results.

SPSS output:

T-Test

Group Statistics

	Restaurant	N	Mean	Std. Deviation	Std. Error Mean
Delivery Times	Local Pizza Restaurant	10	16.700	3.0955	.9789
	National Pizza Chain	10	18.880	2.8662	.9064

Independent Samples Test

		Levene's Test for Equality of Variances		t-test for Equality of Means						
									95% Confidence Interval of the Difference	
		F	Sig.	t	df	Sig. (2-tailed)	Mean Difference	Std. Error Difference	Lower	Upper
Delivery Times	Equal variances assumed	.001	.980	-1.634	18	.120	-2.1800	1.3341	-4.9828	.6228
	Equal variances not assumed			-1.634	17.894	.120	-2.1800	1.3341	-4.9840	.6240

12.2 Comparing the Means of Two Related Populations

The hypothesis-testing procedures presented in Section 12.1 enable you to examine differences between the means of two *independent* populations. In this section, you will learn about a procedure for examining the mean difference between two populations when you collect sample data from populations that are related—that is, when results of the first population are *not* independent of the results of the second population.

There are two situations that involve related data: when you take repeated measurements from the same set of items or individuals or when you match items or individuals according to some characteristic. In either situation, you are interested in the *difference between the two related values* rather than the *individual values* themselves.

When you take **repeated measurements** on the same items or individuals, you assume that the same items or individuals will behave alike if treated alike. Your objective is to show that any differences between two measurements of the same items or individuals are due to different treatments that have been applied to the items or individuals. For example, when performing a taste-testing experiment comparing two beverages, you can use each person in the sample as his or her own control so that you can have *repeated measurements* on the same individual.

Another example of repeated measurements involves the pricing of the same goods from two different vendors. For example, have you ever wondered whether new textbook prices at a local college bookstore are different from the prices offered at a major online retailer? You could take two independent samples—that is, select two different sets of textbooks—and then use the hypothesis tests discussed in Section 12.1.

However, by random chance, the first sample may have many large-format hardcover textbooks and the second sample may have many small trade paperback books. This would imply that the first set of textbooks will always be more expensive than the second set of textbooks, regardless of where they are purchased. This observation means that using the Section 12.1 tests would not be a good choice. The better choice would be to use two related samples—that is, to determine the price of the *same* sample of textbooks at both the local bookstore and the online retailer.

The second situation that involves related data between populations is when you have **matched samples**. Here items or individuals are paired together according to some characteristic of interest. For example, in test marketing a product in two different advertising campaigns, a sample of test markets can be *matched* on the basis of the test-market population size and/or demographic variables. By accounting for the differences in test-market population size and/or demographic variables, you are better able to measure the effects of the two different advertising campaigns.

Regardless of whether you have matched samples or repeated measurements, the objective is to study the difference between two measurements by reducing the effect of the variability that is due to the items or individuals themselves. Table 12.3 shows the differences between the individual values for two related populations. To read this table, let $X_{11}, X_{12}, \ldots, X_{1n}$ represent the n values from the first sample. And let $X_{21}, X_{22}, \ldots, X_{2n}$ represent either the corresponding n matched values from a second sample or the corresponding n repeated measurements from the initial sample. Then $D_1, D_2, \ldots, D_n$ will represent the corresponding set of n *difference scores* such that

$$D_1 = X_{11} - X_{21}, D_2 = X_{12} - X_{22}, \ldots, \text{ and } D_n = X_{1n} - X_{2n}.$$

To test for the mean difference between two related populations, you treat the difference scores, each D_i, as values from a single sample.

TABLE 12.3

Determining the
Difference Between
Two Related Samples

> **Student Tip**
>
> Which sample you define
> as group 1 will determine
> whether you will be doing
> a lower-tail test or an
> upper-tail test if you are
> conducting a one-tail test.

	SAMPLE		
VALUE	**1**	**2**	DIFFERENCE
1	X_{11}	X_{21}	$D_1 = X_{11} - X_{21}$
2	X_{12}	X_{22}	$D_2 = X_{12} - X_{22}$
$\vdots$	$\vdots$	$\vdots$	$\vdots$
i	X_{1i}	X_{2i}	$D_i = X_{1i} - X_{2i}$
$\vdots$	$\vdots$	$\vdots$	$\vdots$
n	X_{1n}	X_{2n}	$D_n = X_{1n} - X_{2n}$

Flow chart for Hypothesis test for means of two related populations

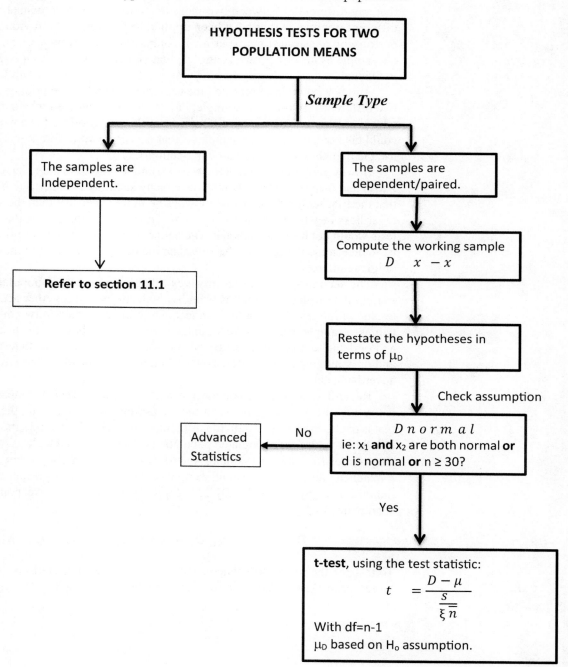

Paired t Test

If you assume that the difference scores are randomly and independently selected from a population that is normally distributed, you can use the **paired t test for the mean difference** in related populations to determine whether there is a significant population mean difference. As with the one-sample t test developed in Section 11.2 [see Equation (11.2) on page 59], the paired t test statistic follows the t distribution with $n - 1$ degrees of freedom. Although the paired t test assumes that the population is normally distributed, since this test is robust, you can use this test as long as the sample size is not very small and the population is not highly skewed.

To test the null hypothesis that there is no difference in the means of two related populations:

$$H_0: \mu_D = 0 \text{ (where } \mu_D = \mu_1 - \mu_2)$$

against the alternative that the means are not the same:

$$H_1: \mu_D \neq 0$$

you compute the t_{STAT} test statistic using Equation (12.3).

PAIRED t TEST FOR THE MEAN DIFFERENCE

$$t_{STAT} = \frac{\overline{D} - \mu_D}{\dfrac{S_D}{\sqrt{n}}} \tag{12.3}$$

where

μ_D = hypothesized mean difference

$$\overline{D} = \frac{\displaystyle\sum_{i=1}^{n} D_i}{n}$$

$$S_D = \sqrt{\frac{\displaystyle\sum_{i=1}^{n} (D_i - \overline{D})^2}{n - 1}}$$

The t_{STAT} test statistic follows a t distribution with $n - 1$ degrees of freedom.

For a two-tail test with a given level of significance, α, you reject the null hypothesis if the computed t_{STAT} test statistic is greater than the upper-tail critical value $t_{\alpha/2}$ from the t distribution, or, if the computed t_{STAT} test statistic is less than the lower-tail critical value $-t_{\alpha/2}$, from the t distribution. The decision rule is

$$\text{Reject } H_0 \text{ if } t_{STAT} > t_{\alpha/2}$$

$$\text{or if } t_{STAT} < -t_{\alpha/2};$$

$$\text{otherwise, do not reject } H_0.$$

You can use the paired t test for the mean difference to investigate a question raised earlier in this section: Are new textbook prices at a local college bookstore different from the prices offered at a major online retailer?

In this repeated-measurements experiment, you use one set of textbooks. For each textbook, you determine the price at the local bookstore and the price at the online retailer. By determining the two prices for the same textbooks, you can reduce the variability in the prices compared with what would occur if you used two independent sets of textbooks. This approach focuses on the differences between the prices of the same textbooks offered by the two retailers.

You collect data by conducting an experiment from a sample of $n = 16$ textbooks used primarily in business school courses during a recent semester at a local college. You determine the college bookstore price and the online price (which includes shipping costs, if any). You organize and store the data in BookPrices . Table 12.4 shows the results. Notice that each row of the table shows the bookstore price and online retailer price for a specific book.

TABLE 12.4

Prices of Textbooks at the College Bookstore and at the Online Retailer

Author	Title	Bookstore	Online
Bade	*Foundations of Microeconomics* 6/e	200.00	121.49
Brigham	*Financial Management* 13/e	304.00	235.88
Clauretie	*Real Estate Finance: Theory and Practice*	179.35	107.61
Foner	*Give Me Liberty! (Brief)* Vol. 2 3/e	72.00	59.99
Garrison	*Managerial Accounting*	277.15	146.99
Grewal	*M: Marketing* 3/e	73.75	63.49
Hill	*Global Business Today*	171.65	138.99
Lafore	*Object-Oriented Programming in C++*	65.00	42.26
Lank	*Modern Real Estate Practice* 11/e	47.45	65.99
Meyer	*Entrepreneurship*	106.00	37.83
Mitchell	*Public Affairs in the Nation and New York*	55.95	102.99
Pindyck	*Microeconomics* 8/e	224.40	144.99
Robbins	*Organizational Behavior* 15/e	223.20	179.39
Ross	*Fundamentals of Corporate Finance* 9/e	250.65	191.49
Schneier	*New York Politics: Tale of Two States*	34.95	28.66
Wilson	*American Government: The Essentials* 12/e	172.65	108.49

Your objective is to determine whether there is any difference between the mean textbook price at the college bookstore and at the online retailer. In other words, is there evidence that the mean price is different between the two textbook sellers? Thus, the null and alternative hypotheses are

H_0: $\mu_D = 0$ (There is no difference in the mean price between the college bookstore and the online retailer.)

H_1: $\mu_D \neq 0$ (There is a difference in the mean price between the college bookstore and the online retailer.)

Choosing the level of significance $\alpha = 0.05$ and assuming that the differences are normally distributed, you use the paired t test [Equation (12.3)]. For a sample of $n = 16$ textbooks, there are $n - 1 = 15$ degrees of freedom. Using Table E.3, the decision rule is

Reject H_0 if $t_{STAT} > 2.1314$

or if $t_{STAT} < -2.1314$;

otherwise, do not reject H_0.

For the $n = 16$ differences (see Table 12.4), the sample mean difference is

$$\overline{D} = \frac{\sum_{i=1}^{n} D_i}{n} = \frac{681.62}{16} = 42.6013$$

and

$$S_D = \sqrt{\frac{\sum_{i=1}^{n}(D_i - \overline{D})^2}{n - 1}} = 43.797$$

From Equation (12.3) on page 121,

$$t_{STAT} = \frac{\overline{D} - \mu_D}{\dfrac{S_D}{\sqrt{n}}} = \frac{42.6013 - 0}{\dfrac{43.797}{\sqrt{16}}} = 3.8908$$

Because $t_{STAT} = 3.8908 > 2.1314$, you reject the null hypothesis, H_0 (see Figure 12.7). There is evidence of a difference in the mean price of textbooks purchased at the college bookstore and the online retailer. You can conclude that the mean price is higher at the college bookstore than at the online retailer.

FIGURE 12.7

Two-tail paired t test at the 0.05 level of significance with 15 degrees of freedom

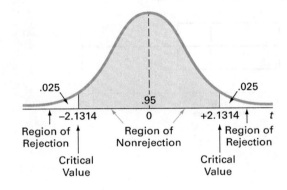

Figure 12.8 presents the results for this example, computing both the t test statistic and the p-value. Because the p-value $= 0.0014 < \alpha = 0.05$, you reject H_0. The p-value indicates that if the two sources for textbooks have the same population mean price, the probability that one

FIGURE 12.8

SPSS paired-samples t test results for the textbook price data

T-Test

Paired Samples Statistics

		Mean	N	Std. Deviation	Std. Error Mean
Pair 1	bookstore	153.6344	16	88.95559	22.23890
	online	111.0331	16	59.95604	14.98901

Paired Samples Correlations

		N	Correlation	Sig.
Pair 1	bookstore & online	16	.899	.000

Paired Samples Test

		Paired Differences							
					95% Confidence Interval of the Difference				
		Mean	Std. Deviation	Std. Error Mean	Lower	Upper	t	df	Sig. (2-tailed)
Pair 1	bookstore - online	42.60125	43.79704	10.94926	19.26345	65.93905	3.891	15	.001

source would have a sample mean \$42.60 more than the other is 0.0014. Because this probability is less than $\alpha = 0.05$, you conclude that there is evidence to reject the null hypothesis.

To evaluate the validity of the assumption of normality, you construct a boxplot of the differences, as shown in Figure 12.9.

The Figure 12.9 boxplots show approximate symmetry and look similar to the boxplot for the normal distribution displayed in Figure 4.5 in Chapter 4. Thus, the distribution of textbook price differences does not greatly contradict the underlying assumption of normality. If a boxplot, histogram, or normal probability plot reveals that the assumption of underlying normality in the population is severely violated, then the t test may be inappropriate, especially if the sample size is small. If you believe that the t test is inappropriate, you can use either a *nonparametric* procedure that does not make the assumption of underlying normality (see references 1 and 2) or make a data transformation (see reference 10) and then check the assumptions again to determine whether you should use the t test.

FIGURE 12.9

Excel and Minitab boxplots for the textbook price differences

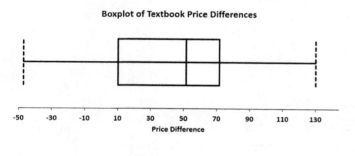

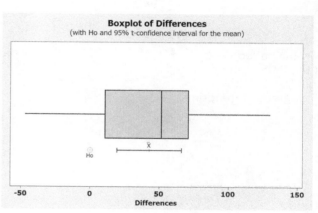

How to Run the "Paired" t Test with a FX-9750GII Calculator

Refer to data in Table 12.4 on page 122.

To run the "paired" t test, follow the instruction below.

First compute the difference in prices as shown below:

Differences
$200.00 - 121.49 = 78.51$
$304.00 - 235.88 = 68.12$
$179.35 - 107.61 = 71.74$
$72.00 - 59.99 = 12.01$
$277.15 - 146.99 = 130.16$
$73.75 - 63.49 = 10.26$
$171.65 - 138.99 = 32.66$
$65.00 - 42.26 = 22.74$
$47.45 - 65.99 = -18.54$
$106.00 - 37.83 = 68.17$
$55.95 - 102.99 = -47.04$
$224.40 - 144.99 = 79.41$
$223.20 - 179.39 = 43.81$
$250.65 - 191.49 = 59.16$
$34.95 - 28.66 = 6.29$
$172.65 - 108.49 = 64.16$

Then enter the "Differences between bookstore and online" data in List 1.

List 1
78.51
68.12
71.74
12.01
130.16
10.26
32.66
22.74
−18.54
68.17
−47.04
79.41
43.81
59.16
6.29
64.16

Now, from the **STAT mode**, select the following:

STAT F3(test) **F2**(t) **F1**(1-s)   then enter the following items:

(Note: Only use the **EXE** key after a new entry. Otherwise, use the cursor ▼ arrow. If you accidentally hit the wrong key, use **AC/ON** or **EXIT** to go back.)

1-Sample t Test

Data	: **List (F1-List)**	▼	
μ	: $\neq \mu 0$ **(F1)**	**EXE**	(Note: Ha: $\mu_D \neq 0$)
$\mu 0$	: 0		
List (1)	: List 1	**EXE (Note: To change the list number, select F1(List).**	
Freq (1)	: 1		
Save Res	: None		
Execute			

Now key **EXE** or **F1**(CALC) or **F6** (DRAW)

If you select **F6** (DRAW), you will see a t distribution.

If you select either **EXE** or **F1**(Calc), the calculator will now show the results:

1-Sample t Test

μ	$\neq 0$	
t	$= 3.89078768$	(Note: this is t stat value)
p	$= 1.4482E\text{-}03$	(Note: this is p-value)
$\bar{X}$	$= 42.60125$	
$\bar{S}x$	$= 43.7970442$	
n	$= 16$	

How to Find t Critical Value Using Calculator?

Calculate the t critical value for $\alpha = 0.05$, using the Casio Calculator fx-9750GII and follow the following calculator steps:

From the **Main Menu** select:

STAT F5 (DIST) **F2** (t) **F3**(Invt)   then enter the following items:

Inverse Student-t

Data	: **F2**(Var)	▼	
Area	: **0.025**	**EXE**	(Note: divide a by 2 because it is a two-tailed test)
df	: **15**	**EXE**	(Note: df = n − 1 = 15)
Save Res	: None		

Execute

Now key **EXE** or **F1**(CALC)

The calculator will now show the results:

Inverse Student-t

x-Inv = 2.13144955   (**Note: this is the critical value for the upper tail. The critical value for the lower tail is −2.1314 (insert a negative sign). See Figure 12.7**)

EXAMPLE 12.2

Paired t Test of Pizza Delivery Times

Recall from Example 12.1 on page 106 that a local pizza restaurant situated across the street from your college campus advertises that it delivers to the dormitories faster than the local branch of a national pizza chain. In order to determine whether this advertisement is valid, you and some friends decided to order 10 pizzas from the local pizza restaurant and 10 pizzas from the national chain. In fact, each time you ordered a pizza from the local pizza restaurant, at the same time, your friends ordered a pizza from the national pizza chain. Thus, you have matched samples. For each of the 10 times that pizzas were ordered, you have one measurement from the local pizza restaurant and one from the national chain. At the 0.05 level of significance, is the mean delivery time for the local pizza restaurant less than the mean delivery time for the national pizza chain?

SOLUTION Use the paired t test to analyze the Table 12.5 data (stored in `PizzaTime`). Figure 12.10 shows the paired t test results for the pizza delivery data.

TABLE 12.5

Delivery Times for Local Pizza Restaurant and National Pizza Chain

Time	Local	Chain	Difference
1	16.8	22.0	−5.2
2	11.7	15.2	−3.5
3	15.6	18.7	−3.1
4	16.7	15.6	1.1
5	17.5	20.8	−3.3
6	18.1	19.5	−1.4
7	14.1	17.0	−2.9
8	21.8	19.5	2.3
9	13.9	16.5	−2.6
10	20.8	24.0	−3.2
			−21.8

The null and alternative hypotheses are

$H_0: \mu_D \geq 0$ (Mean difference in the delivery time between the local pizza restaurant and the national pizza chain is greater than or equal to 0.)

$H_1: \mu_D < 0$ (Mean difference in the delivery time between the local pizza restaurant and the national pizza chain is less than 0.)

Choosing the level of significance $\alpha = 0.05$ and assuming that the differences are normally distributed, you use the paired t test [Equation (12.3) on page 121]. For a sample of $n = 10$ delivery times, there are $n - 1 = 9$ degrees of freedom. Using Table E.3, the decision rule is

$$\text{Reject } H_0 \text{ if } t_{STAT} < -t_{0.05} = -1.8331;$$

otherwise, do not reject H_0.

FIGURE 12.10

SPSS paired-samples t-test result for the pizza delivery data

T-Test

Paired Samples Statistics

		Mean	N	Std. Deviation	Std. Error Mean
Pair 1	Delivery Times for Local	16.700	10	3.0955	.9789
	Delivery Times for Chain	18.8800	10	2.86620	.90637

Paired Samples Correlations

		N	Correlation	Sig.
Pair 1	Delivery Times for Local & Delivery Times for Chain	10	.714	.020

Paired Samples Test

		Paired Differences							
					95% Confidence Interval of the Difference				
		Mean	Std. Deviation	Std. Error Mean	Lower	Upper	t	df	Sig. (2-tailed)
Pair 1	Delivery Times for Local - Delivery Times for Chain	-2.18000	2.26412	.71598	-3.79965	-.56035	-3.045	9	.014

To illustrate the computations, for $n = 10$ differences (see Table 12.5), the sample mean difference is

$$\overline{D} = \frac{\displaystyle\sum_{i=1}^{n} D_i}{n} = \frac{-21.8}{10} = -2.18$$

and the sample standard deviation of the difference is

$$S_D = \sqrt{\frac{\displaystyle\sum_{i=1}^{n}(D_i - \overline{D})^2}{n-1}} = 2.2641$$

From Equation (12.3) on page 121,

$$t_{STAT} = \frac{\overline{D} - \mu_D}{\dfrac{S_D}{\sqrt{n}}} = \frac{-2.18 - 0}{\dfrac{2.2641}{\sqrt{10}}} = -3.0448$$

Because $t_{STAT} = -3.0448$ is less than -1.8331, you reject the null hypothesis, H_0 (the p-value is $0.0070 < 0.05$). There is evidence that the mean delivery time is lower for the local pizza restaurant than for the national pizza chain.

This conclusion differs from the conclusion you reached on page 106 for Example 12.1 when you used the pooled-variance t test for these data. By pairing the delivery times, you are able to focus on the differences between the two pizza delivery services and not the variability created by ordering pizzas at different times of day. The paired t test is a more powerful statistical procedure that reduces the variability in the delivery time because you are controlling for the time of day the pizza was ordered.

(continued)

How to Run the "Paired" *t* Test with a FX-9750GII Calculator

Refer to Example 12.2 and data in Table 12.5 on page 126.

To run the "paired" *t* test, follow the instruction below.

First compute the difference in delivery times as shown below:

Differences
$16.8 - 22.0 = -5.2$
$11.7 - 15.2 = -3.5$
$15.6 - 18.7 = -3.1$
$16.7 - 15.6 = 1.1$
$17.5 - 20.8 = -3.3$
$18.1 - 19.5 = -1.4$
$14.1 - 17.0 = -2.9$
$21.8 - 19.5 = 2.3$
$13.9 - 16.5 = -2.6$
$20.8 - 24.0 = -3.2$

Then enter the "Differences between Local and Chain" data in List 1.

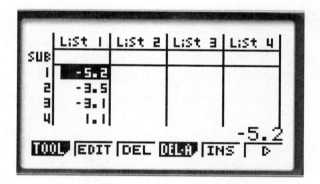

Now, from the **STAT mode**, select the following:

STAT   F3(TEST) **F2**(t) **F1**(1-s)   then enter the following items:

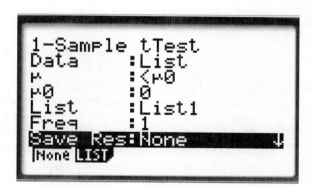

Now press **EXE** or **F1**(CALC) or **F6** (DRAW)

If you select **F6** (DRAW), you will see a *t* distribution.

If you select either **EXE** or **F1**(Calc), the calculator will now show the results:

How to Find *t* Critical Value Using a Calculator?

Calculate the t critical value for $\alpha = 0.05$, using the Casio Calculator fx-9750GII and follow the following calculator steps:

From the **Main Menu** select:

STAT F5 (DIST) **F2** (t) **F3**(Invt)   then enter the following items:

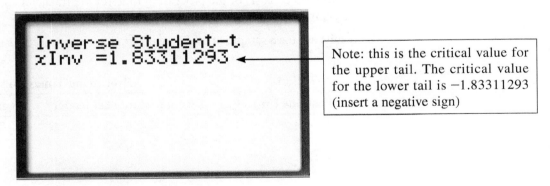

Now press **EXE** or **F1**(CALC)

The calculator will now show the results:

Note: this is the critical value for the upper tail. The critical value for the lower tail is -1.83311293 (insert a negative sign)

Confidence Interval Estimate for the Mean Difference

Instead of, or in addition to, testing for the mean difference between two related populations, you can use Equation (12.4) to construct a confidence interval estimate for the population mean difference.

CONFIDENCE INTERVAL ESTIMATE FOR THE MEAN DIFFERENCE

$$\overline{D} \pm t_{\alpha/2}\frac{S_D}{\sqrt{n}}$$

(12.4)

or

$$\overline{D} - t_{\alpha/2}\frac{S_D}{\sqrt{n}} \leq \mu_D \leq \overline{D} + t_{\alpha/2}\frac{S_D}{\sqrt{n}}$$

where $t_{\alpha/2}$ is the critical value of the t distribution, with $n - 1$ degrees of freedom, for an area of $\alpha/2$ in the upper tail.

Recall the example comparing textbook prices on page 122. Using Equation (12.4), $\overline{D} = 42.6013$, $S_D = 43.797$, $n = 16$, and $t_{\alpha/2} = 2.1314$ (for 95% confidence and $n - 1 = 15$ degrees of freedom),

$$42.6013 \pm (2.1314)\frac{43.797}{\sqrt{16}}$$

$$42.6013 \pm 23.3373$$

$$19.264 \leq \mu_D \leq 65.9386$$

Thus, with 95% confidence, you estimate that the population mean difference in textbook prices between the college bookstore and the online retailer is between \$19.26 and \$65.94. Because the interval estimate does not contain zero, using the 0.05 level of significance and a two-tail test, you can conclude that there is evidence of a difference in the mean prices of textbooks at the college bookstore and the online retailer. Since both the lower and upper limits of the confidence interval are above 0, you can conclude that the mean price is higher at the college bookstore than the online retailer.

How to Run a Paired-samples t-test with SPSS Version 25

We will use the data depicted in Table 1 to demonstrate how to perform paired t test using SPSS. The data consists of the processing time for the financial applications projects that use the current market leader and new software package.

The results are for a sample of 10 financial applications projects as shown below:

Table 1	Processing Times (in seconds)	
Applications Project	**By current market leader**	**By new software package**
1	9.98	9.88
2	9.88	9.86
3	9.84	9.75
4	9.99	9.80
5	9.94	9.87
6	9.84	9.84
7	9.86	9.87
8	10.12	9.86
9	9.90	9.83
10	9.91	9.86

At the 0.05 level of significance, is there evidence that the mean processing time is greater when the financial applications projects use the current market leader rather than the new software package?

Instruction:
Performing a Paired-Samples T Test on SPSS – Version 25
Open a new spreadsheet called the "New Dataset".
Click "New Dataset".

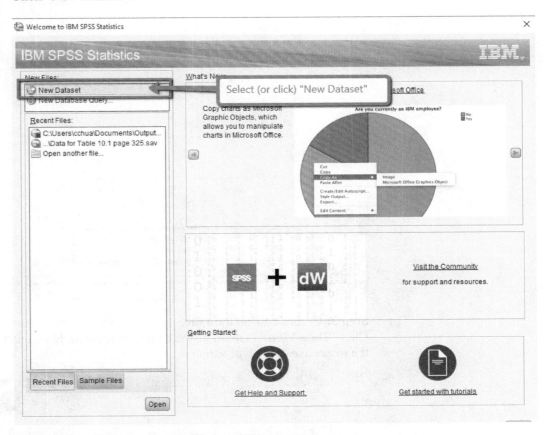

Step 2: Define the variables and give the variables a label.
Click "**Variable View**" (at the bottom of the window) to go to the **variable view** window in order to define the variables and fix the data at zero or one decimal places.

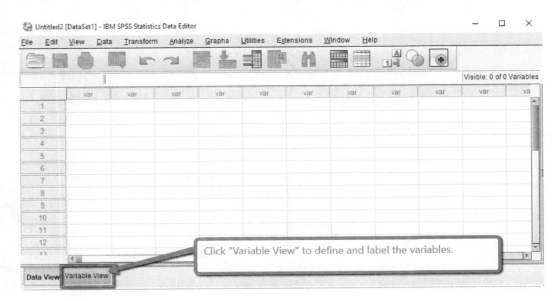

- Enter the first variable name -"current" and give the variable a label '**By current market leader**'.
- Enter the second variable name – "new" and label it as "**By new software package**".

See the Variable View window show below.

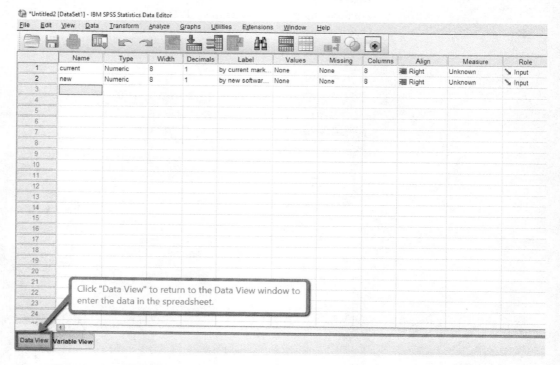

Step 3: Create a SPSS data file.
Click "**Data View**" to return to the data view window. Now, enter the raw data (in Table 1) into the respective column of variables.

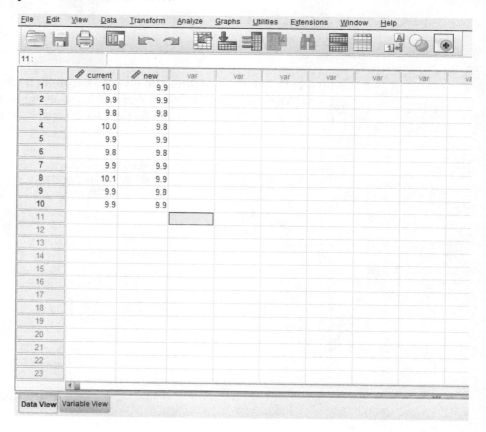

After you have entered all the data, save it as "pairedTtest.sav" (or any filename).

Step 3: Perform Paired-samples t-test.

Make the following menu selections:
Analyze→Compare Means→Paired-Samples T test

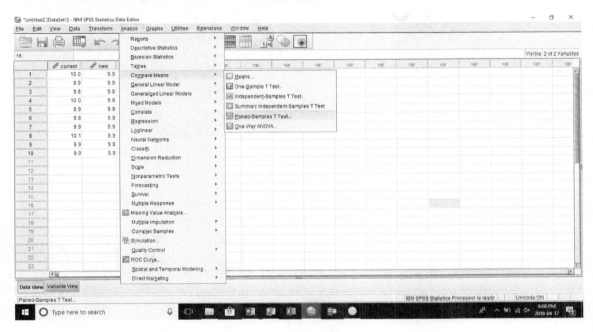

At this point, the **Paired Samples T Test** dialog box will appear. Make these entries in the **Paired-Samples T Test** dialog box:

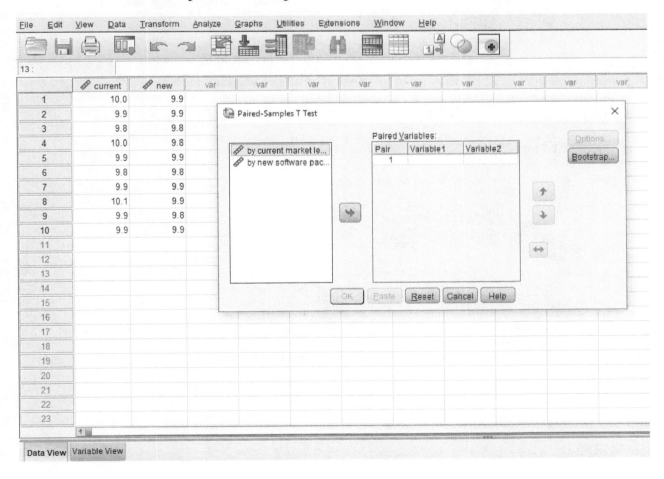

- Highlight on the "**By current market leader**" variable and click on the arrow key (→). The variable will automatically fall into the **Pair 1 – Variable 1** cell.
- Highlight on the "**By new software package**" variable and click on the arrow key (→). The variable will automatically fall into the **Pair 1 – Variable 2** cell.

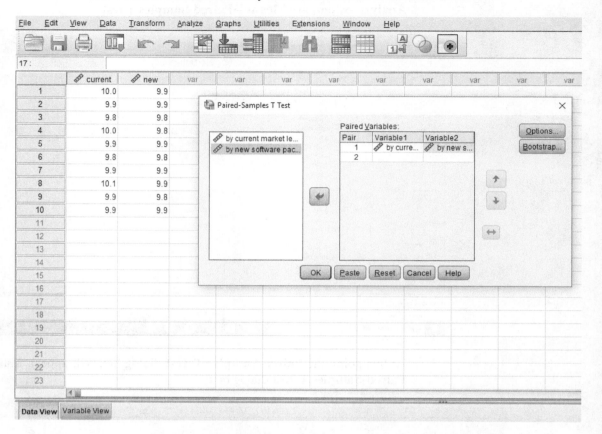

- Click on the **Ok** button to obtain the SPSS results.

Step 3: Go to **SPSS Viewer** to obtain your SPSS results.

SPSS output:

T-Test

Paired Samples Statistics

		Mean	N	Std. Deviation	Std. Error Mean
Pair 1	by current market leader	9.920	10	.0919	.0291
	by new software package	9.860	10	.0516	.0163

Paired Samples Correlations

		N	Correlation	Sig.
Pair 1	by current market leader & by new software package	10	.421	.225

Paired Samples Test

		Paired Differences							
					95% Confidence Interval of the Difference				
		Mean	Std. Deviation	Std. Error Mean	Lower	Upper	t	df	Sig. (2-tailed)
Pair 1	by current market leader - by new software package	.0600	.0843	.0267	-.0003	.1203	2.250	9	.051

12.3 Comparing the Proportions of Two Independent Populations

Often, you need to make comparisons and analyze differences between two population proportions. You can perform a test for the difference between two proportions selected from independent populations by using two different methods. This section presents a procedure whose test statistic, Z_{STAT}, is approximated by a standardized normal distribution. In Section 14.1, a procedure whose test statistic, χ^2_{STAT}, is approximated by a chi-square distribution is used. As explained in the latter section, the results from these two tests are equivalent.

Z Test for the Difference Between Two Proportions

In evaluating differences between two population proportions, you can use a **Z test for the difference between two proportions**. The Z_{STAT} test statistic is based on the difference between two sample proportions $(p_1 - p_2)$. This test statistic, given in Equation (12.5), approximately follows a standardized normal distribution for large enough sample sizes.

Z TEST FOR THE DIFFERENCE BETWEEN TWO PROPORTIONS

$$Z_{STAT} = \frac{(p_1 - p_2) - (\pi_1 - \pi_2)}{\sqrt{\bar{p}(1 - \bar{p})\left(\dfrac{1}{n_1} + \dfrac{1}{n_2}\right)}} \qquad (12.5)$$

where

$$\bar{p} = \frac{X_1 + X_2}{n_1 + n_2} \qquad p_1 = \frac{X_1}{n_1} \qquad p_2 = \frac{X_2}{n_2}$$

and

p_1 = proportion of items of interest in sample 1
X_1 = number of items of interest in sample 1
n_1 = sample size of sample 1
π_1 = proportion of items of interest in population 1
p_2 = proportion of items of interest in sample 2
X_2 = number of items of interest in sample 2
n_2 = sample size of sample 2
π_2 = proportion of items of interest in population 2
$\bar{p}$ = pooled estimate of the population proportion of items of interest

The Z_{STAT} test statistic approximately follows a standardized normal distribution.

> **Student Tip**
> Do not confuse this use of the Greek letter pi, π, to represent the population proportion with the mathematical constant that uses the same letter to represent the ratio of the circumference to a diameter of a circle—approximately 3.14159.

The null hypothesis in the Z test for the difference between two proportions states that the two population proportions are equal $(\pi_1 = \pi_2)$. Because the pooled estimate for the population proportion is based on the null hypothesis, you combine, or pool, the two sample proportions to compute $\bar{p}$, an overall estimate of the common population proportion. This estimate is equal to the number of items of interest in the two samples $(X_1 + X_2)$ divided by the total sample size from the two samples $(n_1 + n_2)$.

As shown in the following table, you can use this Z test for the difference between population proportions to determine whether there is a difference in the proportion of items of interest in the two populations (two-tail test) or whether one population has a higher proportion of items of interest than the other population (one-tail test):

Two-Tail Test	One-Tail Test	One-Tail Test
$H_0: \pi_1 = \pi_2$	$H_0: \pi_1 \geq \pi_2$	$H_0: \pi_1 \leq \pi_2$
$H_1: \pi_1 \neq \pi_2$	$H_1: \pi_1 < \pi_2$	$H_1: \pi_1 > \pi_2$

where

π_1 = proportion of items of interest in population 1

π_2 = proportion of items of interest in population 2

To test the null hypothesis that there is no difference between the proportions of two independent populations:

$$H_0: \pi_1 = \pi_2$$

against the alternative that the two population proportions are not the same:

$$H_1: \pi_1 \neq \pi_2$$

you use the Z_{STAT} test statistic, given by Equation (12.5). For a given level of significance, α, you reject the null hypothesis if the computed Z_{STAT} test statistic is greater than the upper-tail critical value from the standardized normal distribution or if the computed Z_{STAT} test statistic is less than the lower-tail critical value from the standardized normal distribution.

To illustrate the use of the Z test for the equality of two proportions, suppose that you are the manager of T.C. Resort Properties, a collection of five upscale resort hotels located on two tropical islands. On one of the islands, T.C. Resort Properties has two hotels, the Beachcomber and the Windsurfer. Using the DCOVA problem-solving approach, you have defined the business objective as improving the return rate of guests at the Beachcomber and the Windsurfer hotels. On the survey completed by hotel guests upon or after their departure, one question asked is whether the guest is likely to return to the hotel. Responses to this and other questions were collected from 227 guests at the Beachcomber and 262 guests at the Windsurfer. The results for this question indicated that 163 of 227 guests at the Beachcomber responded yes, they were likely to return to the hotel and 154 of 262 guests at the Windsurfer responded yes, they were likely to return to the hotel. At the 0.05 level of significance, is there evidence of a significant difference in guest satisfaction (as measured by the likelihood to return to the hotel) between the two hotels?

The null and alternative hypotheses are

$$H_0: \pi_1 = \pi_2 \quad \text{or} \quad \pi_1 - \pi_2 = 0$$
$$H_1: \pi_1 \neq \pi_2 \quad \text{or} \quad \pi_1 - \pi_2 \neq 0$$

Using the 0.05 level of significance, the critical values are -1.96 and $+1.96$ (see Figure 12.11), and the decision rule is

Reject H_0 if $Z_{STAT} < -1.96$
or if $Z_{STAT} > +1.96$;
otherwise, do not reject H_0.

FIGURE 12.11

Regions of rejection and nonrejection when testing a hypothesis for the difference between two proportions at the 0.05 level of significance

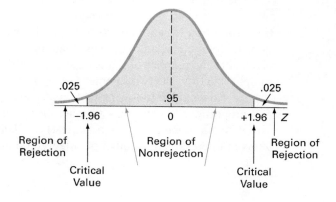

Using Equation (12.5) on page 135,

$$Z_{STAT} = \frac{(p_1 - p_2) - (\pi_1 - \pi_2)}{\sqrt{\bar{p}(1 - \bar{p})\left(\dfrac{1}{n_1} + \dfrac{1}{n_2}\right)}}$$

where

$$p_1 = \frac{X_1}{n_1} = \frac{163}{227} = 0.7181 \quad p_2 = \frac{X_2}{n_2} = \frac{154}{262} = 0.5878$$

and

$$\bar{p} = \frac{X_1 + X_2}{n_1 + n_2} = \frac{163 + 154}{227 + 262} = \frac{317}{489} = 0.6483$$

so that

$$
\begin{aligned}
Z_{STAT} &= \frac{(0.7181 - 0.5878) - (0)}{\sqrt{0.6483(1 - 0.6483)\left(\dfrac{1}{227} + \dfrac{1}{262}\right)}} \\
&= \frac{0.1303}{\sqrt{(0.228)(0.0082)}} \\
&= \frac{0.1303}{\sqrt{0.00187}} \\
&= \frac{0.1303}{0.0432} = +3.0088
\end{aligned}
$$

Using the 0.05 level of significance, you reject the null hypothesis because $Z_{STAT} = +3.0088 > +1.96$. The p-value is 0.0026 (computed using Table E.2 or from Figure 12.12) and indicates that if the null hypothesis is true, the probability that a Z_{STAT} test statistic is less than -3.0088 is 0.0013, and, similarly, the probability that a Z_{STAT} test statistic is greater than $+3.0088$ is 0.0013. Thus, for this two-tail test, the p-value is $0.0013 + 0.0013 = 0.0026$. Because $0.0026 < \alpha = 0.05$, you reject the null hypothesis. There is evidence to conclude that the two hotels are significantly different with respect to guest satisfaction; a greater proportion of guests are willing to return to the Beachcomber than to the Windsurfer.

FIGURE 12.12

Calculator result for the Z test for the difference two proportions for the hotel guest satisfaction problem

Perform z-test of hypothesis for the proportion using the calculator.

From the **Main Menu** select:

STAT F3(TEST) **F1**(Z) **F4**(2-p)   then enter the following items:

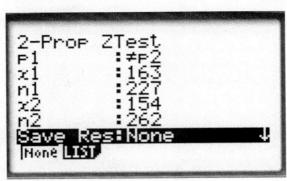

Now press **EXE** or **F1**(CALC) or **F6** (DRAW)

If you select **F6** (DRAW), you will see a normal distribution.

If you select either **EXE** or **F1**(Calc), the calculator will now show the results:

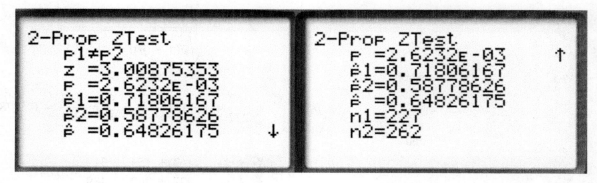

Statistical Decision: Do Not Reject the null hypothesis.

EXAMPLE 12.3

Testing for the Difference Between Two Proportions

Are men less likely than women to say that a major reason they use Facebook is to share with many people at once? A survey reported that 42% of men (193 out of 459 sampled) and 50% of women (250 out of 501 sampled) said that a major reason they use Facebook is to share with many people at once. (Source: "6 new facts about Facebook," **bit.ly/1kENZcA**.)

SOLUTION   Because you want to know whether there is evidence that the proportion of men who say that a major reason they use Facebook is to share with many people at once is *less* than the proportion of women who say that a major reason they use Facebook is to share with many people at once, you have a one-tail test. The null and alternative hypotheses are

$H_0: \pi_1 \geq \pi_2$ (The proportion of men who say that a major reason they use Facebook is to share with many people at once is greater than or equal to the proportion of women who say that a major reason they use Facebook is to share with many people at once.)

$H_1: \pi_1 < \pi_2$ (The proportion of men who say that a major reason they use Facebook is to share with many people at once is less than the proportion of women who say that a major reason they use Facebook is to share with many people at once.)

Using the 0.05 level of significance, for the one-tail test in the lower tail, the critical value is $+1.645$. The decision rule is

$$\text{Reject } H_0 \text{ if } Z_{STAT} < -1.645;$$

$$\text{otherwise, do not reject } H_0.$$

Using Equation (12.5) on page 135,

$$Z_{STAT} = \frac{(p_1 - p_2) - (\pi_1 - \pi_2)}{\sqrt{\bar{p}(1 - \bar{p})\left(\dfrac{1}{n_1} + \dfrac{1}{n_2}\right)}}$$

where

$$p_1 = \frac{X_1}{n_1} = \frac{193}{459} = 0.4205 \quad p_2 = \frac{X_2}{n_2} = \frac{250}{501} = 0.4990$$

and

$$\bar{p} = \frac{X_1 + X_2}{n_1 + n_2} = \frac{193 + 250}{459 + 501} = \frac{443}{960} = 0.4615$$

(*continued*)

so that

$$Z_{STAT} = \frac{(0.4205 - 0.4990) - (0)}{\sqrt{0.4615(1 - 0.4615)\left(\dfrac{1}{459} + \dfrac{1}{501}\right)}}$$

$$= \frac{-0.0785}{\sqrt{(0.2485)(0.0042)}}$$

$$= \frac{-0.0785}{\sqrt{0.0010437}}$$

$$= \frac{-0.0785}{0.0322} = -2.4379$$

Using the 0.05 level of significance, you reject the null hypothesis because $Z_{STAT} = -2.4379$ < -1.645. The p-value is 0.0074. Therefore, if the null hypothesis is true, the probability that a Z_{STAT} test statistic is less than -2.4379 is 0.0074 (which is less than $\alpha = 0.05$). You conclude that there is evidence that the proportion of men who say that a major reason they use Facebook is to share with many people at once is less than the proportion of women who say that a major reason they use Facebook is to share with many people at once.

How to Run a z Test for Two Proportions with a FX-9750GII Calculator

Refer to Example 12.3: At the 0.05 level of significance, is there evidence that the proportion of men who say that a major reason they use Facebook is to share with many people at once is less than the proportion of women who say that a major reason they use Facebook is to share with many people at once?

Null Hypothesis: $\pi_1 \geq \pi_2$

Alternative Hypothesis: $\pi_1 < \pi_2$

where π_1 is defined as the population proportion of men who say that a major reason they use Facebook is to share with many people at once.
π_2 is defined as the population proportion of women who say that a major reason they use Facebook is to share with many people at once.

To test the hypothesis, follow these calculator steps:
From the **Main Menu** select:

STAT   F3(TEST)   **F1**(Z)   **F4**(2-P)   then enter the following items:

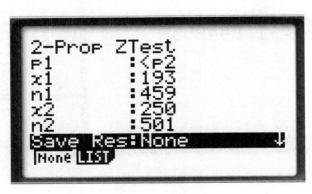

Now press **EXE** or **F1**(Calc) or **F6** (DRAW)

If you select **F6** (DRAW), you will see a normal distribution.

If you select either **EXE** or **F1**(CALC), the calculator will now show the results:

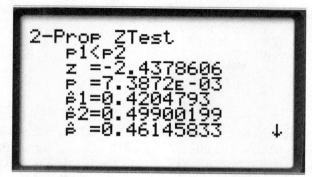

Since the p-value of 0.0074 is less than 0.05, the conclusion is to reject the null hypothesis. In other words there is evidence that the proportion of men who say that a major reason they use Facebook is to share with many people at once is less than the proportion of women who say that a major reason they use Facebook is to share with many people at once.

To find z critical value:

From the **Main Menu** select:

STAT   F5(Dist)   **F1**(Norm)   **F3**(InvN)   then enter the following items:

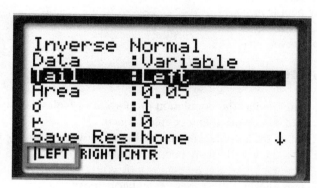

The calculator will now show the results:

Inverse Normal
 xInv=-1.6448536

Confidence Interval Estimate for the Difference Between Two Proportions

Instead of, or in addition to, testing for the difference between the proportions of two independent populations, you can construct a confidence interval estimate for the difference between the two proportions using Equation (12.6).

CONFIDENCE INTERVAL ESTIMATE FOR THE DIFFERENCE BETWEEN TWO PROPORTIONS

$$(p_1 - p_2) \pm Z_{\alpha/2}\sqrt{\frac{p_1(1 - p_1)}{n_1} + \frac{p_2(1 - p_2)}{n_2}} \tag{12.6}$$

or

$$(p_1 - p_2) - Z_{\alpha/2}\sqrt{\frac{p_1(1 - p_1)}{n_1} + \frac{p_2(1 - p_2)}{n_2}} \le (\pi_1 - \pi_2)$$

$$\le (p_1 - p_2) + Z_{\alpha/2}\sqrt{\frac{p_1(1 - p_1)}{n_1} + \frac{p_2(1 - p_2)}{n_2}}$$

To construct a 95% confidence interval estimate for the population difference between the proportion of guests who would return to the Beachcomber and who would return to the Windsurfer, you use the results on page 136 or from Figure 12.12 on page 137:

$$p_1 = \frac{X_1}{n_1} = \frac{163}{227} = 0.7181 \quad p_2 = \frac{X_2}{n_2} = \frac{154}{262} = 0.5878$$

Using Equation (12.6),

$$(0.7181 - 0.5878) \pm (1.96)\sqrt{\frac{0.7181(1 - 0.7181)}{227} + \frac{0.5878(1 - 0.5878)}{262}}$$

$$0.1303 \pm (1.96)(0.0426)$$

$$0.1303 \pm 0.0835$$

$$0.0468 \le (\pi_1 - \pi_2) \le 0.2138$$

Thus, you have 95% confidence that the difference between the population proportion of guests who would return to the Beachcomber and the Windsurfer is between 0.0468 and 0.2138. In percentages, the difference is between 4.68% and 21.38%. Guest satisfaction is higher at the Beachcomber than at the Windsurfer.

12.4 *F* Test for the Ratio of Two Variances

Often you need to determine whether two independent populations have the same variability. By testing variances, you can detect differences in the variability in two independent populations. One important reason to test for the difference between the variances of two populations is to determine whether to use the pooled-variance *t* test (which assumes equal variances) or the separate-variance *t* test (which does not assume equal variances) while comparing the means of two independent populations.

The test for the difference between the variances of two independent populations is based on the ratio of the two sample variances. If you assume that each population is normally distributed, then the ratio S_1^2/S_2^2 follows the F distribution (see Table E.5). The critical values of the **F distribution** in Table E.5 depend on the degrees of freedom in the two samples. The degrees of freedom in the numerator of the ratio are for the first sample, and the degrees of freedom in the denominator are for the second sample. Equation (12.2) defines the **F test for the ratio of two variances**.

F TEST STATISTIC FOR TESTING THE RATIO OF TWO VARIANCES

The F_{STAT} test statistic is equal to the variance of sample 1 divided by the variance of sample 2.

$$F_{STAT} = \frac{S_1^2}{S_2^2} \tag{12.7}$$

where

S_1^2 = variance of sample 1
S_2^2 = variance of sample 2
n_1 = sample size selected from population 1
n_2 = sample size selected from population 2
$n_1 - 1$ = degrees of freedom from sample 1 (i.e., the numerator degrees of freedom)
$n_2 - 1$ = degrees of freedom from sample 2 (i.e., the denominator degrees of freedom)

The F_{STAT} test statistic follows an F distribution with $n_1 - 1$ and $n_2 - 1$ degrees of freedom.

F Critical Value

1. For a two tail test: The two critical values are F_U (F **Upper**) and F_L (F **Lower**)

$$F_U = F_{a/2, n_1 - 1, n_2 - 1}$$

$$F_L = F_{1 - a/2, n_1 - 1, n_2 - 1} = \frac{1}{F_{a/2, n_2 - 1, n_1 - 1}}$$

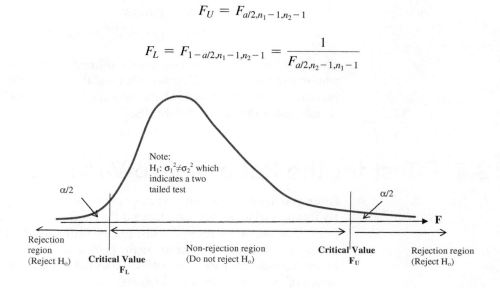

2. For a lower-tailed test (left tailed test): The critical value is F_L (*F* **Lower**)

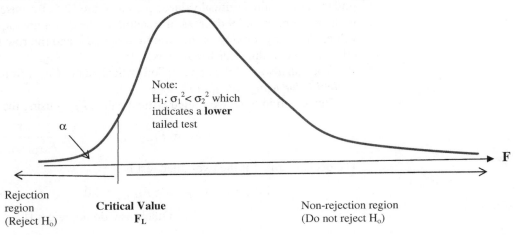

Note:
$H_1: \sigma_1^2 < \sigma_2^2$ which
indicates a **lower**
tailed test

α

| Rejection region (Reject H_o) | **Critical Value** $\mathbf{F_L}$ | Non-rejection region (Do not reject H_o) |

3. For a upper-tailed test (right tailed test): The critical value is F_U (*F* **Upper**)

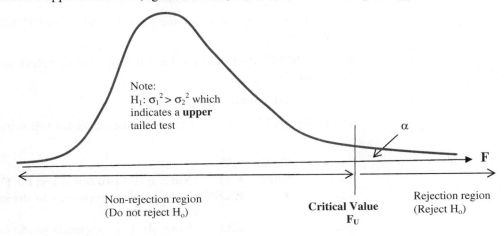

Note:
$H_1: \sigma_1^2 > \sigma_2^2$ which
indicates a **upper**
tailed test

α

| Non-rejection region (Do not reject H_o) | **Critical Value** $\mathbf{F_U}$ | Rejection region (Reject H_o) |

For a given level of significance, α, to test the null hypothesis of equality of population variances:

$$H_0: \sigma_1^2 = \sigma_2^2$$

against the alternative hypothesis that the two population variances are not equal:

$$H_1: \sigma_1^2 \neq \sigma_2^2$$

you reject the null hypothesis if the computed F_{STAT} test statistic is greater than the upper-tail critical value, $F_{U\alpha/2}$ or F_{CALC} test statistic is less than the lower-tail critical value, $F_{L,\alpha/2}$ from the F distribution, with $n_1 - 1$ degrees of freedom in the numerator and $n_2 - 1$ degrees of freedom in the denominator. Thus, the decision rule is

$$\text{Reject } H_0 \text{ if } F_{STAT} > F_{U\alpha/2}; \text{ or } F_{STAT} < F_{U\alpha/2}$$

otherwise, do not reject H_0.

To illustrate how to use the *F* test to determine whether the two variances are equal, return to the BLK Beverages scenario on page 102 and refer to the data in Table 12.1 concerning the sales of BLK Cola in two different display locations. To determine whether to use the pooled-variance *t* test or the separate-variance *t* test in Section 12.1, you can test the equality of the two population variances. The null and alternative hypotheses are

$$H_0: \sigma_1^2 = \sigma_2^2$$

$$H_1: \sigma_1^2 \neq \sigma_2^2$$

The hypothesis test is a two-tailed test and therefore you have to compute the upper-tailed critical value, $F_{U,\alpha/2}$ and the lower-tailed critical value, $F_{L,\alpha/2}$. First find the upper-tailed critical value, $F_{U,\alpha/2}$. The numerator degrees of freedom (corresponds to sample 1) is $10 - 1 = 9$ and the denominator degrees of freedom (corresponds to sample 2) is also $10 - 1 = 9$. You can find the upper-tailed critical value, $F_{U,\alpha/2}$ in Table 12.6. Because there are 9 degrees of freedom in the numerator and 9 degrees of freedom in the denominator, you find the upper-tail critical value, $F_{U,\alpha/2}$, by looking in the column labelled 9 and the row labelled 9. Thus, the upper-tail critical value of this F distribution is 4.03.

You can also find the upper-tailed critical value, $F_{U,\alpha/2}$ from the calculator (refer to *Find F critical value using calculator*).

You can find the lower-tailed critical value, $F_{L,\alpha/2}$.using the following formula.

$$F_L = F_{1-a/2, n_1-1, n_2-1} = \frac{1}{F_{a/2, n_2-1, n_1-1}}$$

The decision rule for the two-tailed test is

Reject H_0 if $F_{CALC} > F_{U,\alpha/2} = 4.03$ or $F_{CALC} < F_{L,\alpha/2} = 0.248$

Otherwise, do not reject H_0.

Find F critical value using calculator:

To find the F critical value, use the Casio Calculator fx-9750GII and follow the following calculator steps:

Note: Fx-9750G Plus does not have this option; therefore you have to use the Table A.5 in the Appendix.

From the **Main Menu** select:

STAT   F5 (DIST)   **F4** (F)   **F3**(InvF)   then enter the following items:

Inverse F
Data   : **F2**(Var)   ▼
Area   : **0.025**   **EXE**   (**Note: It is a two tailed test for F distribution, $\alpha \div 2$**)
n:df   : **9**   **EXE**   (**Note: n:df corresponds to the sample 1 happens to be in the numerator**)
d:df   : **9**   **EXE**   (**Note: d:df corresponds to the sample 2 happens to be in the denominator**)
Save Res : None

Execute

Now key **EXE** or **F1**(CALC)

The calculator will now show the results:

Inverse F

x-Inv = 4.02599416

The critical value defines the rejection and non-rejection regions.

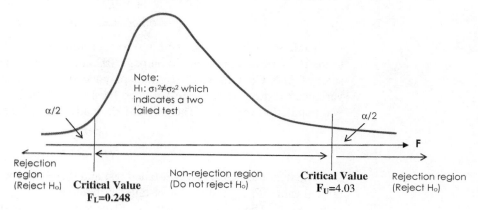

Note:
H_1: $\sigma_1^2 \neq \sigma_2^2$ which indicates a two tailed test

$\alpha/2$ $\alpha/2$

F

Rejection region
(Reject H_0)   **Critical Value**   Non-rejection region   **Critical Value**   Rejection region
                F_L=0.248   (Do not reject H_0)   **F_U=4.03**   (Reject H_0)

Note:
Apply the formula to compute F_L.

$$F_L = F_{1-a/2, n_1-1, n_2-1} = \frac{1}{F_{a/2, n_2-1, n_1-1}} = \frac{1}{F_{0.025, 9, 9}} = \frac{1}{4.02599416} = 0.248386$$

TABLE 12.6

Finding the Upper-Tail Critical Value of *F* with 9 and 9 Degrees of Freedom for an Upper-Tail Area of 0.025

Denominator df_2	1	2	3	...	7	8	9
			Cumulative Probabilities = 0.975				
			Upper-Tail Area = 0.025				
			Numerator df_1				
1	647.80	799.50	864.20	...	948.20	956.70	963.30
2	38.51	39.00	39.17	...	39.36	39.37	39.39
3	17.44	16.04	15.44	...	14.62	14.54	14.47
⋮	⋮	⋮	⋮	⋮	⋮	⋮	⋮
7	8.07	6.54	5.89	...	4.99	4.90	4.82
8	7.57	6.06	5.42	...	4.53	4.43	4.36
9	7.21	5.71	5.08	...	4.20	4.10	4.03

Source: Extracted from Table E.5.

Using Equation (12.7) on page 142 and the cola sales data (see Table 12.1 on page 102),

$$S_1^2 = (18.7264)^2 = 350.6778 \quad S_2^2 = (12.5433)^2 = 157.3333$$

so that

$$F_{STAT} = \frac{S_1^2}{S_2^2}$$

$$= \frac{350.6778}{157.3333} = 2.2289$$

Because $F_{STAT} = 2.2289 < 4.03$, you do not reject H_0. Figure 12.13 shows the results for this test, including the *p*-value, 0.248. Because $0.248 > 0.05$, you conclude that there is no evidence of a significant difference in the variability of the sales of cola for the two display locations.

In testing for a difference between two variances using the *F* test described in this section, you assume that each of the two populations is normally distributed. The *F* test is very sensitive to the normality assumption. If boxplots or normal probability plots suggest even a mild departure from normality for either of the two populations, you should not use the *F* test. If this happens, you should use the Levene test or a nonparametric approach (see references 1 and 2).

In testing for the equality of variances as part of assessing the validity of the pooled-variance *t* test procedure, the *F* test is a two-tail test with $\alpha/2$ in the upper tail. However, when you are interested in examining the variability in situations other than the pooled-variance *t* test, the *F* test is often a one-tail test. Example 12.4 illustrates a one-tail test.

FIGURE 12.13
Casio calculator *F*-test results for the BLK Cola sales data

Solution: From the **Main Menu** select the following:

STAT **F3**(test) **F4**(F). Then enter the following items:

2-Sample FTest

Data	: **F2**(Var) ▼
$\sigma 1$	: **F1**($\neq\sigma 2$) ▼
x1σn-1	: **18.72639255** **EXE**
n1	: **10** **EXE**
x2σn-1	: **12.54325848** **EXE**
n2	: **10** **EXE**

Now press **EXE** or **F1** (Calc).

The calculator will now show the results:

2-Sample FTest

$\sigma 1$	$\neq\sigma 2$
F	=2.2289
p	=0.2482
x1σn-1	=18.726
x2σn-1	=12.543
n1	=10
n2	=10

EXAMPLE 12.4

A One-Tail Test for the Difference Between Two Variances

A professor in the accounting department of a business school would like to determine whether there is more variability in the final exam scores of students taking the introductory accounting course who are not majoring in accounting than for students taking the course who are majoring in accounting. Random samples of 13 non-accounting majors and 10 accounting majors are selected from the professor's class roster in his large lecture, and the following results are computed based on the final exam scores:

$$\text{Non-accounting:} \quad n_1 = 13 \quad S_1^2 = 210.2$$

$$\text{Accounting:} \quad n_2 = 10 \quad S_2^2 = 36.5$$

At the 0.05 level of significance, is there evidence that there is more variability in the final exam scores of students taking the introductory accounting course who are not majoring in accounting than for students taking the course who are majoring in accounting? Assume that the population final exam scores are normally distributed.

SOLUTION The null and alternative hypotheses are

$$H_0: \sigma_{NA}^2 \leq \sigma_A^2$$

$$H_1: \sigma_{NA}^2 > \sigma_A^2$$

The F_{STAT} test statistic is given by Equation (12.7) on page 142:

$$F_{STAT} = \frac{S_1^2}{S_2^2}$$

You use Table E.5 to find the upper critical value of the F distribution. With $n_1 - 1 = 13 - 1 = 12$ degrees of freedom in the numerator, $n_2 - 1 = 10 - 1 = 9$ degrees of freedom in the denominator, and $\alpha = 0.05$, the upper-tail critical value, $F_{0.05}$, is 3.07. The decision rule is

$$\text{Reject } H_0 \text{ if } F_{STAT} > 3.07;$$

$$\text{otherwise, do not reject } H_0.$$

From Equation (12.2) on page 109,

$$F_{STAT} = \frac{S_1^2}{S_2^2}$$

$$= \frac{210.2}{36.5} = 5.7589$$

Because $F_{STAT} = 5.7589 > 3.07$, you reject H_0. Using a 0.05 level of significance, you conclude that there is evidence that there is more variability in the final exam scores of students taking the introductory accounting course who are not majoring in accounting than for students taking the course who are majoring in accounting.

How to Run the *F* Test with a FX-9750GII Calculator

Refer to the Example 12.4

$$\text{Non-accounting:} \quad n_1 = 13 \text{ and } S_1^2 = 210.2$$

$$\text{Accounting:} \quad n_2 = 10 \text{ and } S_2^2 = 36.5$$

With the following hypotheses:

$$H_0 : \sigma_{NA}^2 \leq \sigma_A^2$$

$$H_a : \sigma_{NA}^2 > \sigma_A^2$$

To run the *F* test, follow the instruction below.

STAT F3(test) **F4**(F)   then enter the following items:

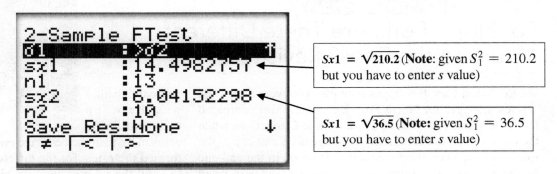

$Sx1 = \sqrt{210.2}$ (**Note:** given $S_1^2 = 210.2$ but you have to enter s value)

$Sx1 = \sqrt{36.5}$ (**Note:** given $S_1^2 = 36.5$ but you have to enter s value)

Now press **EXE** or **F1**(Calc)

The calculator will now show the results:

```
2-Sample FTest
ó1     >ó2
F      =5.75890411
P      =6.6055ᴇ-03
sx1    =14.4982758
sx2    =6.04152299
n1     =13           ↓
```

```
2-Sample FTest
F      =5.75890411   ↑
P      =6.6055ᴇ-03
sx1    =14.4982758
sx2    =6.04152299
n1     =13
n2     =10
```

How to Find *F* Critical Value Using a Calculator

Refer to Example 12.4

Calculate the *F* critical value for $\alpha = 0.05$ with 12 and 9 degree of freedoms, using the Casio Calculator fx-9750GII and follow the following calculator steps:

From the **Main Menu** select:

STAT F5 (DIST) **F4** (F) **F3**(InvF)   then enter the following items:

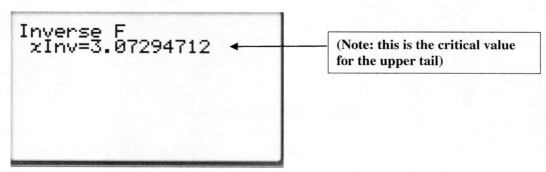

Inverse F
Data   : **F2** (Var)   ▼
Area   : **0.05**   **EXE**
n: df   : **12**   **EXE**
d: df   : **9**   **EXE**
Save Res   : None
Execute

Now key **EXE** or **F1**(CALC)
The calculator will now show the results:

```
Inverse F
  xInv=3.07294712
```

(Note: this is the critical value
for the upper tail)

For North Fork, Are There Different Means to the Ends? Revisited

Fotolia

In the North Fork Beverages scenario, you were a regional sales manager for North Fork Beverages. You compared the sales volume of your new HandMade Citrus Cola when the product was featured in the beverage aisle end-cap to the sales volume when the product was featured in the end-cap by the produce department. An experiment was performed in which 10 stores used the beverage end-cap location and 10 stores used the produce end-cap location. Using a *t* test for the difference between two means, you were able to conclude that the mean sales using the produce end-cap location are higher than the mean sales for the beverage end-cap location. A confidence interval allowed you to infer with 95% confidence that population mean amount sold at the produce end-cap location was between 6.73 and 36.67 cases more than the beverage end-cap location. You also performed the *F* test for the difference between two variances to see if the store-to-store variability in sales in stores using the produce end-cap location differed from the store-to-store variability in sales in stores using the beverage end-cap location. You concluded that there was no significant difference in the variability of the sales of cola for the two display locations. As a regional sales manager, you decide to lease the produce end-cap location in all FoodPlace Supermarkets during your next sales promotional period.

SUMMARY

In this chapter, you were introduced to a variety of tests for two or more samples. For situations in which the samples are independent, you learned statistical test procedures for analyzing possible differences between means, proportions, and variances. In addition, you learned a test procedure that is frequently used when analyzing differences between the means of two related samples. Remember that you need to select the test that is most appropriate for a given set of conditions and to critically investigate the validity of the assumptions underlying each of the hypothesis-testing procedures.

Table 12.12 provides a list of topics covered in this chapter. The roadmap in Figure 12.22 illustrates the steps needed in determining which two-sample test of hypothesis to use. The following are the questions you need to consider:

1. What type of variables do you have? If you are dealing with categorical variables, use the *Z* test for the difference between two proportions. (This test assumes independent samples.)

2. If you have a numerical variable, determine whether you have independent samples or related samples. If you have related samples, and you can assume approximate normality, use the paired *t* test.

3. If you have independent samples, is your focus on variability or central tendency? If the focus is on variability, and you can assume approximate normality, use the *F* test.

4. If your focus is central tendency and you can assume approximate normality, determine whether you can assume that the variances of the two populations are equal. (This assumption can be tested using the *F* test.)

5. If you can assume that the two populations have equal variances, use the pooled-variance *t* test. If you cannot assume that the two populations have equal variances, use the separate-variance *t* test.

6. If you have more than two independent samples, you can use the one-way ANOVA.)

TABLE 12.7

Summary of Topics in Chapter 12

	TYPES OF DATA	
TYPE OF ANALYSIS	**Numerical**	**Categorical**
Compare two populations	*t* tests for the difference in the means of two independent populations (Section 12.1)	*Z* test for the difference between two proportions (Section 12.3)
	Paired *t* test (Section 12.2)	
	F test for the difference between two variances (Section 12.4)	
Compare more than two populations	One-way ANOVA (Section 12.5)	

FIGURE 12.14

Roadmap for selecting a test of hypothesis for two or more samples

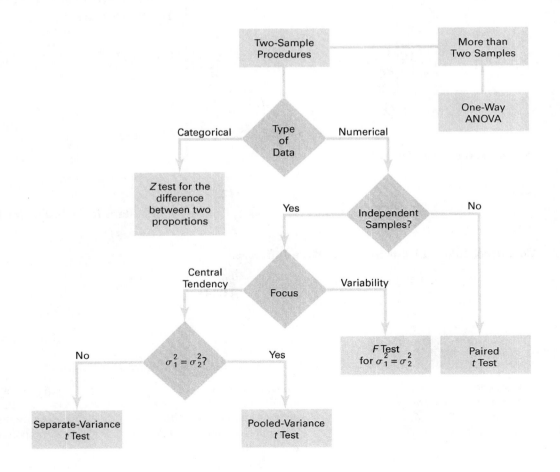

REFERENCES

1. Conover, W. J. *Practical Nonparametric Statistics*, 3rd ed. New York: Wiley, 2000.
2. Daniel, W. *Applied Nonparametric Statistics*, 2nd ed. Boston: Houghton Mifflin, 1990.
3. Hicks, C. R., and K. V. *Turner. Fundamental Concepts in the Design of Experiments*, 5th ed. New York: Oxford University Press, 1999.
4. Kutner, M. H., J. Neter, C. Nachtsheim, and W. Li. *Applied Linear Statistical Models*, 5th ed. New York: McGraw-Hill-Irwin, 2005.
5. Levine, D. M. *Statistics for Six Sigma Green Belts*. Upper Saddle River, NJ: Financial Times/Prentice Hall, 2006.
6. *Microsoft Excel 2013*. Redmond, WA: Microsoft Corp., 2012.
7. *Minitab Release 16* State College, PA: Minitab, 2010.
8. Montgomery, D. M. *Design and Analysis of Experiments*, 6th ed. New York: Wiley, 2005.
9. Satterthwaite, F. E. "An Approximate Distribution of Estimates of Variance Components." *Biometrics Bulletin*, 2(1946): 110–114.
10. Snedecor, G. W., and W. G. Cochran. *Statistical Methods*, 8th ed. Ames, IA: Iowa State University Press, 1989.

KEY EQUATIONS

Pooled-Variance t Test for the Difference Between Two Means

$$t_{STAT} = \frac{(\overline{X}_1 - \overline{X}_2) - (\mu_1 - \mu_2)}{\sqrt{S_p^2\left(\frac{1}{n_1} + \frac{1}{n_2}\right)}} \quad (12.1)$$

Confidence Interval Estimate for the Difference Between the Means of Two Independent Populations

$$(\overline{X}_1 - \overline{X}_2) \pm t_{\alpha/2}\sqrt{S_p^2\left(\frac{1}{n_1} + \frac{1}{n_2}\right)} \quad (12.2)$$

or

$$(\overline{X}_1 - \overline{X}_2) - t_{\alpha/2}\sqrt{S_p^2\left(\frac{1}{n_1} + \frac{1}{n_2}\right)} \leq \mu_1 - \mu_2$$

$$\leq (\overline{X}_1 - \overline{X}_2) + t_{\alpha/2}\sqrt{S_p^2\left(\frac{1}{n_1} + \frac{1}{n_2}\right)}$$

Paired t Test for the Mean Difference

$$t_{STAT} = \frac{\overline{D} - \mu_D}{\frac{S_D}{\sqrt{n}}} \quad (12.3)$$

Confidence Interval Estimate for the Mean Difference

$$\overline{D} \pm t_{\alpha/2}\frac{S_D}{\sqrt{n}} \quad (12.4)$$

or

$$\overline{D} - t_{\alpha/2}\frac{S_D}{\sqrt{n}} \leq \mu_D \leq \overline{D} + t_{\alpha/2}\frac{S_D}{\sqrt{n}}$$

Z Test for the Difference Between Two Proportions

$$Z_{STAT} = \frac{(p_1 - p_2) - (\pi_1 - \pi_2)}{\sqrt{\overline{p}(1 - \overline{p})\left(\frac{1}{n_1} + \frac{1}{n_2}\right)}} \quad (12.5)$$

Confidence Interval Estimate for the Difference Between Two Proportions

$$(p_1 - p_2) \pm Z_{\alpha/2}\sqrt{\left(\frac{p_1(1 - p_1)}{n_1} + \frac{p_2(1 - p_2)}{n_2}\right)} \quad (12.6)$$

or

$$(p_1 - p_2) - Z_{\alpha/2}\sqrt{\frac{p_1(1 - p_1)}{n_1} + \frac{p_2(1 - p_2)}{n_2}} \leq (\pi_1 - \pi_2)$$

$$\leq (p_1 - p_2) + Z_{\alpha/2}\sqrt{\frac{p_1(1 - p_1)}{n_1} + \frac{p_2(1 - p_2)}{n_2}}$$

F Test Statistic for Testing the Ratio of Two Variances

$$F_{STAT} = \frac{S_1^2}{S_2^2} \quad (12.7)$$

KEY TERMS

F distribution 142
F test for the ratio of two variances 142
matched samples 119

paired t test for the mean difference 121
pooled-variance t test 101
repeated measurements 119
robust 106

separate-variance t test 110
two-sample tests 100
Z test for the difference between two proportions 135

CHECKING YOUR UNDERSTANDING

12.1 What are some of the criteria used in the selection of a particular hypothesis-testing procedure?

12.2 Under what conditions should you use the pooled-variance t test to examine possible differences in the means of two independent populations?

12.3 Under what conditions should you use the F test to examine possible differences in the variances of two independent populations?

12.4 What is the distinction between two independent populations and two related populations?

12.5 What is the distinction between repeated measurements and matched items?

12.6 When you have two independent populations, explain the similarities and differences between the test of hypothesis for the difference between the means and the confidence interval estimate for the difference between the means.

12.7 Under what conditions should you use the paired t test for the mean difference between two related populations?

12.8 In a one-way ANOVA, what is the difference between the among-groups variance MSA and the within-groups variance MSW?

12.9 What are the assumptions of ANOVA?

12.10 Under what conditions should you use the one-way ANOVA F test to examine possible differences among the means of c independent populations?

12.11 What is the difference between the one-way ANOVA F test and the Levene test?

PROBLEMS

Section 12.1

12.12 If you have samples of $n_1 = 12$ and $n_2 = 15$, in performing the pooled-variance t test, how many degrees of freedom do you have?

12.13 Assume that you have a sample of $n_1 = 8$, with the sample mean $\overline{X}_1 = 42$, and a sample standard deviation $S_1 = 4$, and you have an independent sample of $n_2 = 15$ from another population with a sample mean of $\overline{X}_2 = 34$ and a sample standard deviation $S_2 = 5$.
a. What is the value of the pooled-variance t_{STAT} test statistic for testing $H_0: \mu_1 = \mu_2$?
b. In finding the critical value, how many degrees of freedom are there?
c. Using the level of significance $\alpha = 0.01$, what is the critical value for a one-tail test of the hypothesis $H_0: \mu_1 \leq \mu_2$ against the alternative, $H_1: \mu_1 > \mu_2$?
d. What is your statistical decision?

12.14 What assumptions about the two populations are necessary in Problem 12.13?

12.15 Referring to Problem 12.13, construct a 95% confidence interval estimate of the population mean difference between μ_1 and μ_2.

12.16 Referring to Problem 12.13, if $n_1 = 5$ and $n_2 = 4$, how many degrees of freedom do you have?

12.17 Referring to Problem 12.13, if $n_1 = 5$ and $n_2 = 4$, at the 0.01 level of significance, is there evidence that $\mu_1 > \mu_2$?

12.18 When people make estimates, they are influenced by anchors to their estimates. A study was conducted in which students were asked to estimate the number of calories in a cheeseburger. One group was asked to do this after thinking about a calorie-laden cheesecake. A second group was asked to do this after thinking about an organic fruit salad. The mean number of calories estimated in a cheeseburger was 780 for the group that thought about the cheesecake and 1,041 for the group that thought about the organic fruit salad. (Data extracted from "Drilling Down, Sizing Up a Cheeseburger's Caloric Heft," *The New York Times*, October 4, 2010, p. B2.) Suppose that the study was based on a sample of 20 people who thought about the cheesecake first and 20 people who thought about the organic fruit salad first, and the standard deviation of the number of calories in the cheeseburger was 128 for the people who thought about the cheesecake first and 140 for the people who thought about the organic fruit salad first.
a. State the null and alternative hypotheses if you want to determine whether the mean estimated number of calories in the cheeseburger is lower for the people who thought about the cheesecake first than for the people who thought about the organic fruit salad first.
b. In the context of this study, what is the meaning of the Type I error?
c. In the context of this study, what is the meaning of the Type II error?
d. At the 0.01 level of significance, is there evidence that the mean estimated number of calories in the cheeseburger is lower for the people who thought about the cheesecake first than for the people who thought about the organic fruit salad first?

12.19 A recent study (data extracted from E. J. Boyland et al., "Food Choice and Overconsumption: Effect of a Premium Sports Celebrity Endorser," *Journal of Pediatrics*, March 13, 2013, **bit.ly/16NR4Bi**) found that 51 children who watched a commercial for Walker Crisps (potato chips) featuring a long-standing sports celebrity endorser ate a mean of 36 grams of Walker Crisps as compared to a mean of 25 grams of Walker Crisps for 41 children who watched a commercial for an alternative food snack. Suppose that the sample standard deviation for the children who watched the sports celebrity–endorsed Walker Crisps commercial was 21.4 grams and the sample standard deviation for the children who watched the alternative food snack commercial was 12.8 grams.
a. Assuming that the population variances are equal and $\alpha = 0.05$, is there evidence that the mean amount of Walker Crisps eaten was significantly higher for the children who watched the sports celebrity–endorsed Walker Crisps commercial?
b. Assuming that the population variances are equal, construct a 95% confidence interval estimate of the difference between the mean amount of Walker Crisps eaten by children who watched the sports celebrity–endorsed Walker Crisps commercial and children who watched the alternative food snack commercial.
c. Compare and discuss the results of (a) and (b).

12.20 A problem with a phone line that prevents a customer from receiving or making calls is upsetting to both the customer and the telecommunications company. The file **Phone** contains samples of 20 problems reported to two different offices of a telecommunications company and the time to clear these problems (in minutes) from the customers' lines:

Central Office I Time to Clear Problems (minutes)

1.48 1.75 0.78 2.85 0.52 1.60 4.15 3.97 1.48 3.10
1.02 0.53 0.93 1.60 0.80 1.05 6.32 3.93 5.45 0.97

Central Office II Time to Clear Problems (minutes)

7.55 3.75 0.10 1.10 0.60 0.52 3.30 2.10 0.58 4.02
3.75 0.65 1.92 0.60 1.53 4.23 0.08 1.48 1.65 0.72

a. Assuming that the population variances from both offices are equal, is there evidence of a difference in the mean waiting time between the two offices? (Use $\alpha = 0.05$.)
b. Find the p-value in (a) and interpret its meaning.
c. What other assumption is necessary in (a)?
d. Assuming that the population variances from both offices are equal, construct and interpret a 95% confidence interval estimate of the difference between the population means in the two offices.

12.21 *Accounting Today* identified the top accounting firms in 10 geographic regions across the United States. All 10 regions reported growth in 2013. The Southeast and Gulf Coast regions reported growth of 4.7% and 13.86%, respectively. A characteristic description of the accounting firms in the Southeast and Gulf Coast regions included the number of partners in the firm. The file AccountingPartners2 contains the number of partners. (Data extracted from **bit.ly/ODuzd3**.)

a. At the 0.05 level of significance, is there evidence of a difference between Southeast region accounting firms and Gulf Coast accounting firms with respect to the mean number of partners?
b. Determine the p-value and interpret its meaning.
c. What assumptions do you have to make about the two populations in order to justify the use of the t test?

12.22 An important feature of tablets is battery life, the number of hours before the battery needs to be recharged. The file Tablets contains the battery life of 12 WiFi-only and 7 3G/4G/WiFi 9- through 12-inch tablets. (Data extracted from "Ratings and recommendations: Tablets," *Consumer Reports*, August 2013, p. 24.)

a. Assuming that the population variances from both types of tablets are equal, is there evidence of a difference in the mean battery life between the two types of tablets? (Use $\alpha = 0.05$.)
b. Determine the p-value in (a) and interpret its meaning.
c. Assuming that the population variances from both types of tablets are equal, construct and interpret a 95% confidence interval estimate of the difference between the population mean battery life of the two types of tablets.

12.23 A bank with a branch located in a commercial district of a city has the business objective of developing an improved process for serving customers during the noon-to-1 P.M. lunch period. Management decides to first study the waiting time in the current process. The waiting time is defined as the number of minutes that elapses from when the customer enters the line until he or she reaches the teller window. Data are collected from a random sample of 15 customers and stored in Bank1. These data are:

4.21 5.55 3.02 5.13 4.77 2.34 3.54 3.20
4.50 6.10 0.38 5.12 6.46 6.19 3.79

Suppose that another branch, located in a residential area, is also concerned with improving the process of serving customers in the noon-to-1 P.M. lunch period. Data are collected from a random sample of 15 customers and stored in Bank2. These data are:

9.66 5.90 8.02 5.79 8.73 3.82 8.01 8.35
10.49 6.68 5.64 4.08 6.17 9.91 5.47

a. Assuming that the population variances from both banks are equal, is there evidence of a difference in the mean waiting time between the two branches? (Use $\alpha = 0.05$.)
b. Determine the p-value in (a) and interpret its meaning.
c. In addition to equal variances, what other assumption is necessary in (a)?
d. Construct and interpret a 95% confidence interval estimate of the difference between the population means in the two branches.

12.24 Repeat Problem 12.23 (a), assuming that the population variances in the two branches are not equal. Compare these results with those of Problem 12.23 (a).

12.25 As a member of the international strategic management team in your company, you are assigned the task of exploring potential foreign market entry. As part of your initial investigation, you want to know if there is a difference between developed markets and emerging markets with respect to the time required to start a business. You select 15 developed countries and 15 emerging countries. The time required to start a business, defined as the number of days needed to complete the procedures to legally operate a business in these countries, is stored in ForeignMarket. (Data extracted from **data.worldbank.org**.)

a. Assuming that the population variances for developed countries and emerging countries are equal, is there evidence of a difference in the mean time required to start a business between developed countries and emerging countries? (Use $\alpha = 0.05$.)
b. Determine the p-value in (a) and interpret its meaning.
c. In addition to equal variances, what other assumption is necessary in (a)?
d. Construct a 95% confidence interval estimate of the difference between the population means of developed countries and emerging countries.

12.26 Repeat Problem 12.25 (a), assuming that the population variances from developed and emerging countries are not equal. Compare these results with those of Problem 12.25 (a).

12.27 Experian Marketing Services reported that the typical American spends 2.4 hours (144 minutes) per day accessing the Internet via a mobile device. (Source: *The 2014 Digital Marketer*, available at **ex.pn/1kXJjfX**.) You wonder if males and females spend differing amounts of time per day accessing the Internet through a mobile device.

You select a sample of 60 friends and family (30 males and 30 females), collect times spent per day accessing the Internet through a mobile device (in minutes), and store the data collected in InternetMobileTime2.

a. Assuming that the variances in the population of times spent per day accessing the Internet via a mobile device are equal, is there evidence of a difference between males and females in the mean time spent per day accessing the Internet via a mobile device? (Use a 0.05 level of significance.)
b. In addition to equal variances, what other assumption is necessary in (a)?

12.28 Brand valuations are critical to CEOs, financial and marketing executives, security analysts, institutional investors, and others who depend on well-researched, reliable information needed for assessments, and comparisons in decision making. Millward Brown Optimor has developed the BrandZ Top 100 Most Valuable Global Brands for WPP, the world's largest communications services group. Unlike other studies, the BrandZ Top 100 Most Valuable Global Brands fuses consumer measures of brand equity with financial measures to place a financial value on brands. The file `BrandZTechFin` contains the brand values for two sectors in the BrandZ Top 100 Most Valuable Global Brands for 2014: the technology sector and the financial institutions sector. (Data extracted from **bit.ly/18OL5Mu**.)

a. Assuming that the population variances are equal, is there evidence of a difference between the technology sector and the financial institutions sector with respect to mean brand value? (Use $\alpha = .05$.)

b. Repeat (a), assuming that the population variances are not equal.

c. Compare the results of (a) and (b).

Section 12.2

12.29 An experimental design for a paired t test has 20 pairs of identical twins. How many degrees of freedom are there in this t test?

12.30 Fifteen volunteers are recruited to participate in an experiment. A measurement is made (such as blood pressure) before each volunteer is asked to read a particularly upsetting passage from a book and after each volunteer reads the passage from the book. In the analysis of the data collected from this experiment, how many degrees of freedom are there in the test?

12.31 Nine experts rated two brands of Colombian coffee in a taste-testing experiment. A rating on a 7-point scale (1 = extremely unpleasing, 7 = extremely pleasing) is given for each of four characteristics: taste, aroma, richness, and acidity. The following data stored in `Coffee` contain the ratings accumulated over all four characteristics:

EXPERT	BRAND	
	A	**B**
C.C.	24	26
S.E.	27	27
E.G.	19	22
B.L.	24	27
C.M.	22	25
C.N.	26	27
G.N.	27	26
R.M.	25	27
P.V.	22	23

a. At the 0.05 level of significance, is there evidence of a difference in the mean ratings between the two brands?

b. What assumption is necessary about the population distribution in order to perform this test?

c. Determine the p-value in (a) and interpret its meaning.

d. Construct and interpret a 95% confidence interval estimate of the difference in the mean ratings between the two brands.

12.32 How do the ratings of TV and Internet services compare? The file `Telecom` contains the rating of 14 different providers. (Data extracted from "Ratings: TV, Phone, and Internet Services," *Consumer Reports*, May 2014, pp. 28–29.)

a. At the 0.05 level of significance, is there evidence of a difference in the mean service rating between TV and Internet services?

b. What assumption is necessary about the population distribution in order to perform this test?

c. Use a graphical method to evaluate the validity of the assumption in (a).

d. Construct and interpret a 95% confidence interval estimate of the difference in the mean service rating between TV and Internet services.

12.33 Super Target versus Walmart: Who has the lowest prices? Given Walmart's slogan "Save Money—Live Better," you suspect that Walmart does. The prices of 33 foods were compared (data extracted from "Supermarket Showdown," *The Palm Beach Post*, February 13, 2011, pp. 1F, 2F) and the results are stored in `TargetWalmart`.

a. At the 0.05 level of significance, is there evidence that the mean price of items is higher at Super Target than at Walmart?

b. What assumption is necessary about the population distribution in order to perform this test?

c. Find the p-value in (a) and interpret its meaning.

12.34 What motivates employees? The Great Place to Work Institute evaluated nonfinancial factors both globally and in the United States. (Data extracted from L. Petrecca, "Tech Companies Top List of 'Great Workplaces,'" *USA Today*, October 31, 2011, p. 7B.) The results, which indicate the importance rating of each factor, are stored in `Motivation`.

a. At the 0.05 level of significance, is there evidence of a difference in the mean rating between global and U.S. employees?

b. What assumption is necessary about the population distribution in order to perform this test?

c. Use a graphical method to evaluate the validity of the assumption in (b).

12.35 Multiple myeloma, or blood plasma cancer, is characterized by increased blood vessel formulation (angiogenesis) in the bone marrow that is a predictive factor in survival. One treatment approach used for multiple myeloma is stem cell transplantation with the patient's own stem cells. The data stored in `Myeloma`, and shown on page 152 represent the bone marrow microvessel density for patients who had a complete response to the stem cell transplant (as measured by blood and urine tests). The measurements were taken immediately prior to the stem cell transplant and at the time the complete response was determined.

Patient	Before	After
1	158	284
2	189	214
3	202	101
4	353	227
5	416	290
6	426	176
7	441	290

Data extracted from S. V. Rajkumar, R. Fonseca, T. E. Witzig, M. A. Gertz, and P. R. Greipp, "Bone Marrow Angiogenesis in Patients Achieving Complete Response After Stem Cell Transplantation for Multiple Myeloma," *Leukemia* 13 (1999): 469–472.

a. At the 0.05 level of significance, is there evidence that the mean bone marrow microvessel density is higher before the stem cell transplant than after the stem cell transplant?

b. Interpret the meaning of the p-value in (a).

c. Construct and interpret a 95% confidence interval estimate of the mean difference in bone marrow microvessel density before and after the stem cell transplant.

d. What assumption is necessary about the population distribution in order to perform the test in (a)?

12.36 To assess the effectiveness of a cola video ad, a random sample of 38 individuals from a target audience was selected to participate in a copy test. Participants viewed two ads, one of which was the ad being tested. Participants then answered a series of questions about how much they liked the ads. An adindex measure was created and stored in Adindex ; the higher the adindex value, the more likeable the ad. Compute descriptive statistics and perform a paired t test. State your findings and conclusions in a report. (Use the 0.05 level of significance.)

12.37 The file Concrete1 contains the compressive strength, in thousands of pounds per square inch (psi), of 40 samples of concrete taken two and seven days after pouring. (Data extracted from O. Carrillo-Gamboa and R. F. Gunst, "Measurement-Error-Model Collinearities," *Technometrics*, 34 (1992): 454–464.)

a. At the 0.01 level of significance, is there evidence that the mean strength is lower at two days than at seven days?

b. What assumption is necessary about the population distribution in order to perform this test?

c. Find the p-value in (a) and interpret its meaning.

Section 12.3

12.38 Let $n_1 = 100, X_1 = 50, n_2 = 100$, and $X_2 = 30$.

a. At the 0.05 level of significance, is there evidence of a significant difference between the two population proportions?

b. Construct a 95% confidence interval estimate for the difference between the two population proportions.

12.39 Let $n_1 = 100, X_1 = 45, n_2 = 50$, and $X_2 = 25$.

a. At the 0.01 level of significance, is there evidence of a significant difference between the two population proportions?

b. Construct a 99% confidence interval estimate for the difference between the two population proportions.

12.40 An online survey asked 1,000 adults "What do you buy from your mobile device?" The results indicated that 61% of the females and 39% of the males answered clothes. (Source: *Ebates. com 2014 Mobile Shopping Survey: Nearly Half of Americans Shop from a Mobile Device,* available from **bit.ly/1hi6kyX**.)

The sample sizes for males and females were not provided. Suppose that both sample sizes were 500 and that 195 out of 500 males and 305 out of 500 females reported they buy clothing from their mobile device.

a. Is there evidence of a difference between males and females in the proportion who said they buy clothing from their mobile device at the 0.01 level of significance?

b. Find the p-value in (a) and interpret its meaning.

c. Construct and interpret a 99% confidence interval estimate for the difference between the proportion of males and females who said they buy clothing from their mobile device.

d. What are your answers to (a) through (c) if 270 males said they buy clothing from their mobile device?

12.41 Do social recommendations increase ad effectiveness? A study of online video viewers compared viewers who arrived at an advertising video for a particular brand by following a social media recommendation link to viewers who arrived at the same video by web browsing. Data were collected on whether the viewer could correctly recall the brand being advertised after seeing the video. The results were:

	CORRECTLY RECALLED THE BRAND	
ARRIVAL METHOD	**Yes**	**No**
Recommendation	407	150
Browsing	193	91

Source: Data extracted from "Social Ad Effectiveness: An Unruly White Paper," **www.unrulymedia.com**, January 2012, p.3.

a. Set up the null and alternative hypotheses to try to determine whether brand recall is higher following a social media recommendation than with only web browsing.

b. Conduct the hypothesis test defined in (a), using the 0.05 level of significance.

c. Does the result of your test in (b) make it appropriate to claim that brand recall is higher following a social media recommendation than by web browsing?

12.42 A/B testing is a testing method that businesses use to test different designs and formats of a web page to determine whether a new web page is more effective than a current web page. Web designers tested a new call to action button on its web page. Every visitor to the web page was randomly shown either the original call to action button (the control) or the new call to action button. The metric used to measure success was the download rate: the number of people who downloaded the file divided by the number of people who saw that particular call to action button. The experiment yielded the following results:

Variations	Downloads	Visitors
Original call to action button	351	3,642
New call to action button	485	3,556

a. What is the proportion (download rate) of visitors who saw the original call to action button and downloaded the file?

b. What is the proportion (download rate) of visitors who saw the new call to action button and downloaded the file?

c. At the 0.05 level of significance, is there evidence that the new call to action button is more effective than the original?

12.43 The consumer research firm Scarborough analyzed the 10% of American adults that are either "Superbanked" or "Unbanked." Superbanked consumers are defined as U.S. adults who live in a household that has multiple asset accounts at financial institutions, as well as some additional investments; Unbanked consumers are U.S. adults who live in a household that does not use a bank or credit union. By finding the 5% of Americans that are Superbanked, Scarborough identifies financially savvy consumers who might be open to diversifying their financial portfolios; by identifying the Unbanked, Scarborough provides insight into the ultimate prospective client for banks and financial institutions. As part of its analysis, Scarborough reported that 93% of Superbanked consumers use credit cards in the past three months as compared to 23% of Unbanked consumers. (Data extracted from **bit.ly/QlABwO**.) Suppose that these results were based on 1,000 Superbanked consumers and 1,000 Unbanked consumers.

a. At the 0.01 level of significance, is there evidence of a significant difference between the Superbanked and the Unbanked with respect to the proportion that use credit cards?

b. Find the p-value in (a) and interpret its meaning.

c. Construct and interpret a 99% confidence interval estimate for the difference between the Superbanked and the Unbanked with respect to the proportion that use credit cards.

12.44 What social media tools do marketers commonly use? A survey by Social Media Examiner (data extracted from "2014 Social Media Marketing Industry Report," April 2014) of B2B marketers (marketers that focus primarily on attracting businesses) and B2C marketers (marketers that primarily target consumers) reported that 519 (88%) of B2B marketers and 242 (59%) of B2C marketers commonly use LinkedIn as a social media tool. The study also revealed that 307 (52%) of B2B marketers and 246 (60%) of B2C marketers commonly use YouTube as a social media tool. Suppose the survey was based on 590 B2B marketers and 410 B2C marketers.

a. At the 0.05 level of significance, is there evidence of a difference between B2B marketers and B2C marketers in the proportion that commonly use LinkedIn as a social media tool?

b. Find the p-value in (a) and interpret its value.

c. At the 0.05 level of significance, is there evidence of a difference between B2B marketers and B2C marketers in the proportion that commonly use YouTube as a social media tool?

12.45 Does co-browsing have positive effects on the customer experience? Co-browsing refers to the ability to have a contact center agent and customer jointly navigate an online document or mobile application on a real-time basis through the web. A study of businesses indicates that 81 of 129 co-browsing organizations use skills-based routing to match the caller with the *right* agent, whereas 65 of 176 non-co-browsing organizations use skills-based routing to match the caller with the *right* agent. (Source: *Cobrowsing Presents a 'Lucrative' Customer Service Opportunity,* available at **bit.ly/1wwALWr**.)

a. At the 0.05 level of significance, is there evidence of a difference between co-browsing organizations and non-co-browsing organizations in the proportion that use skills-based routing to match the caller with the *right* agent?

b. Find the p-value in (a) and interpret its meaning.

12.46 One of the most impressive, innovative advances in online fundraising over the past decade is the rise of crowd-funding websites. While features differ from site to site, crowd-funding sites are websites that allow you to set up an online fundraising campaign based around a fundraising page, and accept money directly from that page using the website's own credit card processor. Kickstarter, one crowd-funding website, reported that 124 of 355 *technology* crowd-funding projects were successfully launched in the past year and 349 of 873 *film and video* crowd-funding projects were successfully launched in the past year. (Data extracted from **kickstarter.com/help/stats**.)

a. Is there evidence of a significant difference in the proportion of *technology* crowd-funding projects and *film and video* crowd-funding projects that were successful? (Use $\alpha = 0.05$.)

b. Determine the p-value in (a) and interpret its meaning.

c. Construct and interpret a 95% confidence interval estimate for the difference between the proportion of *technology* crowd-funding projects and *film and video* crowd-funding projects that are successful.

Section 12.4

12.47 Determine the upper-tail critical values of F in each of the following two-tail tests.

a. $\alpha = 0.10, n_1 = 16, n_2 = 21$

b. $\alpha = 0.05, n_1 = 16, n_2 = 21$

c. $\alpha = 0.01, n_1 = 16, n_2 = 21$

12.48 Determine the upper-tail critical value of F in each of the following one-tail tests.

a. $\alpha = 0.05, n_1 = 16, n_2 = 21$

b. $\alpha = 0.01, n_1 = 16, n_2 = 21$

12.49 The following information is available for two samples selected from independent normally distributed populations:

$$\text{Population A: } n_1 = 25 \quad S_1^2 = 16$$

$$\text{Population B: } n_2 = 25 \quad S_2^2 = 25$$

a. Which sample variance do you place in the numerator of F_{STAT}?

b. What is the value of F_{STAT}?

12.50 The following information is available for two samples selected from independent normally distributed populations:

$$\text{Population A: } n_1 = 25 \quad S_1^2 = 161.9$$

$$\text{Population B: } n_2 = 25 \quad S_2^2 = 133.7$$

What is the value of F_{STAT} if you are testing the null hypothesis $H_0: \sigma_1^2 = \sigma_2^2$?

12.51 In Problem 12.50, how many degrees of freedom are there in the numerator and denominator of the F test?

12.52 In Problems 12.50 and 12.51, what is the upper-tail critical value for F if the level of significance, α, is 0.05 and the alternative hypothesis is $H_1: \sigma_1^2 \neq \sigma_2^2$?

12.53 In Problems 12.39 through 12.41, what is your statistical decision?

12.54 The following information is available for two samples selected from independent but very right-skewed populations:

$$\text{Population A: } n_1 = 16 \quad S_1^2 = 47.3$$

$$\text{Population B: } n_2 = 13 \quad S_2^2 = 36.4$$

Should you use the F test to test the null hypothesis of equality of variances? Discuss.

12.55 In Problem 12.54, assume that two samples are selected from independent normally distributed populations.

a. At the 0.05 level of significance, is there evidence of a difference between σ_1^2 and σ_2^2?

b. Suppose that you want to perform a one-tail test. At the 0.05 level of significance, what is the upper-tail critical value of F to determine whether there is evidence that $\sigma_1^2 > \sigma_2^2$? What is your statistical decision?

12.56 A problem with a telephone line that prevents a customer from receiving or making calls is upsetting to both the customer and the telecommunications company. The file Phone contains samples of 20 problems reported to two different offices of a telecommunications company and the time to clear these problems (in minutes) from the customers' lines.

a. At the 0.05 level of significance, is there evidence of a difference in the variability of the time to clear problems between the two central offices?

b. Determine the p-value in (a) and interpret its meaning.

c. What assumption do you need to make in (a) about the two populations in order to justify your use of the F test?

d. Based on the results of (a) and (b), which t test defined in Section 12.1 should you use to compare the mean time to clear problems in the two central offices?

12.57 *Accounting Today* identified the top accounting firms in 10 geographic regions across the United States. All 10 regions reported growth in 2013. The Southeast and Gulf Coast regions reported growth of 4.7% and 13.86%, respectively. A characteristic description of the accounting firms in the Southeast and Gulf Coast regions included the number of partners in the firm. The file AccountingPartners2 contains the number of partners. (Data extracted from **bit.ly/ODuzd3**.)

a. At the 0.05 level of significance, is there evidence of a difference in the variability in numbers of partners for Southeast region accounting firms and Gulf Coast accounting firms?

b. Determine the p-value in (a) and interpret its meaning.

c. What assumption do you have to make about the two populations in order to justify the use of the F test?

d. Based on (a) and (b), which t test defined in Section 12.1 should you use to test whether there is a significant difference in the mean number of partners for Southeast region accounting firms and Gulf Coast accounting firms?

12.58 A bank with a branch located in a commercial district of a city has the business objective of improving the process for serving customers during the noon-to-1 P.M. lunch period. To do so, the waiting time (defined as the number of minutes that elapses from when the customer enters the line until he or she reaches the teller window) needs to be shortened to increase customer satisfaction. A random sample of 15 customers is selected and the waiting times are collected and stored in Bank1. These data are:

4.21	5.55	3.02	5.13	4.77	2.34	3.54	3.20
4.50	6.10	0.38	5.12	6.46	6.19	3.79	

Suppose that another branch, located in a residential area, is also concerned with the noon-to-1 P.M. lunch period. A random sample of 15 customers is selected and the waiting times are collected and stored in Bank2. These data are:

9.66	5.90	8.02	5.79	8.73	3.82	8.01	8.35
10.49	6.68	5.64	4.08	6.17	9.91	5.47	

a. Is there evidence of a difference in the variability of the waiting time between the two branches? (Use $\alpha = 0.05$.)

b. Determine the p-value in (a) and interpret its meaning.

c. What assumption about the population distribution of each bank is necessary in (a)? Is the assumption valid for these data?

d. Based on the results of (a), is it appropriate to use the pooled-variance t test to compare the means of the two branches?

12.59 An important feature of tablets is battery life, the number of hours before the battery needs to be recharged. The file Tablets contains the battery life of 12 WiFi-only and 7 3G/4G/WiFi 9- through 12-inch tablets. (Data extracted from "Ratings and recommendations: Tablets," *Consumer Reports*, August 2013, p. 24.)

a. Is there evidence of a difference in the variability of the battery life between the two types of tablets? (Use $\alpha = 0.05$.)

b. Determine the p-value in (a) and interpret its meaning.

c. What assumption about the population distribution of the two types of tablets is necessary in (a)? Is the assumption valid for these data?

d. Based on the results of (a), which t test defined in Section 12.1 should you use to compare the mean battery life of the two types of tablets?

12.60 Experian Marketing Services reported that the typical American spends 144 minutes (2.4 hours) per day accessing the Internet through a mobile device. (Source: *The 2014 Digital Marketer*, available at **ex.pn/1kXJjfX**.) You wonder if males and females spend differing amounts of time per day accessing the Internet through a mobile device.

You select a sample of 60 friends and family (30 males and 30 females), collect times spent per day accessing the Internet through a mobile device (in minutes), and store the data collected in InternetMobileTime2.

a. Using a 0.05 level of significance, is there evidence of a difference in the variances of time spent per day accessing the Internet via mobile device between males and females?

b. On the basis of the results in (a), which t test defined in Section 12.1 should you use to compare the means of males and females? Discuss.

12.61 Is there a difference in the variation of the yield of five-year certificates of deposit (CDs) in different cities? The file FiveYearCDRate contains the yields for a five-year CD for ten banks in New York and eight banks in Los Angeles, as of April 19, 2014. (Data extracted from **www.Bankrate.com**, April 19, 2014.) At the 0.05 level of significance, is there evidence of a difference in the variance of the yield of five-year CDs in the two cities? Assume that the population yields are normally distributed.

CASES FOR CHAPTER 12

Managing Ashland MultiComm Services

Part 1 AMS communicates with customers who subscribe to cable television services through a special secured email system that sends messages about service changes, new features, and billing information to in-home digital set-top boxes for later display. To enhance customer service, the operations department established the business objective of reducing the amount of time to fully update each subscriber's set of messages. The department selected two candidate messaging systems and conducted an experiment in which 30 randomly chosen cable subscribers were assigned one of the two systems (15 assigned to each system). Update times were measured, and the results are organized in Table AMS12.1 and stored in `AMS12-1`.

TABLE AMS12.1

Update Times (in seconds) for Two Different Email Interfaces

Email Interface 1	Email Interface 2
4.13	3.71
3.75	3.89
3.93	4.22
3.74	4.57
3.36	4.24
3.85	3.90
3.26	4.09
3.73	4.05
4.06	4.07
3.33	3.80
3.96	4.36
3.57	4.38
3.13	3.49
3.68	3.57
3.63	4.74

1. Analyze the data in Table AMS12.1 and write a report to the computer operations department that indicates your findings. Include an appendix in which you discuss the reason you selected a particular statistical test to compare the two independent groups of callers.

2. Suppose that instead of the research design described in the case, there were only 15 subscribers sampled, and the update process for each subscriber email was measured for each of the two messaging systems. Suppose that the results were organized in Table AMS12.1—making each row in the table a pair of values for an individual subscriber. Using these suppositions, reanalyze the Table AMS12.1 data and write a report for presentation to the team that indicates your findings.

Part 2   The computer operations department had a business objective of reducing the amount of time to fully update each subscriber's set of messages in a special secured email system. An experiment was conducted in which 24 subscribers were selected and three different messaging systems were used. Eight subscribers were assigned to each system, and the update times were measured. The results, stored in `AMS12-2`, are presented in Table AMS12.2.

TABLE AMS12.2

Update Times (in seconds) for Three Different Systems

System 1	System 2	System 3
38.8	41.8	32.9
42.1	36.4	36.1
45.2	39.1	39.2
34.8	28.7	29.3
48.3	36.4	41.9
37.8	36.1	31.7
41.1	35.8	35.2
43.6	33.7	38.1

3. Analyze the data in Table AMS12.2 and write a report to the computer operations department that indicates your findings. Include an appendix in which you discuss the reason you selected a particular statistical test to compare the three email interfaces.

Digital Case

Apply your knowledge about hypothesis testing in this Digital Case, which continues the cereal-fill packaging dispute Digital Case from Chapters 8 and 11.

Part 1   Even after the recent public experiment about cereal box weights, Consumers Concerned About Cereal Cheaters (CCACC) remains convinced that Oxford Cereals has misled the public. The group has created and circulated **MoreCheating.pdf**, a document in which it claims that cereal boxes produced at Plant Number 2 in Springville weigh less than the claimed mean of 368 grams. Review this document and then answer the following questions:

1. Do the CCACC's results prove that there is a statistically significant difference in the mean weights of cereal boxes produced at Plant Numbers 1 and 2?

2. Perform the appropriate analysis to test the CCACC's hypothesis. What conclusions can you reach based on the data?

Part 2   *Apply your knowledge about ANOVA in this part, which continues the cereal-fill packaging dispute Digital Case.*

After reviewing the CCACC's **MoreCheating.pdf** document, Oxford Cereals has released **SecondAnalysis.pdf**, a press kit that Oxford Cereals has assembled to refute the claim that it is guilty of using selective data. Review the Oxford Cereals press kit and then answer the following questions.

3. Does Oxford Cereals have a legitimate argument? Why or why not?

4. Assuming that the samples Oxford Cereals has posted were randomly selected, perform the appropriate analysis to resolve the ongoing weight dispute.

5. What conclusions can you reach from your results? If you were called as an expert witness, would you support the claims of the CCACC or the claims of Oxford Cereals? Explain.

Sure Value Convenience Stores

Part 1   You continue to work in the corporate office for a nationwide convenience store franchise that operates nearly 10,000 stores. The per-store daily customer count (i.e., the mean number of customers in a store in one day) has been steady, at 900, for some time. To increase the customer count, the chain is considering cutting prices for coffee beverages. The small size will now be either $0.59 or $0.79 instead of $0.99. Even with this reduction in price, the chain will have a 40% gross margin on coffee.

The question to be determined is how much to cut prices to increase the daily customer count without reducing the gross margin on coffee sales too much. The chain decides to carry out an experiment in a sample of 30 stores where customer counts have been running almost exactly at the national average of 900. In 15 of the stores, the price of a small coffee will now be $0.59 instead of $0.99, and in 15 other stores, the price of a small coffee will now be $0.79. After four weeks, the 15 stores that priced the small coffee at $0.59 had a mean daily customer count of 964 and a standard deviation of 88, and the 15 stores that priced the small coffee at $0.79 had a mean daily customer count of 941 and a standard deviation of 76. Analyze these data (using the 0.05 level of significance) and answer the following questions.

1. Does reducing the price of a small coffee to either $0.59 or $0.79 increase the mean per-store daily customer count?

2. If reducing the price of a small coffee to either $0.59 or $0.79 increases the mean per-store daily customer count, is there any difference in the mean per-store daily customer count between stores in which a small coffee was priced at $0.59 and stores in which a small coffee was priced at $0.79?

3. What price do you recommend for a small coffee?

Part 2   As you continue to work in the corporate office for a nationwide convenience store franchise that operates nearly 10,000 stores, you decide to carry out an experiment in a sample of 24 stores where customer counts have been running almost exactly at the national average of 900. In 6 of the stores, the price of a small coffee will now be $0.59, in 6 stores the price of a small coffee will now be $0.69, in 6 stores, the price of a small coffee will now be $0.79, and in 6 stores, the price of a small coffee will now be $0.89. After four weeks of selling the coffee at the new price, the daily customer counts in the stores were recorded and stored in CoffeeSales .

4. Analyze the data and determine whether there is evidence of a difference in the daily customer count, based on the price of a small coffee.

5. If appropriate, determine which mean prices differ in daily customer counts.

6. What price do you recommend for a small coffee?

CardioGood Fitness

Return to the CardioGood Fitness case first presented on Chapter 1. Using the data stored in CardioGood Fitness :

1. Determine whether differences exist between males and females in their age in years, education in years, annual household income ($), mean number of times the customer plans to use the treadmill each week, and mean number of miles the customer expects to walk or run each week.

2. Determine whether differences exist between customers based on the product purchased (TM195, TM498, TM798) in their age in years, education in years, annual household income ($), mean number of times the customer plans to use the treadmill each week, and mean number of miles the customer expects to walk or run each week.

3. Write a report to be presented to the management of CardioGood Fitness detailing your findings.

More Descriptive Choices Follow-Up

Follow up the Using Statistics scenario "More Descriptive Choices, Revisited" on Chapter 3.

1. Determine whether there is a difference in the 3-year return percentage, 5-year return percentages, and 10-year return percentages of the growth and value funds (stored in Retirement Funds).

2. Determine whether there is a difference between the small, mid-cap, and large market cap funds in the three-year return percentages, five-year return percentages, and ten-year return percentages (stored in Retirement Funds).

Clear Mountain State Student Surveys

1. The Student News Service at Clear Mountain State University (CMSU) has decided to gather data about the undergraduate students that attend CMSU. It creates and distributes a survey of 14 questions and receives responses from 62 undergraduates (stored in UndergradSurvey).

   a. At the 0.05 level of significance, is there evidence of a difference between males and females in grade point average, expected starting salary, number of social networking sites registered for, age, spending on textbooks and supplies, text messages sent in a week, and the wealth needed to feel rich?

   b. At the 0.05 level of significance, is there evidence of a difference between students who plan to go to graduate school and those who do not plan to go to graduate school in grade point average, expected starting salary, number of social networking sites registered for, age, spending on textbooks and supplies, text messages sent in a week, and the wealth needed to feel rich?

   c. At the 0.05 level of significance, is there evidence of a difference based on academic major in expected starting salary, number of social networking sites registered for, age, spending on textbooks and supplies, text messages sent in a week, and the wealth needed to feel rich?

   d. At the 0.05 level of significance, is there evidence of a difference based on graduate school intention in grade point average, expected starting salary, number of social networking sites registered for, age, spending on textbooks and supplies, text messages sent in a week, and the wealth needed to feel rich?

2. The dean of students at CMSU has learned about the undergraduate survey and has decided to undertake a similar survey for graduate students at Clear Mountain State. She creates and distributes a survey of 14 questions and receives responses from 44 graduate students (stored in GradSurvey). For these data, at the 0.05 level of significance.

   a. Is there evidence of a difference between males and females in age, undergraduate grade point average, graduate grade point average, expected salary upon graduation, spending on textbooks and supplies, text messages sent in a week, and the wealth needed to feel rich?

   b. Is there evidence of a difference based on undergraduate major in age, undergraduate grade point average, graduate grade point average, expected salary upon graduation, spending on textbooks and supplies, text messages sent in a week, and the wealth needed to feel rich?

   c. Is there evidence of a difference based on graduate major in age, undergraduate grade point average, graduate grade point average, expected salary upon graduation, spending on textbooks and supplies, text messages sent in a week, and the wealth needed to feel rich?

   d. Is there evidence of a difference based on employment status in age, undergraduate grade point average, graduate grade point average, expected salary upon graduation, spending on textbooks and supplies, text messages sent in a week, and the wealth needed to feel rich?

CHAPTER 12 CASIO CALCULATOR GUIDE

CALCULATOR LESSON 12A

CFX-9850GB CALCULATOR

Lesson 12A—Z Test and t Test of Two Means

EXAMPLE 12.9

A company that makes bolts that are used on an automotive component uses two machines to make these bolts. It has been determined by past studies that the standard deviation of the bolt diameters made by machine 1 is 0.025 mm and the standard deviation of the bolt diameters of machine 2 is 0.022 mm. Both machines have a dial to set for the desired diameter. Recently, the company used both machines to fill a large order. The customer found that many of the bolts from a certain package were too large and made a complaint. It was determined that the package in question was made by machine 2. The manufacturer decided to take samples of the bolts from both machines to test to see whether the mean diameter of the bolts from machine 2 was significantly larger than the mean diameter from machine 1 when the dial was set to the same diameter on each machine. The sample of 100 bolts from machine 1 had a mean diameter of 5.02 mm, and the sample of 100 bolts from machine 2 had a mean diameter of 5.09 mm. At the 5% level of significance, what is the conclusion?

Solution: From the **Main Menu** select the following:

STAT   F3(test)   F1(Z)   **F2**(2-S). Then enter the following items:

2-Sample ZTest

Data	: **F2**(Var)	▼
$\mu 1$	: **F2**(<$\mu 2$)	▼
$\sigma 1$	: **0.025**	**EXE**
$\sigma 2$	: **0.022**	**EXE**
$\bar{x}1$	: **5.02**	**EXE**
n1	: **100**	**EXE**
$\bar{x}2$	: **5.09**	**EXE**
n2	: **100**	**EXE**

Now key **EXE** or **F1**(Calc)

The calculator will now show the results:

2-Sample ZTest

$\mu 1$	< $\mu 2$
z_{CALC}	$= -21.019978$
p	$= 2.1531E-98$
$\bar{x}1$	$= 5.02$
$\bar{x}2$	$= 5.09$
n1	$= 100$
n2	$= 100$

Since the *p*-value < 0.05, the conclusion is to *reject* the null hypothesis. In other words, the mean diameter of bolts produced by machine 2 is greater than the mean of machine 1.

EXAMPLE 12.10

A work team has developed a new process to assemble a certain component. Its members would like to know if this new process has significantly reduced the time to assemble the component. They have taken samples of 50 components produced by the existing process and 40 components produced by the new process. The mean and standard deviation of the assembly times for the existing process were 73.2 minutes and 3.6 minutes, respectively. The mean time was 71.4 minutes, with a standard deviation of 3.2 minutes for the components assembled by the new process. Assume that the times for both processes are normally distributed, with the same variance. At the 1% level of significance, does this evidence indicate that the new process is quicker than the old process?

Solution: Let sample 1 be the existing process sample and sample 2 the new process. From the **Main Menu** select the following:

STAT F3(test) **F2**(t) **F2**(2-S). Then enter the following items:

2-Sample tTest

Data	: **F2**(Var)	▼
$\mu 1$	: **F3**($>\mu 2$)	▼
$\bar{x}1$	: **73.2**	**EXE**
x1_n-1	: **3.6**	**EXE**
n1	: **50**	**EXE**
$\bar{x}12$	: **71.4**	**EXE**
x2σn-1	: **3.2**	**EXE**
n2	: **40**	**EXE**
Pooled	: **F1**(On)	**EXE**

(Note: If you select **F1(On)**, you are using the *t* test pooled-variance procedure; if you select **F2(OFF)**, you are using the *t* test separate variance.)

The calculator will now show the results:

2-Sample tTest

$\mu 1$	$> \mu 2$
t	$=2.4749$
p	$=7.6215E-03$ ($=0.0076215$)
df	$=88$
1	$=73.2$
2	$=71.4$
$\bar{x}1$σn-1	$=3.6$
$\bar{x}2$σn-1	$=3.2$
xPσn-1	$=3.4285$
n1	$=50$
n2	$=40$

Since the *p*-value < 0.01, the conclusion is to reject the null hypothesis. In other words, the evidence does indicate that the average time to assemble the component by the new process is less than the average time to assemble the component by the existing process, (i.e., the new process is faster).

EXAMPLE 12.11   We wish to determine if there is a difference in the braking distances for two types of tires. Use the 5% level of significance and assume that the braking distances for each type of tire are normally distributed, with the same variance. Based on the data for the samples of tires shown, at the 5% level of significance, should we conclude that there is a difference in the mean braking distance?

Braking distance (metres)

Tire A	Tire B
83	75
79	84
82	76
84	83
80	85
81	78
	83

Solution: Enter the data for Tire A in List 1 and the data for Tire B in List 2. From the **Main Menu** select the following:

STAT   F3(test)   **F2**(t)   **F2**(2-S). Then enter the following items:

2-Sample tTest

Data	: **F1**(List) ▼
μ1	: **F1**($\neq$μ2) ▼
List1	: **F1**(List1) ▼
List2	: **F2**(List2) ▼
Freq	: **1** ▼
Freq	: **1** ▼
Pooled	: **F1**(On) **EXE**

The calculator will now show the results:

2-Sample tTest

μ1	$\neq$μ2
t	=0.50699
p	=0.62217
df	=11
$\bar{x}$1	=81.5
$\bar{x}$2	=80.571
x1σn-1	=1.8708
x2σn-1	=4.1173
xPσn-1	=3.292
n1	=6
n2	=7

Since the *p*-value > 0.05, the conclusion is to *not reject* the null hypothesis. In other words, the evidence does not indicate that the average stopping distance is different for the two types of tires.

CALCULATOR LESSON 12B

CASIO FX-9750GII CALCULATOR

Lesson 12B—Z Test and t Test of Two Means

EXAMPLE 12.12

A company that makes bolts that are used on an automotive component uses two machines to make these bolts. It has been determined by past studies that the standard deviation of the bolt diameters made by machine 1 is 0.025 mm and the standard deviation of the bolt diameters of machine 2 is 0.022 mm. Both machines have a dial to set for the desired diameter. Recently, the company used both machines to fill a large order. The customer found that many of the bolts from a certain package were too large and made a complaint. It was determined that the package in question was made by machine 2. The manufacturer decided to take samples of the bolts from both machines to test to see whether the mean diameter of the bolts from machine 2 was significantly larger than the mean diameter of the bolts from machine 1 when the dial was set to the same diameter on each machine. The sample of 100 bolts from machine 1 had a mean diameter of 5.02 mm and the sample of 100 bolts from machine 2 had a mean diameter of 5.09 mm when the dial on both machines was set at 5.00 mm. At the 5% level of significance, what is the conclusion?

Solution: From the **Main Menu** select the following:

STAT F3(test) **F1**(Z) **F2**(2-S). Then enter the following items:

2-Sample ZTest

Data	: **F2**(Var)	▼
$\mu 1$	: **F2**($<\mu 2$)	▼
$\sigma 1$	: **0.025**	**EXE**
$\sigma 2$	: **0.022**	**EXE**
$\bar{x}1$	: **5.023**	**EXE**
n1	: **100**	**EXE**
$\bar{x}2$	: **5.031**	**EXE**
n2	: **100**	**EXE**
Save Res	: NONE	

Now press **EXE**, **F1**(Calc), or **F6**(DRAW).

If you select **F6**(DRAW), you will see a normal distribution.

If you select either **EXE** or **F1**(Calc), the calculator will show the results:

2-Sample ZTest

$\mu 1$	$<\mu 2$
z_{CALC}	$=-21.019978$
p	$=2.1531\text{E-}98$
$\bar{x}1$	$=5.02$
$\bar{x}2$	$=5.09$
n1	$=100$
n2	$=100$

Since the *p*-value < 0.05, the conclusion is to *reject* the null hypothesis. In other words, the mean diameter of the bolts produced by machine 2 is greater than the mean diameter of the bolts produced by machine 1.

EXAMPLE 12.13

A work team has developed a new process to assemble a certain component. Its members would like to know if this new process has significantly reduced the time to assemble the component. They have taken samples of 50 components produced by the existing process and 40 components produced by the new process. The mean and standard deviation of the assembly times for the existing process were 73.2 minutes and 3.6 minutes, respectively. The mean time was 71.4 minutes, with a standard deviation of 3.2 minutes for the components assembled by the new process. Assume that the times for both processes are normally distributed with the same variance. At the 1% level of significance, does this evidence indicate that the new process is quicker than the old process?

Solution: Let sample 1 be the existing process sample and sample 2 the new process. From the **Main Menu** select the following:

STAT F3(test) **F2**(t) **F2**(2-S). Then enter the following items:

2-Sample tTest

Data	: **F2**(Var)	▼
$\mu 1$	: **F3**($>\mu 2$)	▼
$\bar{x}1$	: **73.2**	**EXE**
sx1	: **3.6**	**EXE**
n1	: **50**	**EXE**
$\bar{x}2$	: **71.4**	**EXE**
sx2	: **3.2**	**EXE**
n2	: **40**	**EXE**
Pooled	: **F1**(On)	**EXE**
Save Res	: None	

Now press **EXE**, **F1**(Calc), or **F6**(DRAW).

If you select **F6**(DRAW), you will see a normal distribution.

If you select either **EXE** or **F1**(Calc), the calculator will show the results:

2-Sample tTest

$\mu 1$	$>\mu 2$
t	$=2.47493233$
p	$=7.6215\text{E}-03$ $(=0.0076215)$
df	$=88$
$\bar{x}1$	$=73.2$
$\bar{x}2$	$=71.4$
sx1	$=3.6$
sx2	$=3.2$
sp	$=3.42849026$
n1	$=50$
n2	$=40$

Since the *p*-value < 0.01, the conclusion is to *reject* the null hypothesis. In other words, the evidence does indicate that the average time to assemble the component by the new process is less than the average time to assemble the component by the existing process (i.e., the new process is faster).

EXAMPLE 12.14   We wish to determine if there is a difference in the braking distances for two types of tires. Use the 5% level of significance and assume that the braking distances for each type of tire are normally distributed with the same variance. Based on the data for the samples of tires shown, at the 5% level of significance, should we conclude that there is a difference in the mean braking distance?

Braking distance (metres)	
Tire A	Tire B
83	75
79	84
82	76
84	83
80	85
81	78
	83

Solution: Enter the data for Tire A in List 1 and the data for Tire B in List 2. From the **Main Menu** select the following:

STAT   **F3**(test)   **F2**(t)   **F2**(2-S). Then enter the following items:

2-Sample tTest

Data	: **F1**(List)	▼
$\mu 1$	: **F1**($\neq \mu 2$)	▼
List1	: **F1**(List1)	▼
List2	: **F1**(List2)	▼
Freq	: 1	▼
Freq	: 1	▼
Pooled	: **F1**(On)	**EXE**
Save Res	: None	

Now press **EXE**, or **F1**(Calc), or **F6**(DRAW).

If you select **F6**(DRAW), you will see a normal distribution.

If you select either **EXE** or **F1**(Calc), the calculator will show the results:

2-Sample tTest

μ1	≠μ2
t	$=0.50699126$
p	$=0.62216994$
df	$=11$
$\bar{x}1$	$=81.5$
$\bar{x}2$	$=80.5714286$
sx1	$=1.87082869$
sx2	$=4.11732692$
sp	$=3.2920605$
n1	$=6$
n2	$=7$

Since the *p*-value > 0.05, the conclusion is to *not reject* the null hypothesis. In other words, the evidence does not indicate that the average stopping distance is different for the two types of tires.

CALCULATOR LESSON 13A

CFX-9850GB CALCULATOR

EXAMPLE 12.15

Lesson 13A—*F* Test of Two Variances

Recall the following example from Calculator Lesson 10.

A work team has developed a new process to assemble a certain component. Its members would like to know if this new process has significantly reduced the time to assemble the component. They have taken samples of 50 components produced by the existing process and 40 components produced by the new process. The mean and standard deviation of the assembly times for the existing process were 73.2 minutes and 3.6 minutes, respectively. The mean time was 71.4 minutes, with a standard deviation of 3.2 minutes, for the components assembled by the new process. Assume that the times for both processes are normally distributed, with the same variance.

Suppose that instead of assuming that the variances of the assembly times for the two processes are equal, we do an *F* test to see if there is evidence to support such an assumption. Test at the 5% level of significance.

Solution: Let sample 1 be the existing process sample and sample 2 the new process. From the **Main Menu** select the following:

STAT F3(test) **F4**(F). Then enter the following items:

2-Sample FTest

Data	: **F2**(Var)	▼
σ1	: **F1**(≠σ2)	▼
x1σn-1	: **3.6**	**EXE**
n1	: **50**	**EXE**
x2σn-1	: **3.2**	**EXE**
n2	: **40**	**EXE**

Now press **EXE** or **F1**(Calc).

The calculator will now show the results:

2-Sample FTest

$\sigma 1$	$\neq \sigma 2$
F	$=1.2656$
p	$=0.44965$
$x1\sigma n\text{-}1$	$=3.6$
$x2\sigma n\text{-}1$	$=3.2$
n1	$=50$
n2	$=40$

Since the p-value > 0.05, the conclusion is to *not reject* the null hypothesis. In other words, the evidence does not indicate that the variances of the assembly times for the two processes are different (i.e., the variances are approximately the same).

EXAMPLE 12.16   Recall the following example from Lesson 10.

We wish to determine if there is a difference in the braking distances for two types of tires. Use the 5% level of significance and assume that the braking distances for each type of tire are normally distributed, with the same variance. The data are as follows:

Braking distance (metres)

Tire A	Tire B
83	75
79	84
82	76
84	83
80	85
81	78
	83

Suppose we test to see if the assumption about equal variances seems reasonable at the 5% level.

Solution: Enter the data for Tire A in List 1 and the data for Tire B in List 2. From the **Main Menu** select the following:

STAT   F3(test)   **F4**(F). Then enter the following items:

2-Sample FTest

Data	: **F1**(List)	▼
$\sigma 1$	: **F1**($\neq \sigma 2$)	▼
List1	: **F1**(List1)	▼
List2	: **F2**(List2)	▼
Freq	: 1	▼
Freq	: 1	**EXE**

The calculator will now show the results:

$\sigma 1$	$\neq \sigma 2$
F	$=0.20646$
p	$=0.10432$
$x1\sigma n\text{-}1$	$=1.8708$
$x2\sigma n\text{-}1$	$=4.1173$
$\bar{x}1$	$=81.5$
$\bar{x}2$	$=80.571$
n1	$=6$
n2	$=7$

Since the p-value > 0.05, the conclusion is to *not reject* the null hypothesis. In other words, the evidence does not indicate that the variances of the stopping distances for the two types of tires are different (i.e., the variances are approximately the same).

CALCULATOR LESSON 13B

CASIO FX-9750GII CALCULATOR

EXAMPLE 12.17

Lesson 13B—*F* Test of Two Variances

Recall the following example from Calculator Lesson 11.

A work team has developed a new process to assemble a certain component. Its members would like to know if this new process has significantly reduced the time to assemble the component. They have taken samples of 50 components produced by the existing process and 40 components produced by the new process. The mean and standard deviation of the assembly times for the existing process were 73.2 minutes and 3.6 minutes, respectively. The mean time was 71.4 minutes, with a standard deviation of 3.2 minutes, for the components assembled by the new process. Assume that the times for both processes are normally distributed, with the same variance.

Suppose that instead of assuming that the variances of the assembly times for the two processes are equal, we do an *F* test to see if there is evidence to support such an assumption. Test at the 5% level of significance.

Solution: Let sample 1 be the existing process sample, and sample 2 the new process. From the **Main Menu** select the following:

STAT F3(test) **F4**(F). Then enter the following items:

2-Sample F Test

Data	: **F2**(Var)	▼
σ1	: **F1**($\neq$σ2)	▼
sx1	**: 3.6**	**EXE**
n1	**: 50**	**EXE**
sx2	**: 3.2**	**EXE**
n2	**: 40**	**EXE**
Save Res	: None	

Now press **EXE**, **F1**(Calc), or **F6**(DRAW).

If you select **F6**(DRAW), you will see a normal distribution.

If you select either **EXE** or **F1**(Calc), the calculator will show the results:

2-Sample F Test

σ1	$\neq$σ2
F	=1.265625
p	=0.44965583
sx1	=3.6
sx2	=3.2
n1	=50
n2	=40

Since the *p*-value > 0.05, the conclusion is to *not reject* the null hypothesis. In other words, the evidence does not indicate that the variances of the assembly times for the two processes are different (i.e., the variances are approximately the same).

EXAMPLE 12.18   Recall the following example from Lesson 11.
We wish to determine if there is a difference in the braking distances for two types of tires. Use the 5% level of significance and assume that the braking distances for each type of tire are normally distributed with the same variance. Based on the data …

Braking distance (metres)	
Tire A	Tire B
83	75
79	84
82	76
84	83
80	85
81	78
	83

Suppose we test to see if the assumption about equal variances seems reasonable at the 5% level.

Solution: Enter the data for Tire A in List 1 and the data for Tire B in List 2. From the **Main Menu** select the following:

STAT F3(test) **F4**(F). Then enter the following items:

2-Sample FTest

Data	: **F1**(List)	▼
σ1	: **F1**($\neq$σ2)	▼
List1	: **F1**(List1)	▼
List2	: **F2**(List2)	▼
Freq	: 1	▼
Freq	: 1	**EXE**
Save Res	: None	

Now press **EXE**, **F1**(Calc), or **F6**(DRAW).

If you select **F6**(DRAW), you will see a normal distribution.

If you select either **EXE** or **F1**(Calc), the calculator will show the results:

2-Sample FTest

σ1	$\neq$σ2
F	=0.20646067
p	=0.10432125
$\bar{x}1$	=81.5
$\bar{x}2$	=80.5714286
sx1	=1.87082869
sx2	=4.11732692
n1	=6
n2	=7

Since the *p*-value > 0.05, the conclusion is to *not reject* the null hypothesis. In other words, the evidence does not indicate that the variances of the stopping distances for the two types of tires are different (i.e., the variances are approximately the same).

CALCULATOR LESSON 14A

CFX-9850GB CALCULATOR

EXAMPLE 12.19

Lesson 14A—Z Test of Two Proportions

A political candidate thinks that his level of support is different among male and female voters and would like to address this issue if it is true. Random samples of 200 male voters and 100 female voters in his riding revealed that 85 of the men would vote for the candidate but only 35 of the women would. At the 10% level of significance, what conclusion should the candidate make regarding the level of support?

Solution:

Let π_1 = the proportion of male voters that will vote for the candidate

π_2 = the proportion of female voters that will vote for the candidate

From the **Main Menu** select the following:

STAT, **F3**(test), **F1**(Z), and **F4**(2-P). Then enter the following items:

2-Prop ZTest

p1	: **F1**($\neq$p2) ▼	
x1	: **85**	**EXE**
n1	: **200**	**EXE**
x2	: **35**	**EXE**
n2	: **100**	**EXE**

Now press **EXE** or **F1**(Calc),

The calculator will now show the results:

2-Prop ZTest

p1	$\neq$p2
z	=1.25
p	=0.21129
$\hat{p}1$	=0.425
$\hat{p}2$	=0.35
$\hat{p}$	=0.4
n1	=200
n2	=100

Since the *p*-value > 0.10, the conclusion is to *not reject* the null hypothesis. In other words, the evidence indicates that the level of support for the candidate is almost the same among both male and female voters.

CALCULATOR LESSON 14B

CASIO FX-9750GII CALCULATOR

EXAMPLE 12.20

Lesson 14B—Z Test of Two Proportions

A political candidate thinks that his level of support is different among male and female voters and would like to address this issue if it is true. Random samples of 200 male voters and 100 female voters in his riding revealed that 85 of the men would vote for the candidate but only 35 of the women would. At the 10% level of significance, what conclusion should the candidate make regarding the level of support?

Solution:

Let π_1 = the proportion of male voters that will vote for the candidate

π_2 = the proportion of female voters that will vote for the candidate

From the **Main Menu** select the following:

STAT, **F3**(test), **F1**(Z), and **F4**(2-P). Then enter the following items:

2-Prop ZTest

p1	: **F1**($\neq$p2) ▼	
x1	: **85**	**EXE**
n1	: **200**	**EXE**
x2	: **35**	**EXE**
n2	: **100**	**EXE**
Save Res	: None	

Now press **EXE**, **F1**(Calc), or **F6**(DRAW).

If you select **F6**(DRAW), you will see a normal distribution.

If you select either **EXE** or **F1**(Calc), the calculator will show the results:

2-Prop ZTest

p1	$\neq$p2
z	$=1.25$
p	$=0.21129954$
$\hat{p}1$	$=0.425$
$\hat{p}2$	$=0.35$
$\hat{p}$	$=0.4$
n1	$=200$
n2	$=100$

Since the *p*-value > 0.10, the conclusion is to *not reject* the null hypothesis. In other words, the evidence indicates that the level of support for the candidate is almost the same among both male and female voters.

APPENDIX 12.1

SPSS—Version 15 Lesson 3

Introduction

OVERVIEW

We will use SPSS 15.0 Student Version for this course. When you open SPSS, either by clicking the shortcut icon, by selecting **programs/SPSS/spsswin** from the Explorer window, or by clicking **start/SPSS**, a "What would you like to do?" menu appears. It allows you to select one of the following:

Run the tutorial
Type in data
Run an existing query
Create new query using Database Wizard
Open an existing data source

As you gain experience with SPSS, you will probably skip this screen by clicking on Cancel or you will select "Don't show this dialog in the future."

The **Tutorial** feature provides a useful introduction to various aspects of SPSS. To view a tutorial, follow these instructions:

From the opening menu, select **Run the tutorial/OK.**

Or if you have passed this window:

Help/Tutorial

You will now be shown an **Introduction** tutorial on SPSS version 15. Click on the word *Introduction* to view the expanded list of topics and then click *Sample Files*. Use the Next button (right arrow) until you have viewed information on the following topics:

Sample Files
Starting SPSS
Opening a Data File
Running an Analysis*
Viewing Results*
Creating Charts*
Using the Help System
Help Contents Tab
Help Index Tab
Dialog Box Help
Statistics Coach (skip)
Case Studies (skip)
Reading Data
Basic Structure of an SPSS Data File
Reading an SPSS Data File
Reading Data from Spreadsheets

Close the tutorial at this point.

***Do not study** these topics in this tutorial. It is useful to quickly look at the demonstration in order to get an idea of what types of things we will be using SPSS for. You can always go through this tutorial at another time, although you may find it more useful choosing a tutorial on the specific topic that you are interested in learning about.

At the end of the *Introduction* tutorial, return to SPSS Data Editor window by clicking the **Untitled1[DataSet0] – SPSS Data Editor** button at the very bottom of the screen.

Now click on **Help/Topics**/if necessary click **Contents** tab / under **Core System**/select **Data Editor.** Read the information regarding the data editor.

Now choose **Entering Data** from the 'Related Topics' list. Read the general information.

Now choose **To Enter Numeric Data** and **To Enter Non-numeric Data from the 'Related Topics' list.**

You may have to come back to this screen at other times during the course to receive guidance on how to enter various data.

The **Help** feature is also useful for finding information on specific topics. This feature works similarly to the Help feature in MS Word or Excel.

Summary

SPSS uses a routine of four basic steps.

1. Input data into the data editor.
2. Select a procedure from the menus.
3. Select variables for analysis.
4. Examine and modify the results.

SPSS utilizes two important file types: data files, and output files.

Data file: Data are input into an Untitled Data Editor worksheet until it is renamed and saved by the researcher. Data files are identified by the extension **.sav** on the filename chosen by the researcher.

Output file: The SPSS output appears in a viewer window titled **Output1**, which may be renamed and saved by the researcher. Output files are identified by the extension **.spo** (**SP**SS **O**utput). It is possible to edit the viewer window. The output may be rearranged, other output may be inserted, output may be deleted, and tables may be edited using the SPSS word processing capability.

You will switch between windows by using methods similar to those used in other computer packages (i.e., click on the appropriate buttons on the Start button bar at the very bottom of the screen).

Entering, Saving, and Printing Data

The following data were obtained by surveying 25 customers who used a bank machine that has just recently been installed in a downtown restaurant.

The survey took note of the customer's gender, how long the customer waited in line (rounded to the nearest minute), the type of transaction the customer performed, and the amount involved in the transaction. (A simplified scenario is presented in which each customer performed only one transaction.) The results are shown in the table below.

Customer	Gender	Waiting Time (minutes)	Type of Transaction	Amount ($)
1	Male	5	Withdrawal	100
2	Female	6	Bill Payment	83.56
3	Female	12	Withdrawal	60
4	Male	15	Withdrawal	40
5	Male	18	Deposit	512.81
6	Male	4	Bill Payment	56.82
7	Female	5	Withdrawal	200
8	Male	4	Deposit	2,315.23

Customer	Gender	Waiting Time (minutes)	Type of Transaction	Amount ($)
9	Male	14	Withdrawal	120
10	Female	21	Withdrawal	100
11	Female	0	Bill Payment	112.15
12	Male	7	Deposit	648.65
13	Male	8	Withdrawal	80
14	Male	9	Deposit	847.97
15	Female	16	Withdrawal	120
16	Male	6	Withdrawal	100
17	Female	6	Bill Payment	72.49
18	Male	12	Bill Payment	87.63
19	Female	11	Withdrawal	100
20	Male	2	Withdrawal	200
21	Male	1	Deposit	638.92
22	Female	3	Withdrawal	40
23	Female	9	Withdrawal	100
24	Male	14	Bill Payment	38.47
25	Male	3	Withdrawal	100

Example 1a:

Open SPSS and select **Type in data/OK** from the opening menu. Now click on the Variable View tab. A variable definition summary screen now appears. In the first column, enter the four variable names: gender, waittime, transtyp, and amount. Now skip to the decimals column and adjust the first three variables to have '0' decimals. The fourth variable will have the default of '2' decimals.

In the Label column, enter the following labels:

Gender
Waiting Time (minutes)
Type of Transaction
Amount of the Transaction

Now you will perform two labelling procedures. Click on the Values button for the 'gender' variable. Use the value '0' to represent females and the value '1' to represent males. To do this, type '0' in the **Value** Box, type 'Female' in the **Value Label** box, and then click the the **Add** button. Repeat the same process for the 'Male' label. When finished with the label values, click the **OK** button.

Now click on the Values button for the 'transtyp' variable. Use the following values:

1 = Withdrawal
2 = Deposit
3 = Bill Payment

Move the cursor to the **Align** column and click on the ▼ to activate the pop-up menu. Select **Center** for the first three variables.

Move the cursor to the **Type** column for the 'amount' variable. Click on the numeric button. Choose **Dollar/$#,###.##/OK.**

Now click on the Data View tab and enter the data as follows:

1	5	1	100
0	6	3	83.56
0	12	1	60
.	.	.	.
.	.	.	.
.	.	.	.

The input data will now appear exactly as shown below.

To save these data, select the following from the main toolbar:

File / Save as (select the appropriate drive and folder) key in the filename **Lesson1 – Ex. 1a** (in the File name box) and verify that the 'Save as type' box contains SPSS (*.sav). Click **Save.**

To print this file, select the following from the main toolbar:

File / Print / All / OK

You should obtain the printout as shown on the following page. Note that the 'case number' column is included.

	gender	waitingtime	transtype	amount
1	Male	5	Withdrawal	100
2	Female	6	Bill Payment	83.56
3	Female	12	Withdrawal	60
4	Male	15	Withdrawal	40
5	Male	18	Deposit	512.81
6	Male	4	Bill Payment	56.82
7	Female	5	Withdrawal	200
8	Male	4	Deposit	2,315.23
9	Male	14	Withdrawal	120
10	Female	21	Withdrawal	100
11	Female	0	Bill Payment	112.15

	gender	waitingtime	transtype	amount
12	Male	7	Deposit	648.65
13	Male	8	Withdrawal	80
14	Male	9	Deposit	847.97
15	Female	16	Withdrawal	120
16	Male	6	Withdrawal	100
17	Female	6	Bill Payment	72.49
18	Male	12	Bill Payment	87.63
19	Female	11	Withdrawal	100
20	Male	2	Withdrawal	200
21	Male	1	Deposit	638.92
22	Female	3	Withdrawal	40
23	Female	9	Withdrawal	100
24	Male	14	Bill Payment	38.47
25	Male	3	Withdrawal	100

If you want someone else to be able to understand your input data, then you should print a copy showing the labels associated with the variable values. From the main toolbar, select **View / Value Labels.**

In order to read the labels better, you may want to widen the transtyp column by clicking on the **Variable View** tab and placing the cursor in the third variable cell in the **Columns** column and increasing the value from 8 to 11.

The data will now appear as follows:

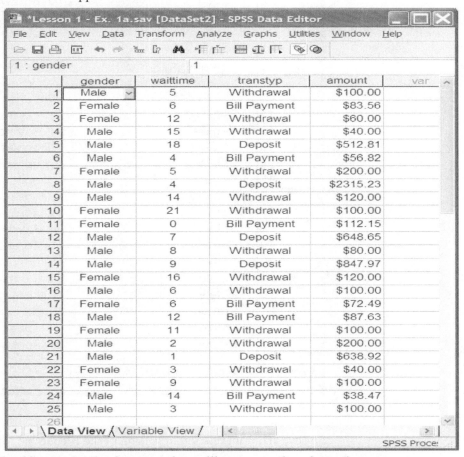

Note that if you print the data now, they will appear as they do on the screen.

Sorting Data

At this stage you should read the following SPSS help feature. Make summary notes as you go along.

Help / Topics / Index / type 'sort' and then click the **Display** button.

Read the Help information.

Example 1b:

Suppose we want to sort the cases in ascending order based on the waiting time and if waiting times are equal then in descending order of the amount of the transaction.

Make sure you are in Data View. Select the following from the main toolbar:

Data / Sort Cases / then highlight **Waiting Time (Minutes) [waittime]** ▶ **Ascending** / then highlight **Amount of Transaction [amount]** ▶ **Descending** / OK.

You should now have the data as shown below.

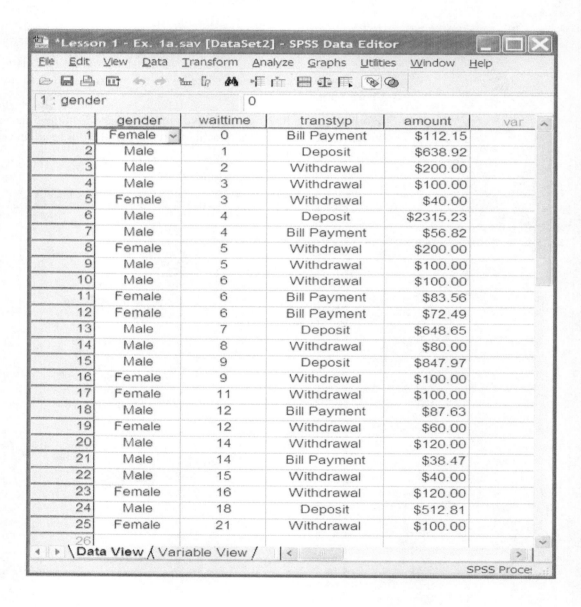

To save and print this sorted version of the file, do the following:

From the main menu toolbar, choose **File/Save as**. Select the appropriate drive, enter the filename **Lesson 1 – Ex. 1b**, and check that the Save as type box contains SPSS(*sav). **Save.**

If you want to print these data, select **File / Print / All / OK**.

Then, to leave SPSS, select **File / Exit.**

CHAPTER

13

One-Way ANOVA

CONTENTS

13.1 One-Way ANOVA

13.2 Effect Size (*online*)

USING STATISTICS: For North Fork, Are There Different Means to the Ends? Revisited

CHAPTER 13 CASIO CALCULATOR GUIDE

13.1 One-Way ANOVA

Section 12.1 through 12.4 discuss hypothesis-testing methods that allow you to reach conclusions about differences between two populations. **Analysis of variance**, known by the acronym **ANOVA**, are methods that allow you to compare *multiple* populations, or **groups**. Unlike the hypothesis-testing methods discussed previously, in ANOVA, you take samples from each group to examine the effects of differences among two or more groups. The criteria that distinguishes the groups are called **factors**, or sometimes the factors of interest. Factors contain **levels** which are analogous to the categories of a categorical variable.

In the simplest method, **one-way ANOVA**, also known as the *completely randomized design*, you examine only one factor and the levels provide the basis for dividing the variable under study into groups. One-way ANOVA is a two-part process. You first determine if there is a significant difference among the group means. If you reject the null hypothesis that there is no difference among the means, you continue with a second method that seeks to identify the groups whose means are significantly different from the other group means.

In one-way ANOVA, you **partition** the total variation into variation that is due to differences among the groups and variation that is due to differences within the groups (see Figure 13.1). The **within-group variation** (SSW) measures random variation. The **among-group variation** (SSA) measures differences from group to group. The symbol n represents the number of values in all groups and the symbol c represents the number of groups.

FIGURE 13.1

Partitioning the total variation in a completely randomized design

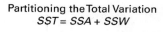

Partitioning the Total Variation
$SST = SSA + SSW$

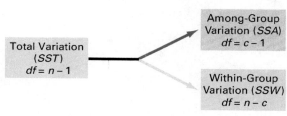

Assuming that the c groups represent populations whose values are randomly and independently selected, follow a normal distribution, and have equal variances, the null hypothesis of no differences in the population means:

$$H_0: \mu_1 = \mu_2 = \cdots = \mu_c$$

is tested against the alternative that not all the c population means are equal:

$$H_1: \text{Not all } \mu_j \text{ are equal (where } j = 1, 2, \ldots, c).$$

The alternative hypothesis, H_1, can also be stated as "at least one population mean is different from the other population means."

To perform an ANOVA test of equality of population means, you subdivide the total variation in the values into two parts—that which is due to variation among the groups and that which is due to variation within the groups. The **total variation** is represented by the **sum of squares total (SST)**. Because the population means of the c groups are assumed to be equal under the null hypothesis, you compute the total variation among all the values by summing the squared differences between each individual value and the **grand mean, $\overline{\overline{X}}$**. The grand mean is the mean of all the values in all the groups combined. Equation (13.8) shows the computation of the total variation.

TOTAL VARIATION IN ONE-WAY ANOVA

$$SST = \sum_{j=1}^{c} \sum_{i=1}^{n_j} (X_{ij} - \bar{\bar{X}})^2 \tag{13.1}$$

where

$$\bar{\bar{X}} = \frac{\sum_{j=1}^{c} \sum_{i=1}^{n_j} X_{ij}}{n} = \text{grand mean}$$

$X_{ij} = i$th value in group j

$n_j = $ number of values in group j

$n = $ total number of values in all groups combined
(that is, $n = n_1 + n_2 + \cdots + n_c$)

$c = $ number of groups

> **Student Tip**
> A sum of squares (SS) cannot be negative.

You compute the among-group variation, usually called the **sum of squares among groups (SSA)**, by summing the squared differences between the sample mean of each group, $\bar{X}_j$, and the grand mean, $\bar{\bar{X}}$, weighted by the sample size, n_j, in each group. Equation (13.2) shows the computation of the among-group variation.

AMONG-GROUP VARIATION IN ONE-WAY ANOVA

$$SSA = \sum_{j=1}^{c} n_j (\bar{X}_j - \bar{\bar{X}})^2 \tag{13.2}$$

where

$c = $ number of groups

$n_j = $ number of values in group j

$\bar{X}_j = $ sample mean of group j

$\bar{\bar{X}} = $ grand mean

The within-group variation, usually called the **sum of squares within groups (SSW)**, measures the difference between each value and the mean of its own group and sums the squares of these differences over all groups. Equation (13.3) shows the computation of the within-group variation.

WITHIN-GROUP VARIATION IN ONE-WAY ANOVA

$$SSW = \sum_{j=1}^{c} \sum_{i=1}^{n_j} (X_{ij} - \bar{X}_j)^2 \tag{13.3}$$

where

$X_{ij} = i$th value in group j

$\bar{X}_j = $ sample mean of group j

Because you are comparing c groups, there are $c - 1$ degrees of freedom associated with the sum of squares among groups. Because each of the c groups contributes $n_j - 1$ degrees of freedom, there are $n - c$ degrees of freedom associated with the sum of squares within groups. In addition, there are $n - 1$ degrees of freedom associated with the sum of squares total because you are comparing each value, X_{ij}, to the grand mean, $\overline{\overline{X}}$, based on all n values.

If you divide each of these sums of squares by its respective degrees of freedom, you have three variances. In ANOVA, these three variances are called the **mean squares** and the three mean squares are defined as MSA (mean square among), MSW (mean square within), and MST (mean square total).

MEAN SQUARES IN ONE-WAY ANOVA

$$MSA = \frac{SSA}{c - 1} \tag{13.4a}$$

$$MSW = \frac{SSW}{n - c} \tag{13.4b}$$

$$MST = \frac{SST}{n - 1} \tag{13.4c}$$

F Test for Differences Among More Than Two Means

To determine if there is a significant difference among the group means, you use the F test for differences among more than two means. If the null hypothesis is true and there are no differences among the c group means, MSA, MSW, and MST, will provide estimates of the overall variance in the population. Thus, to test the null hypothesis:

$$H_0: \mu_1 = \mu_2 = \cdots = \mu_c$$

against the alternative:

$$H_1: \text{Not all } \mu_j \text{ are equal (where } j = 1, 2, \ldots, c)$$

you compute the one-way ANOVA F_{STAT} test statistic as the ratio of MSA to MSW, as in Equation (13.5).

ONE-WAY ANOVA F$_{STAT}$ TEST STATISTIC

$$F_{STAT} = \frac{MSA}{MSW} \tag{13.5}$$

The F_{STAT} test statistic follows an F distribution, with $c - 1$ degrees of freedom in the numerator and $n - c$ degrees of freedom in the denominator.

The test statistic compares mean squares (the variances) because the one-way ANOVA reaches conclusions about possible differences among the means of c groups by examining variances. For a given level of significance, α, you reject the null hypothesis if the F_{STAT} test statistic computed in Equation (13.5) is greater than the upper-tail critical value, F_α, from the F distribution with $c - 1$ degrees of freedom in the numerator and $n - c$ in the denominator (see Table E.5). Thus, as shown in Figure 13.2, the decision rule is

$$\text{Reject } H_0 \text{ if } F_{STAT} > F_\alpha;$$

$$\text{otherwise, do not reject } H_0.$$

FIGURE 13.2

Regions of rejection and
nonrejection when using
ANOVA

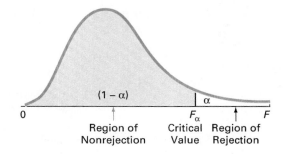

If the null hypothesis is true, the computed F_{STAT} test statistic is expected to be approximately equal to 1 because both the numerator and denominator mean square terms are estimating the overall variance in the population. If H_0 is false (and there are differences in the group means), the computed F_{STAT} test statistic is expected to be larger than 1 because the numerator, *MSA*, is estimating the differences among groups in addition to the overall variability in the values, while the denominator, *MSW*, is measuring only the overall variability in the values. Therefore, you reject the null hypothesis at a selected level of significance, α, only if the computed F_{STAT} test statistic is *greater than* F_α, the upper-tail critical value of the F distribution having $c - 1$ and $n - c$ degrees of freedom.

Table 13.7 presents the **ANOVA summary table** that is typically used to summarize the results of a one-way ANOVA. The table includes entries for the sources of variation (among groups, within groups, and total), the degrees of freedom, the sums of squares, the mean squares (the variances), and the computed F_{STAT} test statistic. The table may also include the *p*-value, the probability of having an F_{STAT} value as large as or larger than the one computed, given that the null hypothesis is true. The *p*-value allows you to reach conclusions about the null hypothesis without needing to refer to a table of critical values of the F distribution. If the *p*-value is less than the chosen level of significance, α, you reject the null hypothesis.

TABLE 13.1

ANOVA Summary Table

Source	Degrees of Freedom	Sum of Squares	Mean Square (Variance)	F
Among groups	$c - 1$	SSA	$MSA = \dfrac{SSA}{c - 1}$	$F_{STAT} = \dfrac{MSA}{MSW}$
Within groups	$n - c$	SSW	$MSW = \dfrac{SSW}{n - c}$	
Total	$n - 1$	SST		

Student Tip

In ordinary English,
you could characterize
this sales experiment
as asking the question
"How much of a *factor* is in-store location
in determining mobile
electronics sales?" echoing the sense of factor as
defined in this section.

To illustrate the one-way ANOVA F test, suppose you were the manager of a general merchandiser looking for ways of increasing sales of mobile electronics items. You decide to experiment with the placement of such items in a store. You devise an experiment to compare sales at the current location in aisle 5 ("in-aisle") with sales at three other locations: at the front of the store near weekly specials ("front"), in an end-of-aisle special kiosk display ("end-cap"), or adjacent to the Expert Counter that is staffed with specially trained salespeople ("expert"). You decide to conduct a one-way ANOVA in which these four in-store locations in-aisle, front, kiosk, and expert are the *levels* of the *factor* in-store location.

To test the comparative effectiveness of the four in-store locations, you conduct a 60-day experiment at 20 same-sized stores that have similar storewide net sales. You randomly assign five stores to use the in-aisle location, five stores to use the front location, five stores to use the end-cap kiosk, and five stores to use the expert location to form the four groups. At the end of the experiment, you organize the mobile electronics sales data by group and store the data in unstacked format in Mobile Electronics . Figure 13.3 presents that unstacked data, along with the sample mean and the sample standard deviation for each group.

FIGURE 13.3

Mobile electronic sales ($000), sample means, and sample standard deviations for four different in-store locations

	In-aisle	Front	Kiosk	Expert
	30.06	32.22	30.78	30.33
	29.96	31.47	30.91	30.29
	30.19	32.13	30.79	30.25
	29.96	31.86	30.95	30.25
	29.74	32.29	31.13	30.55
Sample Mean	29.982	31.994	30.912	30.334
Sample Standard Deviation	0.165	0.335	0.143	0.125

Figure 13.3 shows differences among the sample means for the mobile electronics sales for the four in-store locations. For the original in-aisle location, mean sales were $29.982 thousands, whereas mean sales at the three new locations varied from $30.334 thousands ("expert" location) to $30.912 thousands ("kiosk" location) to $31.994 thousands ("front" location).

Differences in the mobile electronic sales for the four in-store locations can also be presented visually. In Figure 13.4, the cell means plot displays the four sample means and connects the sample means with a straight line. In the same figure, the scatter plot presents the mobile electronics sales at each store in each group, permitting you to observe differences *within* each location as well as among the four locations. (In this example, because the difference within each group is slight, the points for each group overlap and blur together.)

FIGURE 13.4

Scatter plot and main effects plot of mobile electronics sales for four in-store locations

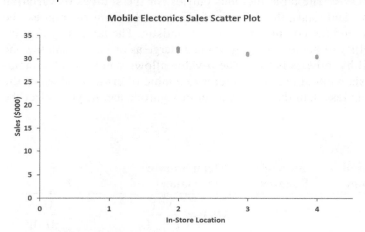

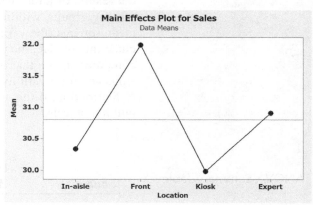

In the Excel scatter plot, the locations in-aisle, front, kiosk, and expert were relabeled 1, 2, 3, and 4 in order to use the scatter plot chart type.

> **Student Tip**
>
> If the sample sizes in each group were larger, you could construct stem-and-leaf displays, boxplots, and normal probability plots as additional ways of visualizing the sales data.

Having observed that the four sample means appear to be different, you use the F test for differences among more than two means to determine if these sample means are sufficiently different to conclude that the *population* means are not all equal. The null hypothesis states that there is no difference in the mean sales among the four in-store locations:

$$H_0: \mu_1 = \mu_2 = \mu_3 = \mu_4$$

The alternative hypothesis states that at least one of the in-store location mean sales differs from the other means:

$$H_1: \text{Not all the means are equal.}$$

To construct the ANOVA summary table, you first compute the sample means in each group (see Figure 13.3 on page 182). Then you compute the grand mean by summing all 20 values and dividing by the total number of values:

$$\overline{\overline{X}} = \frac{\sum_{j=1}^{c} \sum_{j=1}^{n_j} X_{ij}}{n} = \frac{616.12}{20} = 30.806$$

Then, using Equations (13.1) through (13.3) on page 179, you compute the sum of squares:

$$SSA = \sum_{j=1}^{c} n_j (\bar{X}_j - \bar{\bar{X}})^2 = (5)(29.982 - 30.806)^2 + (5)(31.994 - 30.806)^2$$

$$+ (5)(30.912 - 30.806)^2 + (5)(30.334 - 30.806)^2$$

$$= 11.6217$$

$$SSW = \sum_{j=1}^{c} \sum_{i=1}^{n_j} (X_{ij} - \bar{X}_j)^2$$

$$= (30.06 - 29.982)^2 + \cdots + (29.74 - 29.982)^2 + (32.22 - 31.994)^2 + \cdots$$

$$+ (32.29 - 31.994)^2 + (30.78 - 30.912)^2 + \cdots + (31.13 - 30.912)^2$$

$$+ (30.33 - 30.334)^2 + \cdots + (30.55 - 30.334)^2$$

$$= 0.7026$$

$$SST = \sum_{j=1}^{c} \sum_{i=1}^{n_j} (X_{ij} - \bar{\bar{X}})^2$$

$$= (30.06 - 30.806)^2 + (29.96 - 30.806)^2 + \cdots + (30.55 - 30.806)^2$$

$$= 12.3243$$

You compute the mean squares by dividing the sum of squares by the corresponding degrees of freedom [see Equation (13.4) on page 180]. Because $c = 4$ and $n = 20$,

$$MSA = \frac{SSA}{c-1} = \frac{11.6217}{4-1} = 3.8739$$

$$MSW = \frac{SSW}{n-c} = \frac{0.7026}{20-4} = 0.0439$$

so that using Equation (13.5) on page 180,

$$F_{STAT} = \frac{MSA}{MSW} = \frac{3.8739}{0.0439} = 88.2186$$

How to Run the One-way ANOVA with a FX-9750GII Calculator

Refer to data in Figure 13.3 on page 182.

To run the one-way ANOVA, follow the instruction below.

First enter the data in the lists (in your calculator): List 1 and List 2 as shown below:

List 1	List 2	
30.06	1	Note: 1 denotes "In-aisle"
29.96	1	
30.19	1	
29.96	1	
29.74	1	
32.22	2	Note: 2 denotes "Front"
31.47	2	
32.13	2	
31.86	2	
32.29	2	
30.78	3	Note: 3 denotes "Kiosk"

30.91	3
30.79	3
30.95	3
31.13	3
30.33	4
30.29	4
30.25	4
30.25	4
30.55	4

Note: 4 denotes "Expert"

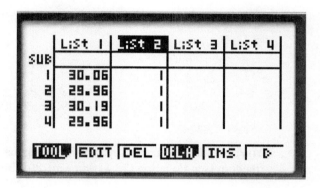

After you have entered the data, go to the **Main Menu** and select the following functions:

STAT   F3(TEST)   **F5**(ANOV)   then enter the following items:

Now press **EXE** or **F1**(CALC)

If you select either **EXE** or **F1**(Calc), the calculator will now show the results:

Because you are trying to determine whether *MSA* is greater than *MSW*, you only reject H_0 if F_{STAT} is greater than the upper critical value of F. For a selected level of significance, α, you

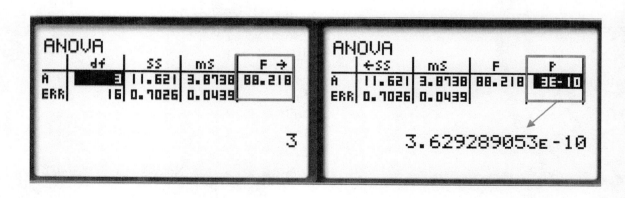

find the upper-tail critical value, F_α, from the F distribution using Table E.5. A portion of Table E.5 is presented in Table 13.2. In the in-store location sales experiment, there are 3 degrees of freedom in the numerator and 16 degrees of freedom in the denominator. F_α, the upper-tail critical value at the 0.05 level of significance, is 3.24.

TABLE 13.2

Finding the Critical Value of F with 3 and 16 Degrees of Freedom at the 0.05 Level of Significance

	Cumulative Probabilities = 0.95								
	Upper-Tail Area = 0.05								
	Numerator df_1								
Denominator df_2	**1**	**2**	**3**	**4**	**5**	**6**	**7**	**8**	**9**
⋮	⋮	⋮	⋮	⋮	⋮	⋮	⋮	⋮	⋮
11	4.84	3.98	3.59	3.36	3.20	3.09	3.01	2.95	2.90
12	4.75	3.89	3.49	3.26	3.11	3.00	2.91	2.85	2.80
13	4.67	3.81	3.41	3.18	3.03	2.92	2.83	2.77	2.71
14	4.60	3.74	3.34	3.11	2.96	2.85	2.76	2.70	2.65
15	4.54	3.68	3.29	3.06	2.90	2.79	2.71	2.64	2.59
16	4.49	3.63	3.24	3.01	2.85	2.74	2.66	2.59	2.54

Source: Extracted from Table E.5.

Because $F_{STAT} = 88.2186$ is greater than $F_\alpha = 3.24$, you reject the null hypothesis (see Figure 13.5). You conclude that there is a significant difference in the mean sales for the four in-store locations.

FIGURE 13.5

Regions of rejection and nonrejection for the one-way ANOVA at the 0.05 level of significance, with 3 and 16 degrees of freedom

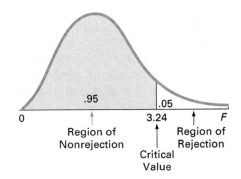

How to Find *F* Critical Value Using Calculator

Refer to Figure 13.5

Calculate the F critical value for $\alpha = 0.05$ with 3 and 16 degree of freedoms, using the Casio Calculator fx-9750GII and follow the following calculator steps:

From the **Main Menu** select:

STAT   F5 (DIST)   **F4** (F)   **F3**(InvF)   then enter the following items:

Inverse F
Data   : **F2** (Var)   ▼
Area   : **0.05**   **EXE**
n: df   : **3**   **EXE**
d: df   : **16**   **EXE**
Save Res   : None
Execute

Now key **EXE** or **F1**(CALC)

The calculator will now show the results:

Inverse F
x-Inv = 3.23887152   **(Note: this is the critical value for the upper tail. See Figure 13.5)**

Figure 13.6 shows the ANOVA results for the in-store location sales experiment, including the *p*-value. In Table 13.1 (on page 181), the between groups is labeled as Among group in the SPSS output as shown in Figure 13.6. The Casio Calculator labels Among group as A (which stands for Among) and Within group as ERR (which stands for error).

FIGURE 13.6

SPSS ANOVA result for the in-store location sales experiment

Oneway

ANOVA

Mobile electronic sales ($000)

	Sum of Squares	df	Mean Square	F	Sig.
Between Groups	11.622	3	3.874	88.219	.000
Within Groups	.703	16	.044		
Total	12.324	19			

The *p*-value, or probability of getting a computed F_{STAT} statistic of 88.2186 or larger when the null hypothesis is true, is 0.0000. Because this *p*-value is less than the specified α of 0.05, you reject the null hypothesis. The *p*-value of 0.0000 indicates that there is a 0.00% chance of observing differences this large or larger if the population means for the four in-store locations are all equal. After performing the one-way ANOVA and finding a significant difference among the in-store locations, you still do not know *which* in-store locations differ. All you know is that there is sufficient evidence to state that the population means are not all the same. In other words, one or more population means are significantly different. Before proceeding to determine which in-store locations differ, you check to see if the assumptions of ANOVA hold.

One-Way ANOVA *F* Test Assumptions

To use the one-way ANOVA *F* test, you must make three assumptions about your data:

- **Randomness and independence** of the samples selected
- **Normality** of the *c* groups from which the samples are selected
- **Homogeneity of variance** (the variances of the *c* groups are equal)

Most critical of all is the first assumption. The validity of any experiment depends on random sampling and/or the randomization process. To avoid biases in the outcomes, you need to select random samples from the *c* groups or use the randomization process to randomly assign the items to the *c* levels of the factor. Selecting a random sample or randomly assigning the levels ensures that a value from one group is independent of any other value in the experiment. Departures from this assumption can seriously affect inferences from the ANOVA. These problems are discussed more thoroughly in references 3 and 10.

As for the second assumption, **normality**, the one-way ANOVA *F* test is fairly robust against departures from the normal distribution. As long as the distributions are not extremely different from a normal distribution, the level of significance of the ANOVA F test is usually not greatly affected, particularly for large samples. You can assess the normality of each of the c samples by constructing a normal probability plot or a boxplot.

As for the third assumption, **homogeneity of variance**, if you have equal sample sizes in each group, inferences based on the F distribution are not seriously affected by unequal variances. However, if you have unequal sample sizes, unequal variances can have a serious effect on inferences from the ANOVA procedure. Thus, when possible, you should have equal sample sizes in all groups. You can use the Levene test for homogeneity of variance discussed below, to test whether the variances of the c groups are equal.

When only the normality assumption is violated, you can use the Kruskal-Wallis rank test, a nonparametric procedure (see references 1 and 2). When only the homogeneity-of-variance assumption is violated, you can use procedures similar to those used in the separate-variance t test of Section 12.1 (see references 1 and 2). When both the normality and homogeneity-of-variance assumptions have been violated, you need to use an appropriate data transformation that both normalizes the data and reduces the differences in variances (see reference 10) or use a more general nonparametric procedure (see reference 1).

Levene Test for Homogeneity of Variance

Although the one-way ANOVA F test is relatively robust with respect to the assumption of equal group variances, large differences in the group variances can seriously affect the level of significance and the power of the F test. One powerful yet simple procedure for testing the equality of the variances is the modified **Levene test** (see reference 5). To test for the homogeneity of variance, you use the following null hypothesis:

$$H_0: \sigma_1^2 = \sigma_2^2 = \cdots = \sigma_c^2$$

> **Student Tip**
>
> Remember when performing the Levene test that you are conducting a one-way ANOVA on the absolute differences from the median in each group, not on the actual values themselves.

against the alternative hypothesis:

$$H_1: \text{Not all } \sigma_j^2 \text{ are equal } (j = 1, 2, 3, \ldots, c)$$

To test the null hypothesis of equal variances, you first compute the absolute value of the difference between each value and the median of the group. Then you perform a one-way ANOVA on these *absolute differences*. Most statisticians suggest using a level of significance of $\alpha = 0.05$ when performing the ANOVA. To illustrate the modified Levene test, return to the Figure 13.3 data and summary statistics on page 182 for the in-store location sales experiment. Table 13.3 summarizes the absolute differences from the median of each location.

TABLE 13.3

Absolute Differences from the Median Sales for Four Locations

In-Aisle (Median = 29.96)	Front (Median = 32.13)	Kiosk (Median = 30.91)	Expert (Median = 30.29)
$\lvert 30.06 - 29.96 \rvert = 0.10$	$\lvert 32.22 - 32.13 \rvert = 0.09$	$\lvert 30.78 - 30.91 \rvert = 0.13$	$\lvert 30.33 - 30.29 \rvert = 0.04$
$\lvert 29.96 - 29.96 \rvert = 0.00$	$\lvert 31.47 - 32.13 \rvert = 0.66$	$\lvert 30.91 - 30.91 \rvert = 0.00$	$\lvert 30.29 - 30.29 \rvert = 0.00$
$\lvert 30.19 - 29.96 \rvert = 0.23$	$\lvert 32.13 - 32.13 \rvert = 0.00$	$\lvert 30.79 - 30.91 \rvert = 0.12$	$\lvert 30.25 - 30.29 \rvert = 0.04$
$\lvert 29.96 - 29.96 \rvert = 0.00$	$\lvert 31.86 - 32.13 \rvert = 0.27$	$\lvert 30.95 - 30.91 \rvert = 0.04$	$\lvert 30.25 - 30.29 \rvert = 0.04$
$\lvert 29.74 - 29.96 \rvert = 0.22$	$\lvert 32.29 - 32.13 \rvert = 0.16$	$\lvert 31.13 - 30.91 \rvert = 0.22$	$\lvert 30.55 - 30.29 \rvert = 0.26$

Using the absolute differences given in Table 13.3, you perform a one-way ANOVA (see Figure 13.7).

From the Figure 13.7 results, observe that Levene Statistic = 1.0556. Because Levene Statistic = 1.0556 < 3.2389 (or the p-value = 0.3953 > 0.05), you do not reject H_0. (The SPSS output labels p-value as Sig.) There is insufficient evidence of a significant difference among the four variances. In other words, it is reasonable to assume that the four in-store locations have an equal amount of variability in sales. Therefore, the homogeneity-of-variance assumption for the ANOVA procedure is justified.

FIGURE 13.7

SPSS Levene test result for the in-store location sales experiment

Oneway

Test of Homogeneity of Variances

		Levene Statistic	df1	df2	Sig.
Mobile electronic sales ($000)	Based on Mean	2.667	3	16	.083
	Based on Median	1.056	3	16	.395
	Based on Median and with adjusted df	1.056	3	8.014	.420
	Based on trimmed mean	2.505	3	16	.096

Levene Test

Levene test is used to test if c samples have equal variances (where c is the number of independent groups). The Homogeneity of Variance is also known as equal variances.

The Levene test statistics can be computed based on mean, median, median with adjusted degree of freedom and trimmed mean as shown in Figure 13.7. The four choices for calculating the Levene test statistic depends on the ability of the test to detect the unequal variance when the data are not normally distributed. The median performed best if the distribution is not normal. In this course, we proposed that you use the Levene test statistic based on median, which is 1.056 and the p-value is 0.395.

The decision rule for critical value approach is

Reject Ho if Levene test statistic is greater than $F_{\alpha, c-1, n-c}$,

Otherwise, do not reject Ho

The decision rule for p-value approach is

Reject Ho if p-value is less than α, otherwise, do not reject Ho.

$F_{\alpha, c-1, n-c}$ is the upper critical value of a F distribution with numerator degree of freedom of $c-1$ and denominator degree of freedom of n-c at a significance level of α, where c = number of groups and n = total sample sizes in the c groups

You can use the recommended calculator to obtain the F critical value by selecting DIST, F and InvF functions.

How to run the Levene Test of Equal Variance with SPSS

First enter the data (in Figure 13.3 on page 182) in the SPSS data sheet as shown below.

File Edit View Data Transform Analyze Graphs Utilities Extensions Window Help

7:

	Sales	Location	var	var	var	var	var	var	va
1	30.06	1							
2	29.96	1							
3	30.19	1							
4	29.96	1							
5	29.74	1							
6	32.22	2							
7	31.47	2							
8	32.13	2							
9	31.86	2							
10	32.29	2							
11	30.78	3							
12	30.91	3							
13	30.79	3							
14	30.95	3							
15	31.13	3							
16	30.33	4							
17	30.29	4							
18	30.25	4							
19	30.25	4							
20	30.55	4							
21									
22									
23									

Data View   Variable View

Make the following menu selections: **Analyze – Compare Means – One-Way ANOVA (as shown below)**

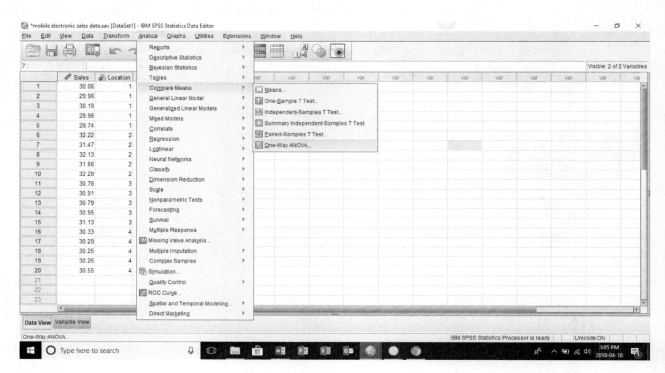

Click "**Option**" button and on the "one-way ANOVA Options" dialog box, check "**Homogeneity of variance test**". Then click **Continue** and then **OK** to run the one-way ANOVA test. You will obtain the result table of test of homogeneity of variances as shown in Figure 13.7.

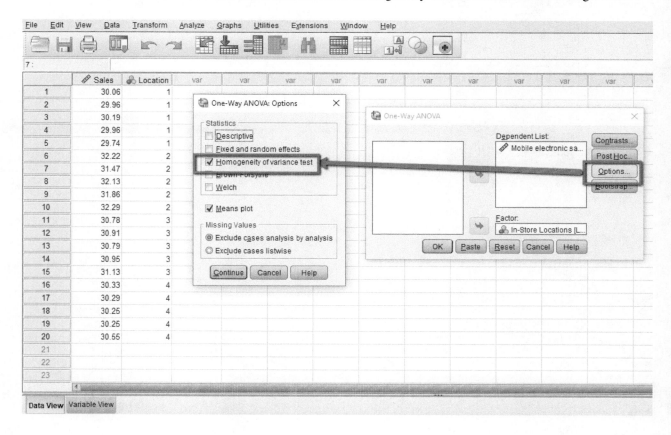

Student Tip
You have an α level of risk in the entire set of comparisons not just a single comparison.

Multiple Comparisons: The Tukey-Kramer Procedure with SPSS

In the mobile electronics sales experiment example, the one-way ANOVA *F* test determined that there was a difference among the four in-store sales locations. Having verified that the assumptions were valid, the next step in one-way ANOVA analysis would be to construct **multiple comparisons** to test the null hypothesis that the differences in the means of all pairs of in-store locations are equal to 0.

Although many methods could be used to determine which of the *c* means are significantly different (see references 3 and 4), one commonly used method is the **Tukey-Kramer multiple comparisons procedure for one-way ANOVA**. This procedure enables you to simultaneously make comparisons between *all* pairs of groups. Use the SPSS to obtain the Tukey-Kramer procedure result, shown in Figure13.8.

FIGURE 13.8

SPSS Tukey-Kramer procedure result for the in-store location sales experiment

Post Hoc Tests

Multiple Comparisons

Dependent Variable: Mobile electronic sales ($000)

Tukey HSD

(I) In-Store Locations	(J) In-Store Locations	Mean Difference (I-J)	Std. Error	Sig.	95% Confidence Interval Lower Bound	Upper Bound
in-aisle	front	-2.01200*	.13253	.000	-2.3912	-1.6328
	kiosk	-.93000*	.13253	.000	-1.3092	-.5508
	expert	-.35200	.13253	.074	-.7312	.0272
front	in-aisle	2.01200*	.13253	.000	1.6328	2.3912
	kiosk	1.08200*	.13253	.000	.7028	1.4612
	expert	1.66000*	.13253	.000	1.2808	2.0392
kiosk	in-aisle	.93000*	.13253	.000	.5508	1.3092
	front	-1.08200*	.13253	.000	-1.4612	-.7028
	expert	.57800*	.13253	.002	.1988	.9572
expert	in-aisle	.35200	.13253	.074	-.0272	.7312
	front	-1.66000*	.13253	.000	-2.0392	-1.2808
	kiosk	-.57800*	.13253	.002	-.9572	-.1988

*. The mean difference is significant at the 0.05 level.

Mobile electronic sales ($000)

Tukey HSD[a]

In-Store Locations	N	Subset for alpha = 0.05: 1	2	3
in-aisle	5	29.9820		
expert	5	30.3340		
kiosk	5		30.9120	
front	5			31.9940
Sig.		.074	1.000	1.000

Means for groups in homogeneous subsets are displayed.

a. Uses Harmonic Mean Sample Size = 5.000.

Figure 13.8 presents the SPSS results for the Tukey-Kramer procedure for the mobile electronics sales in-store location experiment. Note that by using $\alpha = 0.05$, you are able to make all six of the comparisons with an overall error rate of only 5%.

Use the SPSS Tukey-Kramer procedure result in Figure 13.8 to make comparisons between all pairs of groups. The SPSS results show the comparisons in terms of p-value (i.e. sig) and 95% confidence interval. Use a level of significance of $\alpha = 0.05$ when performing the pairwise means comparison. For each pair of groups, compare the p-value with $\alpha = 0.05$. Reject null hypothesis if p-value is less than α and conclude that there is a significant difference between the pair. For example, compare "in-aisle" and "front" location. The mean differences between "in-store" and "front" mean sales is -2.012. The p-value is 0.000 which is less than $\alpha = 0.05$ and you can conclude that there is a significant difference between the mobile electronic sales means of this pair ("in-store" and "front").

Using $\alpha = 0.05$, you are able to make all six unique pairs comparison with the p-value.
Summary of the pair comparison analysis:

Pair 1: comparing "in-aisle" to "front" location, p-value is 0.000 which is less than $\alpha = 0.05$, you can conclude that there is a significant difference between the mobile electronic sales means of this pair

Pair 2: comparing "in-aisle" to "kiosk" location, p-value is 0.000 which is less than $\alpha = 0.05$, you can conclude that you conclude that there is a significant difference between the mobile electronic sales means of this pair

Pair 3: comparing "in-aisle" to "expert" location, p-value is 0.074 which is greater than $\alpha = 0.05$, you can conclude that you conclude that there is no evidence of a difference between the mobile electronic sales means of this pair.

Pair 4: comparing "front" to "kiosk" location, p--value is 0.000 which is less than $\alpha = 0.05$, you can conclude that you conclude that there is a significant difference between the mobile electronic sales means of this pair

Pair 5: comparing "expert" to "front" location, p-value is 0.000 which is less than $\alpha = 0.05$, you can conclude that there is significant difference between the mobile electronic sales means of this pair

Pair 6: comparing "kiosk" to "expert" location, p-value is 0.002 which is less than $\alpha = 0.05$, you can conclude that there is a significant difference between the mobile electronic sales means of this pair

Alternatively, any 95% confidence interval for the comparison that does not include 0 is considered significant. Therefore, all the comparisons are significant except for the comparison of expert to in-aisle location. The 95% confidence interval for that comparison includes 0 since the lower bound is -0.0275 and upper bound is 0.7312.

The mean difference allows you to infer if the sales in a particular location is higher or lower than the other location.

How to run the Tukey-Kramer Procedure with SPSS

First enter the data in the SPSS data sheet as shown below.

File	Edit	View	Data	Transform	Analyze	Graphs	Utilities	Extensions	Window	Help

7 :

	Sales	Location	var	var	var	var	var	var	va
1	30.06	1							
2	29.96	1							
3	30.19	1							
4	29.96	1							
5	29.74	1							
6	32.22	2							
7	31.47	2							
8	32.13	2							
9	31.86	2							
10	32.29	2							
11	30.78	3							
12	30.91	3							
13	30.79	3							
14	30.95	3							
15	31.13	3							
16	30.33	4							
17	30.29	4							
18	30.25	4							
19	30.25	4							
20	30.55	4							
21									
22									
23									

Data View | Variable View

Make the following menu selections: **Analyze – Compare Means – One-Way ANOVA (as shown below)**

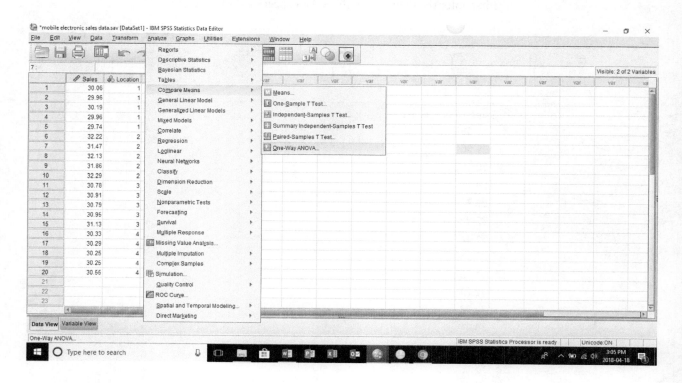

Click "**Post Hoc**" button and on the "one-way ANOVA Post Hoc Multiple comparisons" dialog box, check "**Tukey**". Then click **Continue** and then **OK** to run the one-way ANOVA test. You will obtain the result table of Post Hoc tests as shown in Figure 13.8.

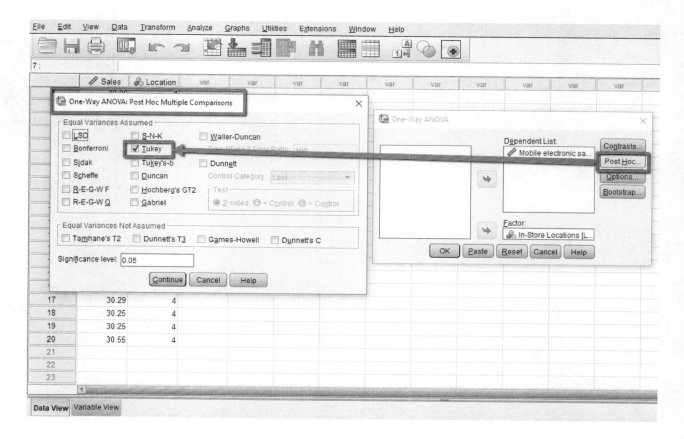

Example 13.1 illustrates another example of the one-way ANOVA.

EXAMPLE 13.1

ANOVA of the Speed of Drive-Through Service at Fast-Food Chains

For fast-food restaurants, the drive-through window is an important revenue source. The chain that offers the fastest service is likely to attract additional customers. Each year *QSR Magazine*, **www.qsrmagazine.com**, publishes its results of a survey of drive-through service times (from menu board to departure) at fast-food chains. In a recent year, the mean time was 129.75 seconds for Wendy's, 149.69 seconds for Taco Bell, 201.33 seconds for Burger King, 188.83 seconds for McDonald's, and 190.06 seconds for Chick-fil-A. Suppose the study was based on 20 customers for each fast-food chain. At the 0.05 level of significance, is there evidence of a difference in the mean drive-through service times of the five chains?

Table 13.5 contains the ANOVA table for this problem.

TABLE 13.5

ANOVA Summary Table of Drive-Through Service Times at Fast-Food Chains

Source	Degrees of Freedom	Sum of Squares	Mean Squares	F	p-value
Among chains	4	75,048.74	18,762.185	143.66	0.0000
Within chains	95	12,407.00	130.60		

SOLUTION

$H_0: \mu_1 = \mu_2 = \mu_3 = \mu_4 = \mu_5$ where 1 = Wendy's, 2 = Taco Bell, 3 = Burger King,

4 = McDonald's, 5 = Chick-fil-A

H_1: Not all μ_j are equal   where $j = 1, 2, 3, 4, 5$

Decision rule: If the *p*-value < 0.05, reject H_0. Because the *p*-value is 0.0000, which is less than $\alpha = 0.05$, reject H_0. You have sufficient evidence to conclude that the mean drive-through times of the five chains are not all equal.

To determine which of the means are significantly different from one another, you have to perform the Tukey-Kramer procedure with SPSS.

SPSS GUIDE– VERSION 21 – ANOVA

We will use the scenario, "The Perfect Parachute Company" to demonstrate how to perform one-way ANOVA using SPSS.

A research was conducted to determine if any significant differences exist in the strength of parachutes woven from synthetic fibers from the four suppliers. Five parachutes were woven for each group – Supplier 1, Supplier 2, Supplier 3 and Supplier 4. The amount of force required to tear the parachute is measured on a tensile-strength scale where the larger the value the stronger the parachute. The data is shown below:

Supplier 1	Supplier 2	Supplier 3	Supplier 4
18.5	26.3	20.6	25.4
24.0	25.3	25.2	19.9
17.2	24.0	20.8	22.6
19.9	21.2	24.7	17.5
18.0	24.5	22.9	20.4

Instruction:
Performing a a one-way ANOVA on SPSS – Version 25
Open a new spreadsheet called the "New Dataset".
Click "New Dataset".

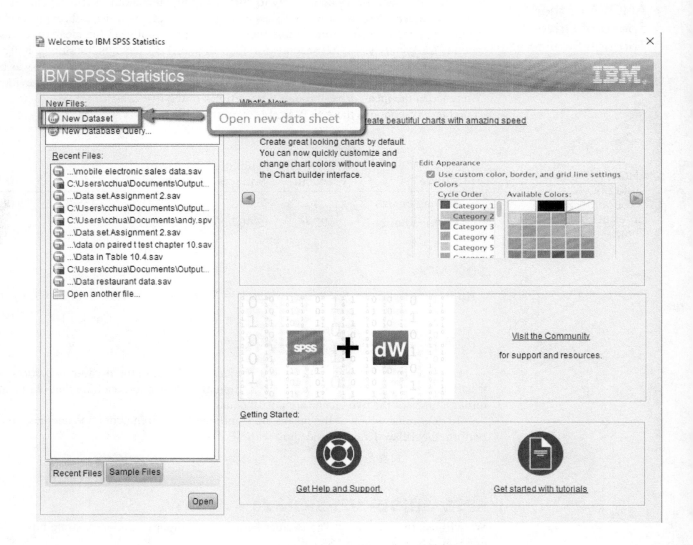

Step 2: Define the variables and give the variables a label.

Click "**Variable View**" (at the bottom of the window) to go to the variable view window to define the variables and fix the data at zero or one decimal places.

- Enter the first variable name -"suppliers" and then click **values.** Key "**1**" in the value box and key "**Supplier 1**" in the Label box, and then click **Add**. Similarly enter for the other three suppliers.
- Enter the second variable name – "Strength" and label it as "Tensile-Strength Scale".

File	Edit	View	Data	Transform	Analyze	Graphs	Utilities	Extensions	Window	Help		

	Name	Type	Width	Decimals	Label	Values	Missing	Columns	Align	Measure	Role
1	suppliers	Numeric	8	0		{1, Supplier ...	None	8	Right	Nominal	Input
2	Strength	Numeric	8	2	Tensile strength	None	None	8	Right	Scale	Input
3											
4											
5											

Step 3: Create a SPSS data file.

Click "**Data View**" to return to the data view window. Now, enter the raw data (in Table 1) into the respective column of variables.

■ *Untitled2 [DataSet1] - IBM SPSS Statistics Data Editor

File Edit View Data Transform Analyze Graphs Utilities Extensions Window Help

21 : suppliers

	suppliers	Strength	var	var	var	var	var	var	va
1	1	18.50							
2	1	24.00							
3	1	17.20							
4	1	19.90							
5	1	18.00							
6	2	26.30							
7	2	25.30							
8	2	24.00							
9	2	21.20							
10	2	24.50							
11	3	20.60							
12	3	25.20							
13	3	20.80							
14	3	24.70							
15	3	22.90							
16	4	25.40							
17	4	19.90							
18	4	22.60							
19	4	17.50							
20	4	20.40							
21									
22									
23									

Data View | Variable View

After you have entered all the data, save it as "Anova.sav" (or any filename).

Step 3: Perform ANOVA.

Make the following menu selections:

Analyze→Compare Means→One-Way Anova

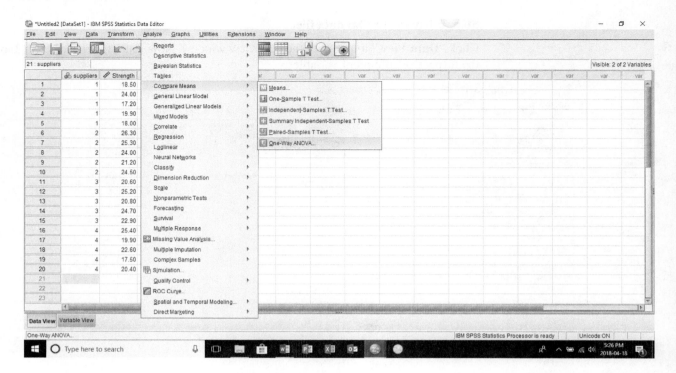

At this point, the **One-Way Anova** dialog box will appear. Make these entries in the **One-Way Anova** dialog box:

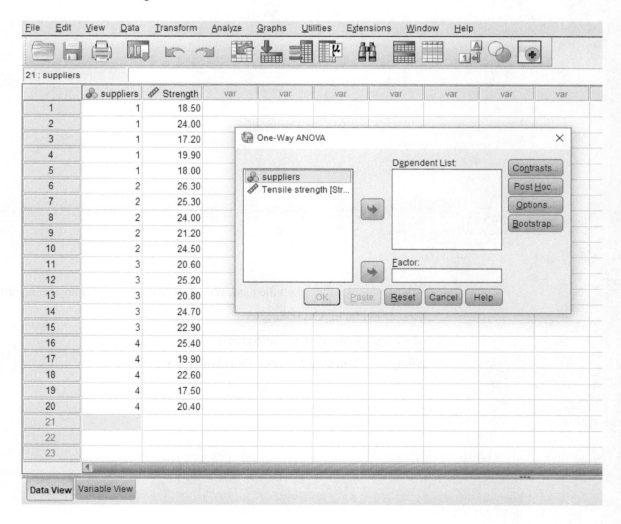

- Highlight on the "**tensile-strength scale**" variable and click on the arrow
  key (➡). The variable will automatically fall into the **Dependent List** box.
- Highlight on the "**Suppliers**" variable and click on the arrow key (➡). The variable
  will automatically fall into the **Factor** box.

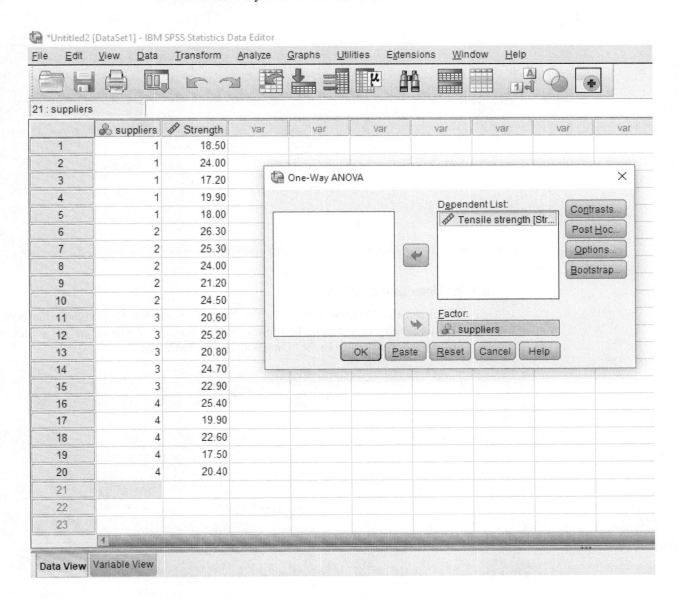

To Perform Tukey-Kramer Procedure

- Click on the **Post-Hoc** button. In the "One-Way Anova: Post Hoc Multiple Comparisons"
  window, select **Tukey** as the comparison method. Then click on **continue** button to
  return to the "One-Way Anova" window.

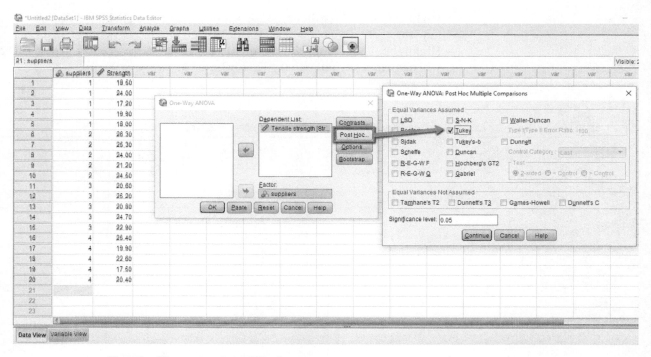

Test for Homogeneity of Variance

- Click on the **Options** button. In the "One-Way Anova: Options" dialog box, select **Homogeneity of variance test** to test for the equality of variances. Then click on **continue** button to return to the "One-Way Anova" window.

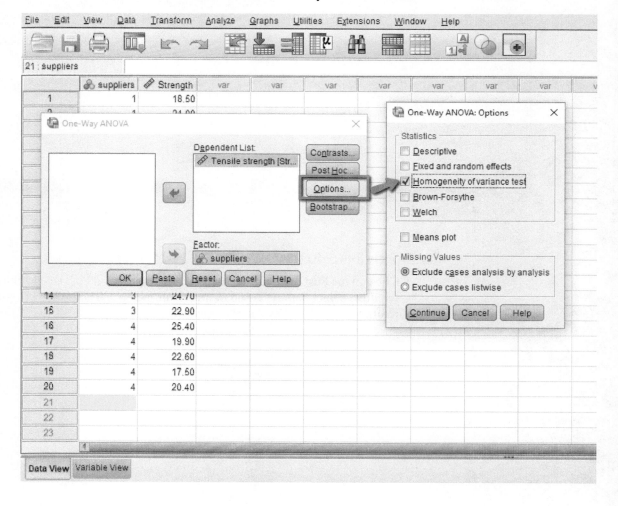

At this point, the **One-Way Anova** dialog box will appear. Click on the **Ok** button to obtain the SPSS results.

Step 3: Go to **SPSS Viewer** to obtain your SPSS results.

SPSS output:

➡️ **Oneway**

[DataSet1]

Test of Homogeneity of Variances

		Levene Statistic	df1	df2	Sig.
Tensile strength	Based on Mean	.430	3	16	.734
	Based on Median	.207	3	16	.890
	Based on Median and with adjusted df	.207	3	12.271	.890
	Based on trimmed mean	.418	3	16	.743

ANOVA

Tensile strength

	Sum of Squares	df	Mean Square	F	Sig.
Between Groups	63.285	3	21.095	3.462	.041
Within Groups	97.504	16	6.094		
Total	160.789	19			

Post Hoc Tests

Multiple Comparisons

Dependent Variable: Tensile strength

Tukey HSD

(I) suppliers	(J) suppliers	Mean Difference (I-J)	Std. Error	Sig.	95% Confidence Interval	
					Lower Bound	Upper Bound
Supplier 1	Supplier 2	-4.74000*	1.56128	.036	-9.2069	-.2731
	supplier 3	-3.32000	1.56128	.187	-7.7869	1.1469
	supplier 4	-1.64000	1.56128	.723	-6.1069	2.8269
Supplier 2	Supplier 1	4.74000*	1.56128	.036	.2731	9.2069
	supplier 3	1.42000	1.56128	.800	-3.0469	5.8869
	supplier 4	3.10000	1.56128	.234	-1.3669	7.5669
supplier 3	Supplier 1	3.32000	1.56128	.187	-1.1469	7.7869
	Supplier 2	-1.42000	1.56128	.800	-5.8869	3.0469
	supplier 4	1.68000	1.56128	.708	-2.7869	6.1469
supplier 4	Supplier 1	1.64000	1.56128	.723	-2.8269	6.1069
	Supplier 2	-3.10000	1.56128	.234	-7.5669	1.3669
	supplier 3	-1.68000	1.56128	.708	-6.1469	2.7869

*. The mean difference is significant at the 0.05 level.

Homogeneous Subsets

Tensile strength

Tukey HSD[a]

suppliers	N	Subset for alpha = 0.05 1	2
Supplier 1	5	19.5200	
supplier 4	5	21.1600	21.1600
supplier 3	5	22.8400	22.8400
Supplier 2	5		24.2600
Sig.		.187	.234

Means for groups in homogeneous subsets are displayed.

a. Uses Harmonic Mean Sample Size = 5.000.

13.2 Effect Size

Section 11.5 discusses the issue of the practical significance of a statistically significant test and explains that when a very large sample is selected, a statistically significant result can be of limited importance. The **Section 13.2 online topic** shows how to measure the effect size of a statistical test.

SUMMARY

In this chapter, you were introduced to a variety of tests for two or more samples. For situations in which the samples are independent, you learned statistical test procedures for analyzing possible differences between means, proportions, and variances. In addition, you learned a test procedure that is frequently used when analyzing differences between the means of two related samples. Remember that you need to select the test that is most appropriate for a given set of conditions and to critically investigate the validity of the assumptions underlying each of the hypothesis-testing procedures.

Table 13.6 provides a list of topics covered in this chapter. The roadmap in Figure 13.9 illustrates the steps needed in determining which two-sample test of hypothesis to use. The following are the questions you need to consider:

1. What type of variables do you have? If you are dealing with categorical variables, use the Z test for the difference between two proportions. (This test assumes independent samples.)

2. If you have a numerical variable, determine whether you have independent samples or related samples. If you have related samples, and you can assume approximate normality, use the paired t test.

3. If you have independent samples, is your focus on variability or central tendency? If the focus is on variability, and you can assume approximate normality, use the F test.

4. If your focus is central tendency and you can assume approximate normality, determine whether you can assume that the variances of the two populations are equal. (This assumption can be tested using the F test.)

5. If you can assume that the two populations have equal variances, use the pooled-variance t test. If you cannot assume that the two populations have equal variances, use the separate-variance t test.

6. If you have more than two independent samples, you can use the one-way ANOVA.)

TABLE 13.6

Summary of Topics in
Chapter 13

TYPE OF ANALYSIS	TYPES OF DATA	
	Numerical	**Categorical**
Compare two populations	t tests for the difference in the means of two independent populations (Section 12.1)	Z test for the difference between two proportions (Section 12.3)
	Paired t test (Section 12.2)	
	F test for the difference between two variances (Section 12.4)	
Compare more than two populations	One-way ANOVA (Section 13.1)	

FIGURE 13.9

Roadmap for selecting
a test of hypothesis for
two or more samples

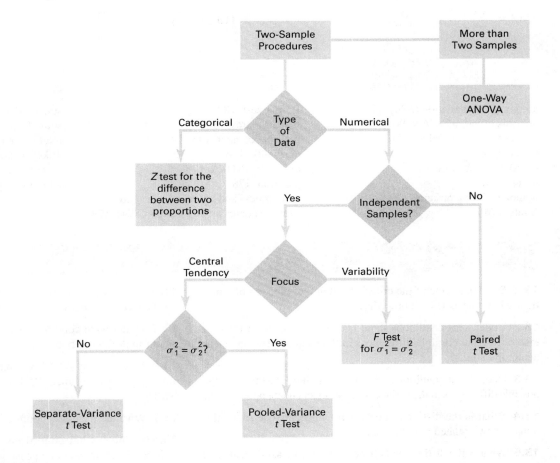

REFERENCES

1. Conover, W. J. *Practical Nonparametric Statistics*, 3rd ed. New York: Wiley, 2000.

2. Daniel, W. *Applied Nonparametric Statistics*, 2nd ed. Boston: Houghton Mifflin, 1990.

3. Hicks, C. R., and K. V. *Turner. Fundamental Concepts in the Design of Experiments,* 5th ed. New York: Oxford University Press, 1999.

4. Kutner, M. H., J. Neter, C. Nachtsheim, and W. Li. *Applied Linear Statistical Models,* 5th ed. New York: McGraw-Hill-Irwin, 2005.

5. Levine, D. M. *Statistics for Six Sigma Green Belts*. Upper Saddle River, NJ: Financial Times/Prentice Hall, 2006.

6. *Microsoft Excel 2013*. Redmond, WA: Microsoft Corp., 2012.

7. *Minitab Release 16* State College, PA: Minitab, 2010.

8. Montgomery, D. M. *Design and Analysis of Experiments*, 6th ed. New York: Wiley, 2005.

9. Satterthwaite, F. E. "An Approximate Distribution of Estimates of Variance Components." *Biometrics Bulletin*, 2(1946): 110–114.

10. Snedecor, G. W., and W. G. Cochran. *Statistical Methods*, 8th ed. Ames, IA: Iowa State University Press, 1989.

KEY EQUATIONS

Total Variation in One-Way ANOVA

$$SST = \sum_{j=1}^{c} \sum_{i=1}^{n_j} (X_{ij} - \overline{\overline{X}})^2 \quad \textbf{(13.1)}$$

Among-Group Variation in One-Way ANOVA

$$SSA = \sum_{j=1}^{c} n_j (\overline{X}_j - \overline{\overline{X}})^2 \quad \textbf{(13.2)}$$

Within-Group Variation in One-Way ANOVA

$$SSW = \sum_{j=1}^{c} \sum_{i=1}^{n_j} (X_{ij} - \overline{X}_j)^2 \quad \textbf{(13.3)}$$

Mean Squares in One-Way ANOVA

$$MSA = \frac{SSA}{c - 1} \quad \textbf{(13.4a)}$$

$$MSW = \frac{SSW}{n - c} \quad \textbf{(13.4b)}$$

$$MST = \frac{SST}{n - 1} \quad \textbf{(13.4c)}$$

One-Way ANOVA F_{STAT} Test Statistic

$$F_{STAT} = \frac{MSA}{MSW} \quad \textbf{(13.5)}$$

KEY TERMS

among-group variation (*SSA*) 178
analysis of variance (ANOVA) 178
ANOVA summary table 181
factor 178
grand mean, $\overline{\overline{X}}$ 178
groups 178
homogeneity of variance 186
levels 178

Levene test 187
mean squares 180
multiple comparisons 191
normality 186
one-way ANOVA 178
partition 178
randomness and independence 186
sum of squares among groups (*SSA*) 179

sum of squares total (*SST*) 178
sum of squares within groups (*SSW*) 179
total variation 178
Tukey-Kramer multiple comparisons
   procedure for one-way ANOVA 191
within-group variation (*SSW*) 178

CHECKING YOUR UNDERSTANDING

13.1 What are some of the criteria used in the selection of a particular hypothesis-testing procedure?

13.2 Under what conditions should you use the pooled-variance *t* test to examine possible differences in the means of two independent populations?

13.3 Under what conditions should you use the *F* test to examine possible differences in the variances of two independent populations?

13.4 What is the distinction between two independent populations and two related populations?

13.5 What is the distinction between repeated measurements and matched items?

13.6 When you have two independent populations, explain the similarities and differences between the test of hypothesis for the

difference between the means and the confidence interval estimate for the difference between the means.

13.7 Under what conditions should you use the paired *t* test for the mean difference between two related populations?

13.8 In a one-way ANOVA, what is the difference between the among-groups variance *MSA* and the within-groups variance *MSW*?

13.9 What are the assumptions of ANOVA?

13.10 Under what conditions should you use the one-way ANOVA *F* test to examine possible differences among the means of *c* independent populations?

13.11 What is the difference between the one-way ANOVA *F* test and the Levene test?

PROBLEMS

Section 13.1

13.12 An experiment has a single factor with five groups and seven values in each group.
a. How many degrees of freedom are there in determining the among-group variation?
b. How many degrees of freedom are there in determining the within-group variation?

c. How many degrees of freedom are there in determining the total variation?

13.13 You are working with the same experiment as in Problem 13.12.
a. If *SSA* = 60 and *SST* = 210, what is *SSW*?
b. What is *MSA*?
c. What is *MSW*?
d. What is the value of F_{STAT}?

13.14 You are working with the same experiment as in Problems 13.12 and 13.13.

a. Construct the ANOVA summary table and fill in all values in the table.

b. At the 0.05 level of significance, what is the upper-tail critical value from the F distribution?

c. State the decision rule for testing the null hypothesis that all five groups have equal population means.

d. What is your statistical decision?

13.15 Consider an experiment with three groups, with seven values in each.

a. How many degrees of freedom are there in determining the among-group variation?

b. How many degrees of freedom are there in determining the within-group variation?

c. How many degrees of freedom are there in determining the total variation?

13.16 Consider an experiment with four groups, with eight values in each. For the ANOVA summary table below, fill in all the missing results:

Source	Degrees of Freedom	Sum of Squares	Mean Square (Variance)	F
Among groups	$c - 1 = ?$	$SSA = ?$	$MSA = 80$	$F_{STAT} = ?$
Within groups	$n - c = ?$	$SSW = 560$	$MSW = ?$	
Total	$n - 1 = ?$	$SST = ?$		

13.17 You are working with the same experiment as in Problem 13.16.

a. At the 0.05 level of significance, state the decision rule for testing the null hypothesis that all four groups have equal population means.

b. What is your statistical decision?

c. At the 0.05 level of significance, what is the upper-tail critical value from the Studentized range distribution?

d. To perform the Tukey-Kramer procedure, what is the critical range?

13.18 *Accounting Today* identified the top accounting firms in 10 geographic regions across the United States. All 10 regions reported growth in 2013, including the Capital, Great Lakes, Mid-Atlantic, and New England regions which reported combined growths of 2.06%, 16.58%, 8.31%, and 9.49%, respectively. A characteristic description of the accounting firms in the Capital, Great Lakes, Mid-Atlantic, and New England regions included the number of partners in the firm.

The file **AccountingPartners4** contains the number of partners. (Data extracted from **bit.ly/ODuzd3**.)

a. At the 0.05 level of significance, is there evidence of a difference among the Capital, Great Lakes, Mid-Atlantic, and New England region accounting firms with respect to the mean number of partners?

b. If the results in (a) indicate that it is appropriate to do so, use the Tukey-Kramer procedure to determine which regions differ in the mean number of partners. Discuss your findings.

13.19 The more costly and time consuming it is to export and import, the more difficult it is for local companies to be competitive

and to reach international markets. As part of an initial investigation exploring foreign market entry, 10 countries were selected from each of four global regions. The cost associated with importing a standardized cargo of goods by sea transport in these countries (in US$ per container) is stored in **ForeignMarket2**. (Data extracted from **doingbusiness.org/data**.)

a. At the 0.05 level of significance, is there evidence of a difference in the mean cost of importing across the four global regions?

b. If appropriate, determine which global regions differ in mean cost of importing.

c. At the 0.05 level of significance, is there evidence of a difference in the variation in cost of importing among the four global regions?

d. Which global region(s) should you consider for foreign market entry? Explain.

13.20 A hospital conducted a study of the waiting time in its emergency room. The hospital has a main campus and three satellite locations. Management had a business objective of reducing waiting time for emergency room cases that did not require immediate attention. To study this, a random sample of 15 emergency room cases that did not require immediate attention at each location were selected on a particular day, and the waiting times (measured from check-in to when the patient was called into the clinic area) were collected and stored in **ERWaiting**.

a. At the 0.05 level of significance, is there evidence of a difference in the mean waiting times in the four locations?

b. If appropriate, determine which locations differ in mean waiting time.

c. At the 0.05 level of significance, is there evidence of a difference in the variation in waiting time among the four locations?

13.21 A manufacturer of pens has hired an advertising agency to develop an advertising campaign for the upcoming holiday season. To prepare for this project, the research director decides to initiate a study of the effect of advertising on product perception. An experiment is designed to compare five different advertisements. Advertisement A greatly undersells the pen's characteristics. Advertisement B slightly undersells the pen's characteristics. Advertisement C slightly oversells the pen's characteristics. Advertisement D greatly oversells the pen's characteristics. Advertisement E attempts to correctly state the pen's characteristics. A sample of 30 adult respondents, taken from a larger focus group, is randomly assigned to the five advertisements (so that there are 6 respondents to each advertisement). After reading the advertisement and developing a sense of "product expectation," all respondents unknowingly receive the same pen to evaluate. The respondents are permitted to test the pen and the plausibility of the advertising copy. The respondents are then asked to rate the pen from 1 to 7 (lowest to highest) on the product characteristic scales of appearance, durability, and writing performance. The *combined* scores of three ratings (appearance, durability, and writing performance) for the 30 respondents, stored in **Pen**, are as follows:

A	B	C	D	E
15	16	8	5	12
18	17	7	6	19
17	21	10	13	18
19	16	15	11	12
19	19	14	9	17
20	17	14	10	14

a. At the 0.05 level of significance, is there evidence of a difference in the mean rating of the pens following exposure to five advertisements?

b. If appropriate, determine which advertisements differ in mean ratings.

c. At the 0.05 level of significance, is there evidence of a difference in the variation in ratings among the five advertisements?

d. Which advertisement(s) should you use, and which advertisement(s) should you avoid? Explain.

13.22 *QSR* magazine reports on the largest quick serve and fast casual restaurants in the United States. Do the various market segments (burger, chicken, sandwich, and pizza) differ in their mean sales per unit? The file FastFoodChain contains the mean sales in a recent year. (Data extracted **bit.ly/1mw56xA.**)

a. At the 0.05 level of significance, is there evidence of a difference in the mean U.S. mean sales per unit ($ thousands) among the food segments?

b. At the 0.05 level of significance, is there a difference in the variation in U.S. average sales per unit ($ thousands) among the food segments?

c. What effect does your result in (b) have on the validity of the results in (a)?

13.23 Researchers conducted a study to determine whether graduates with an academic background in the discipline of leadership studies were better equipped with essential soft skills required to be successful in contemporary organizations than students with no leadership education and/or students with a certificate in leadership. The Teams Skills Questionnaire was used to capture students' self-reported ratings of their soft skills. The researchers found the following:

Source	Degrees of Freedom	Sum of Squares	Mean Squares	F
Among groups	2	1.879		
Within groups	297	31.865		
Total	299	33.744		

Group	N	Mean
No coursework in leadership	109	3.290
Certificate in leadership	90	3.362
Degree in leadership	102	3.471

Source: Data Extracted from C. Brungardt, "The Intersection Between Soft Skill Development and Leadership Education," *Journal of Leadership Education*, 10 (Winter 2011): 1–22.

a. Complete the ANOVA summary table.

b. At the 0.05 level of significance, is there evidence of a difference in the mean soft-skill score reported by different groups?

c. If the results in (b) indicate that it is appropriate, use the Tukey-Kramer procedure to determine which groups differ in mean soft-skill score. Discuss your findings.

13.24 A pet food company has a business objective of expanding its product line beyond its current kidney- and shrimp-based cat foods. The company developed two new products, one based on chicken liver and the other based on salmon. The company conducted an experiment to compare the two new products with its two existing ones, as well as a generic beef-based product sold at a supermarket chain.

For the experiment, a sample of 50 cats from the population at a local animal shelter was selected. Ten cats were randomly assigned to each of the five products being tested. Each of the cats was then presented with 3 ounces of the selected food in a dish at feeding time. The researchers defined the variable to be measured as the number of ounces of food that the cat consumed within a 10-minute time interval that began when the filled dish was presented. The results for this experiment are summarized in the table at top right and stored in CatFood .

a. At the 0.05 level of significance, is there evidence of a difference in the mean amount of food eaten among the various products?

b. If appropriate, determine which products appear to differ significantly in the mean amount of food eaten.

c. At the 0.05 level of significance, is there evidence of a difference in the variation in the amount of food eaten among the various products?

d. What should the pet food company conclude? Fully describe the pet food company's options with respect to the products.

Kidney	Shrimp	Chicken Liver	Salmon	Beef
2.37	2.26	2.29	1.79	2.09
2.62	2.69	2.23	2.33	1.87
2.31	2.25	2.41	1.96	1.67
2.47	2.45	2.68	2.05	1.64
2.59	2.34	2.25	2.26	2.16
2.62	2.37	2.17	2.24	1.75
2.34	2.22	2.37	1.96	1.18
2.47	2.56	2.26	1.58	1.92
2.45	2.36	2.45	2.18	1.32
2.32	2.59	2.57	1.93	1.94

13.25 A sporting goods manufacturing company wanted to compare the distance traveled by golf balls produced using four different designs. Ten balls were manufactured with each design and were brought to the local golf course for the club professional to test. The order in which the balls were hit with the same club from the first tee was randomized so that the pro did not know which type of ball was being hit. All 40 balls were hit in a short period of time, during which the environmental conditions were essentially the same. The results (distance traveled in yards) for the four designs are stored in Golfball and shown in the following table:

Design 1	Design 2	Design 3	Design 4
206.32	217.08	226.77	230.55
207.94	221.43	224.79	227.95
206.19	218.04	229.75	231.84
204.45	224.13	228.51	224.87
209.65	211.82	221.44	229.49
203.81	213.90	223.85	231.10
206.75	221.28	223.97	221.53
205.68	229.43	234.30	235.45
204.49	213.54	219.50	228.35
210.86	214.51	233.00	225.09

a. At the 0.05 level of significance, is there evidence of a difference in the mean distances traveled by the golf balls with different designs?

b. If the results in (a) indicate that it is appropriate to do so, use the Tukey-Kramer procedure to determine which designs differ in mean distances.

c. What assumptions are necessary in (a)?

d. At the 0.05 level of significance, is there evidence of a difference in the variation of the distances traveled by the golf balls with different designs?

e. What golf ball design should the manufacturing manager choose? Explain.

Review

13.26 The American Society for Quality (ASQ) conducted a salary survey of all its members. ASQ members work in all areas of manufacturing and service-related institutions, with a common theme of an interest in quality. Two job titles are black belt and green belt. Descriptive statistics concerning salaries for these two job titles are given in the following table:

Job Title	Sample Size	Mean	Standard Deviation
Black belt	128	93,123	21,186
Green belt	39	73,045	21,272

Source: Data extracted from "QP Salary Survey," *Quality Progress*, December 2013, p. 17.

a. Using a 0.05 level of significance, is there a difference in the variability of salaries between black belts and green belts?

b. Based on the result of (a), which *t* test defined in Section 12.1 is appropriate for comparing mean salaries?

c. Using a 0.05 level of significance, is the mean salary of black belts greater than the mean salary of green belts?

13.27 Do male and female students study the same amount per week? In a recent year, 58 sophomore business students were surveyed at a large university that has more than 1,000 sophomore business students each year. The file **StudyTime** contains the gender and the number of hours spent studying in a typical week for the sampled students.

a. At the 0.05 level of significance, is there a difference in the variance of the study time for male students and female students?

b. Using the results of (a), which *t* test is appropriate for comparing the mean study time for male and female students?

c. At the 0.05 level of significance, conduct the test selected in (b).

d. Write a short summary of your findings.

13.28 Do males and females differ in the amount of time they talk on the phone and the number of text messages they send? A study reported that women spent a mean of 818 minutes per month talking as compared to 716 minutes per month for men. (Data extracted from "Women Talk and Text More," *USA Today*, February 1, 2011, p. 1A.) The sample sizes were not reported. Suppose that the sample sizes were 100 each for women and men and that the standard deviation for women was 125 minutes per month as compared to 100 minutes per month for men.

a. Using a 0.01 level of significance, is there evidence of a difference in the variances of the amount of time spent talking between women and men?

b. To test for a difference in the mean talking time of women and men, is it most appropriate to use the pooled-variance *t* test or the separate-variance *t* test? Use the most appropriate test to determine if there is a difference in the amount of time spent talking on the phone between women and men.

The article also reported that women sent a mean of 716 text messages per month compared to 555 per month for men.

Suppose that the standard deviation for women was 150 text messages per month compared to 125 text messages per month for men.

c. Using a 0.01 level of significance, is there evidence of a difference in the variances of the number of text messages sent per month by women and men?

d. Based on the results of (c), use the most appropriate test to determine, at the 0.01 level of significance, whether there is evidence of a difference in the mean number of text messages sent per month by women and men.

13.29 The file **Restaurants** contains the ratings for food, décor, service, and the price per person for a sample of 50 restaurants located in a city and 50 restaurants located in a suburb. Completely analyze the differences between city and suburban restaurants for the variables food rating, décor rating, service rating, and cost per person, using $\alpha = 0.05$.

Source: Data extracted from *Zagat Survey 2013 New York City Restaurants* and *Zagat Survey 2012–2013 Long Island Restaurants*.

13.30 A computer information systems professor is interested in studying the amount of time it takes students enrolled in the Introduction to Computers course to write a program in VB.NET. The professor hires you to analyze the following results (in minutes), stored in **VB**, from a random sample of nine students:

$$10 \quad 13 \quad 9 \quad 15 \quad 12 \quad 13 \quad 11 \quad 13 \quad 12$$

a. At the 0.05 level of significance, is there evidence that the population mean time is greater than 10 minutes? What will you tell the professor?

b. Suppose that the professor, when checking her results, realizes that the fourth student needed 51 minutes rather than the recorded 15 minutes to write the VB.NET program. At the 0.05 level of significance, reanalyze the question posed in (a), using the revised data. What will you tell the professor now?

c. The professor is perplexed by these paradoxical results and requests an explanation from you regarding the justification for the difference in your findings in (a) and (b). Discuss.

d. A few days later, the professor calls to tell you that the dilemma is completely resolved. The original number 15 (the fourth data value) was correct, and therefore your findings in (a) are being used in the article she is writing for a computer journal. Now she wants to hire you to compare the results from that group of Introduction to Computers students against those from a sample of 11 computer majors in order to determine whether there is evidence that computer majors can write a VB.NET program in less time than introductory students. For the computer majors, the sample mean is 8.5 minutes, and the sample standard deviation is 2.0 minutes. At the 0.05 level of significance, completely analyze these data. What will you tell the professor?

e. A few days later, the professor calls again to tell you that a reviewer of her article wants her to include the *p*-value for the "correct" result in (a). In addition, the professor inquires about an unequal-variances problem, which the reviewer wants her to discuss in her article. In your own words, discuss the concept of *p*-value and also describe the unequal-variances problem. Then, determine the *p*-value in (a) and discuss whether the unequal-variances problem had any meaning in the professor's study.

13.31 Do Pinterest shoppers and Facebook shoppers differ with respect to spending behavior? A study of browser-based shopping sessions reported that Pinterest shoppers spent a mean of $153 per order and Facebook shoppers spent a mean of $85 per order. (Data extracted from **bit.ly/14wG1YI**.) Suppose that the study consisted of 500 Pinterest shoppers and 500 Facebook shoppers, and the standard deviation of the order value was $150 for Pinterest shoppers and $80 for Facebook shoppers. Assume a level of significance of 0.05.

a. Is there evidence of a difference in the variances of the order values between Pinterest shoppers and Facebook shoppers?

b. Is there evidence of a difference in the mean order value between Pinterest shoppers and Facebook shoppers?

c. Construct a 95% confidence interval estimate for the difference in mean order value between Pinterest shoppers and Facebook shoppers.

13.32 The lengths of life (in hours) of a sample of 40 20-watt compact fluorescent light bulbs produced by manufacturer A and a sample of 40 20-watt compact fluorescent light bulbs produced by manufacturer B are stored in Bulbs . Completely analyze the differences between the lengths of life of the compact fluorescent light bulbs produced by the two manufacturers. (Use $\alpha = 0.05$.)

13.33 A hotel manager looks to enhance the initial impressions that hotel guests have when they check in. Contributing to initial impressions is the time it takes to deliver a guest's luggage to the room after check-in. A random sample of 20 deliveries on a particular day were selected in Wing A of the hotel, and a random sample of 20 deliveries were selected in Wing B. The results are stored in Luggage . Analyze the data and determine whether there is a difference between the mean delivery times in the two wings of the hotel. (Use $\alpha = 0.05$.)

13.34 The owner of a restaurant that serves Continental-style entrées has the business objective of learning more about the patterns of patron demand during the Friday-to-Sunday weekend time period. She decided to study the demand for dessert during this time period. In addition to studying whether a dessert was ordered, she will study the gender of the individual and whether a beef entrée was ordered. Data were collected from 630 customers and organized in the following contingency tables:

	GENDER		
DESSERT ORDERED	**Male**	**Female**	**Total**
Yes	50	96	146
No	250	234	484
Total	300	330	630

	BEEF ENTRÉE		
DESSERT ORDERED	**Yes**	**No**	**Total**
Yes	74	68	142
No	123	365	488
Total	197	433	630

a. At the 0.05 level of significance, is there evidence of a difference between males and females in the proportion who order dessert?

b. At the 0.05 level of significance, is there evidence of a difference in the proportion who order dessert based on whether a beef entrée has been ordered?

13.35 The manufacturer of Boston and Vermont asphalt shingles knows that product weight is a major factor in the customer's perception of quality. Moreover, the weight represents the amount of raw materials being used and is therefore very important to the company from a cost standpoint. The last stage of the assembly line packages the shingles before they are placed on wooden pallets. Once a pallet is full (a pallet for most brands holds 16 squares of shingles), it is weighed, and the measurement is recorded. The file Pallet contains the weight (in pounds) from a sample of 368 pallets of Boston shingles and 330 pallets of Vermont shingles. Completely analyze the differences in the weights of the Boston and Vermont shingles, using $\alpha = 0.05$.

13.36 The manufacturer of Boston and Vermont asphalt shingles provides its customers with a 20-year warranty on most of its products. To determine whether a shingle will last as long as the warranty period, the manufacturer conducts accelerated-life testing. Accelerated-life testing exposes the shingle to the stresses it would be subject to in a lifetime of normal use in a laboratory setting via an experiment that takes only a few minutes to conduct. In this test, a shingle is repeatedly scraped with a brush for a short period of time, and the shingle granules removed by the brushing are weighed (in grams). Shingles that experience low amounts of granule loss are expected to last longer in normal use than shingles that experience high amounts of granule loss. In this situation, a shingle should experience no more than 0.8 grams of granule loss if it is expected to last the length of the warranty period. The file Granule contains a sample of 170 measurements made on the company's Boston shingles and 140 measurements made on Vermont shingles. Completely analyze the differences in the granule loss of the Boston and Vermont shingles, using $\alpha = 0.05$.

13.37 There are a very large number of mutual funds from which an investor can choose. Each mutual fund has its own mix of different types of investments. The data in BestFunds1 present the one-year return for the 10 best short-term bond funds and the 10 best long-term bond funds, according to the *U.S. News & World Report*. (Data extracted from **money.usnews.com/mutual-funds**.) Analyze the data and determine whether any differences exist between short-term and long-term bond funds. (Use the 0.05 level of significance.)

13.38 An investor can choose from a very large number of mutual funds. Each mutual fund has its own mix of different types of investments. The data in BestFunds2 present the one-year return for the 10 best short-term bond, long-term bond, and world bond funds, according to the *U.S. News & World Report*. (Data extracted from **money.usnews.com/mutual-funds**.) Analyze the data and determine whether any differences exist in the one-year return between short-term, long-term, and world bond funds. (Use the 0.05 level of significance.)

13.39 An investor can choose from a very large number of mutual funds. Each mutual fund has its own mix of different types of investments. The data in BestFunds3 present the one-year return for the 10 best small cap growth, mid-cap growth, and large cap growth funds, according to the *U.S. News & World Report*. (Data extracted from **money.usnews.com/mutual-funds**.) Analyze the data and determine whether any differences exist in the one-year return between small cap growth, mid-cap growth, and large cap growth funds. (Use the 0.05 level of significance.)

REPORT WRITING EXERCISE

13.40 Referring to the results of Problems 13.35 and 13.36 concerning the weight and granule loss of Boston and Vermont shingles, write a report that summarizes your conclusions.

CASES FOR CHAPTER 13

Managing Ashland MultiComm Services

Part 1   AMS communicates with customers who subscribe to cable television services through a special secured email system that sends messages about service changes, new features, and billing information to in-home digital set-top boxes for later display. To enhance customer service, the operations department established the business objective of reducing the amount of time to fully update each subscriber's set of messages. The department selected two candidate messaging systems and conducted an experiment in which 30 randomly chosen cable subscribers were assigned one of the two systems (15 assigned to each system). Update times were measured, and the results are organized in Table AMS13.1 and stored in AMS13-1 .

1. Analyze the data in Table AMS13.1 and write a report to the computer operations department that indicates your findings. Include an appendix in which you discuss the reason you selected a particular statistical test to compare the two independent groups of callers.

2. Suppose that instead of the research design described in the case, there were only 15 subscribers sampled, and the update process for each subscriber email was measured for each of the two messaging systems. Suppose that the results were organized in Table AMS13.1—making each row in the table a pair of values for an individual subscriber. Using these suppositions, reanalyze the Table AMS13.1 data and write a report for presentation to the team that indicates your findings.

Part 2   The computer operations department had a business objective of reducing the amount of time to fully update each subscriber's set of messages in a special secured email system. An experiment was conducted in which 24 subscribers were selected and three different messaging systems were used. Eight subscribers were assigned to each system, and the update times were measured. The results, stored in AMS13-2 , are presented in Table AMS13.2.

TABLE AMS13.1

Update Times (in seconds) for Two Different Email Interfaces

Email Interface 1	Email Interface 2
4.13	3.71
3.75	3.89
3.93	4.22
3.74	4.57
3.36	4.24
3.85	3.90
3.26	4.09
3.73	4.05
4.06	4.07
3.33	3.80
3.96	4.36
3.57	4.38
3.13	3.49
3.68	3.57
3.63	4.74

TABLE AMS13.2

Update Times (in seconds) for Three Different Systems

System 1	System 2	System 3
38.8	41.8	32.9
42.1	36.4	36.1
45.2	39.1	39.2
34.8	28.7	29.3
48.3	36.4	41.9
37.8	36.1	31.7
41.1	35.8	35.2
43.6	33.7	38.1

3. Analyze the data in Table AMS13.2 and write a report to the computer operations department that indicates your findings. Include an appendix in which you discuss the reason you selected a particular statistical test to compare the three email interfaces.

Digital Case

Apply your knowledge about hypothesis testing in this Digital Case, which continues the cereal-fill packaging dispute Digital Case from Chapters 8 and 11.

Part 1   Even after the recent public experiment about cereal box weights, Consumers Concerned About Cereal Cheaters (CCACC) remains convinced that Oxford Cereals has misled the public. The group has created and circulated **MoreCheating.pdf**, a document in which it claims that cereal boxes produced at Plant Number 2 in Springville weigh less than the claimed mean of 368 grams. Review this document and then answer the following questions:

1. Do the CCACC's results prove that there is a statistically significant difference in the mean weights of cereal boxes produced at Plant Numbers 1 and 2?

2. Perform the appropriate analysis to test the CCACC's hypothesis. What conclusions can you reach based on the data?

Part 2   *Apply your knowledge about ANOVA in this part, which continues the cereal-fill packaging dispute Digital Case.*

After reviewing the CCACC's **MoreCheating.pdf** document, Oxford Cereals has released **SecondAnalysis.pdf**, a press kit that Oxford Cereals has assembled to refute the claim that it is guilty of using selective data. Review the Oxford Cereals press kit and then answer the following questions.

3. Does Oxford Cereals have a legitimate argument? Why or why not?

4. Assuming that the samples Oxford Cereals has posted were randomly selected, perform the appropriate analysis to resolve the ongoing weight dispute.

5. What conclusions can you reach from your results? If you were called as an expert witness, would you support the claims of the CCACC or the claims of Oxford Cereals? Explain.

Sure Value Convenience Stores

Part 1   You continue to work in the corporate office for a nationwide convenience store franchise that operates nearly 10,000 stores. The per-store daily customer count (i.e., the mean number of customers in a store in one day) has been steady, at 900, for some time. To increase the customer count, the chain is considering cutting prices for coffee beverages. The small size will now be either $0.59 or $0.79 instead of $0.99. Even with this reduction in price, the chain will have a 40% gross margin on coffee.

The question to be determined is how much to cut prices to increase the daily customer count without reducing the gross margin on coffee sales too much. The chain decides to carry out an experiment in a sample of 30 stores where customer counts have been running almost exactly at the national average of 900. In 15 of the stores, the price of a small coffee will now be $0.59 instead of $0.99, and in 15 other stores, the price of a small coffee will now be $0.79. After four weeks, the 15 stores that priced the small coffee at $0.59 had a mean daily customer count of 964 and a standard deviation of 88, and the 15 stores that priced the small coffee at $0.79 had a mean daily customer count of 941 and a standard deviation of 76. Analyze these data (using the 0.05 level of significance) and answer the following questions.

1. Does reducing the price of a small coffee to either $0.59 or $0.79 increase the mean per-store daily customer count?

2. If reducing the price of a small coffee to either $0.59 or $0.79 increases the mean per-store daily customer count, is there any difference in the mean per-store daily customer count between stores in which a small coffee was priced at $0.59 and stores in which a small coffee was priced at $0.79?

3. What price do you recommend for a small coffee?

Part 2   As you continue to work in the corporate office for a nationwide convenience store franchise that operates nearly 10,000 stores, you decide to carry out an experiment in a sample of 24 stores where customer counts have been running almost exactly at the national average of 900. In 6 of the stores, the price of a small coffee will now be $0.59, in 6 stores the price of a small coffee will now be $0.69, in 6 stores, the price of a small coffee will now be $0.79, and in 6 stores, the price of a small coffee will now be $0.89. After four weeks of selling the coffee at the new price, the daily customer counts in the stores were recorded and stored in **CoffeeSales**.

4. Analyze the data and determine whether there is evidence of a difference in the daily customer count, based on the price of a small coffee.

5. If appropriate, determine which mean prices differ in daily customer counts.

6. What price do you recommend for a small coffee?

CardioGood Fitness

Return to the CardioGood Fitness case first presented on Chapter 1. Using the data stored in CardioGood Fitness :

1. Determine whether differences exist between males and females in their age in years, education in years, annual household income ($), mean number of times the customer plans to use the treadmill each week, and mean number of miles the customer expects to walk or run each week.

2. Determine whether differences exist between customers based on the product purchased (TM195, TM498, TM798) in their age in years, education in years, annual household income ($), mean number of times the customer plans to use the treadmill each week, and mean number of miles the customer expects to walk or run each week.

3. Write a report to be presented to the management of CardioGood Fitness detailing your findings.

More Descriptive Choices Follow-Up

Follow up the Using Statistics scenario "More Descriptive Choices, Revisited" on Chapter 4.

1. Determine whether there is a difference in the 3-year return percentage, 5-year return percentages, and 10-year return percentages of the growth and value funds (stored in Retirement Funds).

2. Determine whether there is a difference between the small, mid-cap, and large market cap funds in the three-year return percentages, five-year return percentages, and ten-year return percentages (stored in Retirement Funds).

Clear Mountain State Student Surveys

1. The Student News Service at Clear Mountain State University (CMSU) has decided to gather data about the undergraduate students that attend CMSU. It creates and distributes a survey of 14 questions and receives responses from 62 undergraduates (stored in UndergradSurvey).
   a. At the 0.05 level of significance, is there evidence of a difference between males and females in grade point average, expected starting salary, number of social networking sites registered for, age, spending on textbooks and supplies, text messages sent in a week, and the wealth needed to feel rich?
   b. At the 0.05 level of significance, is there evidence of a difference between students who plan to go to graduate school and those who do not plan to go to graduate school in grade point average, expected starting salary, number of social networking sites registered for, age, spending on textbooks and supplies, text messages sent in a week, and the wealth needed to feel rich?
   c. At the 0.05 level of significance, is there evidence of a difference based on academic major in expected starting salary, number of social networking sites registered for, age, spending on textbooks and supplies, text messages sent in a week, and the wealth needed to feel rich?
   d. At the 0.05 level of significance, is there evidence of a difference based on graduate school intention in grade point average, expected starting salary, number of social networking sites registered for, age, spending on textbooks and supplies, text messages sent in a week, and the wealth needed to feel rich?

2. The dean of students at CMSU has learned about the undergraduate survey and has decided to undertake a similar survey for graduate students at Clear Mountain State. She creates and distributes a survey of 14 questions and receives responses from 44 graduate students (stored in GradSurvey). For these data, at the 0.05 level of significance.
   a. Is there evidence of a difference between males and females in age, undergraduate grade point average, graduate grade point average, expected salary upon graduation, spending on textbooks and supplies, text messages sent in a week, and the wealth needed to feel rich?
   b. Is there evidence of a difference based on undergraduate major in age, undergraduate grade point average, graduate grade point average, expected salary upon graduation, spending on textbooks and supplies, text messages sent in a week, and the wealth needed to feel rich?
   c. Is there evidence of a difference based on graduate major in age, undergraduate grade point average, graduate grade point average, expected salary upon graduation, spending on textbooks and supplies, text messages sent in a week, and the wealth needed to feel rich?
   d. Is there evidence of a difference based on employment status in age, undergraduate grade point average, graduate grade point average, expected salary upon graduation, spending on textbooks and supplies, text messages sent in a week, and the wealth needed to feel rich?

CHAPTER 13 CASIO CALCULATOR GUIDE

CALCULATOR LESSON 15A

CFX-9850GB CALCULATOR

EXAMPLE: The Perfect Parachute Company

TABLE 13.7

Summary of the Results of the Four Suppliers

Lesson 15A—One-Way ANOVA

We will use the scenario "The Perfect Parachute Company" to demonstrate how to perform one-way ANOVA on the calculator.

A research was conducted to determine if any significant differences exist in the strength of parachutes woven from synthetic fibers from the four suppliers. Five parachutes were woven for each group—Supplier 1, Supplier 2, Supplier 3, and Supplier 4. The amount of force required to tear the parachute is measured on a tensile-strength scale on which the larger the value, the stronger the parachute. The data are shown below:

Supplier 1	Supplier 2	Supplier 3	Supplier 4
18.5	26.3	20.6	25.4
24.0	25.3	25.2	19.9
17.2	24.0	20.8	22.6
19.9	21.2	24.7	17.5
18.0	24.5	22.9	20.4

Solution: First enter data into **List 1** (corresponding to Supplier 1), **List 2** (corresponding to Supplier 2), **List 3** (corresponding to Supplier 3) and **List 4** (corresponding to Supplier 4).

Now, from the **Main Menu** select the following:

STAT   TEST (F3)   ANOV (F5).   Then enter the following items:

ANOVA
How many : 4 (press **F3**)
List 1   : List 1 (F1)
List 2   : List 2 (F2)
List 3   : List 3 (F3)
List 4   : List 4 (F4)
Execute

Now press **EXE** or **F1** (Calc).

The calculator will show the results:

ANOVA
F	=3.4616
p	=0.041365
xpσn-1	=2.4686
Fdf	=3
SS	=63.285
MS	=21.095
Edf	=16
SSe	=97.504
MSe	=6.094

Since the p-value < 0.05, the conclusion is to reject the null hypothesis. In other words, there is a significant difference in the mean tensile strength among the products from the four suppliers. However, we do not know which suppliers differ. To answer this question, we perform the Tukey procedure using SPSS (see Figure 13.7).

CALCULATOR LESSON 15B

FX-9850GII CALCULATOR

EXAMPLE: The Perfect Parachute Company

Lesson 15B—One-Way ANOVA

We will use the scenario "The Perfect Parachute Company" to demonstrate how to perform one-way ANOVA on the calculator.

A research was conducted to determine if any significant differences exist in the strength of parachutes woven from synthetic fibers from the four suppliers. Five parachutes were woven for each group—Supplier 1, Supplier 2, Supplier 3, and Supplier 4. The amount of force required to tear the parachute is measured on a tensile-strength scale on which the larger the value, the stronger the parachute. The data are shown below:

TABLE 13.8

Summary of the Results of the Four Suppliers

Supplier 1	Supplier 2	Supplier 3	Supplier 4
18.5	26.3	20.6	25.4
24.0	25.3	25.2	19.9
17.2	24.0	20.8	22.6
19.9	21.2	24.7	17.5
18.0	24.5	22.9	20.4

Solution:

A. First enter data in **List 1** and **List 2** as follows:

Factor A	Dependent
List 1	**List 2**
1	18.5
1	24.0
1	17.2
1	19.9
1	18.0
2	26.3
2	25.3
2	24.0
2	21.2
2	24.5
3	20.6
3	25.2
3	20.8
3	24.7
3	22.9
4	25.4
4	19.9
4	22.6
4	17.5
4	20.4

B. Perform the ANOVA procedure

From the **Main Menu** select the following:

STAT   TEST(F3) ANOV(F5).   Then enter the following items:

ANOVA
How many   : 1 (press **F1**)
Factor A   : List 1 (F1)
Dependnt   : List 2 (F1)
Save Res   : None
Execute

Now press **EXE** or **F1**(Calc).
The calculator will show the results:

ANOVA

	df	SS	mS	F	p
A	3	63.285	21.095	3.4616	0.0413
ERR	16	97.504	6.094		

Since the p-value < 0.05, the conclusion is to reject the null hypothesis. In other words, there is a significant difference in the mean tensile strength among the products from the four suppliers. However, we do not know which suppliers differ. To answer this question, we perform the Tukey procedure using SPSS.

SPSS—VERSION 16—ANOVA

We will use the scenario "The Perfect Parachute Company" to demonstrate how to perform one-way ANOVA using SPSS.

A research was conducted to determine if any significant differences exist in the strength of parachutes woven from synthetic fibers from the four suppliers. Five parachutes were woven for each group—Supplier 1, Supplier 2, Supplier 3 and, Supplier 4. The amount of force required to tear the parachute is measured on a tensile-strength scale on which the larger the value, the stronger the parachute. The data are shown below:

FIGURE 13.9

Supplier 1	Supplier 2	Supplier 3	Supplier 4
18.5	26.3	20.6	25.4
24.0	25.3	25.2	19.9
17.2	24.0	20.8	22.6
19.9	21.2	24.7	17.5
18.0	24.5	22.9	20.4

Solution:

Performing a one-way ANOVA on SPSS—Version 16

Step 1: Open the SPSS Data Editor.

Click **Cancel** to cancel the SPSS opening window.

FIGURE 13.10

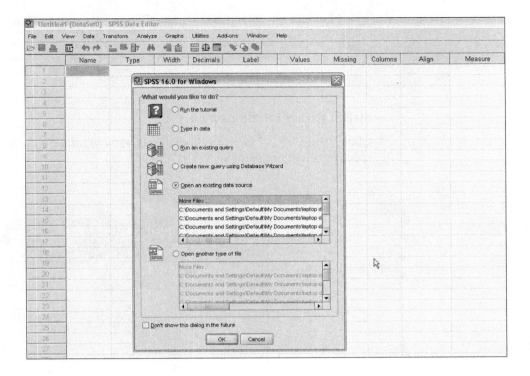

Step 2: Define the variables and give the variables a label.

Click **"Variable View"** (at the bottom of the window) to go to the variable view window to define the variables and fix the data at zero or one decimal places.

- Enter the first variable name, "suppliers," and then click **Values.** Enter "1" in the value box, enter **"Supplier 1"** in the Label box, and then click **Add.** Similarly, enter the data for the other three suppliers.

FIGURE 13.11

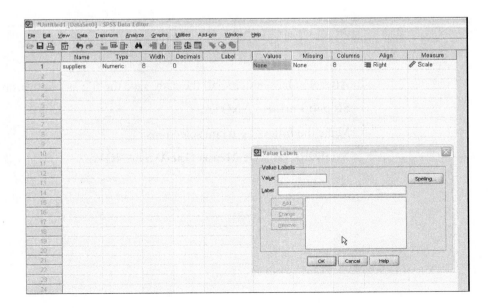

- Enter the second variable name, "Strength" and label it as "tensile-strength scale."

FIGURE 13.12

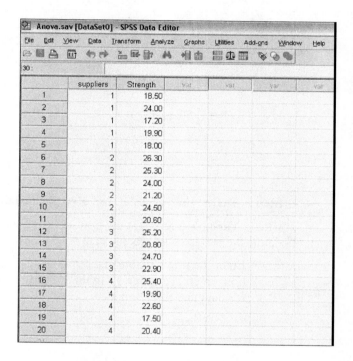

Step 3: Create a SPSS data file.

Click **"Data View"** to return to the Data View window. Now, enter the raw data into the respective column of variables.

FIGURE 13.13

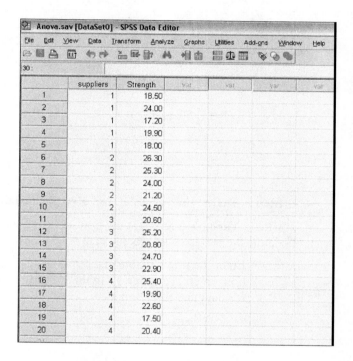

After you have entered all the data, save the file as "Anova.sav" (or any filename).

Step 4: Perform ANOVA.

Make the following menu selections:

Analyze Compare Means One-Way ANOVA

FIGURE 13.14

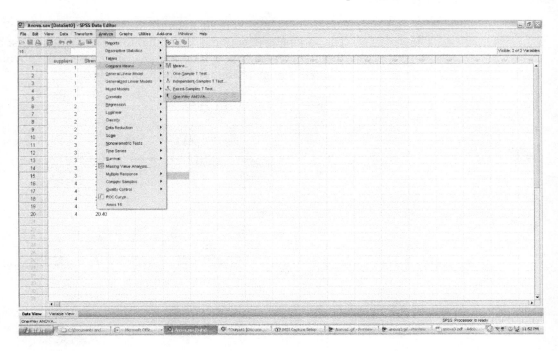

At this point, the **One-Way ANOVA** dialog box will appear. Make these entries in the **One-Way ANOVA** dialog box:

FIGURE 13.15

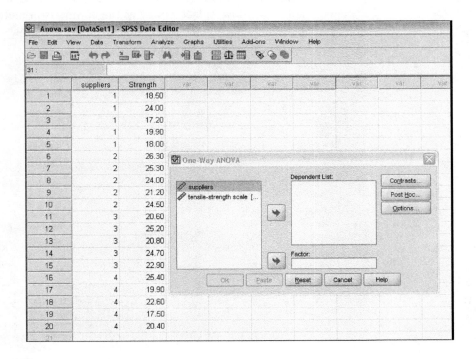

- Highlight on the **"tensile-strength scale"** variable and click on the top arrow key (◆). The variable will automatically fall into the **Dependent List** box.
- Highlight on the **"Suppliers"** variable and click on the bottom arrow key (◆). The variable will automatically fall into the **Factor** box.

FIGURE 13.16

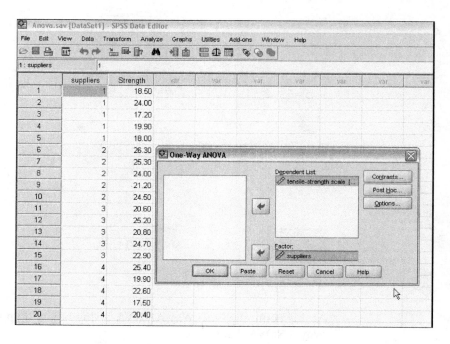

To Perform the Post-Hoc Comparison Procedure

- Click on the **Post-Hoc** button. In the "One-Way ANOVA: Post Hoc Multiple Comparisons" window, select **Tukey** as the comparison method. Then click on the **Continue** button to return to the "One-Way ANOVA" window.

FIGURE 13.17

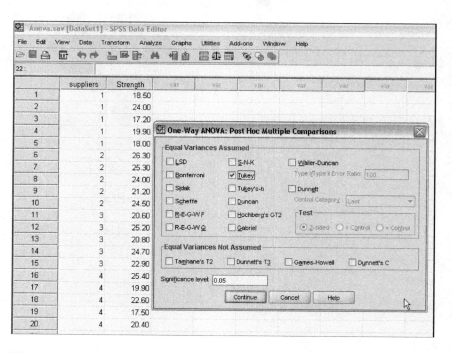

Test for Homogeneity of Variance

- Click on the **Options** button. In the "One-Way ANOVA: Options" window, select **Homogeneity of variance test** to test for the equality of variances. Then click on the **Continue** button to return to the "One-Way ANOVA" window.

FIGURE 13.18

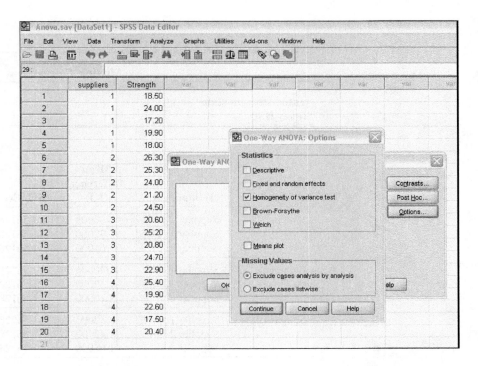

At this point, the **One-Way ANOVA** dialog box will appear. Click on the **OK** button to obtain the SPSS results.

Step 3: Go to **SPSS Viewer** to obtain your SPSS results.

SPSS output:

FIGURE 13.19

Oneway

Test of Homogeneity of Variances

tensile-strength scale

Levene Statistic	df1	df2	Sig.
.430	3	16	.734

ANOVA

tensile-strength scale

	Sum of Squares	df	Mean Square	F	Sig.
Between Groups	63.285	3	21.095	3.462	.041
Within Groups	97.504	16	6.094		
Total	160.789	19			

FIGURE 13.20

Post Hoc Tests

Multiple Comparisons

tensile-strength scale
Tukey HSD

(I) Suppliers	(J) Suppliers	Mean Difference (I-J)	Std. Error	Sig.	95% Confidence Interval	
					Lower Bound	Upper Bound
Supplier 1	Supplier 2	−4.74000*	1.56128	.036	−9.2069	−.2731
	Supplier 3	−3.32000	1.56128	.187	−7.7869	1.1469
	Supplier 4	−1.64000	1.56128	.723	−6.1069	2.8269
Supplier 2	Supplier 1	4.74000*	1.56128	.036	.2731	9.2069
	Supplier 3	1.42000	1.56128	.800	−3.0469	5.8869
	Supplier 4	3.10000	1.56128	.234	−1.3669	7.5669
Supplier 3	Supplier 1	3.32000	1.56128	.187	−1.1469	7.7869
	Supplier 2	−1.42000	1.56128	.800	−5.8869	3.0469
	Supplier 4	1.68000	1.56128	.708	−2.7869	6.1469
Supplier 4	Supplier 1	1.64000	1.56128	.723	−2.8269	6.1069
	Supplier 2	−3.10000	1.56128	.234	−7.5669	1.3669
	Supplier 3	−1.68000	1.56128	.708	−6.1469	2.7869

* The mean difference is significant at the 0.05 level.

Homogeneous Subsets

tensile-strength scale

Tukey HSD

Suppliers	N	Subset for alpha = 0.05	
		1	2
Supplier 1	5	19.5200	
Supplier 4	5	21.1600	21.1600
Supplier 3	5	22.8400	22.8400
Supplier 2	5		24.2600
Sig.		.187	.234

Means for groups in homogeneous subsets are displayed.

CHAPTER
14

Chi-Square Tests

CONTENTS

14.1 Chi-Square Test for the Difference Between Two Proportions

14.2 Chi-Square Test for Differences Among More Than Two Proportions

14.3 Chi-Square Test of Independence

USING STATISTICS: Avoiding Guesswork About Resort Guests, Revisited

CHAPTER 14 CASIO CALCULATOR GUIDE

OBJECTIVE

Learn when to use the chi-square test for contingency tables

Avoiding Guesswork About Resort Guests

You are the manager of T.C. Resort Properties, a collection of five upscale hotels located on two tropical islands. Guests who are satisfied with the quality of services during their stay are more likely to return on a future vacation and to recommend the hotel to friends and relatives. You have defined the business objective as improving the percentage of guests who choose to return to the hotels later. To assess the quality of services being provided by your hotels, your staff encourages guests to complete a satisfaction survey when they check out or via email after they check out.

You need to analyze the data from these surveys to determine the overall satisfaction with the services provided, the likelihood that the guests will return to the hotel, and the reasons some guests indicate that they will not return. For example, on one island, T.C. Resort Properties operates the Beachcomber and Windsurfer hotels. Is the perceived quality at the Beachcomber Hotel the same as at the Windsurfer Hotel? If there is a difference, how can you use this information to improve the overall quality of service at T.C. Resort Properties? Furthermore, if guests indicate that they are not planning to return, what are the most common reasons cited for this decision? Are the reasons cited unique to a certain hotel or common to all hotels operated by T.C. Resort Properties?

Maturos1812/Shutterstock

I n the preceding two chapters, you used hypothesis-testing procedures to analyze both numerical and categorical data. Chapter 11 presented some one-sample tests and Chapter 12 developed several two-sample tests and between discussed the one-way analysis of variance (ANOVA). This chapter extends hypothesis testing to analyze differences between population *proportions* based on two or more samples and to test the hypothesis of independence in the joint responses to two categorical variables.

14.1 Chi-Square Test for the Difference Between Two Proportions

In Section 12.3, you studied the Z test for the difference between two proportions. In this section, the differences between two proportions are examined from a different perspective. The hypothesis-testing procedure uses a test statistic, whose sampling distribution is approximated by a chi-square (χ^2) distribution. The results of this χ^2 test are equivalent to those of the Z test described in Section 12.3.

If you are interested in comparing the counts of categorical responses between two independent groups, you can develop a **two-way contingency table** to display the frequency of occurrence of items of interest and items not of interest for each group. (Contingency tables were first discussed in Section 2.1, and in Chapter 5, contingency tables were used to define and study probability.)

To illustrate a contingency table, return to the Using Statistics scenario concerning T.C. Resort Properties. On one of the islands, T.C. Resort Properties has two hotels (the Beachcomber and the Windsurfer). You collect data from customer satisfaction surveys and focus on the responses to the single question "Are you likely to choose this hotel again?" You organize the results of the survey and determine that 163 of 227 guests at the Beachcomber responded yes to "Are you likely to choose this hotel again?" and 154 of 262 guests at the Windsurfer responded yes to "Are you likely to choose this hotel again?" You want to analyze the results to determine whether, at the 0.05 level of significance, there is evidence of a significant difference in guest satisfaction (as measured by likelihood to return to the hotel) between the two hotels.

The contingency table displayed in Table 14.1, which has two rows and two columns, is called a **2 × 2 contingency table**. The cells in the table indicate the frequency for each row-and-column combination.

TABLE 14.1

Layout of a 2 × 2 Contingency Table

ROW VARIABLE	COLUMN VARIABLE		
	Group 1	**Group 2**	**Totals**
Items of interest	X_1	X_2	X
Items not of interest	$n_1 - X_1$	$n_2 - X_2$	$n - X$
Totals	n_1	n_2	n

where

$$X_1 = \text{number of items of interest in group 1}$$
$$X_2 = \text{number of items of interest in group 2}$$
$$n_1 - X_1 = \text{number of items that are not of interest in group 1}$$
$$n_2 - X_2 = \text{number of items that are not of interest in group 2}$$
$$X = X_1 + X_2, \text{the total number of items of interest}$$
$$n - X = (n_1 - X_1) + (n_2 - X_2), \text{the total number of items that are not of interest}$$

$$n_1 = \text{sample size in group 1}$$
$$n_2 = \text{sample size in group 2}$$
$$n = n_1 + n_2 = \text{total sample size}$$

Table 14.2 is the contingency table for the hotel guest satisfaction study. The contingency table has two rows, indicating whether the guests would return to the hotel or would not return to the hotel, and two columns, one for each hotel. The cells in the table indicate the frequency of each row-and-column combination. The row totals indicate the number of guests who would return to the hotel and the number of guests who would not return to the hotel. The column totals are the sample sizes for each hotel location.

TABLE 14.2

2 × 2 Contingency Table for the Hotel Guest Satisfaction Survey

| | HOTEL | | |
CHOOSE HOTEL AGAIN?	**Beachcomber**	**Windsurfer**	**Total**
Yes	163	154	317
No	64	108	172
Total	227	262	489

To test whether the population proportion of guests who would return to the Beachcomber, π_1, is equal to the population proportion of guests who would return to the Windsurfer, π_2, you can use the **chi-square (χ^2) test for the difference between two proportions**. To test the null hypothesis that there is no difference between the two population proportions:

$$H_0: \pi_1 = \pi_2$$

against the alternative that the two population proportions are not the same:

$$H_1: \pi_1 \neq \pi_2$$

you use the χ^2_{STAT} test statistic, shown in Equation (14.1) whose sampling distribution follows the chi-square distribution.

χ^2 TEST FOR THE DIFFERENCE BETWEEN TWO PROPORTIONS

The χ^2_{STAT} test statistic is equal to the squared difference between the observed and expected frequencies, divided by the expected frequency in each cell of the table, summed over all cells of the table.

$$\chi^2_{STAT} = \sum_{all\ cells} \frac{(f_o - f_e)^2}{f_e} \qquad (14.1)$$

where

f_o = **observed frequency** in a particular cell of a contingency table

f_e = **expected frequency** in a particular cell if the null hypothesis is true

The χ^2_{STAT} test statistic approximately follows a chi-square distribution with 1 degree of freedom.[1]

[1] In general, the degrees of freedom in a contingency table are equal to (number of rows −1) multiplied by (number of columns −1).

To compute the expected frequency, f_e, in any cell, you need to understand that if the null hypothesis is true, the proportion of items of interest in the two populations will be equal. In such situations, the sample proportions you compute from each of the two groups would differ from each other only by chance. Each would provide an estimate of the common population parameter, π. A statistic that combines these two separate estimates together into one overall estimate of the population parameter provides more information than either of the two separate estimates could provide by itself. This statistic, given by the symbol $\bar{p}$, represents the estimated overall proportion of items of interest for the two groups combined (i.e., the total number of items of interest divided by the total sample size). The complement of $\bar{p}$, $1 - \bar{p}$, represents the estimated overall proportion of items that are not of interest in the two groups. Using the notation presented in Table 14.1 on page 222, Equation (14.2) defines $\bar{p}$.

COMPUTING THE ESTIMATED OVERALL PROPORTION FOR TWO GROUPS

$$\bar{p} = \frac{X_1 + X_2}{n_1 + n_2} = \frac{X}{n} \tag{14.2}$$

To compute the expected frequency, f_e, for cells that involve items of interest (i.e., the cells in the first row in the contingency table), you multiply the sample size (or column total) for a group by $\bar{p}$. To compute the expected frequency, f_e, for cells that involve items that are not of interest (i.e., the cells in the second row in the contingency table), you multiply the sample size (or column total) for a group by $1 - \bar{p}$.

The sampling distribution of the χ^2_{STAT} test statistic shown in Equation (14.1) on page 223 approximately follows a **chi-square (χ^2) distribution** (see Table E.4) with 1 degree of freedom. Using a level of significance α, you reject the null hypothesis if the computed χ^2_{STAT} test statistic is greater than χ^2_α, the upper-tail critical value from the χ^2 distribution with 1 degree of freedom. Thus, the decision rule is

Reject H_0 if $\chi^2_{STAT} > \chi^2_\alpha$;

otherwise, do not reject H_0.

Figure 14.1 illustrates the decision rule.

FIGURE 14.1
Regions of rejection and nonrejection when using the chi-square test for the difference between two proportions, with level of significance α

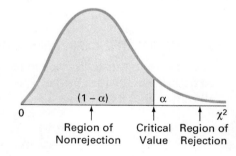

If the null hypothesis is true, the computed χ^2_{STAT} test statistic should be close to zero because the squared difference between what is actually observed in each cell, f_o, and what is theoretically expected, f_e, should be very small. If H_0 is false, then there are differences in the population proportions, and the computed χ^2_{STAT} test statistic is expected to be large. However, what is a large difference in a cell is relative. Because you are dividing by the expected frequencies, the same actual difference between f_o and f_e from a cell with a small number of expected frequencies contributes more to the χ^2_{STAT} test statistic than a cell with a large number of expected frequencies.

To illustrate the use of the chi-square test for the difference between two proportions, return to the Using Statistics scenario concerning T.C. Resort Properties on page 221 and the corresponding contingency table displayed in Table 14.2 on page 223. The null hypothesis

$(H_0: \pi_1 = \pi_2)$ states that there is no difference between the proportion of guests who are likely to choose either of these hotels again. To begin,

$$\bar{p} = \frac{X_1 + X_2}{n_1 + n_2} = \frac{163 + 154}{227 + 262} = \frac{317}{489} = 0.6483$$

$\bar{p}$ is the estimate of the common parameter π, the population proportion of guests who are likely to choose either of these hotels again if the null hypothesis is true. The estimated proportion of guests who are *not* likely to choose these hotels again is the complement of $\bar{p}$, $1 - 0.6483 = 0.3517$. Multiplying these two proportions by the sample size for the Beachcomber Hotel gives the number of guests expected to choose the Beachcomber again and the number not expected to choose this hotel again. In a similar manner, multiplying the two proportions by the Windsurfer Hotel's sample size yields the corresponding expected frequencies for that group.

EXAMPLE 14.1
 	
Computing the
Expected
Frequencies
	Compute the expected frequencies for each of the four cells of Table 14.2 on page 223.
	
	SOLUTION
	    Yes—Beachcomber: $\bar{p} = 0.6483$ and $n_1 = 227$, so $f_e = 147.16$
	    Yes—Windsurfer: $\bar{p} = 0.6483$ and $n_2 = 262$, so $f_e = 169.84$
	    No—Beachcomber: $1 - \bar{p} = 0.3517$ and $n_1 = 227$, so $f_e = 79.84$
	    No—Windsurfer: $1 - \bar{p} = 0.3517$ and $n_2 = 262$, so $f_e = 92.16$
	
	Table 14.3 presents these expected frequencies next to the corresponding observed frequencies.

TABLE 14.3

Comparing the
Observed (f_o)
and Expected (f_e)
Frequencies

	HOTEL				
	Beachcomber		**Windsurfer**		
CHOOSE HOTEL AGAIN?	**Observed**	**Expected**	**Observed**	**Expected**	**Total**
Yes	163	147.16	154	169.84	317
No	64	79.84	108	92.16	172
Total	227	227.00	262	262.00	489

How to Calculate the Expected Frequency by Hand

The expected frequency is a probability count that appears in the contingency table needed to calculate the chi-square test statistic (notation: χ^2_{STAT})

$$f_e = \frac{(row\ total\ of\ i\ cell)\ x\ (column\ total\ of\ i\ cell)}{Grand\ total}$$

Where f_e denotes the expected frequency.

Example: What are the expected cell frequencies for the table 14.2 on page 223?

The observed frequency table

	HOTEL		
CHOOSE HOTEL AGAIN?	**Beachcomber**	**Windsurfer**	**Row Total**
Yes	163	154	317
No	64	108	172
Column Total	227	262	489 = Grand total

The expected frequency table

CHOOSE HOTEL AGAIN?	HOTEL Beachcomber	Windsurfer	Row Total
Yes	$\dfrac{(317) \times (227)}{489}$ $= 147.155$	$\dfrac{(317) \times (262)}{489}$ $= 169.845$	317
No	$\dfrac{(172) \times (227)}{489}$ $= 79.845$	$\dfrac{(172) \times (262)}{489}$ $= 92.155$	172
Column Total	227	262	489 = Grand total

To test the null hypothesis that the population proportions are equal:

$$H_0: \pi_1 = \pi_2$$

against the alternative that the population proportions are not equal:

$$H_1: \pi_1 \neq \pi_2$$

you use the observed and expected frequencies from Table 14.3 to compute the χ^2_{STAT} test statistic given by Equation (14.1) on page 223. Table 14.4 presents these calculations.

TABLE 14.4

Computing the χ^2_{STAT} Test Statistic for the Hotel Guest Satisfaction Survey

f_o	f_e	$(f_o - f_e)$	$(f_o - f_e)^2$	$(f_o - f_e)^2/f_e$
163	147.16	15.84	250.91	1.71
154	169.84	−15.84	250.91	1.48
64	79.84	−15.84	250.91	3.14
108	92.16	15.84	250.91	2.72
				9.05

The chi-square (χ^2) distribution is a right-skewed distribution whose shape depends solely on the number of degrees of freedom. You find the critical value for the χ^2 test from Table E.4, a portion of which is presented in Table 14.5.

TABLE 14.5

Finding the Critical Value from the Chi-Square Distribution with 1 Degree of Freedom, Using the 0.05 Level of Significance

			Cumulative Probabilities				
	.005	.01	...	.95	.975	.99	.995
			Upper-Tail Area				
Degrees of Freedom	.995	.99	...	.05	.025	.01	.005
1			...	3.841	5.024	6.635	7.879
2	0.010	0.020	...	5.991	7.378	9.210	10.597
3	0.072	0.115	...	7.815	9.348	11.345	12.838
4	0.207	0.297	...	9.488	11.143	13.277	14.860
5	0.412	0.554	...	11.071	12.833	15.086	16.750

The values in Table 14.5 refer to selected upper-tail areas of the χ^2 distribution. A 2×2 contingency table has 1 degree of freedom because there are two rows and two columns. [The degrees of freedom are equal to the (number of rows -1)(number of columns -1).] Using $\alpha = 0.05$, with 1 degree of freedom, the critical value of χ^2 from Table 14.5 is 3.841. You reject H_0 if the computed χ^2_{STAT} test statistic is greater than 3.841 (see Figure 14.2). Because $\chi^2_{STAT} = 9.05 > 3.841$, you reject H_0. You conclude that the proportion of guests who would return to the Beachcomber is different from the proportion of guests who would return to the Windsurfer.

FIGURE 14.2

Regions of rejection and nonrejection when finding the χ^2 critical value with 1 degree of freedom, at the 0.05 level of significance

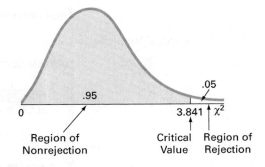

How to Find χ^2 Critical Value Using Calculator

Shown below.
Calculate the χ^2 critical value with 1 degree of freedom for $\alpha = 0.05$, using the Casio Calculator fx-9750GII and follow the following calculator steps:

From the **Main Menu** select:

STAT F5 (DIST) **F3** (CHI) **F3**(InvC) then enter the following items:

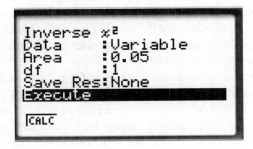

Now press **EXE** or **F1**(CALC)

The calculator will now show the results:

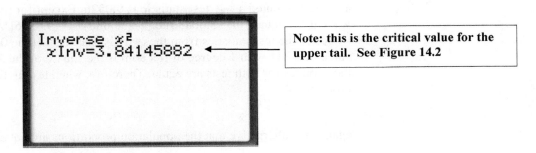

Note: this is the critical value for the upper tail. See Figure 14.2

Figure 14.3 shows the Calculator result for the Table 14.2 guest satisfaction contingency table on page 223.

FIGURE 14.3

Calculator result of
the chi-square test for
the two-hotel guest
satisfaction survey

Calculator result:

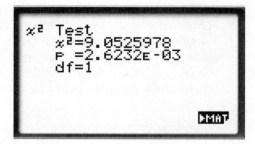

The expected frequencies are:

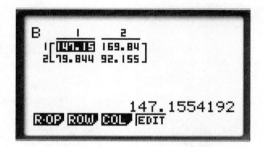

These results include the expected frequencies, χ^2_{STAT}, degrees of freedom, and p-value. The computed χ^2_{STAT} test statistic is 9.0526, which is greater than the critical value of 3.8415 (or the p-value $= 0.0026 < 0.05$), so you reject the null hypothesis that there is no difference in guest satisfaction between the two hotels. The p-value, equal to 0.0026, is the probability of observing sample proportions as different as or more different from the actual difference between the Beachcomber and Windsurfer ($0.718 - 0.588 = 0.13$) observed in the sample data, if the population proportions for the Beachcomber and Windsurfer hotels are equal. Thus, there is strong evidence to conclude that the two hotels are significantly different with respect to guest satisfaction, as measured by whether a guest is likely to return to the hotel again. From Table 14.3 on page 225 you can see that a greater proportion of guests are likely to return to the Beachcomber than to the Windsurfer.

For the χ^2 test to give accurate results for a 2×2 table, you must assume that each expected frequency is at least 5. If this assumption is not satisfied, you can use alternative procedures, such as Fisher's exact test (see references 1, 2, and 4).

In the hotel guest satisfaction survey, both the Z test based on the standardized normal distribution (see Section 12.3) and the χ^2 test based on the chi-square distribution lead to the same conclusion. You can explain this result by the interrelationship between the standardized normal distribution and a chi-square distribution with 1 degree of freedom. For such situations, the χ^2_{STAT} test statistic is the square of the Z_{STAT} test statistic.

For example, in the guest satisfaction study, the computed Z_{STAT} test statistic is $+3.0088$, and the computed χ^2_{STAT} test statistic is 9.0526. Except for rounding differences, this 9.0526 value is the square of $+3.0088$ [i.e., $(+3.0088)^2 \cong 9.0526$]. Also, if you compare the critical values of the test statistics from the two distributions, at the 0.05 level of significance, the χ^2 value of 3.841 with 1 degree of freedom is the square of the Z value of ± 1.96. Furthermore, the p-values for both tests are equal. Therefore, when testing the null hypothesis of equality of proportions:

$$H_0: \pi_1 = \pi_2$$

against the alternative that the population proportions are not equal:

$$H_1: \pi_1 \neq \pi_2$$

the Z test and the χ^2 test are equivalent. If you are interested in determining whether there is evidence of a *directional* difference, such as $\pi_1 > \pi_2$, you must use the Z test, with the entire rejection region located in one tail of the standardized normal distribution.

In Section 14.2, the χ^2 test is extended to make comparisons and evaluate differences between the proportions among more than two groups. However, you cannot use the Z test if there are more than two groups.

How to Run the Chi-Square Test with a FX-9750GII Calculator

To run the Chi-square test, follow the instruction below.

Press **MENU** and select **STAT TEST** (F3) **CHI** (F3)

Under option **CHI,** select **2WAY** (F2)

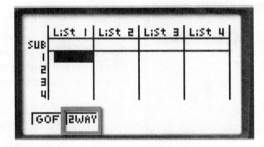

You will see the following on the screen:

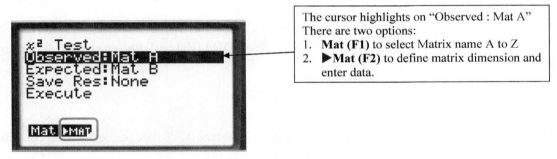

The cursor highlights on "Observed : Mat A"
There are two options:
1. **Mat (F1)** to select Matrix name A to Z
2. **▶Mat (F2)** to define matrix dimension and enter data.

To define dimension and enter data, select ▶Mat (F2) and you will see the following on the screen:

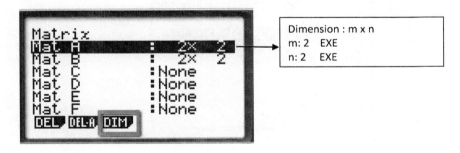

Dimension : m x n
m: 2   EXE
n: 2   EXE

Press DIM(F3) to define or change dimension.

After you have entered the dimension for **Mat A**, you will see the **2 x 2 matrix A** appears on the screen. Use this screen to input your data.

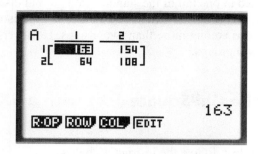

After you have entered your data (i.e. observed frequency) in Matrix A, now press **EXIT** two times until you see the following on the screen:

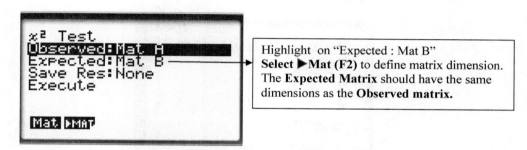

Highlight on "Expected : Mat B"
Select ▶Mat (F2) to define matrix dimension. The **Expected Matrix** should have the same dimensions as the **Observed matrix.**

To define dimension, select ▶Mat (F2) and you will see the following on the screen:

Matrix
Mat A : 2 x 2
Mat B : 2 x 2   **Press DIM (F3) to define or change dimension.** ──▶ Dimention: m x n
Mat C : None   m: 2   EXE
Mat D : None   n: 2   EXE
Mar E : None
Mat F : None

You will see a **2 by 2 matrix B**. You are not required to enter any values. The calculator will give you the expected values.

Now press **EXIT** two times until you see the following on the screen:

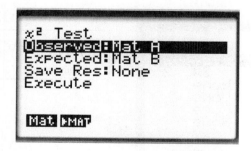

At this point, press either **EXE** or **F1** (CALC)

The calculator will now show the results:

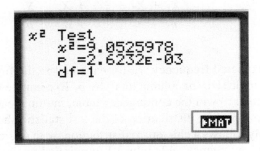

To obtain the expected value matrix select ►**MAT** (F6), and then highlight on **MAT B** and press **EXE**. You will see the expected value matrix displayed on the screen as follows:

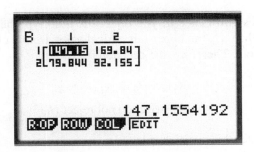

14.2 Chi-Square Test for Differences Among More Than Two Proportions

In this section, the χ^2 test is extended to compare more than two independent populations. The letter c is used to represent the number of independent populations under consideration. Thus, the contingency table now has two rows and c columns. To test the null hypothesis that there are no differences among the c population proportions:

$$H_0: \pi_1 = \pi_2 = \cdots = \pi_c$$

against the alternative that not all the c population proportions are equal:

$$H_1: \text{Not all } \pi_j \text{ are equal (where } j = 1, 2, \ldots, c)$$

you use Equation (14.1) on page 223:

$$\chi^2_{STAT} = \sum_{all\ cells} \frac{(f_o - f_e)^2}{f_e}$$

where

f_o = observed frequency in a particular cell of a $2 \times c$ contingency table

f_e = expected frequency in a particular cell if the null hypothesis is true

If the null hypothesis is true and the proportions are equal across all c populations, the c sample proportions should differ only by chance. In such a situation, a statistic that combines these c separate estimates into one overall estimate of the population proportion, π, provides more information than any one of the c separate estimates alone. To expand on Equation (14.2) on page 224, the statistic $\bar{p}$ in Equation (14.3) represents the estimated overall proportion for all c groups combined.

COMPUTING THE ESTIMATED OVERALL PROPORTION FOR c GROUPS

$$\bar{p} = \frac{X_1 + X_2 + \cdots + X_c}{n_1 + n_2 + \cdots + n_c} = \frac{X}{n} \tag{14.3}$$

To compute the expected frequency, f_e, for each cell in the first row in the contingency table, multiply each sample size (or column total) by $\bar{p}$. To compute the expected frequency, f_e, for each cell in the second row in the contingency table, multiply each sample size (or column total) by $(1 - \bar{p})$. The sampling distribution of the test statistic shown in Equation (14.1) on page 223 approximately follows a chi-square distribution, with degrees of freedom equal to the number of rows in the contingency table minus 1, multiplied by the number of columns in the table minus 1. For a **2 × c contingency table**, there are $c - 1$ degrees of freedom:

$$\text{Degrees of freedom} = (2 - 1)(c - 1) = c - 1$$

Using the level of significance α, you reject the null hypothesis if the computed χ^2_{STAT} test statistic is greater than χ^2_{α}, the upper-tail critical value from a chi-square distribution with $c - 1$ degrees of freedom. Therefore, the decision rule is

$$\text{Reject } H_0 \text{ if } \chi^2_{STAT} > \chi^2_{\alpha};$$

otherwise, do not reject H_0.

Figure 14.4 illustrates this decision rule.

FIGURE 14.4

Regions of rejection and nonrejection when testing for differences among c proportions using the χ^2 test

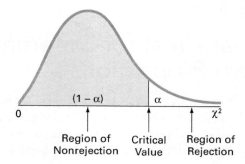

To illustrate the χ^2 test for equality of proportions when there are more than two groups, return to the Using Statistics scenario on page 221 concerning T.C. Resort Properties. Once again, you define the business objective as improving the quality of service, but this time, you are comparing three hotels located on a different island. Data are collected from customer satisfaction surveys at these three hotels. You organize the responses into the contingency table shown in Table 14.6.

TABLE 14.6

2 × 3 Contingency Table for Guest Satisfaction Survey

CHOOSE HOTEL AGAIN?	HOTEL			
	Golden Palm	**Palm Royale**	**Palm Princess**	**Total**
Yes	128	199	186	513
No	88	33	66	187
Total	216	232	252	700

Because the null hypothesis states that there are no differences among the three hotels in the proportion of guests who would likely return again, you use Equation (14.3) to calculate an estimate of π, the population proportion of guests who would likely return again:

$$\bar{p} = \frac{X_1 + X_2 + \cdots + X_c}{n_1 + n_2 + \cdots + n_c} = \frac{X}{n}$$

$$= \frac{(128 + 199 + 186)}{(216 + 232 + 252)} = \frac{513}{700}$$

$$= 0.733$$

The estimated overall proportion of guests who would *not* be likely to return again is the complement, $(1 - \bar{p})$, or 0.267. Multiplying these two proportions by the sample size for each hotel yields the expected number of guests who would and would not likely return.

EXAMPLE 14.2

Computing the Expected Frequencies

Compute the expected frequencies for each of the six cells in Table 14.6.

SOLUTION

Yes—Golden Palm: $\bar{p} = 0.733$ and $n_1 = 216$, so $f_e = 158.30$
Yes—Palm Royale: $\bar{p} = 0.733$ and $n_2 = 232$, so $f_e = 170.02$
Yes—Palm Princess: $\bar{p} = 0.733$ and $n_3 = 252$, so $f_e = 184.68$
No—Golden Palm: $1 - \bar{p} = 0.267$ and $n_1 = 216$, so $f_e = 57.70$
No—Palm Royale: $1 - \bar{p} = 0.267$ and $n_2 = 232$, so $f_e = 61.98$
No—Palm Princess: $1 - \bar{p} = 0.267$ and $n_3 = 252$, so $f_e = 67.32$

Table 14.7 presents these expected frequencies.

TABLE 14.7

Contingency Table of Expected Frequencies from a Guest Satisfaction Survey of Three Hotels

| | HOTEL | | | |
CHOOSE HOTEL AGAIN?	**Golden Palm**	**Palm Royale**	**Palm Princess**	**Total**
Yes	158.30	170.02	184.68	513
No	57.70	61.98	67.32	187
Total	216.00	232.00	252.00	700

To test the null hypothesis that the proportions are equal:

$$H_0: \pi_1 = \pi_2 = \pi_3$$

against the alternative that not all three proportions are equal:

$$H_1: \text{Not all } \pi_j \text{ are equal (where } j = 1, 2, 3)$$

you use the observed frequencies from Table 14.6 and the expected frequencies from Table 14.7 to compute the χ^2_{STAT} test statistic [given by Equation (14.1) on page 223]. Table 14.8 presents the calculations.

TABLE 14.8

Computing the χ^2_{STAT} Test Statistic for the Three-Hotel Guest Satisfaction Survey

f_o	f_e	$(f_o - f_e)$	$(f_o - f_e)^2$	$(f_o - f_e)^2/f_e$
128	158.30	−30.30	918.09	5.80
199	170.02	28.98	839.84	4.94
186	184.68	1.32	1.74	0.01
88	57.70	30.30	918.09	15.91
33	61.98	−28.98	839.84	13.55
66	67.32	−1.32	1.74	0.02
				40.23

You use Table E.4 to find the critical value of the χ^2 test statistic. In the guest satisfaction survey, because there are three hotels, there are $(2 - 1)(3 - 1) = 2$ degrees of freedom. Using $\alpha = 0.05$, the χ^2 critical value with 2 degrees of freedom is 5.991 (see Figure 14.5).

FIGURE 14.5

Regions of rejection and nonrejection when testing for differences in three proportions at the 0.05 level of significance, with 2 degrees of freedom

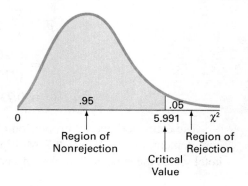

Because the computed χ^2_{STAT} test statistic is 40.23, which is greater than this critical value, you reject the null hypothesis. Figure 14.6 shows the calculator results for this problem. These results also report the p-value. Because the p-value is 0.0000, less than $\alpha = 0.05$, you reject the null hypothesis. Further, this p-value indicates that there is virtually no chance that there will be differences this large or larger among the three sample proportions, if the population proportions for the three hotels are equal. Thus, there is sufficient evidence to conclude that the hotel properties are different with respect to the proportion of guests who are likely to return.

FIGURE 14.6

Calculator result of the Chi-Square test for the three-hotel guest satisfaction survey

Calculator result:

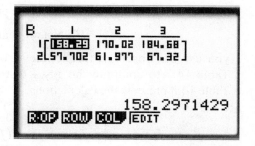

B: Expected frequencies

How to Find χ^2_{STAT} Test Statistic Using Calculator

Using the data Table 14.6.

To run the Chi-square test, follow the instruction below.
Press **MENU** and select **STAT TEST** (F3) **CHI** (F3)
Under option **CHI**, select **2WAY** (F2)

You will see the following on the screen:

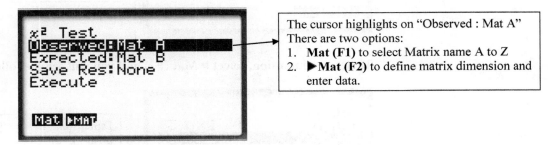

The cursor highlights on "Observed : Mat A"
There are two options:
1. **Mat (F1)** to select Matrix name A to Z
2. **▶Mat (F2)** to define matrix dimension and enter data.

To define dimension and enter data, select ▶Mat (F2) and you will see the following on the screen:

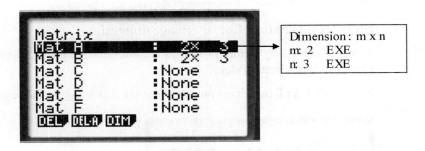

Dimension: m x n
m: 2   EXE
n: 3   EXE

Press DIM(F3) to define or change dimension.

After you have entered the dimension for **Mat A**, you will see the **2 × 3 matrix A** appears on the screen. Use this screen to input your data.

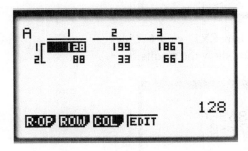

After you have entered your data in Matrix A, now press **EXIT** two times until you see the following on the screen:

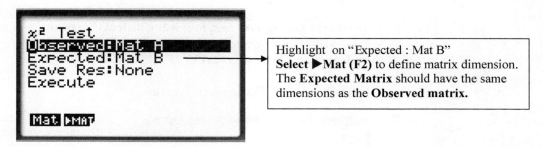

To define dimension, select ▶Mat (F2) and you will see the following on the screen:

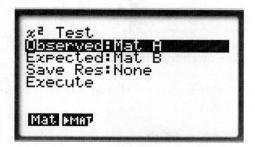

Press DIM (F3) to define or change dimension

You will see a **2 by 3 matrix B**. You are not required to enter any values. The calculator will give you the expected values.

Now press **EXIT** two times until you see the following on the screen:

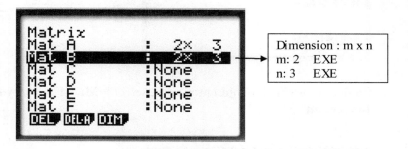

At this point, press either **EXE** or **F1** (Calc)
The calculator will now show the results:

To obtain the expected value matrix select ▶**MAT** (F6), and then highlight on **MAT B** and press **EXE**. You will see the expected value matrix displayed on the screen as follows:

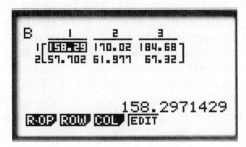

How to Find χ^2 Critical Value Using Calculator

Refer to Figure 14.5

Calculate the χ^2 critical value with 2 degree of freedom for $\alpha = 0.05$, using the Casio Calculator fx-9750GII and follow the following calculator steps:

From the **Main Menu** select:

STAT F5 (DIST) **F3** (CHI) **F3**(InvC) then enter the following items:

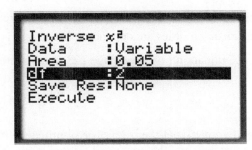

Now press **EXE** or **F1**(CALC)

The calculator will now show the results:

The critical value is used to define the rejection and non-rejection regions as shown in the diagram below.

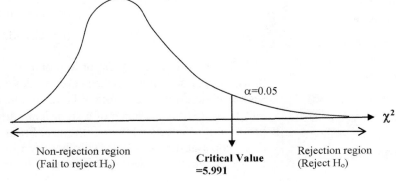

For the χ^2 test to give accurate results when dealing with $2 \times c$ contingency tables, all expected frequencies must be large. The definition of "large" has led to research among statisticians. Some statisticians (see reference 5) have found that the test gives accurate results as long as all expected frequencies are at least 0.5. Other statisticians, more conservative in their approach, believe that no more than 20% of the cells should contain expected frequencies less than 5, and no cells should have expected frequencies less than 1 (see reference 3). As a reasonable compromise between these points of view, to ensure the validity of the test, you should make sure that each expected frequency is at least 1. To do this, you may need to collapse two or more low-expected-frequency categories into one category in the contingency table before performing the test. If combining categories is undesirable, you can use one of the available alternative procedures (see references 1, 2, and 6).

14.3 Chi-Square Test of Independence

In Sections 14.1 and 14.2, you used the χ^2 test to evaluate potential differences among population proportions. For a contingency table that has r rows and c columns, you can generalize the χ^2 test as a *test of independence* for two categorical variables.

For a test of independence, the null and alternative hypotheses follow:

H_0: The two categorical variables are independent (i.e., there is no relationship between them).
H_1: The two categorical variables are dependent (i.e., there is a relationship between them).

Once again, you use Equation (14.1) on page 223 to compute the test statistic:

$$\chi^2_{STAT} = \sum_{all\ cells} \frac{(f_o - f_e)^2}{f_e}$$

You reject the null hypothesis at the α level of significance if the computed value of the χ^2_{STAT} test statistic is greater than χ^2_α, the upper-tail critical value from a chi-square distribution with $(r - 1)(c - 1)$ degrees of freedom (see Figure 14.7).

FIGURE 14.7

Regions of rejection and nonrejection when testing for independence in an $r \times c$ contingency table, using the χ^2 test

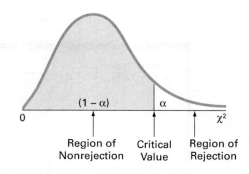

Thus, the decision rule is

Reject H_0 if $\chi^2_{STAT} > \chi^2_\alpha$;

otherwise, do not reject H_0.

Student Tip
Remember that *independence* means no relationship, so you do not reject the null hypothesis. *Dependence* means there is a relationship, so you reject the null hypothesis.

The **chi-square (χ^2) test of independence** is similar to the χ^2 test for equality of proportions. The test statistics and the decision rules are the same, but the null and alternative hypotheses and conclusions are different. For example, in the guest satisfaction survey of Sections 14.1 and 14.2, there is evidence of a significant difference between the hotels with respect to the proportion of guests who would return. From a different viewpoint, you could conclude that there is a significant relationship between the hotels and the likelihood that a guest would return. However, the two types of tests differ in how the samples are selected.

In a test for equality of proportions, there is one factor of interest, with two or more levels. These levels represent samples selected from independent populations. The categorical responses in each group or level are classified into two categories, such as *an item of interest* and *not an item of interest*. The objective is to make comparisons and evaluate differences between the proportions of the *items of interest* among the various levels. However, in a test for independence, there are two factors of interest, each of which has two or more levels. You select one sample and tally the joint responses to the two categorical variables into the cells of a contingency table.

To illustrate the χ^2 test for independence, suppose that, in the three-hotel guest satisfaction survey, respondents who stated that they were not likely to return also indicated the primary reason for their unwillingness to return. Table 14.9 presents the resulting 4×3 contingency table.

From Table 14.9, the primary reasons for not planning to return were price, 67 respondents; location, 60; room accommodation, 31; and some other reason, 29. In Table 14.6 on page 172, there were 88 guests at the Golden Palm, 33 guests at the Palm Royale, and 66 guests at the Palm Princess who were not planning to return.

TABLE 14.9

Contingency Table of Primary Reason for Not Returning and Hotel

PRIMARY REASON FOR NOT RETURNING	HOTEL			Total
	Golden Palm	**Palm Royale**	**Palm Princess**	
Price	23	7	37	67
Location	39	13	8	60
Room accommodation	13	5	13	31
Other	13	8	8	29
Total	88	33	66	187

The observed frequencies in the cells of the 4×3 contingency table represent the joint tallies of the sampled guests with respect to primary reason for not returning and the hotel where they stayed. The null and alternative hypotheses are

H_0: There is no relationship between the primary reason for not returning and the hotel.

H_1: There is a relationship between the primary reason for not returning and the hotel.

To test this null hypothesis of independence against the alternative that there is a relationship between the two categorical variables, you use Equation (14.1) on page 223 to compute the test statistic:

$$\chi^2_{STAT} = \sum_{all\ cells} \frac{(f_o - f_e)^2}{f_e}$$

where

f_o = observed frequency in a particular cell of the $r \times c$ contingency table

f_e = expected frequency in a particular cell if the null hypothesis of independence is true

To compute the expected frequency, f_e, in any cell, you use the multiplication rule for independent events discussed on Chapter 5 [see Equation (5.7)]. For example, under the null hypothesis of independence, the probability of responses expected in the upper-left-corner cell representing primary reason of price for the Golden Palm is the product of the two separate probabilities $P(\text{Price})$ and $P(\text{Golden Palm})$. Here, the proportion of reasons that are due to price, $P(\text{Price})$, is $67/187 = 0.3583$, and the proportion of all responses from the Golden Palm, $P(\text{Golden Palm})$, is $88/187 = 0.4706$. If the null hypothesis is true, then the primary reason for not returning and the hotel are independent:

$$P(\text{Price }and\text{ Golden Palm}) = P(\text{Price}) \times P(\text{Golden Palm})$$
$$= (0.3583) \times (0.4706)$$
$$= 0.1686$$

The expected frequency is the product of the overall sample size, n, and this probability, $187 \times 0.1686 = 31.53$. The f_e values for the remaining cells are shown in Table 14.10.

TABLE 14.10

Contingency Table of
Expected Frequencies
of Primary Reason for
Not Returning with
Hotel

PRIMARY REASON FOR NOT RETURNING	HOTEL			Total
	Golden Palm	**Palm Royale**	**Palm Princess**	
Price	31.53	11.82	23.65	67
Location	28.24	10.59	21.18	60
Room accommodation	14.59	5.47	10.94	31
Other	13.65	5.12	10.24	29
Total	88.00	33.00	66.00	187

You can also compute the expected frequency by taking the product of the row total and column total for a cell and dividing this product by the overall sample size, as Equation (14.4) shows.

COMPUTING THE EXPECTED FREQUENCY

The expected frequency in a cell is the product of its row total and column total, divided by the overall sample size.

$$f_e = \frac{\text{Row total} \times \text{Column total}}{n} \tag{14.4}$$

where

$$\text{Row total} = \text{sum of the frequencies in the row}$$
$$\text{Column total} = \text{sum of the frequencies in the column}$$
$$n = \text{overall sample size}$$

This alternate method results in simpler computations. For example, using Equation (14.4) for the upper-left-corner cell (price for the Golden Palm),

$$f_e = \frac{\text{Row total} \times \text{Column total}}{n} = \frac{(67)(88)}{187} = 31.53$$

and for the lower-right-corner cell (other reason for the Palm Princess),

$$f_e = \frac{\text{Row total} \times \text{Column total}}{n} = \frac{(29)(66)}{187} = 10.24$$

To perform the test of independence, you use the χ^2_{STAT} test statistic shown in Equation (14.1) on page 223. The sampling distribution of the χ^2_{STAT} test statistic approximately follows a chi-square distribution, with degrees of freedom equal to the number of rows in the contingency table minus 1, multiplied by the number of columns in the table minus 1:

$$\text{Degrees of freedom} = (r - 1)(c - 1)$$
$$= (4 - 1)(3 - 1) = 6$$

Table 14.11 presents the computations for the χ^2_{STAT} test statistic.

TABLE 14.11

Computing the χ^2_{STAT} Test Statistic for the Test of Independence

Cell	f_o	f_e	$(f_o - f_e)$	$(f_o - f_e)^2$	$(f_o - f_e)^2/f_e$
Price/Golden Palm	23	31.53	−8.53	72.76	2.31
Price/Palm Royale	7	11.82	−4.82	23.23	1.97
Price/Palm Princess	37	23.65	13.35	178.22	7.54
Location/Golden Palm	39	28.24	10.76	115.78	4.10
Location/Palm Royale	13	10.59	2.41	5.81	0.55
Location/Palm Princess	8	21.18	−13.18	173.71	8.20
Room/Golden Palm	13	14.59	−1.59	2.53	0.17
Room/Palm Royale	5	5.47	−0.47	0.22	0.04
Room/Palm Princess	13	10.94	2.06	4.24	0.39
Other/Golden Palm	13	13.65	−0.65	0.42	0.03
Other/Palm Royale	8	5.12	2.88	8.29	1.62
Other/Palm Princess	8	10.24	−2.24	5.02	0.49
					27.41

Using the $\alpha = 0.05$ level of significance, the upper-tail critical value from the chi-square distribution with 6 degrees of freedom is 12.592 (see Table E.4). Because $\chi^2_{STAT} = 27.41 > 12.592$, you reject the null hypothesis of independence (see Figure 14.8).

FIGURE 14.8

Regions of rejection and nonrejection when testing for independence in the three hotel guest satisfaction survey example at the 0.05 level of significance, with 6 degrees of freedom

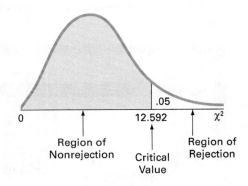

Figure 14.9 shows the calculator results for this test, which are identical when rounded to three decimal places. Because $\chi^2_{STAT} = 27.410 > 12.592$, you reject the null hypothesis of independence. Using the p-value approach, you reject the null hypothesis of independence because the p-value $= 0.000 < 0.05$. The p-value indicates that there is virtually no chance of having a relationship this strong or stronger between the hotel and the primary reasons for not returning in a sample, if the primary reasons for not returning are independent of the specific hotels in the entire population. Thus, there is strong evidence of a relationship between the primary reason for not returning and the hotel.

FIGURE 14.9

Calculator result of the Chi-Square test for the Table 14.9 primary reason for not returning to hotel data

Calculator result:

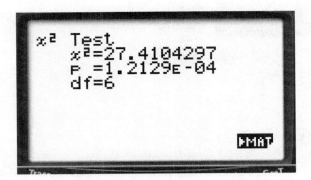

B : Expected frequencies

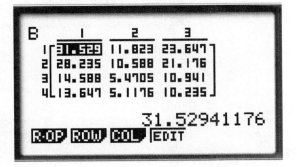

How to Find χ^2_{STAT} Test Statistic Using Calculator

Using the data Table 14.9

To run the Chi-square test, follow the instruction below.

Press **MENU** and select **STAT TEST** (F3) **CHI** (F3)
Under option **CHI,** select **2WAY** (F2)

You will see the following on the screen:

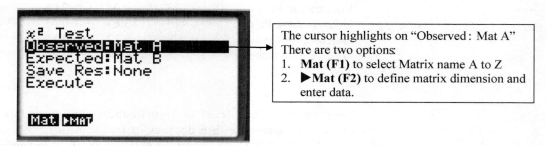

The cursor highlights on "Observed : Mat A"
There are two options:
1. **Mat (F1)** to select Matrix name A to Z
2. **▶Mat (F2)** to define matrix dimension and enter data.

To define dimension and enter data, select ▶Mat (F2) and you will see the following on the screen:

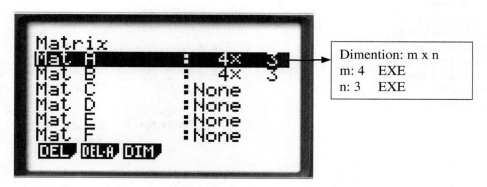

Dimention: m x n
m: 4   EXE
n: 3   EXE

After you have entered the dimension for **Mat A**, you will see the **4 x 3 matrix A** appears on the screen. Use this screen to input your data.

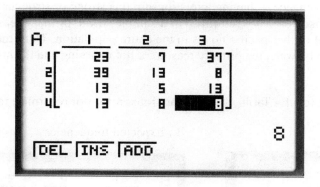

After you have entered your data in Matrix A, now press **EXIT** two times until you see the following on the screen:

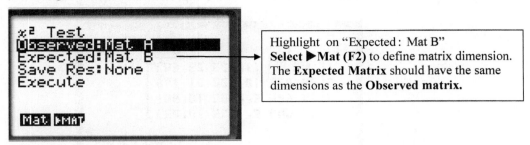

To define dimension, select ▶Mat (F2) and you will see the following on the screen:

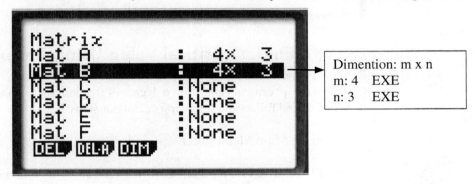

Press DIM (F3) to define or change dimension.

You will see a **4 by 3 matrix B**. You are not required to enter any values. The calculator will give you the expected values.

Now press **EXIT** two times until you see the following on the screen:

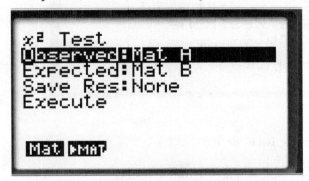

At this point, press either **EXE** or **F1** (Calc)
The calculator will now show the results:

To obtain the expected value matrix select ▶**MAT** (F6), and then highlight on **MAT B** and press **EXE**. You will see the expected value matrix displayed on the screen as follows:

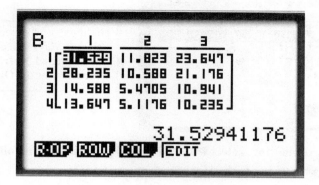

How to Find χ^2 Critical Value Using Calculator

Refer to Figure 14.8

Calculate the χ^2 critical value with 6 degree of freedom for $\alpha = 0.05$, using the Casio Calculator fx-9750GII and follow the following calculator steps:

From the **Main Menu** select:

STAT F5 (DIST) **F3** (CHI) **F3**(Invc) then enter the following items:

Now press **EXE** or **F1**(CALC)

The calculator will now show the results:

The critical value defines the rejection and non-rejection regions.

The critical value defines the rejection and non-rejection regions.

		$\alpha=0.05$
		χ^2
Non-rejection region (Fail to reject H$_o$)	**Critical Value 12.592**	Rejection region (Reject H$_o$)

Examination of the observed and expected frequencies (see Table 14.11 above on page 241) reveals that price is underrepresented as a reason for not returning to the Golden Palm (i.e., $f_o = 23$ and $f_e = 31.53$) but is overrepresented at the Palm Princess. Guests are more satisfied with the price at the Golden Palm than at the Palm Princess. Location is overrepresented as a reason for not returning to the Golden Palm but greatly underrepresented at the Palm Princess. Thus, guests are much more satisfied with the location of the Palm Princess than with that of the Golden Palm.

To ensure accurate results, all expected frequencies need to be large in order to use the χ^2 test when dealing with $r \times c$ contingency tables. As in the case of $2 \times c$ contingency tables in Section 14.2, all expected frequencies should be at least 1. For contingency tables in which one or more expected frequencies are less than 1, you can use the chi-square test after collapsing two or more low-frequency rows into one row (or collapsing two or more low-frequency columns into one column). Merging rows or columns usually results in expected frequencies sufficiently large to ensure the accuracy of the χ^2 test.

USING STATISTICS

Avoiding Guesswork About Resort Guests, Revisited

Maturos1812/Shutterstock

In the Using Statistics scenario, you were the manager of T.C. Resort Properties, a collection of five upscale hotels located on two tropical islands. To assess the quality of services being provided by your hotels, guests are encouraged to complete a satisfaction survey when they check out or via email after they check out. You analyzed the data from these surveys to determine the overall satisfaction with the services provided, the likelihood that the guests will return to the hotel, and the reasons given by some guests for not wanting to return.

On one island, T.C. Resort Properties operates the Beachcomber and Windsurfer hotels. You performed a chi-square test for the difference in two proportions and concluded that a greater proportion of guests are willing to return to the Beachcomber Hotel than to the Windsurfer. On the other island, T.C. Resort Properties operates the Golden Palm, Palm Royale, and Palm Princess hotels. To see if guest satisfaction was the same among the three hotels, you performed a chi-square test for the differences among more than two proportions. The test confirmed that the three proportions are not equal, and guests seem to be most likely to return to the Palm Royale and least likely to return to the Golden Palm.

In addition, you investigated whether the reasons given for not returning to the Golden Palm, Palm Royale, and Palm Princess were unique to a certain hotel or common to all three hotels. By performing a chi-square test of independence, you determined that the reasons given for wanting to return or not depended on the hotel where the guests had been staying. By examining the observed and expected frequencies, you concluded that guests were more satisfied with the price at the Golden Palm and were much more satisfied with the location of the Palm Princess. Guest satisfaction with room accommodations was not significantly different among the three hotels.

SUMMARY

Figure 14.10 presents a roadmap for this chapter. First, you used hypothesis testing for analyzing categorical data from two independent samples and from more than two independent samples. In addition, the rules of probability from Section 5.2 were extended to the hypothesis of independence in the joint responses to two categorical variables.

FIGURE 14.10
Roadmap of Chapter 14

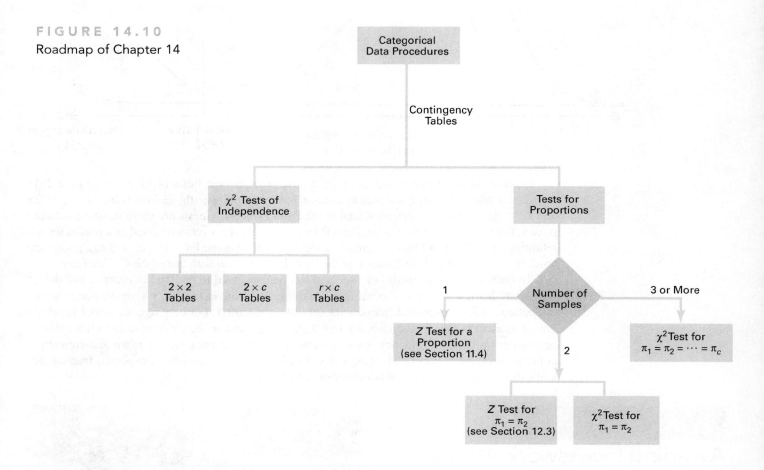

REFERENCES

1. Conover, W. J. *Practical Nonparametric Statistics*, 3rd ed. New York: Wiley, 2000.
2. Daniel, W. W. *Applied Nonparametric Statistics*, 2nd ed. Boston: PWS Kent, 1990.
3. Dixon, W. J., and F. J. Massey, Jr. *Introduction to Statistical Analysis*, 4th ed. New York: McGraw-Hill, 1983.
4. Hollander, M., and D. A. Wolfe. *Nonparametric Statistical Methods*, 2nd ed. New York: Wiley, 1999.
5. Lewontin, R. C., and J. Felsenstein. "Robustness of Homogeneity Tests in 2 × *n* Tables," *Biometrics*, 21 (March 1965): 19–33.
6. Marascuilo, L. A., and M. McSweeney. *Nonparametric and Distribution-Free Methods for the Social Sciences*. Monterey, CA: Brooks/Cole, 1977.
7. *Microsoft Excel 2013*. Redmond, WA: Microsoft Corp., 2012.
8. *Minitab Release 16*. State College, PA: Minitab Inc., 2010.

KEY EQUATIONS

χ^2 Test for the Difference Between Two Proportions

$$\chi^2_{STAT} = \sum_{\text{all cells}} \frac{(f_o - f_e)^2}{f_e} \tag{14.1}$$

Computing the Estimated Overall Proportion for Two Groups

$$\bar{p} = \frac{X_1 + X_2}{n_1 + n_2} = \frac{X}{n} \tag{14.2}$$

Computing the Estimated Overall Proportion for c Groups

$$\bar{p} = \frac{X_1 + X_2 + \cdots + X_c}{n_1 + n_2 + \cdots + n_c} = \frac{X}{n} \tag{14.3}$$

Computing the Expected Frequency

$$f_e = \frac{\text{Row total} \times \text{Column total}}{n} \tag{14.4}$$

KEY TERMS

chi-square (χ^2) distribution 224
chi-square (χ^2) test for the difference
   between two proportions 223
chi-square (χ^2) test of independence 238
expected frequency (f_e) 223
observed frequency (f_o) 223
$2 \times c$ contingency table 232
2×2 contingency table 222
two-way contingency table 222

CHECKING YOUR UNDERSTANDING

14.1 Under what conditions should you use the χ^2 test to determine whether there is a difference between the proportions of two independent populations?

14.2 Under what conditions should you use the χ^2 test to determine whether there is a difference among the proportions of more than two independent populations?

14.3 Under what conditions should you use the χ^2 test of independence?

PROBLEMS

Section 14.1

14.4 Determine the critical value of χ^2 with 1 degree of freedom in each of the following circumstances:
a. $\alpha = 0.01$
b. $\alpha = 0.005$
c. $\alpha = 0.10$

14.5 Determine the critical value of χ^2 with 1 degree of freedom in each of the following circumstances:
a. $\alpha = 0.05$
b. $\alpha = 0.025$
c. $\alpha = 0.01$

14.6 Use the following contingency table:

	A	B	Total
1	20	30	50
2	30	45	75
Total	50	75	125

a. Compute the expected frequency for each cell.
b. Compare the observed and expected frequencies for each cell.
c. Compute χ^2_{STAT}. Is it significant at $\alpha = 0.05$?

14.7 Use the following contingency table:

	A	B	Total
1	20	30	50
2	30	20	50
Total	50	50	100

a. Compute the expected frequency for each cell.
b. Compute χ^2_{STAT}. Is it significant at $\alpha = 0.05$?

14.8 An online survey of 1,000 adults asked, "What do you buy from your mobile device?" The results indicated that 61% of the females said clothes as compared to 39% of the males. (Data extracted from *Ebates.com 2014 Mobile Shopping Survey: Nearly Half of Americans Shop from a Mobile Device*, available from

bit.ly/1hi6kyX.) The sample sizes of males and females were not provided. Suppose that the results were as shown in the following table:

BUY CLOTHES FROM THEIR MOBILE DEVICE	GENDER		
	Male	**Female**	**Total**
Yes	195	305	500
No	305	195	500
Total	500	500	1,000

a. Is there evidence of a significant difference between the proportion of males and females who say they buy clothing from their mobile device at the 0.01 level of significance?

b. Determine the p-value in (a) and interpret its meaning.

c. What are your answers to (a) and (b) if 270 males say they buy clothing from their mobile device and 230 did not?

d. Compare the results of (a) through (c) to those of Problem 12.40 (a), (b), and (d) on page 153.

14.9 Do social recommendations increase ad effectiveness? A study of online video viewers compared viewers who arrived at an advertising video for a particular brand by following a social media recommendation link to viewers who arrived at the same video by web browsing. Data were collected on whether the viewer could correctly recall the brand being advertised after seeing the video. The results were:

ARRIVAL METHOD	CORRECTLY RECALLED THE BRAND	
	Yes	**No**
Recommendation	407	150
Browsing	193	91

Source: Data extracted from "Social Ad Effectiveness: An Unruly White Paper," January 2012, p. 3, **www.unrulymedia.com**.

a. Set up the null and alternative hypotheses to determine whether there is a difference in brand recall between viewers who arrived by following a social media recommendation and those who arrived by web browsing.

b. Conduct the hypothesis test defined in (a), using the 0.05 level of significance.

c. Compare the results of (a) and (b) to those of Problem 12.41 (a) and (b) on page 153.

14.10 Do males or females feel more tense or stressed out at work? A survey of employed adults conducted online by Harris Interactive on behalf of the American Psychological Association revealed the following:

GENDER	FELT TENSE OR STRESSED OUT AT WORK	
	Yes	**No**
Male	244	495
Female	282	480

Source: Data extracted from "The 2013 Work and Well-Being Survey," American Psychological Association and Harris Interactive, March 2013, p. 5, **bit.ly/11JGcPf**.

a. At the 0.05 level of significance, is there evidence of a difference between males and females in the proportion who feel stressed out at work?

b. Determine the p-value in (a) and interpret its meaning.

14.11 Consumer research firm Scarborough analyzed the 10% of American adults who are either "Superbanked" or "Unbanked." Superbanked consumers are defined as U.S. adults who live in a household that has multiple asset accounts at financial institutions, as well as some additional investments; Unbanked consumers are U.S. adults who live in a household that does not use a bank or credit union. By finding the 5% of Americans who are Superbanked, Scarborough identifies financially savvy consumers who might be open to diversifying their financial portfolios; by identifying the Unbanked, Scarborough provides insight into the ultimate prospective client for banks and financial institutions. As part of its analysis, Scarborough reported that 93% of Superbanked consumers use credit cards as compared to 23% of Unbanked consumers. (Data extracted from **bit.ly/Syi9kN**.) Suppose that these results were based on 1,000 Superbanked consumers and 1,000 Unbanked consumers.

a. At the 0.01 level of significance, is there evidence of a significant difference between the Superbanked and the Unbanked with respect to the proportion that use credit cards?

b. Determine the p-value in (a) and interpret is meaning.

c. Compare the results of (a) and (b) to those of Problem 12.43 on page 153.

14.12 A/B testing is a method used by businesses to test different designs and formats of a web page to determine if a new web page is more effective than a current web page. Web designers tested a new call-to-action button on its web page. Every visitor to the web page was randomly shown either the original call-to-action button (the control) or the new variation. The metric used to measure success was the download rate: the number of people who downloaded the file divided by the number of people who saw that particular call-to-action button. Results of the experiment yielded the following:

Variations	**Downloads**	**Visitors**
Original call-to-action button	351	3,642
New call-to-action button	485	3,556

a. At the 0.05 level of significance, is there evidence of a difference in the download rate between the original call-to-action button and the new call-to-action button?

b. Find the p-value in (a) and interpret its value.

c. Compare the results of (a) and (b) to those of Problem 12.42 on page 153.

14.13 Does co-browsing have positive effects on the customer experience? Co-browsing refers to the ability to have a contact center agent and customer jointly navigate an application (e.g., web page, digital document, or mobile application) on a real time basis through the web. A study of businesses indicates that 81 of 129 co-browsing organizations use skills-based routing to match the caller with the *right* agent, whereas 65 of 176 non-co-browsing organizations use skills-based routing to match the caller with the *right* agent. (Source: *Cobrowsing Presents a "Lucrative" Customer Service Opportunity*, available at **bit.ly/1wwALWr**.)

a. Construct a 2×2 contingency table.

b. At the 0.05 level of significance, is there evidence of a difference between co-browsing organizations and non-co-browsing organizations in the proportion that use skills-based routing to match the caller with the *right* agent?

c. Find the p-value in (a) and interpret its meaning.

d. Compare the results of (a) and (b) to those of Problem 12.45 on page 154.

Section 14.2

14.14 Consider a contingency table with two rows and five columns.
a. How many degrees of freedom are there in the contingency table?
b. Determine the critical value for $\alpha = 0.05$.
c. Determine the critical value for $\alpha = 0.01$.

14.15 Use the following contingency table:

	A	B	C	Total
1	10	30	50	90
2	40	45	50	135
Total	50	75	100	225

a. Compute the expected frequency for each cell.
b. Compute χ^2_{STAT}. Is it significant at $\alpha = 0.05$?

14.16 Use the following contingency table:

	A	B	C	Total
1	20	30	25	75
2	30	20	25	75
Total	50	50	50	150

a. Compute the expected frequency for each cell.
b. Compute χ^2_{STAT}. Is it significant at $\alpha = 0.05$?

14.17 How common is online personal data theft? A survey of internet users found that 15% of the 18- to 29-year-olds, 20% of the 30- to 49-year-olds, 20% of the 50- to 64-year-olds, and 13% of the 65+-year-olds have had important personal information stolen. (Data extracted from *How Common is Online Personal Data Theft?* available at **bit.ly/1rKlqRW**.) Suppose the survey was based on 200 Internet users in each of the four age groups: 18–29, 30–49, 50–64, and 65+.
a. At the 0.05 level of significance, is there evidence of a difference among the age groups in the proportion of internet users who have had important personal information stolen?
b. Determine the *p*-value in (a) and interpret its meaning.

14.18 A digital CEO is one of five behaviors important to raising an organization's Digital IQ. A survey of business and IT executives found that 80% of automotive executives, 70% of financial services executives, 82% of health care executives, 59% of retail & consumer executives, and 76% of technology executives say their CEOs are active champions of using digital technology to achieve strategy. (Data extracted from *PwC's 2014 Global Digital IQ Survey*, available at **pwc.to/1tGKCVa**.)

Suppose these results were based on 500 business and IT executives in each of the five industries: automotive, financial services, health care, retail & consumer, and technology.
a. At the 0.05 level of significance, is there evidence of a difference among the industries with respect to the proportion of executives that say their CEOs are active champions of using digital technology to achieve strategy?
b. Compute the *p*-value and interpret its meaning.

14.19 Most companies consider Big Data analytics critical to success. However, is there a difference among small (<100 employees), mid-sized (100–999 employees), and large (1,000+ employees) companies in the proportion of companies that have already deployed Big Data projects? A study showed the results for the different company sizes. (Data extracted from *2014 Big*

Data Outlook: Big Data Is Transformative—Where Is Your Company? available at: **bit.ly/1o8kaEo**.)

HAVE ALREADY DEPLOYED BIG DATA PROJECTS	COMPANY SIZE		
	Small	Mid-Sized	Large
Yes	9%	37%	26%
No	91%	63%	74%

Assume that 200 decision makers involved in Big Data purchases within each company size were surveyed.
a. At the 0.05 level of significance, is there evidence of a difference among companies of different sizes with respect to the proportion of companies that have already deployed Big Data projects?
b. Determine the *p*-value in (a) and interpret its meaning.

14.20 Repeat (a) and (b) of Problem 14.19, assuming that only 50 decision makers involved in Big Data purchases for each company size were surveyed. Discuss the implications of sample size on the χ^2 test for differences among more than two populations.

14.21 Most marketers at mid-size companies feel overwhelmed by the number of technology vendor relationships they must manage. A study by DNN based on samples of 57 companies with 50–99 employees, 93 companies with 100–499 employees, 69 companies with 500–999 employees, and 81 companies with 1,000–5,000 employees reported that 19 of the companies with 50–99 employees, 44 of the companies with 100–499 employees, 43 of the companies with 500–999 employees, and 61 of the companies with 1,000–5,000 employees are working simultaneously with five or more vendors. (Data extracted from *Marketing Got Complicated: Challenges (and Opportunities) for Marketers at Mid-Sized Companies*, **bit.ly/S6PIOj**.)
a. Is there evidence of a significant difference among companies of different sizes with respect to the proportion that are working simultaneously with five or more vendors ? (Use $\alpha = 0.05$).
b. Determine the *p*-value and interpret its meaning.

14.22 The GMI Ratings' 2013 Women on Boards Survey showed that progress on most measures of female board representation continues to be slow. The study reported that 68 of 101 (67%) of French companies sampled, 148 of 212 (70%) of Australian companies sampled, 28 of 30 (93%) of Norwegian companies sampled, 31 of 58 (53%) of Singaporean companies, and 96 of 145 (66%) of Canadian companies sampled have at least one female director on their boards. (Data extracted from *GMI Ratings' 2013 Woman on Boards Survey*, **http://bit.ly/1jPXYc4**.)
a. Is there evidence of a significant difference among the countries with respect to the proportion of companies that have at least one female director on their boards? (Use $\alpha = 0.05$).
b. Determine the *p*-value and interpret its meaning.

Section 14.3

14.23 If a contingency table has three rows and four columns, how many degrees of freedom are there for the χ^2 test of independence?

14.24 When performing a χ^2 test of independence in a contingency table with *r* rows and *c* columns, determine the upper-tail critical value of the test statistic in each of the following circumstances:
a. $\alpha = 0.05$, $r = 4$ rows, $c = 5$ columns
b. $\alpha = 0.01$, $r = 4$ rows, $c = 5$ columns
c. $\alpha = 0.01$, $r = 4$ rows, $c = 6$ columns

d. $\alpha = 0.01$, $r = 3$ rows, $c = 6$ columns
e. $\alpha = 0.01$, $r = 6$ rows, $c = 3$ columns

14.25 The owner of a restaurant serving Continental-style entrées has the business objective of learning more about the patterns of patron demand during the Friday-to-Sunday weekend time period. Data were collected from 630 customers on the type of entrée ordered and the type of dessert ordered and organized into the following table:

TYPE OF DESSERT	TYPE OF ENTRÉE				
	Beef	**Poultry**	**Fish**	**Pasta**	**Total**
Ice cream	13	8	12	14	47
Cake	98	12	29	6	145
Fruit	8	10	6	2	26
None	124	98	149	41	412
Total	243	128	196	63	630

At the 0.05 level of significance, is there evidence of a relationship between type of dessert and type of entrée?

14.26 Is there a generation gap in the type of music that people listen to? The following table represents the type of favorite music for a sample of 1,000 respondents classified according to their age group:

FAVORITE TYPE	AGE				
	16–29	**30–49**	**50–64**	**65 and over**	**Total**
Rock	71	62	51	27	211
Rap or hip-hop	40	21	7	3	71
Rhythm and blues	48	46	46	40	180
Country	43	53	59	79	234
Classical	22	28	33	46	129
Jazz	18	26	36	43	123
Salsa	8	14	18	12	52
Total	250	250	250	250	1,000

At the 0.05 level of significance, is there evidence of a relationship between favorite type of music and age group?

14.27 How many airline loyalty programs do nonbusiness travelers belong to? A study by Parago, Inc., revealed the following results:

NUMBER OF LOYALTY PROGRAMS	AGE						
	18–22	**23–29**	**30–39**	**40–49**	**50–59**	**60+**	**Total**
0	78	113	79	74	88	88	520
1	36	50	41	48	69	82	326
2–3	12	34	36	48	52	85	267
4–5	4	4	6	7	13	25	59
6+	0	0	3	0	2	3	8
Total	130	201	165	177	224	283	1,180

Source: The Great American Vacation Study, **parago.com/travel-study**.

At the 0.01 level of significance, is there evidence of a significant relationship between number of airline loyalty programs and age?

14.28 Where people look for news is different for various age groups. A study indicated where different age groups primarily get their news:

MEDIA	AGE GROUP		
	Under 36	**36–50**	**50+**
Local TV	107	119	133
National TV	73	102	127
Radio	75	97	109
Local newspaper	52	79	107
Internet	95	83	76

At the 0.05 level of significance, is there evidence of a significant relationship between the age group and where people primarily get their news? If so, explain the relationship.

14.29 PwC takes a closer look at what CEOs are looking for and are finding as new sources of value in their businesses and industries. The results of the 2014 Global CEO survey, summarized in the table below, classified CEOs by the main opportunity that they identified for business growth in their companies as well as their geographic region.

IDENTIFIED MAIN OPPORTUNITY	GEOGRAPHIC REGION				
	U.S.	**China & Hong Kong**	**Japan**	**Germany**	**Total**
Product or service innovation	58	58	45	21	182
Increased share in existing markets	60	30	31	15	136
Mergers and acquisitions	23	10	12	4	49
New geographic markets	16	18	31	2	67
New joint ventures and/or strategic alliances	5	18	8	3	34
Total	162	134	127	45	468

Source: *17th Annual Global CEO Survey*, **pwc.com/gx/en/ceo-survey/index.jhtml**.

At the 0.05 level of significance, is there evidence of a significant relationship between the identified main opportunity and geographic region?

Review

14.30 Undergraduate students at Miami University in Oxford, Ohio, were surveyed in order to evaluate the effect of gender and price on purchasing a pizza from Pizza Hut. Students were told to suppose that they were planning to have a large two-topping pizza delivered to their residence that evening. The students had to decide between ordering from Pizza Hut at a reduced price of $8.49 (the regular price for a large two-topping pizza from the Oxford Pizza Hut at the time was $11.49) and ordering a pizza from a different pizzeria. The results from this question are summarized in the following contingency table:

GENDER	PIZZERIA		
	Pizza Hut	**Other**	**Total**
Female	4	13	17
Male	6	12	18
Total	10	25	35

a. Using a 0.05 level of significance, is there evidence of a difference between males and females in their pizzeria selection?

b. What is your answer to (a) if nine of the male students selected Pizza Hut and nine selected another pizzeria?

A subsequent survey evaluated purchase decisions at other prices. These results are summarized in the following contingency table:

| PIZZERIA | PRICE | | | |
	$8.49	$11.49	$14.49	Total
Pizza Hut	10	5	2	17
Other	25	23	27	75
Total	35	28	29	92

c. Using a 0.05 level of significance and using the data in the second contingency table, is there evidence of a difference in pizzeria selection based on price?

d. Determine the p-value in (c) and interpret its meaning.

14.31 What social media tools do marketers commonly use? *Social Media Examiner* surveyed B2B and B2C marketers who commonly use an indicated social media tool. (B2B marketers are marketers that focus primarily on attracting businesses. B2C marketers are marketers that primarily target consumers.) Suppose the survey was based on 500 B2B marketers and 500 B2C marketers and yielded the results in the following table. (Data extracted from *2014 Social Media Marketing Industry Report*, available from **socialmediaexaminer.com**.)

| SOCIAL MEDIA TOOL | BUSINESS FOCUS | |
	B2B	B2C
Facebook	89%	97%
Twitter	86%	81%
LinkedIn	88%	59%
YouTube	52%	60%

For *each social media tool*, at the 0.05 level of significance, determine whether there is a difference between B2B marketers and B2C marketers in the proportion who used each social media tool.

14.32 A company is considering an organizational change involving the use of self-managed work teams. To assess the attitudes of employees of the company toward this change, a sample of 400 employees is selected and asked whether they favor the institution of self-managed work teams in the organization. Three responses are permitted: favor, neutral, or oppose. The results of the survey, cross-classified by type of job and attitude toward self-managed work teams, are summarized as follows:

| TYPE OF JOB | SELF-MANAGED WORK TEAMS | | | |
	Favor	Neutral	Oppose	Total
Hourly worker	108	46	71	225
Supervisor	18	12	30	60
Middle management	35	14	26	75
Upper management	24	7	9	40
Total	185	79	136	400

a. At the 0.05 level of significance, is there evidence of a relationship between attitude toward self-managed work teams and type of job?

The survey also asked respondents about their attitudes toward instituting a policy whereby an employee could take one additional vacation day per month without pay. The results, cross-classified by type of job, are as follows:

| TYPE OF JOB | VACATION TIME WITHOUT PAY | | | |
	Favor	Neutral	Oppose	Total
Hourly worker	135	23	67	225
Supervisor	39	7	14	60
Middle management	47	6	22	75
Upper management	26	6	8	40
Total	247	42	111	400

b. At the 0.05 level of significance, is there evidence of a relationship between attitude toward vacation time without pay and type of job?

14.33 Do Americans trust advertisements? The following table summarizes the results of a YouGov.com survey that asked Americans who see advertisements at least once a month how honest advertisements are.

| HONEST? | GEOGRAPHIC REGION | | | | |
	Northeast	Midwest	South	West	Total
Yes	102	118	220	115	555
No	74	93	135	130	432
Total	176	211	355	245	987

Source: "Truth in advertising: 50% don't trust what they see, read and hear," **bit.ly/1jPXYc4**.

a. At the 0.05 level of significance, is there evidence of a difference in the proportion of Americans who say advertisements are honest on the basis of geographic region?

YouGov.com also asked Americans who see advertisements at least once a month whether they trust the advertisements that they see, read, and hear. The following table summarizes the results of this second survey.

| TRUST? | GEOGRAPHIC REGION | | | | |
	Northeast	Midwest	South	West	Total
Yes	88	108	202	93	491
No	88	103	153	152	496
Total	176	211	355	245	987

Source: "Truth in advertising: 50% don't trust what they see, read and hear," **bit.ly/1ivIlLX**.

b. At the 0.05 level of significance is there evidence of a difference in the proportion of Americans who say they trust advertisements on the basis of geographic region?

CASES FOR CHAPTER 14

Managing Ashland MultiComm Services

PHASE 1

Reviewing the results of its research, the marketing department team concluded that a segment of Ashland households might be interested in a discounted trial subscription to the AMS *3-For-All* cable/phone/Internet service. The team decided to test various discounts before determining the type of discount to offer during the trial period. It decided to conduct an experiment using three types of discounts plus a plan that offered no discount during the trial period:

1. No discount for the *3-For-All* cable/phone/Internet service. Subscribers would pay $24.99 per week for the *3-For-All* cable/phone/Internet service during the 90-day trial period.

2. Moderate discount for the *3-For-All* cable/phone/ Internet service. Subscribers would pay $19.99 per week for the *3-For-All* cable/phone/Internet service during the 90-day trial period.

3. Substantial discount for the *3-For-All* cable/phone/ Internet service. Subscribers would pay $14.99 per week for the *3-For-All* cable/phone/Internet service during the 90-day trial period.

4. Discount restaurant card. Subscribers would be given a special card providing a discount of 15% at selected restaurants in Ashland during the trial period.

Each participant in the experiment was randomly assigned to a discount plan. A random sample of 100 subscribers to each plan during the trial period was tracked to determine how many would continue to subscribe to the *3-For-All* service after the trial period. The following table summarizes the results.

CONTINUE SUBSCRIPTIONS AFTER TRIAL PERIOD	DISCOUNT PLANS				
	No Discount	Moderate Discount	Substantial Discount	Restaurant Card	Total
Yes	24	30	38	51	143
No	76	70	62	49	257
Total	100	100	100	100	400

1. Analyze the results of the experiment. Write a report to the team that includes your recommendation for which discount plan to use. Be prepared to discuss the limitations and assumptions of the experiment.

PHASE 2

The marketing department team discussed the results of the survey presented in Chapter 10, on pages 35 and 36. The team realized that the evaluation of individual questions was providing only limited information. In order to further understand the market for the *3-For-All* cable/phone/Internet service, the data were organized in the following contingency tables:

HAS AMS TELEPHONE SERVICE	HAS AMS INTERNET SERVICE		
	Yes	No	Total
Yes	55	28	83
No	207	128	335
Total	262	156	418

TYPE OF SERVICE	DISCOUNT TRIAL		
	Yes	No	Total
Basic	8	156	164
Enhanced	32	222	254
Total	40	378	418

TYPE OF SERVICE	WATCHES PREMIUM OR ON-DEMAND SERVICES				
	Almost Every Day	Several Times a Week	Almost Never	Never	Total
Basic	2	5	127	30	164
Enhanced	12	30	186	26	254
Total	14	35	313	56	418

DISCOUNT	WATCHES PREMIUM OR ON-DEMAND SERVICES				
	Almost Every Day	Several Times a Week	Almost Never	Never	Total
Yes	4	5	27	4	40
No	10	30	286	52	378
Total	14	35	313	56	418

| | METHOD FOR CURRENT SUBSCRIPTION | | | | | |
DISCOUNT	Toll-Free Phone	AMS Website	Direct Mail Reply Card	Good Tunes & More	Other	Total
Yes	11	21	5	1	2	40
No	219	85	41	9	24	378
Total	230	106	46	10	26	418

| | METHOD FOR CURRENT SUBSCRIPTION | | | | | |
GOLD CARD	Toll-Free Phone	AMS Website	Direct Mail Reply Card	Good Tunes & More	Other	Total
Yes	10	20	5	1	2	38
No	220	86	41	9	24	380
Total	230	106	46	10	26	418

2. Analyze the results of the contingency tables. Write a report for the marketing department team, discussing the marketing implications of the results for Ashland MultiComm Services.

Digital Case

Apply your knowledge of testing for the difference between two proportions in this Digital Case, which extends the T.C. Resort Properties Using Statistics scenario of this chapter.

As T.C. Resort Properties seeks to improve its customer service, the company faces new competition from SunLow Resorts. SunLow has recently opened resort hotels on the islands where T.C. Resort Properties has its five hotels. SunLow is currently advertising that a random survey of 300 customers revealed that about 60% of the customers preferred its "Concierge Class" travel reward program over the T.C. Resorts "TCRewards Plus" program.

Open and review **ConciergeClass.pdf**, an electronic brochure that describes the Concierge Class program and compares it to the T.C. Resorts program. Then answer the following questions:

1. Are the claims made by SunLow valid?

2. What analyses of the survey data would lead to a more favorable impression about T.C. Resort Properties?

3. Perform one of the analyses identified in your answer to step 2.

4. Review the data about the T.C. Resort Properties customers presented in this chapter. Are there any other questions that you might include in a future survey of travel reward programs? Explain.

CardioGood Fitness

Return to the CardioGood Fitness case first presented on Chapter 1. The data for this case are stored in CardioGood Fitness.

1. Determine whether differences exist in the relationship status (single or partnered), and the self-rated fitness based on the product purchased (TM195, TM498, TM798).

2. Write a report to be presented to the management of CardioGood Fitness, detailing your findings.

Clear Mountain State Student Surveys

1. The Student News Service at Clear Mountain State University (CMSU) has decided to gather data about the undergraduate students that attend CMSU. It creates and distributes a survey of 14 questions and receives responses from 62 undergraduates, which it stores in UndergradSurvey .

Construct contingency tables using gender, major, plans to go to graduate school, and employment status. (You need to construct six tables, taking two variables at a time.) Analyze the data at the 0.05 level of significance to determine whether any significant relationships exist among these variables.

2. The dean of students at CMSU has learned about the undergraduate survey and has decided to undertake a similar survey for graduate students at CMSU. She creates and distributes a survey of 14 questions and receives responses from 44 graduate students, which she stores them in GradSurvey . For these data, at the 0.05 level of significance:

Construct contingency tables using gender, undergraduate major, graduate major, and employment status. (You need to construct six tables, taking two variables at a time.) Analyze the data to determine whether any significant relationships exist among these variables.

CHAPTER 14 CASIO CALCULATOR GUIDE

CALCULATOR LESSON 16A

**CFX-9850GB
CALCULATOR**

EXAMPLE 14.3

Lesson 16A—Chi-Square Test for Differences Among More Than Two Proportions

(A) Lesson 16A—Chi-Square Test for Differences among more than two proportions

Example

Five printers of different brands are tested using the same paper and graphic output. The results are judged as conforming or nonconforming. At a 5% level of significance, test for a difference in proportion of nonconforming pages. The results are as follows.

TABLE 14.12

| | Number of Pages Printed | | | | |
| | Brand of the Printer | | | | |
Classification	A	B	C	D	E
Nonconforming	13	10	16	9	12
Conforming	187	190	184	191	188

Solution: From the **Main Menu**, select the folllowing:

MAT and **EXE**

Enter the following in response to the screen prompts.

Matrix

Mat A	:	**2 EXE**	**5EXE**
Mat B	:	None	
Mat C	:	None	
Mat D	:	None	
Mat E	:	None	
Mat F	:	None	

You will see a part of the matrix appear on the screen. Use this screen to input your data.

A	1	2	3	4 →
1	0	0	0	0
2	0	0	0	0

Enter the data values into the appropriate cells. To begin entering your data, use the arrow key to highlight the cell 1,1 (top left corner of the cell). Type 13 and press **EXE.** The cursor will automatically scroll to the next cell.

A	1	2	3	4	5
1	13 EXE	10 EXE	16 EXE	9 EXE	12 EXE
2	187 EXE	190 EXE	184 EXE	191 EXE	188 EXE

After you enter your data in Matrix A, press **MENU** and select the following:

STAT, EXE, TEST (F3), and **CHI** (F3). Then enter the following items:

χ^2 Test
Observed: Mat A (F1)
Execute
Now press **EXE**.

The calculator will now show the results:

χ^2 Test
$\quad \chi^2 = 2.6595$
$\quad p = 0.6163$
$\quad df = 2$
Expected = Mat Ans

We may obtain the expected value matrix by making the following selection:

MENU, MAT, and **EXE**

Use the cursor ▼ arrow to scroll down to the bottom of the matrix list until the cursor is on;

Mat Ans   : 2 x 5
EXE

The expected value matrix will be displayed on the screen as follows:

Ans	1	2	3	4	5
1	12	12	12	12	12
2	188	188	188	188	188

Conclusion:

Since p-value $= 0.6163$ is greater than α, we do not reject H_0.

The statistical evidence does not indicate that we may conclude that there is a difference in the proportion of nonconforming pages produced by the printers.

CALCULATOR LESSON 16B

FX-9850GII CALCULATOR

Lesson 16B—Chi-Square Test for Differences Among More Than Two Proportions

EXAMPLE 14.4

(A) Lesson 16B—Chi-Square Test for Differences among more than two Proportions

Example.

Five printers of different brands are tested using the same paper and graphic output. The results are judged as conforming or nonconforming. At a 5% level of significance, test for a difference in proportion of nonconforming pages. The results are as followed.

TABLE 14.13

	Number of Pages Printed				
	Brand of the Printer				
Classification	**A**	**B**	**C**	**D**	**E**
Nonconforming	13	10	16	9	12
Conforming	187	190	184	191	188

Solution:

Press **MENU** and select **STAT**, **TEST** (F3), and **CHI** (F3).
Under option **CHI**, select **2WAY** (F2).

You will see the following on the screen:

χ^2 Test

Observed   : Mat A

Expected   : Mat B
Save Res   : none
Execute

The cursor highlights "Observed : Mat A."
There are two options:
1. **Mat (F1)** to select matrix name (A to Z)
2. **▶Mat (F2)** to define matrix dimension and enter data

To define dimension and enter data, select ▶Mat (F2). You will see the following on the screen:

Matrx
Mat A   : 2 × 5   **Press DIM(F3) to define or**   Dimension : m × n
Mat B   : None   **change dimension.**   m: 2   EXE
Mat C   : None   n: 5   EXE
Mat D   : None
Mar E   : None
Mat F   : None

After you have entered the dimension for **Mat A**, you will see the **2 × 5 matrix A** appears on the screen. Use this screen to input your data. Enter the data values into the appropriate cells. To begin entering your data, use the arrow key to highlight the cell 1,1 (top left corner of the cell). Type 13 and press **EXE**. The cursor will automatically scroll to the next cell.

A	1	2	3	4⟶	5
1	13 EXE	10 EXE	16 EXE	9 EXE	12 EXE
2	187 EXE	190 EXE	184 EXE	191 EXE	188 EXE

After you enter your data in Matrix A, press **EXIT** two times until you see the following on the screen:

χ^2 Test

Observed : Mat A

| **Expected   : Mat B** |

Save Res   : none
Execute

Highlight "Expected : Mat B"
Select ▶**Mat (F2)** to define matrix dimension.
The **expected matrix** should have the same
dimensions as the **observed matrix**.

To define dimension, select ▶Mat (F2). You will see the following on the screen:

Matrix
Mat A   : 2 × 5
Mat B   : 2 × 5
Mat C   : None
Mat D   : None
Mar E   : None
Mat F   : None

**Press DIM (F3) to define or
change dimension.**

Dimension : m × n
m: 2   EXE
n: 5   EXE

You will see **2 × 5 Matrix B**. You are not required to enter any values; the calculator will give you the expected values.

Now press **EXIT** two times until you see the following on the screen:

χ^2 Test
Observed : Mat A
Expected : Mat B
Save Res   : none
Execute

At this point, press either **EXE** or **F1** (Calc).
The calculator will now show the results:

χ^2 Test

$\chi^2 = 2.65957447$
$p = 0.61630686$
$df = 4$

To obtain the expected value matrix, select ▶**Mat** (F6), highlight **MAT B**, and press **EXE**. The expected value matrix will be displayed on the screen as follows:

Ans	**1**	**2**	**3**	**4**	**5**
1	12	12	12	12	12
2	188	188	188	188	188

Conclusion:
Since p-value = 0.6163 is greater than α, we do not reject H_0.
The statistical evidence does not indicate that we may conclude that there is a difference in the proportion of nonconforming pages produced by the printers.

CALCULATOR LESSON 17A

**CFX-9850GB
CALCULATOR**

EXAMPLE 14.5

Lesson 17A—Chi-Square Test for Independence

Lesson 17A—Chi-Square Test for Independence

Example

A copier service has two laser printers used to produce colour transparencies. The thickness of a transparency can create printing problems. Four common problems are smearing, streaking, skipping, and fogging. A random sample reveals the following information. We wish to test whether the problems depend on the printer used. We will use a significance level of 0.05.

TABLE 14.14

		Problems		
Printer	**Smearing**	**Streaking**	**Skipping**	**Fogging**
A	20	32	44	10
B	10	48	21	15

Solution: From the **Main Menu**, select the following:

MAT and **EXE**

Enter the following in response to the screen prompts.

Matrix

Mat A	:	**2 EXE**	**4EXE**
Mat B	:	None	
Mat C	:	None	
Mat D	:	None	
Mat E	:	None	
Mat F	:	None	

You will see the part of the matrix appears on the screen. Use this screen to input your data.

A	1	2	3	4 →
1	0	0	0	0
2	0	0	0	0

Enter the data values into the appropriate cells. To begin entering your data, use the arrow key to highlight the cell 1,1 (top left corner of the cell). Type 20 and press **EXE.** The cursor will automatically scroll to the next cell.

A	1	2	3	4 →
1	20 EXE	32 EXE	44 EXE	10 EXE
2	10 EXE	48 EXE	21 EXE	15 EXE

After you enter your data in Matrix A, press **MENU** and select the following:

STAT, EXE, TEST (F3), and **CHI** (F3). Then enter the following items:

χ^2 Test
Observed: Mat A (F1)
Execute
Now Press **EXE.**

The calculator will now show the results:

χ^2 Test
      $\chi^2 = 15.005$
      $p = 1.8116\text{E-}03$ $(= 0.0018116)$
      $df = 3$
Expected = Mat Ans

You may obtain the expected value matrix by making the following selection:

MENU, MAT, and **EXE**

Use the cursor ▼ arrow to scroll down to the bottom of the matrix list until the cursor is on

Mat Ans   : 2 x 4
EXE

You will see the expected value matrix displayed on the screen as follows:

Ans	1	2	3	4 →
1	15.9	42.4	34.45	13.25
2	14.1	37.6	30.55	11.75

Conclusion:

Since p-value $= 0.0018$ is smaller than α, we reject H_0.

The statistical evidence indicates that we may conclude that there is a difference in the proportion of nonconforming pages produced by the printers.

CALCULATOR LESSON 17B

FX-9850GII CALCULATOR

EXAMPLE 14.6

Lesson 17B—Chi-Square Test for Independence

Lesson 17B—Chi-Square Test for Independence

Example

A copier service has two laser printers used to produce colour transparencies. The thickness of a transparency can create printing problems. Four common problems are smearing, streaking, skipping, and fogging. A random sample reveals the following information. We wish to test whether the problems depend on the printer used. We will use a significance level of 0.05.

TABLE 14.15

	Problems			
Printer	**Smearing**	**Streaking**	**Skipping**	**Fogging**
A	20	32	44	10
B	10	48	21	15

Solution:

Press **MENU** and select **STAT**, **TEST** (F3), and **CHI** (F3).
Under option **CHI**, select **2WAY** (F2).

You will see the following on the screen:

χ^2 Test

Observed	**: Mat A**

Expected : Mat B
Save Res : none
Execute

> The cursor highlights "Observed : Mat A."
> There are two options:
> 1. **Mat (F1)** to select matrix name (A to Z)
> 2. **▶Mat (F2)** to define matrix dimension and enter data

To define dimension and enter data, select ▶Mat (F2). You will see the following on the screen:

Matrx
Mat A : 2 × 4   **Press DIM(F3) to define or**
Mat B : None   **change dimension.**
Mat C : None
Mat D : None
Mar E : None
Mat F : None

> Dimension : m × n
> m: 2   EXE
> n: 4   EXE

After you have entered the dimension for **Mat A**, you will see the **2 × 4 matrix** A appear on the screen. Use this screen to input your data.

A	1	2	3	4→
1	0	0	0	0
2	0	0	0	0

Enter the data values into the appropriate cells. To begin entering your data, use the arrow key to highlight the cell 1,1 (top left corner of the cell). Type 20 and press **EXE**. The cursor will automatically scroll to the next cell.

A	1	2	3	4
1	20 EXE	32 EXE	44 EXE	10 EXE
2	10 EXE	48 EXE	21 EXE	15 EXE

After you enter your data in Matrix A, press **EXIT** two times until you see the following on the screen:

χ^2 Test

Observed : Mat A

Expected   : Mat B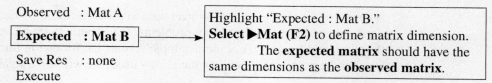

Save Res : none
Execute

> Highlight "Expected : Mat B."
> **Select ▶Mat (F2)** to define matrix dimension.
> The **expected matrix** should have the same dimensions as the **observed matrix**.

To define dimension, select ▶Mat (F2). You will see the following on the screen:

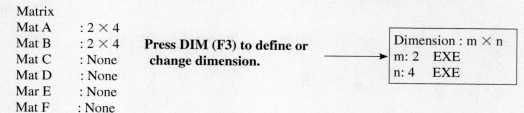

Matrix
Mat A   : 2 × 4
Mat B   : 2 × 4   **Press DIM (F3) to define or**   Dimension : m × n
Mat C   : None   **change dimension.**   ⟶   m: 2   EXE
Mat D   : None   n: 4   EXE
Mar E   : None
Mat F   : None

You will see **2 × 4 Matrix B**. You are not required to enter any values; the calculator will give you the expected values.

Now press **EXIT** two times until you see the following on the screen:

χ^2 Test
Observed : Mat A
Expected : Mat B
Save Res : none
Execute

At this point, press either **EXE** or **F1** (Calc).
The calculator will now show the results:

χ^2 Test

$\chi^2 = 15.0058158$
$p = 1.8117_{E}\text{-}03 \ (0.0018117)$
$df = 3$

To obtain the expected value matrix, select **▶Mat** (F6), highlight **MAT B**, and press **EXE**. The expected value matrix will be displayed on the screen as follows:

Ans	1	2	3	4 ⟶
1	15.9	42.4	34.45	13.25
2	14.1	37.6	30.55	11.75

Conclusion:
Since p-value = 0.0018 is less than α, we do not reject H_0.
The statistical evidence does not indicate that we may conclude that there is a difference in the proportion of nonconforming pages produced by the printers.

CHAPTER
15

Simple Linear Regression

CONTENTS

15.1 Types of Regression Models

15.2 Determining the Simple Linear Regression Equation

VISUAL EXPLORATIONS: Exploring Simple Linear Regression Coefficients

15.3 Measures of Variation

15.4 Assumptions of Regression

15.5 Residual Analysis

15.6 Measuring Autocorrelation: The Durbin-Watson Statistic

15.7 Inferences About the Slope and Correlation Coefficient

15.8 Estimation of Mean Values and Prediction of Individual Values

15.9 Potential Pitfalls in Regression

Six Steps for Avoiding the Potential Pitfalls

USING STATISTICS: Knowing Customers at Sunflowers Apparel, Revisited

CHAPTER 15 CASIO CALCULATOR GUIDE

CHAPTER 15 SPSS GUIDE

OBJECTIVES

Learn to use regression analysis to predict the value of a dependent variable based on the value of an independent variable

Understand the meaning of the regression coefficients b_0 and b_1

Learn to evaluate the assumptions of regression analysis and what to do if the assumptions are violated

Make inferences about the slope and correlation coefficient

Estimate mean values and predict individual values

USING STATISTICS

Knowing Customers at Sunflowers Apparel

Having survived recent economic slowdowns that have diminished their competitors, Sunflowers Apparel, a chain of upscale fashion stores for women, is in the midst of a companywide review that includes researching the factors that make their stores successful. Until recently, Sunflowers managers did not use data analysis to help select where to open stores, relying instead on subjective factors, such as the availability of an inexpensive lease or the perception that a particular location seemed ideal for one of their stores.

As the new director of planning, you have already consulted with marketing data firms that specialize in identifying and classifying groups of consumers. Based on such preliminary analyses, you have already tentatively discovered that the profile of Sunflowers shoppers may not only be the upper middle class long suspected of being the chain's clientele but may also include younger, aspirational families with young children, and, surprisingly, urban hipsters that set trends and are mostly single.

You seek to develop a systematic approach that will lead to making better decisions during the site-selection process. As a starting point, you have asked one marketing data firm to collect and organize data for the number of people in the identified groups of interest who live within a fixed radius of each store. You believe that the greater numbers of profiled customers contribute to store sales, and you want to explore the possible use of this relationship in the decision-making process. How can you use statistics so that you can forecast the annual sales of a proposed store based on the number of profiled customers that reside within a fixed radius of a Sunflowers store?

Fotolia

I n this chapter and the next chapter, you learn **regression analysis** techniques that help uncover relationships between variables. Regression analysis leads to selection of a **model** that expresses how one or more **independent variables** can be used to predict the value of another variable, called the **dependent variable**. Regression models identify the type of mathematical relationship that exists between a dependent variable and an independent variable, thereby enabling you to quantify the effect that a change in the independent variable has on the dependent variable. Models also help you identify unusual values that may be outliers (see references 2, 3, and 4).

This chapter discusses **simple linear regression** models that use a single numerical independent variable, X, to predict the numerical dependent variable, Y. (Chapter 16 discusses *multiple* regression models that use several independent variables to predict the dependent variable.) In the Sunflowers scenario, your initial belief reflects a possible simple linear regression model in which the number of profiled customers is the single numerical independent variable, X, being used to predict the annual sales of the store, the dependent variable, Y.

15.1 Types of Regression Models

Using a **scatter plot** (also known as **scatter diagram**) to visualize the X and Y variables, a technique, can help suggest a starting point for regression analysis. The scatter plots in Figure 15.1 illustrates six possible relationships between an X and Y variable.

FIGURE 15.1

Six types of relationships found in scatter plots

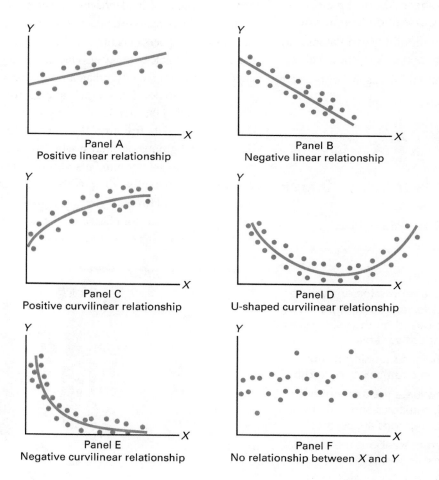

Panel A
Positive linear relationship

Panel B
Negative linear relationship

Panel C
Positive curvilinear relationship

Panel D
U-shaped curvilinear relationship

Panel E
Negative curvilinear relationship

Panel F
No relationship between X and Y

In Panel A, values of Y are generally increasing linearly as X increases. This panel is similar to Figure 15.3 on page 266, which illustrates the positive relationship between the number of profiled customers of the store and the store's annual sales for the Sunflowers Apparel women's clothing store chain.

Panel B is an example of a negative linear relationship. As X increases, the values of Y are generally decreasing. An example of this type of relationship might be the price of a particular product and the amount of sales. As the price charged for the product increases, the amount of sales may tend to decrease.

Panel C shows a positive curvilinear relationship between X and Y. The values of Y increase as X increases, but this increase tapers off beyond certain values of X. An example of a positive curvilinear relationship might be the age and maintenance cost of a machine. As a machine gets older, the maintenance cost may rise rapidly at first but then level off beyond a certain number of years.

Panel D shows a U-shaped relationship between X and Y. As X increases, at first Y generally decreases; but as X continues to increase, Y not only stops decreasing but actually increases above its minimum value. An example of this type of relationship might be entrepreneurial activity and levels of economic development as measured by GDP per capita. Entrepreneurial activity occurs more in the least and most developed countries.

Panel E illustrates an exponential relationship between X and Y. In this case, Y decreases very rapidly as X first increases, but then it decreases much less rapidly as X increases further. An example of an exponential relationship could be the value of an automobile and its age. The value drops drastically from its original price in the first year, but it decreases much less rapidly in subsequent years.

Finally, Panel F shows a set of data in which there is very little or no relationship between X and Y. High and low values of Y appear at each value of X.

Simple Linear Regression Models

Although scatter plots provide preliminary analysis, more sophisticated statistical procedures determine the most appropriate model for a set of variables. Simple linear regression models represent the simplest relationship of a straight-line or **linear relationship**. Figure 15.2 illustrates this relationship.

FIGURE 15.2

A straight-line relationship

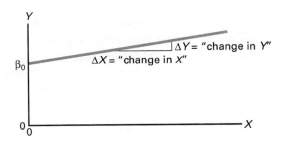

Equation (15.1) expresses this relationship mathematically by defining the simple linear regression model.

SIMPLE LINEAR REGRESSION MODEL

$$Y_i = \beta_0 + \beta_1 X_i + \varepsilon_i \tag{15.1}$$

where

$\beta_0 = Y$ intercept for the population

$\beta_1 =$ slope for the population

$\varepsilon_i =$ random error in Y for observation i

$Y_i =$ dependent variable (sometimes referred to as the **response variable**) for observation i

$X_i =$ independent variable (sometimes referred to as the predictor, or **explanatory variable**) for observation i

The $Y_i = \beta_0 + \beta_1 X_i$ portion of the simple linear regression model expressed in Equation (15.1) is a straight line. The **slope** of the line, β_1, represents the expected change in Y per unit change in X. It represents the mean amount that Y changes (either positively or negatively) for a one-unit change in X. The **Y intercept**, β_0, represents the mean value of Y when X equals 0. The last component of the model, ε_i, represents the random error in Y for each observation, i. In other words, ε_i is the vertical distance of the actual value of Y_i above or below the expected value of Y_i on the line.

15.2 Determining the Simple Linear Regression Equation

In the Sunflowers Apparel scenario on page 263, the business objective of the director of planning is to forecast annual sales for all new stores, based on the number of profiled customers who live no more than 30 minutes from a Sunflowers store. To examine the relationship between the number of profiled customers (in millions) who live within a fixed radius from a Sunflowers store and its annual sales ($millions), data were collected from a sample of 14 stores. Table 15.1 shows the organized data, which are stored in SiteSelection .

TABLE 15.1

Number of Profiled Customers (in millions) and Annual Sales (in $millions) for a Sample of 14 Sunflowers Apparel Stores

Store	Profiled Customers (millions)	Annual Sales ($millions)	Store	Profiled Customers (millions)	Annual Sales ($millions)
1	3.7	5.7	8	3.1	4.7
2	3.6	5.9	9	3.2	6.1
3	2.8	6.7	10	3.5	4.9
4	5.6	9.5	11	5.2	10.7
5	3.3	5.4	12	4.6	7.6
6	2.2	3.5	13	5.8	11.8
7	3.3	6.2	14	3.0	4.1

Figure 15.3 displays the scatter plot for the data in Table 15.1. Observe the increasing relationship between profiled customers (X) and annual sales (Y). As the number of profiled customers increases, annual sales increase approximately as a straight line (superimposed on the scatter plot). Thus, you can assume that a straight line provides a useful mathematical model of this relationship. Now you need to determine the specific straight line that is the *best* fit to these data.

FIGURE 15.3

Scatter plot for the Sunflowers Apparel data

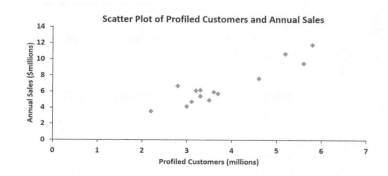

How to Create a Scatter Plot Using Casio Calculator fx-9750GII

Use your Casio calculator and follow the instructions below to create a scatterplot.

First enter the data (Table 15.1) in **List 1** and **List 2** as shown below.

Profiled Customers (millions) :X	Annual sales ($millions): Y
3.7	5.7
3.6	5.9
2.8	6.7
5.6	9.5
3.3	5.4
2.2	3.5
3.3	6.2
3.1	4.7
3.2	6.1
3.5	4.9
5.2	10.7
4.6	7.6
5.8	11.8
3.0	4.1

Input these values in **List 1**
(in your calculator)

Input these values in **List 2**
(in your calculator)

From the **Main Menu** select the following:

STAT   **F1**(GRPH)   **F6**(SET)   and you will see the following screen.

StatGraph1
Graph Type   : Scatter (F1)
Xlist   : List1
Ylist   : List2
Frequency   : 1
Mark Type   : ☐ (F1)

Press **EXE** and then press **F1**(GPH1) to obtain the scatterplot.

The scatterplot created with the calculator is shown below:

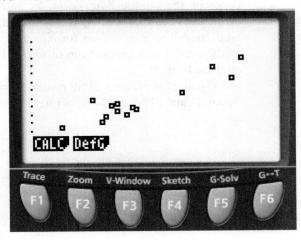

The Least-Squares Method

In the preceding section, a statistical model is hypothesized to represent the relationship between two variables—number of profiled customers and sales—in the entire population of Sunflowers Apparel stores. However, as shown in Table 15.1, the data are collected from a random sample of stores. If certain assumptions are valid (see Section 15.4), you can use the sample Y intercept, b_0, and the sample slope, b_1, as estimates of the respective population parameters, β_0 and β_1. Equation (15.2) uses these estimates to form the **simple linear regression equation**. This straight line is often referred to as the **prediction line**.

SIMPLE LINEAR REGRESSION EQUATION: THE PREDICTION LINE

The predicted value of Y equals the Y intercept plus the slope multiplied by the value of X.

$$\hat{Y}_i = b_0 + b_1 X_i \tag{15.2}$$

where

$\hat{Y}_i$ = predicted value of Y for observation i

X_i = value of X for observation i

b_0 = sample Y intercept

b_1 = sample slope

Equation (15.2) requires you to determine two **regression coefficients**—b_0 (the sample Y intercept) and b_1 (the sample slope). The most common approach to finding b_0 and b_1 is using the least-squares method. This method minimizes the sum of the squared differences between the actual values (Y_i) and the predicted values ($\hat{Y}_i$), using the simple linear regression equation [i.e., the prediction line; see Equation (15.2)]. This sum of squared differences is equal to

$$\sum_{i=1}^{n} (Y_i - \hat{Y}_i)^2$$

Because $\hat{Y}_i = b_0 + b_1 X_i$,

$$\sum_{i=1}^{n} (Y_i - \hat{Y}_i)^2 = \sum_{i=1}^{n} [Y_i - (b_0 + b_1 X_i)]^2$$

Because this equation has two unknowns, b_0 and b_1, the sum of squared differences depends on the sample Y intercept, b_0, and the sample slope, b_1. The **least-squares method** determines the values of b_0 and b_1 that minimize the sum of squared differences around the prediction line. Any values for b_0 and b_1 other than those determined by the least-squares method result in a greater sum of squared differences between the actual values (Y_i) and the predicted values ($\hat{Y}_i$).

Figure 15.4 presents SPSS results for the simple linear regression model for the Sunflower Apparel data. SPSS labels b_0 as Intercept and labels b_1 as Profiled Customers.

FIGURE 15.4

SPSS simple linear regression model for Sunflowers Apparel data

Regression

Model Summary

Model	R	R Square	Adjusted R Square	Std. Error of the Estimate	R Square Change	F Change	df1	df2	Sig. F Change
					Change Statistics				
1	.921ᵃ	.848	.835	.9993	.848	66.879	1	12	.000

a. Predictors: (Constant), Profiled Custers (Millions)

ANOVAᵃ

Model		Sum of Squares	df	Mean Square	F	Sig.
1	Regression	66.785	1	66.785	66.879	.000ᵇ
	Residual	11.983	12	.999		
	Total	78.769	13			

a. Dependent Variable: Annual Sales ($million)

b. Predictors: (Constant), Profiled Custers (Millions)

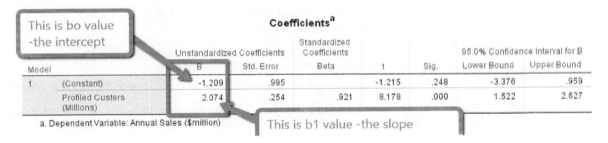

This is bo value -the intercept

Coefficientsᵃ

Model		Unstandardized Coefficients		Standardized Coefficients	t	Sig.	95.0% Confidence Interval for B	
		B	Std. Error	Beta			Lower Bound	Upper Bound
1	(Constant)	-1.209	.995		-1.215	.248	-3.376	.959
	Profiled Custers (Millions)	2.074	.254	.921	8.178	.000	1.522	2.627

a. Dependent Variable: Annual Sales ($million)

This is b1 value -the slope

In Figure 15.4, observe that $b_0 = -1.2088$ and $b_1 = 2.0742$. Using Equation (15.2) on page 268, the prediction line for these data is

$$\hat{Y}_i = -1.2088 + 2.0742X_i$$

> **Student Tip**
>
> Remember that a positive slope means that as X increases, Y is predicted to increase. A negative slope means that as X increases, Y is predicted to decrease.

The slope, b_1, is +2.0742. This means that for each increase of 1 unit in X, the predicted mean value of Y is estimated to increase by 2.0742 units. In other words, for each increase of 1.0 million profiled customers within 30 minutes of the store, the predicted mean annual sales are estimated to increase by $2.0742 million. Thus, the slope represents the portion of the annual sales that are estimated to vary according to the number of profiled customers.

The Y intercept, b_0, is -1.2088. The Y intercept represents the predicted value of Y when X equals 0. Because the number of profiled customers of the store cannot be 0, this Y intercept has little or no practical interpretation. Also, the Y intercept for this example is outside the range of the observed values of the X variable, and therefore interpretations of the value of b_0 should be made cautiously. Figure 15.5 displays the actual values and the prediction line.

FIGURE 15.5

Scatter plot and prediction line for Sunflowers Apparel data

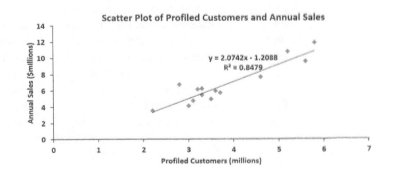

Example 15.1 illustrates a situation in which there is a direct interpretation for the Y intercept, b_0.

EXAMPLE 15.1

Interpreting the Y Intercept, b_0, and the Slope, b_1

A statistics professor wants to use the number of hours a student studies for a statistics final exam (X) to predict the final exam score (Y). A regression model is fit based on data collected from a class during the previous semester, with the following results:

$$\hat{Y}_i = 35.0 + 3X_i$$

What is the interpretation of the Y intercept, b_0, and the slope, b_1?

SOLUTION The Y intercept $b_0 = 35.0$ indicates that when the student does not study for the final exam, the predicted mean final exam score is 35.0. The slope $b_1 = 3$ indicates that for each increase of one hour in studying time, the predicted change in the mean final exam score is $+3.0$. In other words, the final exam score is predicted to increase by a mean of 3 points for each one-hour increase in studying time.

Return to the Sunflowers Apparel scenario on page 263. Example 15.2 illustrates how you use the prediction line to predict the annual sales.

EXAMPLE 15.2

Predicting Annual Sales Based on Number of Profiled Customers

Use the prediction line to predict the annual sales for a store with 4 million profiled customers.

SOLUTION You can determine the predicted value of annual sales by substituting $X = 4$ (millions of profiled customers) into the simple linear regression equation:

$$\hat{Y}_i = -1.2088 + 2.0742X_i$$
$$\hat{Y}_i = -1.2088 + 2.0742(4) = 7.0879 \text{ or } \$7,087,900$$

Thus, a store with 4 million profiled customers has predicted mean annual sales of $7,087,900.

Predictions in Regression Analysis: Interpolation Versus Extrapolation

When using a regression model for prediction purposes, you should consider only the **relevant range** of the independent variable in making predictions. This relevant range includes all values from the smallest to the largest X used in developing the regression model. Hence, when predicting Y for a given value of X, you can interpolate within this relevant range of the X values, but you should not extrapolate beyond the range of X values. When you use the number of profiled customers to predict annual sales, the number of profiled customers (in millions) varies from 2.2 to 5.8 (see Table 15.1 on page 266). Therefore, you should predict annual sales *only* for stores that have between 2.2 and 5.8 million profiled customers. Any prediction of annual sales for stores outside this range assumes that the observed relationship between sales and the number of profiled customers for stores that have between 2.2 and 5.8 million profiled customers is the same as for stores outside this range. For example, you cannot extrapolate the linear relationship beyond 5.8 million profiled customers in Example 15.2. It would be improper to use the prediction line to forecast the sales for a new store that has 8 million profiled customers because the relationship between sales and the number of profiled customers may have a point of diminishing returns. If that is true, as the number of profiled customers increases beyond 5.8 million, the effect on sales may become smaller and smaller.

How to Find Prediction Value Using the Calculator

Use your Casio calculator and follow the instructions below to find the prediction value of annual sales for a store with 8 million profiled customers (X=8).

You have to make sure that the data (Table 15.1) is recorded in the calculator and the simple linear regression is performed prior to computing the prediction value.

To perform the simple linear regression, first enter the data (Table 15.1) in **List 1** and **List 2** as shown below.

Profiled Customers (millions) :X	Annual sales ($millions): Y
3.7	5.7
3.6	5.9
2.8	6.7
5.6	9.5
3.3	5.4
2.2	3.5
3.3	6.2
3.1	4.7
3.2	6.1
3.5	4.9
5.2	10.7
4.6	7.6
5.8	11.8
3.0	4.1

Input these values in **List 1** (in your calculator)   Input these values in **List 2** (in your calculator)

From the **Main Menu** select the following option:

STAT   **F2**(CALC)   **F6**(SET)   and you will see the following screen.

1 Var XList   : List 1
1 Var Freq   : List 2
2 Var XList   : List 1   (Note: set for "2 Var XList)
2 Var YList   : List 2   (Note: set for "2 Var YList)
2 Var Freq   : 1

Press **Exe**

For the regression result select **F3**(REG)   **F1**(X)   **F1**(aX+b)

To obtain predicted value for X=8, go to the main menu and select:

MENU RUN-MAT   EXE   then enter **8** **OPTN** (a black key just under function key F2)

Use the following options at the bottom of the display.
Select   **STAT (F5)** $\bar{y}$ **(F2)**   **EXE**

The calculator will now show the result:

We interpret the value as follows:

$\hat{y} = -1.208839 + 2.07417291\,(8) = 15.3845442$
We predict that the annual sales will be \$15.3845442 (in millions of dollars) if the number of profiled customers is 8 (millions).

Computing the Y Intercept, b_0, and the Slope, b_1 Using Equations

For small data sets, you can use a hand calculator to compute the least-squares regression coefficients. Equations (15.3) and (15.4) give the values of b_0 and b_1, which minimize

$$\sum_{i=1}^{n}(Y_i - \hat{Y}_i)^2 = \sum_{i=1}^{n}[Y_i - (b_0 + b_1 X_i)]^2$$

COMPUTATIONAL FORMULA FOR THE SLOPE, b_1

$$b_1 = \frac{SSXY}{SSX} \tag{15.3}$$

where

$$SSXY = \sum_{i=1}^{n}(X_i - \overline{X})(Y_i - \overline{Y}) = \sum_{i=1}^{n}X_i Y_i - \frac{\left(\sum_{i=1}^{n}X_i\right)\left(\sum_{i=1}^{n}Y_i\right)}{n}$$

$$SSX = \sum_{i=1}^{n}(X_i - \overline{X})^2 = \sum_{i=1}^{n}X_i^2 - \frac{\left(\sum_{i=1}^{n}X_i\right)^2}{n}$$

COMPUTATIONAL FORMULA FOR THE Y INTERCEPT, b_0

$$b_0 = \overline{Y} - b_1\overline{X} \tag{15.4}$$

where

$$\overline{Y} = \frac{\sum_{i=1}^{n}Y_i}{n}$$

$$\overline{X} = \frac{\sum_{i=1}^{n}X_i}{n}$$

EXAMPLE 15.3

Computing the Y Intercept, b_0, and the Slope, b_1

Compute the Y intercept, b_0, and the slope, b_1, for the Sunflowers Apparel data.

SOLUTION In Equations (15.3) and (15.4), five quantities need to be computed to determine b_1 and b_0. These are n, the sample size; $\sum_{i=1}^{n} X_i$, the sum of the X values; $\sum_{i=1}^{n} Y_i$, the sum of the Y values; $\sum_{i=1}^{n} X_i^2$, the sum of the squared X values; and $\sum_{i=1}^{n} X_i Y_i$, the sum of the product of X and Y.

For the Sunflowers Apparel data, the number of profiled customers (X) is used to predict the annual sales (Y) in a store. Table 15.2 presents the computations of the sums needed for the site selection problem. The table also includes $\sum_{i=1}^{n} Y_i^2$, the sum of the squared Y values that will be used to compute SST in Section 15.3.

TABLE 15.2

Computations for the Sunflowers Apparel Data

Store	Profiled Customers (X)	Annual Sales (Y)	X^2	Y^2	XY
1	3.7	5.7	13.69	32.49	21.09
2	3.6	5.9	12.96	34.81	21.24
3	2.8	6.7	7.84	44.89	18.76
4	5.6	9.5	31.36	90.25	53.20
5	3.3	5.4	10.89	29.16	17.82
6	2.2	3.5	4.84	12.25	7.70
7	3.3	6.2	10.89	38.44	20.46
8	3.1	4.7	9.61	22.09	14.57
9	3.2	6.1	10.24	37.21	19.52
10	3.5	4.9	12.25	24.01	17.15
11	5.2	10.7	27.04	114.49	55.64
12	4.6	7.6	21.16	57.76	34.96
13	5.8	11.8	33.64	139.24	68.44
14	3.0	4.1	9.00	16.81	12.30
Totals	52.9	92.8	215.41	693.90	382.85

Student Tip
Coefficients computed manually with the assistance of handheld calculators may differ slightly because of rounding errors caused by the limited number of decimal places that your calculator might use.

Using Equations (15.3) and (15.4), you can compute b_0 and b_1:

$$SSXY = \sum_{i=1}^{n}(X_i - \bar{X})(Y_i - \bar{Y}) = \sum_{i=1}^{n} X_i Y_i - \frac{\left(\sum_{i=1}^{n} X_i\right)\left(\sum_{i=1}^{n} Y_i\right)}{n}$$

$$= 382.85 - \frac{(52.9)(92.8)}{14}$$

$$= 382.85 - 350.65142$$

$$= 32.19858$$

$$SSX = \sum_{i=1}^{n}(X_i - \bar{X})^2 = \sum_{i=1}^{n} X_i^2 - \frac{\left(\sum_{i=1}^{n} X_i\right)^2}{n}$$

$$= 215.41 - \frac{(52.9)^2}{14}$$

$$= 215.41 - 199.88642$$

$$= 15.52358$$

With these values, compute b_1:

$$b_1 = \frac{SSXY}{SSX}$$

$$= \frac{32.19858}{15.52358}$$

$$= 2.07417$$

and:

$$\overline{Y} = \frac{\sum\limits_{i=1}^{n} Y_i}{n} = \frac{92.8}{14} = 6.62857$$

$$\overline{X} = \frac{\sum\limits_{i=1}^{n} X_i}{n} = \frac{52.9}{14} = 3.77857$$

With these values, compute b_0:

$$b_0 = \overline{Y} - b_1\overline{X}$$
$$= 6.62857 - 2.07417(3.77857)$$
$$= -1.2088265$$

Compute the Y Intercept, b_0, and the Slope, b_1, Using the Calculator with the Sunflowers Apparel Data

Refer to Example 15.3. Compute the Y intercept, b_0 and the slope, b_1, for the Sunflowers Apparel data.

The *Casio Calculator fx-9750GII* can perform a simple linear regression. Follow the following calculator steps to run a simple linear regression.

First, enter the data in **List 1** and **List 2**.

Profiled Customers (millions) :X LIST 1	Annual sales ($millions): Y LIST 2
3.7	5.7
3.6	5.9
2.8	6.7
5.6	9.5
3.3	5.4
2.2	3.5
3.3	6.2
3.1	4.7
3.2	6.1
3.5	4.9
5.2	10.7
4.6	7.6
5.8	11.8
3.0	.1

From the **Main Menu** select:

STAT   F2(CALC)   **F6**(SET)   then set the following items:

1Var XList	:	} Do not need to set for **1Var**
1Var Freq	:	
2Var XList	:	**List 1**
2Var YList	:	**List 2**
2Var Freq	:	**1**

Press **EXIT or EXE,** then select **F3 (REG), F1 (X)**

Either press F1(aX+b) or F2(a+bX) to determine the simple linear regression equation.

If you press F1 (aX+b), you will see the following result:

Note: Casio Calculator labels b as intercept (b_0) and labels a as slope.

```
LinearReg(ax+b)
   a =2.07417291
   b =-1.208839
   r =0.92079785
   r²=0.84786868
 MSe=0.99859721
y=ax+b
                  COPY
```

From the results given by the calculator, the simple linear regression equation (line) would be
Y= 2.07417291X-1.208839

If you press F2 (a+bX), you will see the following result:

Note: Casio Calculator labels a as intercept (b_0) and labels b as slope (b_1).

```
LinearReg(a+bx)
   a =-1.208839
   b =2.07417291
   r =0.92079785
   r²=0.84786868
 MSe=0.99859721
y=a+bx
                  COPY
```

From the results given by the calculator, the simple linear regression equation (line) would be
Y= -1.208839 + 2.07417291X   **(Note: This form is preferred)**

Note: Both forms give you the same simple linear regression equation (line).

Exploring Simple Linear Regression Coefficients

Open the **VE-Simple Linear Regression add-in workbook** to explore the coefficients. (See Appendix C to learn more about using this workbook.) When this workbook opens properly, it adds a **Simple Linear Regression** menu in either the Add-ins tab (Microsoft Windows) or the Apple menu bar (OS X).

To explore the effects of changing the simple linear regression coefficients, select **Simple Linear Regression → Explore Coefficients**. In the Explore Coefficients floating control panel (shown inset below), click the spinner buttons for b_1 **slope** (the slope of the prediction line) and b_0 **intercept** (the Y intercept of the prediction line) to change the prediction line. Using the visual feedback of the chart, try to create a prediction line that is as close as possible to the prediction line defined by the least-squares estimates. In other words, try to make the **Difference from Target SSE** value as small as possible. (See page 427 for an explanation of SSE.)

At any time, click **Reset** to reset the b_1 and b_0 values or **Solution** to reveal the prediction line defined by the least-squares method. Click **Finish** when you are finished with this exercise.

Using Your Own Regression Data

Select **Simple Linear Regression using your worksheet data** from the **Simple Linear Regression** menu to explore the simple linear regression coefficients using data you supply from a worksheet. In the procedure's dialog box, enter the cell range of your Y variable as the **Y Variable Cell Range** and the cell range of your X variable as the **X Variable Cell Range**. Click **First cells in both ranges contain a label**, enter a **Title**, and click **OK**. After the scatter plot appears onscreen, continue with the Explore Coefficients floating control panel as described in the left column.

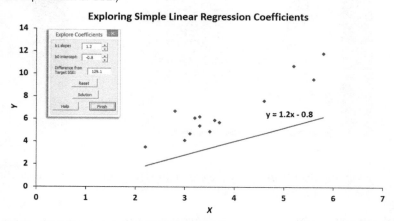

15.3 Measures of Variation

When using the least-squares method to determine the regression coefficients you need to compute three measures of variation. The first measure, the **total sum of squares (SST)**, is a measure of variation of the Y_i values around their mean, $\overline{Y}$. The **total variation**, or total sum of squares, is subdivided into **explained variation** and **unexplained variation**. The explained variation, or **regression sum of squares (SSR)**, represents variation that is explained by the relationship between X and Y, and the unexplained variation, or **error sum of squares (SSE)**, represents variation due to factors other than the relationship between X and Y. Figure 15.6 shows the different measures of variation for a single Y_i value.

FIGURE 15.6
Measures of variation

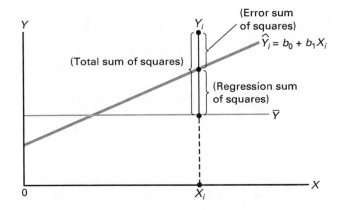

Computing the Sum of Squares

The regression sum of squares (SSR) is based on the difference between $\hat{Y}_i$ (the predicted value of Y from the prediction line) and $\bar{Y}$ (the mean value of Y). The error sum of squares (SSE) represents the part of the variation in Y that is not explained by the regression. It is based on the difference between Y_i and $\hat{Y}_i$. The total sum of squares (SST) is equal to the regression sum of squares (SSR) plus the error sum of squares (SSE). Equations (15.5), (15.6), (15.7), and (15.8) define these measures of variation and the total sum of squares (SST).

MEASURES OF VARIATION IN REGRESSION

The total sum of squares (SST) is equal to the regression sum of squares (SSR) plus the error sum of squares (SSE).

$$SST = SSR + SSE \tag{15.5}$$

TOTAL SUM OF SQUARES (SST)

The total sum of squares (SST) is equal to the sum of the squared differences between each observed value of Y and the mean value of Y.

$$SST = \text{Total sum of squares}$$

$$= \sum_{i=1}^{n} (Y_i - \bar{Y})^2 \tag{15.6}$$

REGRESSION SUM OF SQUARES (SSR)

The regression sum of squares (SSR) is equal to the sum of the squared differences between each predicted value of Y and the mean value of Y.

$$SSR = \text{Explained variation or regression sum of squares}$$

$$= \sum_{i=1}^{n} (\hat{Y}_i - \bar{Y})^2 \tag{15.7}$$

ERROR SUM OF SQUARES (*SSE*)

The error sum of squares (*SSE*) is equal to the sum of the squared differences between each observed value of *Y* and the predicted value of *Y*.

$$SSE = \text{Unexplained variation or error sum of squares}$$

$$= \sum_{i=1}^{n}(Y_i - \hat{Y}_i)^2 \tag{15.8}$$

Figure 15.7 shows the sum of squares portion of the Figure 15.4 results for the Sunflowers Apparel data. The total variation, *SST*, is equal to 78.7686. This amount is subdivided into the sum of squares explained by the regression (*SSR*), equal to 66.7854, and the sum of squares unexplained by the regression (*SSE*), equal to 11.9832. From Equation (15.5) on page 277:

$$SST = SSR + SSE$$
$$78.7686 = 66.7854 + 11.9832$$

FIGURE 15.7

SPSS sum of squares portion for the Sunflowers Apparel data

Regression

ANOVA[a]

Model		Sum of Squares	df	Mean Square	F	Sig.
1	Regression	66.785	1	66.785	66.879	.000[b]
	Residual	11.983	12	.999		
	Total	78.769	13			

a. Dependent Variable: Annual Sales ($million)
b. Predictors: (Constant), Profiled Custers (Millions)

Coefficients[a]

Model		Unstandardized Coefficients B	Std. Error	Standardized Coefficients Beta	t	Sig.	95.0% Confidence Interval for B Lower Bound	Upper Bound
1	(Constant)	-1.209	.995		-1.215	.248	-3.376	.959
	Profiled Custers (Millions)	2.074	.254	.921	8.178	.000	1.522	2.627

a. Dependent Variable: Annual Sales ($million)

The Coefficient of Determination

By themselves, *SSR*, *SSE*, and *SST* provide little information. However, the ratio of the regression sum of squares (*SSR*) to the total sum of squares (*SST*) measures the proportion of variation in *Y* that is explained by the linear relationship of the independent variable *X* with the dependent variable *Y* in the regression model. This ratio, called the coefficient of determination, r^2, is defined in Equation (15.9).

COEFFICIENT OF DETERMINATION

The coefficient of determination is equal to the regression sum of squares (i.e., explained variation) divided by the total sum of squares (i.e., total variation).

$$r^2 = \frac{\text{Regression sum of squares}}{\text{Total sum of squares}} = \frac{SSR}{SST} \tag{15.9}$$

Student Tip
r^2 must be a value between 0 and 1. It cannot be negative.

The **coefficient of determination** measures the proportion of variation in Y that is explained by the variation in the independent variable X in the regression model.

For the Sunflowers Apparel data, with $SSR = 66.7854$, $SSE = 11.9832$, and $SST = 78.7686$,

$$r^2 = \frac{66.7854}{78.7686} = 0.8479$$

Therefore, 84.79% of the variation in annual sales is explained by the variability in the number of profiled customers. This large r^2 indicates a strong linear relationship between these two variables because the regression model has explained 84.79% of the variability in predicting annual sales. Only 15.21% of the sample variability in annual sales is due to factors other than what is accounted for by the linear regression model that uses the number of profiled customers.

Figure 15.8 presents the regression statistics table portion of the Figure 15.4 results for the Sunflowers Apparel data. This table contains the coefficient of determination.

FIGURE 15.8
SPSS regression statistics for the Sunflowers Apparel data

Regression

Model Summary

					Change Statistics				
Model	R	R Square	Adjusted R Square	Std. Error of the Estimate	R Square Change	F Change	df1	df2	Sig. F Change
1	.921[a]	.848	.835	.9993	.848	66.879	1	12	.000

a. Predictors: (Constant), Profiled Custers (Millions)

ANOVA[a]

Model		Sum of Squares	df	Mean Square	F	Sig.
1	Regression	66.785	1	66.785	66.879	.000[b]
	Residual	11.983	12	.999		
	Total	78.769	13			

a. Dependent Variable: Annual Sales ($million)

b. Predictors: (Constant), Profiled Custers (Millions)

EXAMPLE 15.4

Computing the Coefficient of Determination

Compute the coefficient of determination, r^2, for the Sunflowers Apparel data.

SOLUTION You can compute SST, SSR, and SSE, which are defined in Equations (15.6), (15.7), and (15.8) on pages 277 and 278, by using Equations (15.10), (15.11), and (15.12).

COMPUTATIONAL FORMULA FOR *SST*

$$SST = \sum_{i=1}^{n}(Y_i - \overline{Y})^2 = \sum_{i=1}^{n}Y_i^2 - \frac{\left(\sum_{i=1}^{n}Y_i\right)^2}{n} \quad (15.10)$$

COMPUTATIONAL FORMULA FOR *SSR*

$$SSR = \sum_{i=1}^{n}(\hat{Y}_i - \overline{Y})^2$$

$$= b_0\sum_{i=1}^{n}Y_i + b_1\sum_{i=1}^{n}X_iY_i - \frac{\left(\sum_{i=1}^{n}Y_i\right)^2}{n} \quad (15.11)$$

COMPUTATIONAL FORMULA FOR *SSE*

$$SSE = \sum_{i=1}^{n}(Y_i - \hat{Y}_i)^2 = \sum_{i=1}^{n}Y_i^2 - b_0\sum_{i=1}^{n}Y_i - b_1\sum_{i=1}^{n}X_iY_i \qquad (15.12)$$

Using the summary results from Table 15.2 on page 273,

$$SST = \sum_{i=1}^{n}(Y_i - \overline{Y})^2 = \sum_{i=1}^{n}Y_i^2 - \frac{\left(\sum_{i=1}^{n}Y_i\right)^2}{n}$$

$$= 693.9 - \frac{(92.8)^2}{14}$$

$$= 693.9 - 615.13142$$

$$= 78.76858$$

$$SSR = \sum_{i=1}^{n}(\hat{Y}_i - \overline{Y})^2$$

$$= b_0\sum_{i=1}^{n}Y_i + b_1\sum_{i=1}^{n}X_iY_i - \frac{\left(\sum_{i=1}^{n}Y_i\right)^2}{n}$$

$$= (-1.2088265)(92.8) + (2.07417)(382.85) - \frac{(92.8)^2}{14}$$

$$= 66.7854$$

$$SSE = \sum_{i=1}^{n}(Y_i - \hat{Y}_i)^2$$

$$= \sum_{i=1}^{n}Y_i^2 - b_0\sum_{i=1}^{n}Y_i - b_1\sum_{i=1}^{n}X_iY_i$$

$$= 693.9 - (-1.2088265)(92.8) - (2.07417)(382.85)$$

$$= 11.9832$$

> **Student Tip**
> Coefficients computed manually with the assistance of handheld calculators may differ slightly.

Therefore,

$$r^2 = \frac{66.7854}{78.7686} = 0.8479$$

Standard Error of the Estimate

Although the least-squares method produces the line that fits the data with the minimum amount of prediction error, unless all the observed data points fall on a straight line, the prediction line is not a perfect predictor. Just as all data values cannot be expected to be exactly equal to their mean, neither can all the values in a regression analysis be expected to be located exactly on the prediction line. Figure 15.5 on page 269 illustrates the variability around the prediction line for the Sunflowers Apparel data. Notice that many of the observed values of Y fall near the prediction line, but none of the values are exactly on the line.

The **standard error of the estimate** measures the variability of the observed Y values from the predicted Y values in the same way that the standard deviation in Chapter 2 measures the variability of each value around the sample mean. In other words, the standard error of the estimate is the standard deviation *around* the prediction line, whereas the standard deviation in Chapter 2 is the standard deviation *around* the sample mean. Equation (15.13) defines the standard error of the estimate, represented by the symbol S_{YX}.

STANDARD ERROR OF THE ESTIMATE

$$S_{YX} = \sqrt{\frac{SSE}{n-2}} = \sqrt{\frac{\sum_{i=1}^{n}(Y_i - \hat{Y}_i)^2}{n-2}} \qquad \textbf{(15.13)}$$

where

$$Y_i = \text{actual value of } Y \text{ for a given } X_i$$
$$\hat{Y}_i = \text{predicted value of } Y \text{ for a given } X_i$$
$$SSE = \text{error sum of squares}$$

From Equation (15.8) and Figure 15.4 or Figure 15.7 on pages 269 or 648, $SSE = 11.9832$. Thus,

$$S_{YX} = \sqrt{\frac{11.9832}{14-2}} = 0.9993$$

This standard error of the estimate, equal to 0.9993 millions of dollars (i.e., $999,300), is labeled Std. error of the estimates in the Figure 15.8 SPSS results. The standard error of the estimate represents a measure of the variation around the prediction line. It is measured in the same units as the dependent variable Y. The interpretation of the standard error of the estimate is similar to that of the standard deviation. Just as the standard deviation measures variability around the mean, the standard error of the estimate measures variability around the prediction line. For Sunflowers Apparel, the typical difference between actual annual sales at a store and the predicted annual sales using the regression equation is approximately $999,300.

Calculator and SPSS standard error of the estimate for the Sunflower Apparel data.

(I) Using the calculator to compute the standard error of the estimate:

First, you have to run the simple linear regression and the result is shown below.

Then using the MSe value provided above to compute the standard error of the estimate,

$$S_{YX} = \sqrt{MSE} = \sqrt{0.99859721} = 0.9993$$

(II) Using the SPSS to compute the standard error of the estimate:

The SPSS standard error of the estimate is highlighted below:

Regression

Model Summary

Model	R	R Square	Adjusted R Square	Std. Error of the Estimate	R Square Change	F Change	df1	df2	Sig. F Change
						Change Statistics			
1	.921[a]	.848	.835	.9993	.848	66.879	1	12	.000

a. Predictors: (Constant), Profiled Custers (Millions)

S_{yx}

15.4 Assumptions of Regression

When hypothesis testing and the analysis of variance were discussed in Chapters 11 through 14, the importance of the assumptions to the validity of any conclusions reached was emphasized. The assumptions necessary for regression are similar to those of the analysis of variance because both are part of the general category of *linear models* (reference 4).

The four **assumptions of regression** (known by the acronym LINE) are:

- Linearity
- Independence of errors
- Normality of error
- Equal variance

The first assumption, **linearity**, states that the relationship between variables is linear. Relationships between variables that are not linear are discussed in reference 4.

The second assumption, **independence of errors**, requires that the errors (ε_i) be independent of one another. This assumption is particularly important when data are collected over a period of time. In such situations, the errors in a specific time period are sometimes correlated with those of the previous time period.

The third assumption, **normality**, requires that the errors (ε_i) be normally distributed at each value of X. Like the t test and the ANOVA F test, regression analysis is fairly robust against departures from the normality assumption. As long as the distribution of the errors at each level of X is not extremely different from a normal distribution, inferences about β_0 and β_1 are not seriously affected.

The fourth assumption, **equal variance**, or **homoscedasticity**, requires that the variance of the errors (ε_i) be constant for all values of X. In other words, the variability of Y values is the same when X is a low value as when X is a high value. The equal-variance assumption is important when making inferences about β_0 and β_1. If there are serious departures from this assumption, you can use either data transformations or weighted least-squares methods (see reference 4).

15.5 Residual Analysis

Sections 15.2 and 15.3 developed a regression model using the least-squares method for the Sunflowers Apparel data. Is this the correct model for these data? Are the assumptions presented in Section 15.4 valid? **Residual analysis** visually evaluates these assumptions and helps you determine whether the regression model that has been selected is appropriate.

The **residual**, or estimated error value, e_i, is the difference between the observed (Y_i) and predicted $(\hat{Y}_i)$ values of the dependent variable for a given value of X_i. A residual appears on a scatter plot as the vertical distance between an observed value of Y and the prediction line. Equation (15.14) defines the residual.

RESIDUAL

The residual is equal to the difference between the observed value of Y and the predicted value of Y.

$$e_i = Y_i - \hat{Y}_i \qquad\qquad (15.14)$$

Evaluating the Assumptions

Recall from Section 15.4 that the four assumptions of regression (known by the acronym LINE) are linearity, independence, normality, and equal variance.

Linearity To evaluate linearity, you plot the residuals on the vertical axis against the corresponding X_i values of the independent variable on the horizontal axis. If the linear model is appropriate for the data, you will not see any apparent pattern in the plot. However, if the linear model is not appropriate, in the residual plot, there will be a relationship between the X_i values and the residuals, e_i.

You can see such a pattern in the residuals in Figure 15.9. Panel A shows a situation in which, although there is an increasing trend in Y as X increases, the relationship seems curvilinear because the upward trend decreases for increasing values of X. This effect is even more apparent in Panel B, where there is a clear relationship between X_i and e_i. By removing the linear trend of X with Y, the residual plot has exposed the lack of fit in the simple linear model more clearly than the scatter plot in Panel A. For these data, a quadratic or curvilinear model (see reference 4) is a better fit and should be used instead of the simple linear model.

FIGURE 15.9

Studying the appropriateness of the simple linear regression model

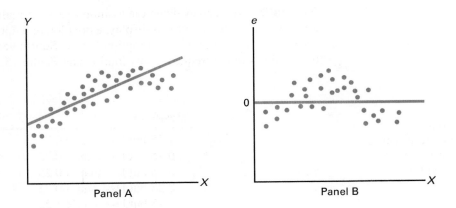

Panel A   Panel B

To determine whether the simple linear regression model for the Sunflowers Apparel data is appropriate, you need to determine the residuals. Figure 15.10 displays the predicted annual sales values and residuals for the Sunflowers Apparel data.

FIGURE 15.10

Table of residuals for the Sunflowers Apparel data

Store	Profiled Customers	Predicted Annual Sales	Annual Sales	Residuals
1	3.7	6.4656	5.7	-0.7656
2	3.6	6.2582	5.9	-0.3582
3	2.8	4.5988	6.7	2.1012
4	5.6	10.4065	9.5	-0.9065
5	3.3	5.6359	5.4	-0.2359
6	2.2	3.3543	3.5	0.1457
7	3.3	5.6359	6.2	0.5641
8	3.1	5.2211	4.7	-0.5211
9	3.2	5.4285	6.1	0.6715
10	3.5	6.0508	4.9	-1.1508
11	5.2	9.5769	10.7	1.1231
12	4.6	8.3324	7.6	-0.7324
13	5.8	10.8214	11.8	0.9786
14	3	5.0137	4.1	-0.9137

To assess linearity, you plot the residuals against the independent variable (number of profiled customers, in millions) in Figure 15.11. Although there is widespread scatter in the residual plot, there is no clear pattern or relationship between the residuals and X_i. The residuals appear to be evenly spread above and below 0 for different values of X. You can conclude that the linear model is appropriate for the Sunflowers Apparel data.

FIGURE 15.11

Plot of residuals against the profiled customers of a store for the Sunflowers Apparel data

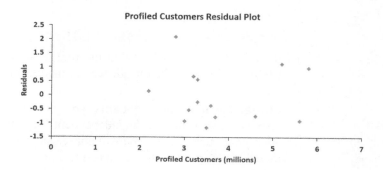

Independence   You can evaluate the assumption of independence of the errors by plotting the residuals in the order or sequence in which the data were collected. If the values of Y are part of a time series, a residual may sometimes be related to the residual that precedes it. If this relationship exists between consecutive residuals (which violates the assumption of independence), the plot of the residuals versus the time in which the data were collected will often show a cyclical pattern. Because the Sunflowers Apparel data were collected during the same time period, you do not need to evaluate the independence assumption for these data.

Normality   You can evaluate the assumption of normality in the errors by constructing a histogram, using a stem-and-leaf display, a boxplot, or a normal probability plot (see Section 7.3). To evaluate the normality assumption for the Sunflowers Apparel data, Table 15.3 organizes the residuals into a frequency distribution and Figure 15.12 is a normal probability plot.

TABLE 15.3

Frequency Distribution of 14 Residual Values for the Sunflowers Apparel Data

Residuals	Frequency
-1.25 but less than -0.75	4
-0.75 but less than -0.25	3
-0.25 but less than $+0.25$	2
$+0.25$ but less than $+0.75$	2
$+0.75$ but less than $+1.25$	2
$+1.25$ but less than $+1.75$	0
$+1.75$ but less than $+2.25$	1
	14

Although the small sample size makes it difficult to evaluate normality, from the normal probability plot of the residuals in Figure 15.12, the data do not appear to depart substantially from a normal distribution. The robustness of regression analysis with modest departures from normality enables you to conclude that you should not be overly concerned about departures from this normality assumption in the Sunflowers Apparel data.

FIGURE 15.12
Normal probability plots of the residuals for the Sunflowers Apparel data

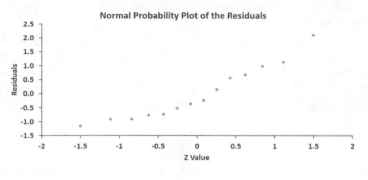

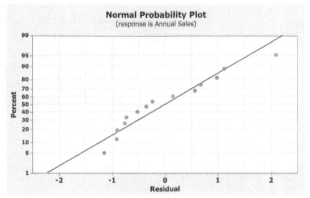

Equal Variance   You can evaluate the assumption of equal variance from a plot of the residuals with X_i. You examine the plot to see if there is approximately the same amount of variation in the residuals at each value of X. For the Sunflowers Apparel data of Figure 15.11 on page 284, there do not appear to be major differences in the variability of the residuals for different X_i values. Thus, you can conclude that there is no apparent violation in the assumption of equal variance at each level of X.

To examine a case in which the equal-variance assumption is violated, observe Figure 15.13, which is a plot of the residuals with X_i for a hypothetical set of data. This plot is fan shaped because the variability of the residuals increases dramatically as X increases. Because this plot shows unequal variances of the residuals at different levels of X, the equal-variance assumption is invalid.

FIGURE 15.13

Violation of equal variance

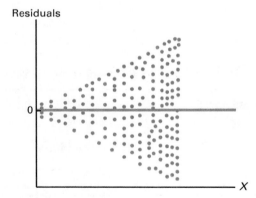

15.6 Measuring Autocorrelation: The Durbin-Watson Statistic

One of the basic assumptions of the regression model is the independence of the errors. This assumption is sometimes violated when data are collected over sequential time periods because a residual at any one time period sometimes is similar to residuals at adjacent time periods. This pattern in the residuals is called **autocorrelation**. When a set of data has substantial autocorrelation, the validity of a regression model is in serious doubt.

Residual Plots to Detect Autocorrelation

As mentioned in Section 15.5, one way to detect autocorrelation is to plot the residuals in time order. If a positive autocorrelation effect exists, there will be clusters of residuals with the same sign, and you will readily detect an apparent pattern. If negative autocorrelation exists, residuals will tend to jump back and forth from positive to negative to positive, and so on. Because negative autocorrelation is very rarely seen in regression analysis, the example in this section illustrates positive autocorrelation.

To illustrate positive autocorrelation, consider the case of a package delivery store manager who wants to be able to predict weekly sales. In approaching this problem, the manager has decided to develop a regression model to use the number of customers making purchases as an independent variable. She collects data for a period of 15 weeks and then organizes and stores these data in FifteenWeeks. Table 15.4 presents these data.

TABLE 15.4

Customers and Sales for a Period of 15 Consecutive Weeks

Week	Customers	Sales ($thousands)	Week	Customers	Sales ($thousands)
1	794	9.33	9	880	12.07
2	799	8.26	10	905	12.55
3	837	7.48	11	886	11.92
4	855	9.08	12	843	10.27
5	845	9.83	13	904	11.80
6	844	10.09	14	950	12.15
7	863	11.01	15	841	9.64
8	875	11.49			

Because the data are collected over a period of 15 consecutive weeks at the same store, you need to determine whether there is autocorrelation. First, you can develop the simple linear regression model you can use to predict sales based on the number of customers assuming there is no autocorrelation in the residuals. Figure 15.14 presents SPSS results for these data.

FIGURE 15.14

SPSS regression results for the Table 15.4 package delivery store data

Regression

Model Summary[b]

Model	R	R Square	Adjusted R Square	Std. Error of the Estimate	Durbin-Watson
1	.811[a]	.657	.631	.93604	.883

a. Predictors: (Constant), Customer

b. Dependent Variable: Sales($ thousands)

ANOVA[a]

Model		Sum of Squares	df	Mean Square	F	Sig.
1	Regression	21.860	1	21.860	24.950	.000[b]
	Residual	11.390	13	.876		
	Total	33.251	14			

a. Dependent Variable: Sales($ thousands)

b. Predictors: (Constant), Customer

(continued)

FIGURE 15.14
Continued

Coefficients[a]

Model		Unstandardized Coefficients B	Std. Error	Standardized Coefficients Beta	t	Sig.
1	(Constant)	-16.032	5.310		-3.019	.010
	Customer	.031	.006	.811	4.995	.000

a. Dependent Variable: Sales($ thousands)

The regression equation is

Sales= −16.032 + 0.031 Customer

From Figure 15.14, observe that r^2 is 0.6574, indicating that 65.74% of the variation in sales is explained by variation in the number of customers. In addition, the Y intercept, b_0, is −16.0322 and the slope, b_1, is 0.0308. However, before using this model for prediction, you must perform a residual analysis. Because the data have been collected over a consecutive period of 15 weeks, in addition to checking the linearity, normality, and equal-variance assumptions, you must investigate the independence-of-errors assumption. To do this, you plot the residuals versus time in Figure 15.15 in order to examine whether a pattern in the residuals exists. In Figure 15.15, you can see that the residuals tend to fluctuate up and down in a cyclical pattern. This cyclical pattern provides strong cause for concern about the existence of autocorrelation in the residuals and, therefore, a violation of the independence-of-errors assumption.

FIGURE 15.15

Residual plot for the Table 15.4 package delivery store data

Package Delivery Store Sales Analysis Residual Plot

The Durbin-Watson Statistic

The **Durbin-Watson statistic** is used to measure autocorrelation. This statistic measures the correlation between each residual and the residual for the previous time period. Equation (15.15) defines the Durbin-Watson statistic.

DURBIN-WATSON STATISTIC

$$D = \frac{\sum_{i=2}^{n}(e_i - e_{i-1})^2}{\sum_{i=1}^{n}e_i^2}$$

(15.15)

where

$$e_i = \text{residual at the time period } i$$

In Equation (15.15), the numerator, $\sum_{i=2}^{n}(e_i - e_{i-1})^2$, represents the squared difference between two successive residuals, summed from the second value to the nth value and the denominator, $\sum_{i=1}^{n}e_i^2$, represents the sum of the squared residuals. This means that the value of the Durbin-Watson statistic, D, will approach 0 if successive residuals are positively autocorrelated. If the residuals are not correlated, the value of D will be close to 2. (If the residuals are negatively autocorrelated, D will be greater than 2 and could even approach its maximum value of 4.) For the package delivery store data, the Durbin-Watson statistic, D, is 0.883. (See the Figure 15.16 SPSS results.)

FIGURE 15.16

SPSS Durbin-Watson
statistics worksheet for
the package delivery
store data

SPSS reports the Durbin-
Watson statistic as part of
the regression results (see
Figure 15.14 on page 286).

Regression

Model Summary[b]

Model	R	R Square	Adjusted R Square	Std. Error of the Estimate	Durbin-Watson
1	.811[a]	.657	.631	.93604	.883

a. Predictors: (Constant), Customer

b. Dependent Variable: Sales($ thousands)

You need to determine when the autocorrelation is large enough to conclude that there is significant positive autocorrelation. To do so, you compare D to the critical values of the Durbin-Watson statistic found in Table E.8, a portion of which is presented in Table 15.5. The critical values depend on α, the significance level chosen, n, the sample size, and k, the number of independent variables in the model (in simple linear regression, $k = 1$).

TABLE 15.5

Finding Critical Values
of the Durbin-Watson
Statistic

					$\alpha = .05$					
	$k = 1$		$k = 2$		$k = 3$		$k = 4$		$k = 5$	
n	d_L	d_U	d_L	d_U	d_L	d_U	d_L	d_U	d_L	d_U
15	1.08	1.36	.95	1.54	.82	1.75	.69	1.97	.56	2.21
16	1.10	1.37	.98	1.54	.86	1.73	.74	1.93	.62	2.15
17	1.13	1.38	1.02	1.54	.90	1.71	.78	1.90	.67	2.10
18	1.16	1.39	1.05	1.53	.93	1.69	.82	1.87	.71	2.06

In Table 15.5, two values are shown for each combination of α (level of significance), n (sample size), and k (number of independent variables in the model). The first value, d_L, represents the lower critical value. If D is below d_L, you conclude that there is evidence of positive autocorrelation among the residuals. If this occurs, the least-squares method used in this chapter is inappropriate, and you should use alternative methods (see reference 4). The second value, d_U, represents the upper critical value of D, above which you would conclude that there is no evidence of positive autocorrelation among the residuals. If D is between d_L and d_U, you are unable to arrive at a definite conclusion.

For the package delivery store data, with one independent variable ($k = 1$) and 15 values ($n = 15$), $d_L = 1.08$ and $d_U = 1.36$. Because $D = 0.8830 < 1.08$, you conclude that there is positive autocorrelation among the residuals. The least-squares regression analysis of the data shown in Figure 15.14 on page 287 is inappropriate because of the presence of significant positive autocorrelation among the residuals. In other words, the independence-of-errors assumption is invalid. You need to use alternative approaches, discussed in reference 4.

15.7 Inferences About the Slope and Correlation Coefficient

In Sections 15.1 through 15.3, regression was used solely for descriptive purposes. You learned how to determine the regression coefficients using the least-squares method and how to predict Y for a given value of X. In addition, you learned how to compute and interpret the standard error of the estimate and the coefficient of determination.

When residual analysis, as discussed in Section 15.5, indicates that the assumptions of a least-squares regression model are not seriously violated and that the straight-line model is appropriate, you can make inferences about the linear relationship between the variables in the population.

t Test for the Slope

To determine the existence of a significant linear relationship between the X and Y variables, you test whether β_1 (the population slope) is equal to 0. The null and alternative hypotheses are as follows:

$$H_0: \beta_1 = 0 \ [\text{There is no linear relationship (the slope is zero).}]$$
$$H_1: \beta_1 \neq 0 \ [\text{There is a linear relationship (the slope is not zero).}]$$

If you reject the null hypothesis, you conclude that there is evidence of a linear relationship. Equation (15.16) defines the test statistic for the slope, which is based on the sampling distribution of the slope.

TESTING A HYPOTHESIS FOR A POPULATION SLOPE, β_1, USING THE t TEST

The t_{STAT} test statistic equals the difference between the sample slope and hypothesized value of the population slope divided by S_{b_1}, the standard error of the slope.

$$t_{STAT} = \frac{b_1 - \beta_1}{S_{b_1}} \tag{15.16}$$

where

$$S_{b_1} = \frac{S_{YX}}{\sqrt{SSX}}$$

$$SSX = \sum_{i=1}^{n} (X_i - \overline{X})^2$$

The t_{STAT} test statistic follows a t distribution with $n - 2$ degrees of freedom.

Return to the Sunflowers Apparel scenario on page 263. To test whether there is a significant linear relationship between the number of profiled customers and the annual sales at the 0.05 level of significance, refer to the t test results shown in Figure 15.17.

FIGURE 15.17
SPSS *t* test for the slope results for the Sunflower Apparel data

Coefficients[a]

Model		Unstandardized Coefficients B	Std. Error	Standardized Coefficients Beta	t	Sig.
1	(Constant)	-1.209	.995		-1.215	.248
	Profiled Custers (Millions)	2.074	.254	.921	8.178	.000

a. Dependent Variable: Annual Sales ($million)

From Figure 15.17,

$$b_1 = +2.0742 \quad n = 14 \quad S_{b_1} = 0.2536$$

and

$$t_{STAT} = \frac{b_1 - \beta_1}{S_{b_1}}$$

$$= \frac{2.0742 - 0}{0.2536} = 8.178$$

Using the 0.05 level of significance, the critical values of t with $n - 2 = 12$ degrees of freedom are ± 2.1788. Because $t_{STAT} = 8.178 > 2.1788$ or because the *p*-value is 0.0000, which is less than $\alpha = 0.05$, you reject H_0 (see Figure 15.18). Hence, you can conclude that there is a significant linear relationship between mean annual sales and the number of profiled customers.

FIGURE 15.18

Testing a hypothesis about the population slope at the 0.05 level of significance, with 12 degrees of freedom

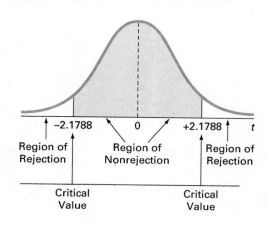

How to Find *t* Critical Value Using Calculator

Calculate the t critical values for a two tail (as shown in Figure 15.18) test with $\alpha = 0.05$, using the Casio Calculator fx-9750GII and follow the following calculator steps:

From the **Main Menu** select:

STAT F5 (DIST) **F2** (t) **F3**(Invt)   then enter the following items:

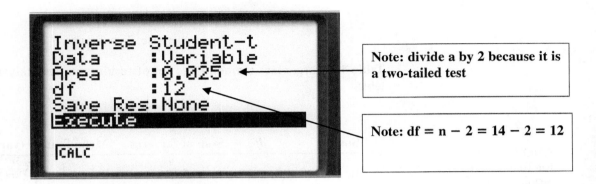

Now key **EXE** or **F1**(CALC)

The calculator will now show the results:

(Note: this is the critical value for the upper tail. The critical value for the lower tail is −2.1788 (insert a negative sign). See Figure 15.18)

F Test for the Slope

As an alternative to the *t* test, in simple linear regression, you can use an *F* test to determine whether the slope is statistically significant. In Section 12.4, you used the *F* distribution to test the ratio of two variances. Equation (15.17) defines the *F* test for the slope as the ratio of the variance that is due to the regression (*MSR*) divided by the error variance ($MSE = S_{YX}^2$).

TESTING A HYPOTHESIS FOR A POPULATION SLOPE, β_1, USING THE *F* TEST

The F_{STAT} test statistic is equal to the regression mean square (*MSR*) divided by the mean square error (*MSE*).

$$F_{STAT} = \frac{MSR}{MSE} \tag{15.17}$$

where

$$MSR = \frac{SSR}{1} = SSR$$

$$MSE = \frac{SSE}{n-2}$$

The F_{STAT} test statistic follows an F distribution with 1 and $n-2$ degrees of freedom.

Using a level of significance α, the decision rule is

$$\text{Reject } H_0 \text{ if } F_{STAT} > F_\alpha;$$

otherwise, do not reject H_0.

Table 15.6 organizes the complete set of results into an analysis of variance (ANOVA) table.

TABLE 15.6

ANOVA Table for Testing the Significance of a Regression Coefficient

Source	df	Sum of Squares	Mean Square (variance)	F
Regression	1	SSR	$MSR = \frac{SSR}{1} = SSR$	$F_{STAT} = \frac{MSR}{MSE}$
Error	$n-2$	SSE	$MSE = \frac{SSE}{n-2}$	
Total	$n-1$	SST		

Figure 15.19, a completed ANOVA table for the Sunflowers sales data (extracted from Figure 15.4), shows that the computed F_{STAT} test statistic is 66.879 and the p-value is 0.0000.

FIGURE 15.19

SPSS F test results for the Sunflower Apparel data

Regression

ANOVA^a

Model		Sum of Squares	df	Mean Square	F	Sig.
1	Regression	66.785	1	66.785	66.879	.000^b
	Residual	11.983	12	.999		
	Total	78.769	13			

a. Dependent Variable: Annual Sales ($million)

b. Predictors: (Constant), Profiled Custers (Millions)

In simple linear regression, $t^2 = F$.

Using a level of significance of 0.05, from Table E.5, the critical value of the F distribution, with 1 and 12 degrees of freedom, is 4.75 (see Figure 15.20). Because $F_{STAT} = 66.8792 > 4.75$ or because the p-value $= 0.0000 < 0.05$, you reject H_0 and conclude that there is a significant linear relationship between the number of profiled customers and annual sales. Because the F test in Equation (15.17) on page 291 is equivalent to the t test in Equation (15.16) on page 289, you reach the same conclusion.

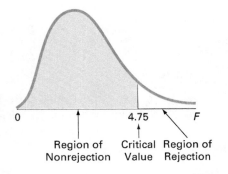

FIGURE 15.20

Regions of rejection and nonrejection when testing for the significance of the slope at the 0.05 level of significance, with 1 and 12 degrees of freedom

How to Find *F* Critical Value Using Calculator

Calculate the *F* critical value for $\alpha = 0.05$ (in Figure 15.20), using the Casio Calculator fx-9750GII and follow the following calculator steps:

From the **Main Menu** select:

STAT F5 (DIST) **F4** (F) **F3**(InvF)   then enter the following items:

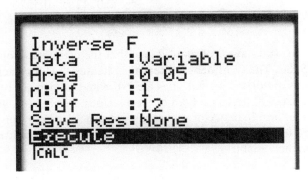

Now key **EXE** or **F1**(CALC)

The calculator will now show the results:

Confidence Interval Estimate for the Slope

As an alternative to testing for the existence of a linear relationship between the variables, you can construct a confidence interval estimate of β_1 using Equation (15.18).

CONFIDENCE INTERVAL ESTIMATE OF THE SLOPE, β_1

The confidence interval estimate for the population slope can be constructed by taking the sample slope, b_1, and adding and subtracting the critical *t* value multiplied by the standard error of the slope.

$$b_1 \pm t_{\alpha/2} S_{b_1}$$

$$b_1 - t_{\alpha/2} S_{b_1} \leq \beta_1 \leq b_1 + t_{\alpha/2} S_{b_1} \tag{15.18}$$

where

$t_{\alpha/2}$ = critical value corresponding to an upper-tail probability of $\alpha/2$ from the t distribution with $n - 2$ degrees of freedom (i.e., a cumulative area of $1 - \alpha/2$)

From the Figure 15.17 results on page 290,

$$b_1 = 2.0742 \quad n = 14 \quad S_{b_1} = 0.2536$$

To construct a 95% confidence interval estimate, $\alpha/2 = 0.025$, and from Table E.3, $t_{\alpha/2} = 2.1788$. Thus,

$$b_1 \pm t_{\alpha/2} S_{b_1} = 2.0742 \pm (2.1788)(0.2536)$$
$$= 2.0742 \pm 0.5526$$
$$1.5216 \leq \beta_1 \leq 2.6268$$

Therefore, you have 95% confidence that the estimated population slope is between 1.5216 and 2.6268. The confidence interval indicates that for each increase of 1 million profiled customers, predicted annual sales are estimated to increase by at least $1,521,600 but no more than $2,626,800. Because both of these values are above 0, you have evidence of a significant linear relationship between annual sales and the number of profiled customers. Had the interval included 0, you would have concluded that there is no evidence of a significant relationship between the variables.

FIGURE 15.21

SPSS confidence interval for the slope for the Sunflower Apparel data.

Regression

Coefficients[a]

Model		Unstandardized Coefficients B	Std. Error	Standardized Coefficients Beta	t	Sig.	95.0% Confidence Interval for B Lower Bound	Upper Bound
1	(Constant)	-1.209	.995		-1.215	.248	-3.376	.959
	Profiled Custers (Millions)	2.074	.254	.921	8.178	.000	1.522	2.627

a. Dependent Variable: Annual Sales ($million)

Instead of using the formula 15.18 to compute the confidence interval for the slope, you can run the SPSS Linear Regression. The SPSS coefficients table gives the 95% confidence interval estimate for the population slope.

t Test for the Correlation Coefficient

The strength of the relationship between two numerical variables was measured using the **correlation coefficient**, r. The values of the coefficient of correlation range from -1 for a perfect negative correlation to $+1$ for a perfect positive correlation. You can use the correlation coefficient to determine whether there is a statistically significant linear relationship between X and Y. To do so, you hypothesize that the population correlation coefficient, ρ, is 0. Thus, the null and alternative hypotheses are

$$H_0: \rho = 0 \quad \text{(no correlation)}$$
$$H_1: \rho \neq 0 \quad \text{(correlation)}$$

Equation (15.19) defines the test statistic for determining the existence of a significant correlation.

TESTING FOR THE EXISTENCE OF CORRELATION

$$t_{STAT} = \frac{r - \rho}{\sqrt{\dfrac{1 - r^2}{n - 2}}} \tag{15.19a}$$

where

$$r = +\sqrt{r^2} \quad \text{if} \quad b_1 > 0$$
$$r = -\sqrt{r^2} \quad \text{if} \quad b_1 < 0$$

The t_{STAT} test statistic follows a t distribution with $n - 2$ degrees of freedom. r is calculated:

$$r = \frac{\text{cov}(X, Y)}{S_X S_Y} \tag{15.19b}$$

where

$$\text{cov}(X, Y) = \frac{\displaystyle\sum_{i=1}^{n}(X_i - \bar{X})(Y_i - \bar{Y})}{n - 1}$$

$$S_X = \sqrt{\frac{\displaystyle\sum_{i=1}^{n}(X_i - \bar{X})^2}{n - 1}}$$

$$S_Y = \sqrt{\frac{\displaystyle\sum_{i=1}^{n}(Y_i - \bar{Y})^2}{n - 1}}$$

In the Sunflowers Apparel problem, $r^2 = 0.8479$ and $b_1 = +2.0742$ (see Figure 15.4 on page 269). Because $b_1 > 0$, the correlation coefficient for annual sales and profiled customers is the positive square root of r^2—that is, $r = +\sqrt{0.8479} = +0.9208$. You use Equation (15.19a) to test the null hypothesis that there is no correlation between these two variables. This results in the following t_{STAT} statistic:

$$t_{STAT} = \frac{r - 0}{\sqrt{\dfrac{1 - r^2}{n - 2}}}$$

$$= \frac{0.9208 - 0}{\sqrt{\dfrac{1 - (0.9208)^2}{14 - 2}}} = 8.178$$

Using the 0.05 level of significance, because $t_{STAT} = 8.178 > 2.1788$, you reject the null hypothesis. You conclude that there is a significant association between annual sales and the number of profiled customers. This t_{STAT} test statistic is equivalent to the t_{STAT} test statistic found when testing whether the population slope, β_1, is equal to zero.

How to Run *t*-test for the Slope with the Casio Calculator

Refer to Table 15.1. To test the slope and the correlation coefficient, use the Casio Calculator fx-9750GII and follow the following calculator steps:

First, enter the data in **List 1** and **List 2**.

List 1 Profiled Customers (X)	List 2 Annual Sales (Y)
3.7	5.7
3.6	5.9
2.8	6.7
5.6	9.5
3.3	5.4
2.2	3.5
3.3	6.2
3.1	4.7
3.2	6.1
3.5	4.9
5.2	10.7
4.6	7.6
5.8	11.8
3.0	4.1

From the **Main Menu** select:

STAT   F3 (TEST)   **F2** (t)   **F3** (REG)   then set the following items:

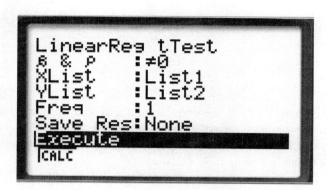

Press **EXE** to obtain the result.

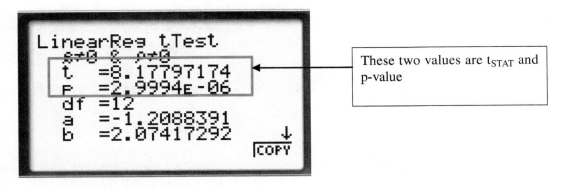

These two values are t_{STAT} and p-value

Scroll down for more result:

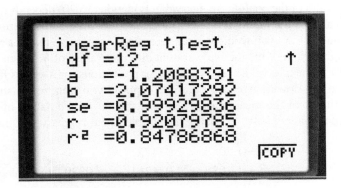

15.8 Estimation of Mean Values and Prediction of Individual Values

In Chapter 10, you studied the concept of the confidence interval estimate of the population mean. In Example 15.2 on page 270, you used the prediction line to predict the mean value of Y for a given X. The mean annual sales for stores that had 4 million profiled customers within a fixed radius was predicted to be 7.0879 millions of dollars ($7,087,900). This estimate, however, is a *point estimate* of the population mean. This section presents methods to develop a confidence interval estimate for the mean response for a given X and for developing a prediction interval for an individual response, Y, for a given value of X.

The Confidence Interval Estimate for the Mean Response

Equation (15.20) defines the **confidence interval estimate for the mean response** for a given X.

CONFIDENCE INTERVAL ESTIMATE FOR THE MEAN OF Y

$$\hat{Y}_i \pm t_{\alpha/2} S_{YX} \sqrt{h_i}$$

$$\hat{Y}_i - t_{\alpha/2} S_{YX} \sqrt{h_i} \leq \mu_{Y|X=X_i} \leq \hat{Y}_i + t_{\alpha/2} S_{YX} \sqrt{h_i} \qquad \textbf{(15.20)}$$

where

$$h_i = \frac{1}{n} + \frac{(X_i - \bar{X})^2}{SSX}$$

$$\hat{Y}_i = \text{predicted value of } Y; \hat{Y}_i = b_0 + b_1 X_i$$

$$S_{YX} = \text{standard error of the estimate}$$
$$n = \text{sample size}$$
$$X_i = \text{given value of } X$$
$$\mu_{Y|X=X_i} = \text{mean value of } Y \text{ when } X = X_i$$

$$SSX = \sum_{i=1}^{n}(X_i - \overline{X})^2$$

$t_{\alpha/2}$ = critical value corresponding to an upper-tail probability of $\alpha/2$ from the t distribution with $n-2$ degrees of freedom (i.e., a cumulative area of $1 - \alpha/2$)

The width of the confidence interval in Equation (15.20) depends on several factors. Increased variation around the prediction line, as measured by the standard error of the estimate, results in a wider interval. As you would expect, increased sample size reduces the width of the interval. In addition, the width of the interval varies at different values of X. When you predict Y for values of X close to $\overline{X}$, the interval is narrower than for predictions for X values farther away from $\overline{X}$.

In the Sunflowers Apparel example, suppose you want to construct a 95% confidence interval estimate of the mean annual sales for the entire population of stores that have 4 million profiled customers ($X = 4$). Using the simple linear regression equation,

$$\hat{Y}_i = -1.2088 + 2.0742X_i$$
$$= -1.2088 + 2.0742(4) = 7.0879 \text{ (millions of dollars)}$$

Also, given the following:

$$\overline{X} = 3.7786 \quad S_{YX} = 0.9993$$

$$SSX = \sum_{i=1}^{n}(X_i - \overline{X})^2 = 15.5236$$

From Table E.3, $t_{\alpha/2} = 2.1788$. Thus,

$$\hat{Y}_i \pm t_{\alpha/2}S_{YX}\sqrt{h_i}$$

where

$$h_i = \frac{1}{n} + \frac{(X_i - \overline{X})^2}{SSX}$$

so that

$$\hat{Y}_i \pm t_{\alpha/2}S_{YX}\sqrt{\frac{1}{n} + \frac{(X_i - \overline{X})^2}{SSX}}$$

$$= 7.0879 \pm (2.1788)(0.9993)\sqrt{\frac{1}{14} + \frac{(4 - 3.7786)^2}{15.5236}}$$

$$= 7.0879 \pm 0.5946$$

so

$$6.4932 \leq \mu_{Y|X=4} \leq 7.6825$$

Therefore, the 95% confidence interval estimate is that the population mean annual sales are between \$6,493,200 and \$7,682,500 for stores with 4 million profiled customers.

The Prediction Interval for an Individual Response

In addition to constructing a confidence interval for the mean value of Y, you can also construct a prediction interval for an individual value of Y. Although the form of this interval is similar to that of the confidence interval estimate of Equation (15.20), the prediction interval is predicting an individual value, not estimating a mean. Equation (15.21) defines the **prediction interval for an individual response**, Y, at a given value, X_i, denoted by $Y_{X=X_i}$.

PREDICTION INTERVAL FOR AN INDIVIDUAL RESPONSE, Y

$$\hat{Y}_i \pm t_{\alpha/2} S_{YX} \sqrt{1 + h_i} \qquad \textbf{(15.21)}$$

$$\hat{Y}_i - t_{\alpha/2} S_{YX} \sqrt{1 + h_i} \leq Y_{X=X_i} \leq \hat{Y}_i + t_{\alpha/2} S_{YX} \sqrt{1 + h_i}$$

where

$Y_{X=X_i}$ = future value of Y when $X = X_i$

$t_{\alpha/2}$ = critical value corresponding to an upper-tail probability of $\alpha/2$ from the t distribution with $n - 2$ degrees of freedom (i.e., a cumulative area of $1 - \alpha/2$)

In addition, h_i, $\hat{Y}_i$, S_{YX}, n, and X_i are defined as in Equation (15.20) on page 297.

To construct a 95% prediction interval of the annual sales for an individual store that has 4 million profiled customers ($X = 4$), you first compute $\hat{Y}_i$. Using the prediction line:

$$\hat{Y}_i = -1.2088 + 2.0742X_i$$
$$= -1.2088 + 2.0742(4)$$
$$= 7.0879 \text{ (millions of dollars)}$$

Also, given the following:

$$\overline{X} = 3.7786 \quad S_{YX} = 0.9993$$

$$SSX = \sum_{i=1}^{n}(X_i - \overline{X})^2 = 15.5236$$

From Table E.3, $t_{\alpha/2} = 2.1788$. Thus,

$$\hat{Y}_i \pm t_{\alpha/2} S_{YX} \sqrt{1 + h_i}$$

where

$$h_i = \frac{1}{n} + \frac{(X_i - \overline{X})^2}{\sum_{i=1}^{n}(X_i - \overline{X})^2}$$

so that

$$\hat{Y}_i \pm t_{\alpha/2} S_{YX} \sqrt{1 + \frac{1}{n} + \frac{(X_i - \overline{X})^2}{SSX}}$$

$$= 7.0879 \pm (2.1788)(0.9993) \sqrt{1 + \frac{1}{14} + \frac{(4 - 3.7786)^2}{15.5236}}$$

$$= 7.0879 \pm 2.2570$$

so

$$4.8308 \leq Y_{X=4} \leq 9.3449$$

Therefore, with 95% confidence, you predict that the annual sales for an individual store with 4 million profiled customers is between $4,830,800 and $9,344,900.

Figure 15.22 presents SPSS results for the confidence interval estimate and the prediction interval for the Sunflowers Apparel data. If you compare the results of the confidence interval estimate and the prediction interval, you see that the width of the prediction interval for an individual store is much wider than the confidence interval estimate for the mean. Remember that there is much more variation in predicting an individual value than in estimating a mean value.

FIGURE 15.22

SPSS confidence interval estimate and predicted interval for the Sunflower Apparel data

	Customer	sales	PRE_1	RES_1	LMCI_1	UMCI_1	LICI_1	UICI_1
1	3.7	5.7	6.46560	-.76560	5.88208	7.04912	4.21148	8.71972
2	3.6	5.9	6.25818	-.35818	5.66797	6.84839	4.00232	8.51405
3	2.8	6.7	4.59885	2.10115	3.80446	5.39323	2.28117	6.91652
4	5.6	9.5	10.40653	-.90653	9.24389	11.56917	7.93827	12.87479
5	3.3	5.4	5.63593	-.23593	4.99675	6.27511	3.36676	7.90510
6	2.2	3.5	3.35434	.14566	2.30573	4.40295	.93770	5.77098
7	3.3	6.2	5.63593	.56407	4.99675	6.27511	3.36676	7.90510
8	3.1	4.7	5.22110	-.52110	4.52884	5.91336	2.93641	7.50578
9	3.2	6.1	5.42851	.67149	4.76456	6.09247	3.15224	7.70478
10	3.5	4.9	6.05077	-1.15077	5.44884	6.65269	3.79181	8.30972
11	5.2	10.7	9.57686	1.12314	8.59930	10.55442	7.19019	11.96353
12	4.6	7.6	8.33236	-.73236	7.59434	9.07037	6.03339	10.63132
13	5.8	11.8	10.82136	.97864	9.56182	12.08090	8.30601	13.33672
14	3.0	4.1	5.01368	-.91368	4.28999	5.73737	2.71928	7.30808
15								

The confidence interval values and prediction values are displayed on the SPSS Data Editor under the variables PRE_1, RES_1, LMCI_1, UMCI_1, LICI_1 and UICI_1.

Note: Model 1 comprises y= Annual Sales ($millions) and X1= Profiled Customers (millions)

Based on Model 1

PRE – Unstandardized Predicted Value

RES – Unstandardized Residual Value

LMCI – 95% Lower Confidence Interval for y mean

UMCI – 95% Upper Confidence Interval for y mean

LICI – 95% Lower Confidence Interval for y individual

UICI – 95% Upper Confidence Interval for y individual

15.9 Potential Pitfalls in Regression

When using regression analysis, some of the potential pitfalls are:

- Lacking awareness of the assumptions of least-squares regression
- Not knowing how to evaluate the assumptions of least-squares regression
- Not knowing what the alternatives are to least-squares regression if a particular assumption is violated
- Using a regression model without knowledge of the subject matter
- Extrapolating outside the relevant range
- Concluding that a significant relationship identified in an observational study is due to a cause-and-effect relationship

The widespread availability of spreadsheet and statistical applications has made regression analysis much more feasible today than it once was. However, many users who have access to such applications do not understand how to use regression analysis properly. Someone who is not familiar with either the assumptions of regression or how to evaluate the assumptions cannot be expected to know what the alternatives to least-squares regression are if a particular assumption is violated.

The data in Table 15.7 (stored in `Anscombe`) illustrate the importance of using scatter plots and residual analysis to go beyond the basic number crunching of computing the Y intercept, the slope, and r^2.

TABLE 15.7

Four Sets of Artificial Data

Data Set A		Data Set B		Data Set C		Data Set D	
X_i	Y_i	X_i	Y_i	X_i	Y_i	X_i	Y_i
10	8.04	10	9.14	10	7.46	8	6.58
14	9.96	14	8.10	14	8.84	8	5.76
5	5.68	5	4.74	5	5.73	8	7.71
8	6.95	8	8.14	8	6.77	8	8.84
9	8.81	9	8.77	9	7.11	8	8.47
12	10.84	12	9.13	12	8.15	8	7.04
4	4.26	4	3.10	4	5.39	8	5.25
7	4.82	7	7.26	7	6.42	19	12.50
11	8.33	11	9.26	11	7.81	8	5.56
13	7.58	13	8.74	13	12.74	8	7.91
6	7.24	6	6.13	6	6.08	8	6.89

Source: Data extracted from F. J. Anscombe, "Graphs in Statistical Analysis," *The American Statistician*, 27 (1973), pp. 17–21.

Anscombe (reference 1) showed that all four data sets given in Table 15.7 have the following identical results:

$$\hat{Y}_i = 3.0 + 0.5X_i$$
$$S_{YX} = 1.237$$
$$S_{b_1} = 0.118$$
$$r^2 = 0.667$$

$$SSR = \text{Explained variation} = \sum_{i=1}^{n}(\hat{Y}_i - \overline{Y})^2 = 27.51$$

$$SSE = \text{Unexplained variation} = \sum_{i=1}^{n}(Y_i - \hat{Y}_i)^2 = 13.76$$

$$SST = \text{Total variation} = \sum_{i=1}^{n}(Y_i - \overline{Y})^2 = 41.27$$

If you stopped the analysis at this point, you would fail to observe the important differences among the four data sets that scatter plots and residual plots can reveal.

From the scatter plots and the residual plots of Figure 15.23, you see how different the data sets are. Each has a different relationship between X and Y. The only data set that seems to approximately follow a straight line is data set A. The residual plot for data set A does not show any obvious patterns or outlying residuals. This is certainly not true for data sets B, C, and D. The scatter plot for data set B shows that a curvilinear regression model is more appropriate. This conclusion is reinforced by the residual plot for data set B. The scatter plot and the residual plot for data set C clearly show an outlying observation. In this case, one approach used is to remove the outlier and reestimate the regression model (see reference 4). The scatter plot for data set D represents a situation in which the model is heavily dependent on the outcome of a single data point ($X_8 = 19$ and $Y_8 = 12.50$). Any regression model with this characteristic should be used with caution.

FIGURE 15.23

Scatter plots and residual plots for the data sets A, B, C, and D

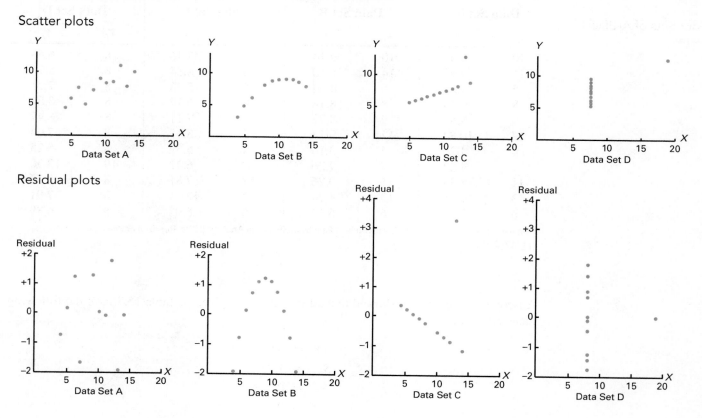

Scatter plots

Residual plots

Six Steps for Avoiding the Potential Pitfalls

Apply the following six-step strategy to avoid the potential pitfalls in the regression analyses you undertake.

Step 1 Construct a scatter plot to observe the possible relationship between X and Y.

Step 2 Perform a residual analysis to check the assumptions of regression (linearity, independence, normality, equal variance):

a. Plot the residuals versus the independent variable to determine whether the linear model is appropriate and to check for equal variance.

b. Construct a histogram, stem-and-leaf display, boxplot, or normal probability plot of the residuals to check for normality.

c. Plot the residuals versus time to check for independence. (This step is necessary only if the data are collected over time.)

Step 3 If there are violations of the assumptions, use alternative methods to least-squares regression or alternative least-squares models (see reference 4).

Step 4 If there are no violations of the assumptions, carry out tests for the significance of the regression coefficients and develop confidence and prediction intervals.

Step 5 Refrain from making predictions and forecasts outside the relevant range of the independent variable.

Step 6 Remember that the relationships identified in observational studies may or may not be due to cause-and-effect relationships. (While causation implies correlation, correlation does not imply causation.)

USING STATISTICS

Knowing Customers at Sunflowers Apparel, Revisited

Fotolia

In the Knowing Customers at Sunflowers Apparel scenario, you were the director of planning for a chain of upscale clothing stores for women. Until now, Sunflowers managers selected sites based on factors such as the availability of a good lease or a subjective opinion that a location seemed like a good place for a store. To make more objective decisions, you used the more systematic DCOVA approach to identify and classify groups of consumers and developed a regression model to analyze the relationship between the number of profiled customers that live within a fixed radius of a Sunflowers store and the annual sales of the store. The model indicated that about 84.8% of the variation in sales was explained by the number of profiled customers that live within a fixed radius of a Sunflowers store. Furthermore, for each increase of 1 million profiled customers, mean annual sales were estimated to increase by $2.0742 million. You can now use your model to help make better decisions when selecting new sites for stores as well as to forecast sales for existing stores.

SUMMARY

As you can see from the chapter roadmap in Figure 15.24, this chapter develops the simple linear regression model and discusses the assumptions and how to evaluate them. Once you are assured that the model is appropriate, you can predict values by using the prediction line and test for the significance of the slope. Chapter 13 extends regression analysis to situations in which more than one independent variable is used to predict the value of a dependent variable.

FIGURE 15.24

Roadmap for simple linear regression

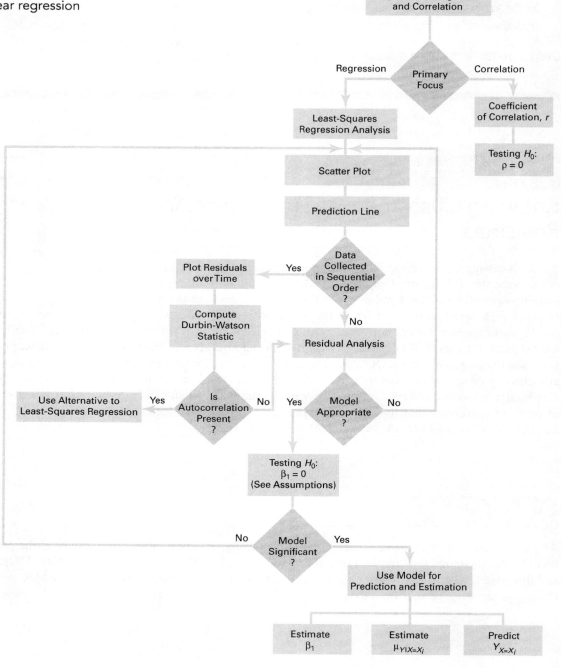

REFERENCES

1. Anscombe, F. J. "Graphs in Statistical Analysis." *The American Statistician*, 27(1973): 17–21.

2. Hoaglin, D. C., and R. Welsch. "The Hat Matrix in Regression and ANOVA." *The American Statistician*, 32(1978): 17–22.

3. Hocking, R. R. "Developments in Linear Regression Methodology: 1959–1982." *Technometrics*, 25(1983): 219–250.

4. Kutner, M. H., C. J. Nachtsheim, J. Neter, and W. Li. *Applied Linear Statistical Models*, 5th ed. New York: McGraw-Hill/Irwin, 2005.

5. *Microsoft Excel 2013*. Redmond, WA: Microsoft Corp., 2012.

6. *Minitab Release 16*. State College, PA: Minitab Inc., 2010.

KEY EQUATIONS

Simple Linear Regression Model

$$Y_i = \beta_0 + \beta_1 X_i + \varepsilon_i \tag{15.1}$$

**Simple Linear Regression Equation:
The Prediction Line**

$$\hat{Y}_i = b_0 + b_1 X_i \tag{15.2}$$

Computational Formula for the Slope, b_1

$$b_1 = \frac{SSXY}{SSX} \tag{15.3}$$

Computational Formula for the Y Intercept, b_0

$$b_0 = \overline{Y} - b_1\overline{X} \tag{15.4}$$

Measures of Variation in Regression

$$SST = SSR + SSE \tag{15.5}$$

Total Sum of Squares (SST)

$$SST = \text{Total sum of squares} = \sum_{i=1}^{n}(Y_i - \overline{Y})^2 \tag{15.6}$$

Regression Sum of Squares (SSR)

SSR = Explained variation or regression sum of squares

$$= \sum_{i=1}^{n}(\hat{Y}_i - \overline{Y})^2 \tag{15.7}$$

Error Sum of Squares (SSE)

SSE = Unexplained variation or error sum of squares

$$= \sum_{i=1}^{n}(Y_i - \hat{Y}_i)^2 \tag{15.8}$$

Coefficient of Determination

$$r^2 = \frac{\text{Regression sum of squares}}{\text{Total sum of squares}} = \frac{SSR}{SST} \tag{15.9}$$

Computational Formula for SST

$$SST = \sum_{i=1}^{n}(Y_i - \overline{Y})^2 = \sum_{i=1}^{n}Y_i^2 - \frac{\left(\sum_{i=1}^{n}Y_i\right)^2}{n} \tag{15.10}$$

Computational Formula for SSR

$$SSR = \sum_{i=1}^{n}(\hat{Y}_i - \overline{Y})^2$$

$$= b_0\sum_{i=1}^{n}Y_i + b_1\sum_{i=1}^{n}X_iY_i - \frac{\left(\sum_{i=1}^{n}Y_i\right)^2}{n} \tag{15.11}$$

Computational Formula for SSE

$$SSE = \sum_{i=1}^{n}(Y_i - \hat{Y}_i)^2 = \sum_{i=1}^{n}Y_i^2 - b_0\sum_{i=1}^{n}Y_i - b_1\sum_{i=1}^{n}X_iY_i \tag{15.12}$$

Standard Error of the Estimate

$$S_{YX} = \sqrt{\frac{SSE}{n-2}} = \sqrt{\frac{\sum_{i=1}^{n}(Y_i - \hat{Y}_i)^2}{n-2}} \tag{15.13}$$

Residual

$$e_i = Y_i - \hat{Y}_i \tag{15.14}$$

Durbin-Watson Statistic

$$D = \frac{\sum_{i=2}^{n}(e_i - e_{i-1})^2}{\sum_{i=1}^{n}e_i^2} \tag{15.15}$$

Testing a Hypothesis for a Population Slope, β_1, Using the t Test

$$t_{STAT} = \frac{b_1 - \beta_1}{S_{b_1}} \tag{15.16}$$

Testing a Hypothesis for a Population Slope, β_1, Using the F Test

$$F_{STAT} = \frac{MSR}{MSE} \tag{15.17}$$

Confidence Interval Estimate of the Slope, β_1

$$b_1 \pm t_{\alpha/2}S_{b_1}$$
$$b_1 - t_{\alpha/2}S_{b_1} \leq \beta_1 \leq b_1 + t_{\alpha/2}S_{b_1} \tag{15.18}$$

Testing for the Existence of Correlation

$$t_{STAT} = \frac{r - \rho}{\sqrt{\frac{1 - r^2}{n-2}}} \tag{15.19a}$$

$$r = \frac{\text{cov}(X, Y)}{S_X S_Y} \tag{15.19b}$$

Confidence Interval Estimate for the Mean of Y

$$\hat{Y}_i \pm t_{\alpha/2}S_{YX}\sqrt{h_i}$$
$$\hat{Y}_i - t_{\alpha/2}S_{YX}\sqrt{h_i} \leq \mu_{Y|X=X_i} \leq \hat{Y}_i + t_{\alpha/2}S_{YX}\sqrt{h_i} \tag{15.20}$$

Prediction Interval for an Individual Response, Y

$$\hat{Y}_i \pm t_{\alpha/2}S_{YX}\sqrt{1 + h_i}$$
$$\hat{Y}_i - t_{\alpha/2}S_{YX}\sqrt{1 + h_i} \leq Y_{X=X_i} \leq \hat{Y}_i + t_{\alpha/2}S_{YX}\sqrt{1 + h_i} \tag{15.21}$$

KEY TERMS

assumptions of regression 222
autocorrelation 225
coefficient of determination 219
confidence interval estimate for the mean
   response 237
correlation coefficient 234
dependent variable 204
Durbin-Watson statistic 227
equal variance 222
error sum of squares (SSE) 216
explained variation 216
explanatory variable 205
homoscedasticity 222
independence of errors 222

independent variable 204
least-squares method 208
linearity 222
linear relationship 205
model 204
normality 222
prediction interval for an individual
   response, Y 239
prediction line 208
regression analysis 204
regression coefficient 208
regression sum of squares (SSR) 216
relevant range 210
residual 222

residual analysis 222
response variable 205
scatter diagram 204
scatter plot 204
simple linear regression 204
simple linear regression equation 208
slope 206
standard error of the estimate 220
total sum of squares (SST) 216
total variation 216
unexplained variation 216
Y intercept 206

CHECKING YOUR UNDERSTANDING

15.1 What is the interpretation of the Y intercept and the slope in the simple linear regression equation?

15.2 What is the interpretation of the coefficient of determination?

15.3 When is the unexplained variation (i.e., error sum of squares) equal to 0?

15.4 When is the explained variation (i.e., regression sum of squares) equal to 0?

15.5 Why should you always carry out a residual analysis as part of a regression model?

15.6 What are the assumptions of regression analysis?

15.7 How do you evaluate the assumptions of regression analysis?

15.8 When and how do you use the Durbin-Watson statistic?

15.9 What is the difference between a confidence interval estimate of the mean response, $\mu_{Y|X=X_i}$, and a prediction interval of $Y_{X=X_i}$?

PROBLEMS

Section 15.2

15.10 Fitting a straight line to a set of data yields the following prediction line:

$$\hat{Y}_i = 2 + 5X_i$$

a. Interpret the meaning of the Y intercept, b_0.
b. Interpret the meaning of the slope, b_1.
c. Predict the value of Y for $X = 3$.

15.11 If the values of X in Problem 15.1 range from 2 to 25, should you use this model to predict the mean value of Y when X equals
a. 3?   **b.** −3?   **c.** 0?   **d.** 24?

15.12 Fitting a straight line to a set of data yields the following prediction line:

$$\hat{Y}_i = 16 - 0.5X_i$$

a. Interpret the meaning of the Y intercept, b_0.
b. Interpret the meaning of the slope, b_1.
c. Predict the value of Y for $X = 6$.

15.13 The production of wine is a multibillion-dollar worldwide industry. In an attempt to develop a model of wine quality as judged by wine experts, data was collected from red wine variants of Portuguese "Vinho Verde" wine. (Data extracted from P. Cortez, Cerdeira, A., Almeida, F., Matos, T., and Reis, J., "Modeling Wine Preferences by Data Mining from Physiochemical Properties," *Decision Support Systems*, 47, 2009, pp. 547–553 and **bit.ly/9xKlEa**.) A sample of 50 wines is stored in VinhoVerde . Develop a simple linear regression model to predict wine quality, measured on a scale from 0 (very bad) to 10 (excellent), based on alcohol content (%).

a. Construct a scatter plot.
    For these data, $b_0 = -0.3529$ and $b_1 = 0.5624$.
b. Interpret the meaning of the slope, b_1, in this problem.
c. Predict the mean wine quality for wines with a 10% alcohol content.
d. What conclusion can you reach based on the results of (a)–(c)?

15.14 Zagat's publishes restaurant ratings for various locations in the United States. The file Restaurants contains the Zagat rating for food, décor, service, and the cost per person for a sample of 100 restaurants located in New York City and in a suburb of New York City. Develop a regression model to predict the cost per person, based on a variable that represents the sum of the ratings for food, décor, and service.

Sources: Extracted from *Zagat Survey 2013, New York City Restaurants*; and *Zagat Survey 2012–2013, Long Island Restaurants*.

a. Construct a scatter plot.
  For these data, $b_0 = -46.7718$ and $b_1 = 1.4963$.
b. Assuming a linear relationship, use the least-squares method to compute the regression coefficients b_0 and b_1.
c. Interpret the meaning of the Y intercept, b_0, and the slope, b_1, in this problem.
d. Predict the mean cost per person for a restaurant with a summated rating of 50.
e. What should you tell the owner of a group of restaurants in this geographical area about the relationship between the summated rating and the cost of a meal?

15.15 The owner of a moving company typically has his most experienced manager predict the total number of labor hours that will be required to complete an upcoming move. This approach has proved useful in the past, but the owner has the business objective of developing a more accurate method of predicting labor hours. In a preliminary effort to provide a more accurate method, the owner has decided to use the number of cubic feet moved as the independent variable and has collected data for 36 moves in which the origin and destination were within the borough of Manhattan in New York City and in which the travel time was an insignificant portion of the hours worked. The data are stored in Moving .
a. Construct a scatter plot.
b. Assuming a linear relationship, use the least-squares method to determine the regression coefficients b_0 and b_1.
c. Interpret the meaning of the slope, b_1, in this problem.
d. Predict the mean labor hours for moving 500 cubic feet.
e. What should you tell the owner of the moving company about the relationship between cubic feet moved and labor hours?

15.16 Starbucks Coffee Co. uses a data-based approach to improving the quality and customer satisfaction of its products. When survey data indicated that Starbucks needed to improve its package-sealing process, an experiment was conducted to determine the factors in the bag-sealing equipment that might be affecting the ease of opening the bag without tearing the inner liner of the bag. (Data extracted from L. Johnson and S. Burrows, "For Starbucks, It's in the Bag," *Quality Progress*, March 2011, pp. 17–23.) One factor that could affect the rating of the ability of the bag to resist tears was the plate gap on the bag-sealing equipment. Data were collected on 19 bags in which the plate gap was varied. The results are stored in Starbucks .
a. Construct a scatter plot.
b. Assuming a linear relationship, use the least-squares method to determine the regression coefficients b_0 and b_1.
c. Interpret the meaning of the slope, b_1, in this problem.
d. Predict the mean tear rating when the plate gap is equal to 0.
e. What should you tell management of Starbucks about the relationship between the plate gap and the tear rating?

15.17 The value of a sports franchise is directly related to the amount of revenue that a franchise can generate. The file BBValues represents the value in 2014 (in $millions) and the annual revenue (in $millions) for the 30 Major League Baseball franchises. (Data extracted from **www.forbes.com/mlb-valuations/list**.) Suppose you want to develop a simple linear regression model to predict franchise value based on annual revenue generated.
a. Construct a scatter plot.
b. Use the least-squares method to determine the regression coefficients b_0 and b_1.
c. Interpret the meaning of b_0 and b_1 in this problem.

d. Predict the mean value of a baseball franchise that generates $250 million of annual revenue.
e. What would you tell a group considering an investment in a major league baseball team about the relationship between revenue and the value of a team?

15.18 An agent for a residential real estate company in a suburb located outside of Washington, DC, has the business objective of developing more accurate estimates of the monthly rental cost for apartments. Toward that goal, the agent would like to use the size of an apartment, as defined by square footage to predict the monthly rental cost. The agent selects a sample of 48 one-bedroom apartments and collects and stores the data in RentSilverSpring .
a. Construct a scatter plot.
b. Use the least-squares method to determine the regression coefficients b_0 and b_1.
c. Interpret the meaning of b_0 and b_1 in this problem.
d. Predict the mean monthly rent for an apartment that has 800 square feet.
e. Why would it not be appropriate to use the model to predict the monthly rent for apartments that have 1,500 square feet?
f. Your friends Jim and Jennifer are considering signing a lease for a one-bedroom apartment in this residential neighborhood. They are trying to decide between two apartments, one with 800 square feet for a monthly rent of $1,130 and the other with 830 square feet for a monthly rent of $1,410. Based on (a) through (d), which apartment do you think is a better deal?

15.19 A company that holds the DVD distribution rights to movies previously released only in theaters has the business objective of developing estimates of the sales revenue of DVDs. Toward this goal, a company analyst plans to use box office gross to predict DVD sales revenue. For 26 movies, the analyst collects the box office gross (in $millions) in the year that they were released and the DVD revenue (in $millions) in the following year and stores these data in Movie . (Data extracted from "Annual Movie Chart–2012," **bit.ly/1kVJIF3** and "Top-Selling DVDs in the United States 2013," **bit.ly/UpTep9**.)

For these data,
a. Construct a scatter plot.
b. Assuming a linear relationship, use the least-squares method to determine the regression coefficients b_0 and b_1.
c. Interpret the meaning of the slope, b_1, in this problem.
d. Predict the mean sales revenue for a movie DVD that had a box office gross of $100 million.
e. What conclusions can you reach about predicting DVD revenue from movie gross?

Section 15.3

15.20 How do you interpret a coefficient of determination, r^2, equal to 0.80?

15.21 If $SSR = 36$ and $SSE = 4$, determine SST and then compute the coefficient of determination, r^2, and interpret its meaning.

15.22 If $SSR = 66$ and $SST = 88$, compute the coefficient of determination, r^2, and interpret its meaning.

15.23 If $SSE = 10$ and $SSR = 30$, compute the coefficient of determination, r^2, and interpret its meaning.

15.24 If $SSR = 120$, why is it impossible for SST to equal 110?

15.25 In Problem 15.13 on page 306, the percentage of alcohol was used to predict wine quality (stored in `VinhoVerde`). For those data, $SSR = 21.8677$ and $SST = 64.0000$.
a. Determine the coefficient of determination, r^2, and interpret its meaning.
b. Determine the standard error of the estimate.
c. How useful do you think this regression model is for predicting sales?

15.26 In Problem 15.14 on page 306, you used the summated rating to predict the cost of a restaurant meal (stored in `Restaurants`). For those data, $SSR = 9,740.0629$ and $SST = 17,844.75$.
a. Determine the coefficient of determination, r^2, and interpret its meaning.
b. Determine the standard error of the estimate.
c. How useful do you think this regression model is for predicting the cost of a restaurant meal?

15.27 In Problem 15.15 on page 307, an owner of a moving company wanted to predict labor hours, based on the cubic feet moved (stored in `Moving`). Using the results of that problem,
a. determine the coefficient of determination, r^2, and interpret its meaning.
b. determine the standard error of the estimate.
c. How useful do you think this regression model is for predicting labor hours?

15.28 In Problem 15.16 on page 307, you used the plate gap on the bag-sealing equipment to predict the tear rating of a bag of coffee (stored in `Starbucks`). Using the results of that problem,
a. determine the coefficient of determination, r^2, and interpret its meaning.
b. determine the standard error of the estimate.
c. How useful do you think this regression model is for predicting the tear rating based on the plate gap in the bag-sealing equipment?

15.29 In Problem 15.17 on page 307, you used annual revenues to predict the value of a baseball franchise (stored in `BBValues`). Using the results of that problem,
a. determine the coefficient of determination, r^2, and interpret its meaning.
b. determine the standard error of the estimate.
c. How useful do you think this regression model is for predicting the value of a baseball franchise?

15.30 In Problem 15.18 on page 307, an agent for a real estate company wanted to predict the monthly rent for one-bedroom apartments, based on the size of the apartment (stored in `Rent-SilverSpring`). Using the results of that problem,
a. determine the coefficient of determination, r^2, and interpret its meaning.
b. determine the standard error of the estimate.
c. How useful do you think this regression model is for predicting the monthly rent?
d. Can you think of other variables that might explain the variation in monthly rent?

15.31 In Problem 15.19 on page 307, you used box office gross to predict DVD revenue (stored in `Movie`). Using the results of that problem,
a. determine the coefficient of determination, r^2, and interpret its meaning.
b. determine the standard error of the estimate.

c. How useful do you think this regression model is for predicting DVD revenue?
d. Can you think of other variables that might explain the variation in DVD revenue?

Section 15.5

15.32 The following results provide the X values, residuals, and a residual plot from a regression analysis:

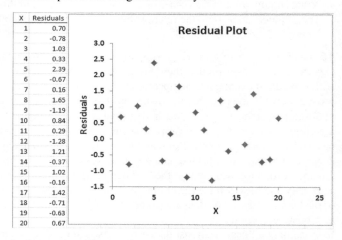

X	Residuals
1	0.70
2	-0.78
3	1.03
4	0.33
5	2.39
6	-0.67
7	0.16
8	1.65
9	-1.19
10	0.84
11	0.29
12	-1.28
13	1.21
14	-0.37
15	1.02
16	-0.16
17	1.42
18	-0.71
19	-0.63
20	0.67

Is there any evidence of a pattern in the residuals? Explain.

15.33 The following results show the X values, residuals, and a residual plot from a regression analysis:

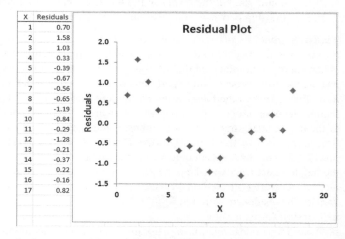

X	Residuals
1	0.70
2	1.58
3	1.03
4	0.33
5	-0.39
6	-0.67
7	-0.56
8	-0.65
9	-1.19
10	-0.84
11	-0.29
12	-1.28
13	-0.21
14	-0.37
15	0.22
16	-0.16
17	0.82

Is there any evidence of a pattern in the residuals? Explain.

15.34 In Problem 15.14 on page 306, you used the summated rating to predict the cost of a restaurant meal. Perform a residual analysis for these data (stored in `Restaurants`). Evaluate whether the assumptions of regression have been seriously violated.

15.35 In Problem 15.13 on page 306, you used the percentage of alcohol to predict wine quality. Perform a residual analysis for these data (stored in `VinhoVerde`). Evaluate whether the assumptions of regression have been seriously violated.

15.36 In Problem 15.16 on page 307, you used the plate gap on the bag-sealing equipment to predict the tear rating of a bag of coffee. Perform a residual analysis for these data (stored in `Starbucks`). Based on these results, evaluate whether the assumptions of regression have been seriously violated.

15.37 In Problem 15.15 on page 307, the owner of a moving company wanted to predict labor hours based on the cubic feet moved. Perform a residual analysis for these data (stored in Moving). Based on these results, evaluate whether the assumptions of regression have been seriously violated.

15.38 In Problem 15.18 on page 307, an agent for a real estate company wanted to predict the monthly rent for one-bedroom apartments, based on the size of the apartments. Perform a residual analysis for these data (stored in RentSilverSpring). Based on these results, evaluate whether the assumptions of regression have been seriously violated.

15.39 In Problem 15.17 on page 307, you used annual revenues to predict the value of a baseball franchise. Perform a residual analysis for these data (stored in BBValues). Based on these results, evaluate whether the assumptions of regression have been seriously violated.

15.40 In Problem 15.19 on page 307, you used box office gross to predict DVD revenue. Perform a residual analysis for these data (stored in Movie). Based on these results, evaluate whether the assumptions of regression have been seriously violated.

Section 15.6

15.41 The residuals for 10 consecutive time periods are as follows:

Time Period	Residual	Time Period	Residual
1	−5	6	+1
2	−4	7	+2
3	−3	8	+3
4	−2	9	+4
5	−1	10	+5

a. Plot the residuals over time. What conclusion can you reach about the pattern of the residuals over time?
b. Based on (a), what conclusion can you reach about the autocorrelation of the residuals?

15.42 The residuals for 15 consecutive time periods are as follows:

Time Period	Residual	Time Period	Residual
1	+4	9	+6
2	−6	10	−3
3	−1	11	+1
4	−5	12	+3
5	+2	13	0
6	+5	14	−4
7	−2	15	−7
8	+7		

a. Plot the residuals over time. What conclusion can you reach about the pattern of the residuals over time?
b. Compute the Durbin-Watson statistic. At the 0.05 level of significance, is there evidence of positive autocorrelation among the residuals?
c. Based on (a) and (b), what conclusion can you reach about the autocorrelation of the residuals?

15.43 In Problem 15.16 on page 307 concerning the bag-sealing equipment at Starbucks, you used the plate gap to predict the tear rating.
a. Is it necessary to compute the Durbin-Watson statistic in this case? Explain.
b. Under what circumstances is it necessary to compute the Durbin-Watson statistic before proceeding with the least-squares method of regression analysis?

15.44 What is the relationship between the price of crude oil and the price you pay at the pump for gasoline? The file Oil & Gasoline contains the price ($) for a barrel of crude oil (Cushing, Oklahoma, spot price) and a gallon of gasoline (U.S. average conventional spot price) for 231 weeks, ending May 30, 2014. (Data extracted from Energy Information Administration, U.S. Department of Energy, **www.eia.doe.gov**.)
a. Construct a scatter plot with the price of oil on the horizontal axis and the price of gasoline on the vertical axis.
b. Use the least-squares method to develop a simple linear regression equation to predict the price of a gallon of gasoline using the price of a barrel of crude oil as the independent variable.
c. Interpret the meaning of the slope, b_1, in this problem.
d. Plot the residuals versus the time period.
e. Compute the Durbin-Watson statistic.
f. At the 0.05 level of significance, is there evidence of positive autocorrelation among the residuals?
g. Based on the results of (d) through (f), is there reason to question the validity of the model?
h. What conclusions can you reach concerning the relationship between the price of a barrel of crude oil and the price of a gallon of gasoline?

15.45 A mail-order catalog business that sells personal computer supplies, software, and hardware maintains a centralized warehouse for the distribution of products ordered. Management is currently examining the process of distribution from the warehouse and has the business objective of determining the factors that affect warehouse distribution costs. Currently, a handling fee is added to the order, regardless of the amount of the order. Data that indicate the warehouse distribution costs and the number of orders received have been collected over the past 24 months and are stored in Warecost.
a. Assuming a linear relationship, use the least-squares method to find the regression coefficients b_0 and b_1.
b. Predict the monthly warehouse distribution costs when the number of orders is 4,500.
c. Plot the residuals versus the time period.
d. Compute the Durbin-Watson statistic. At the 0.05 level of significance, is there evidence of positive autocorrelation among the residuals?
e. Based on the results of (c) and (d), is there reason to question the validity of the model?
f. What conclusions can you reach concerning the factors that affect distribution costs?

15.46 A freshly brewed shot of espresso has three distinct components: the heart, body, and crema. The separation of these three components typically lasts only 10 to 20 seconds. To use the espresso shot in making a latte, a cappuccino, or another drink, the shot must be poured into the beverage during the separation of the heart, body, and crema. If the shot is used after the separation occurs, the drink becomes excessively bitter and acidic, ruining the final drink. Thus, a longer separation time allows the drink-maker more time to pour the shot and ensure that the beverage will meet expectations. An employee at a coffee shop hypothesized that the harder the espresso grounds were tamped down into the portafilter before brewing, the longer the separation time would be. An experiment using 24 observations was conducted to test this relationship. The independent variable Tamp measures the distance, in inches, between the espresso grounds and the top of the portafilter (i.e., the harder the tamp, the greater the distance). The dependent variable Time is the number of seconds the heart, body, and crema are separated (i.e., the amount of time after the shot is poured before it must be used for the customer's beverage). The data are stored in **Espresso** .

a. Use the least-squares method to develop a simple regression equation with Time as the dependent variable and Tamp as the independent variable.

b. Predict the separation time for a tamp distance of 0.50 inch.

c. Plot the residuals versus the time order of experimentation. Are there any noticeable patterns?

d. Compute the Durbin-Watson statistic. At the 0.05 level of significance, is there evidence of positive autocorrelation among the residuals?

e. Based on the results of (c) and (d), is there reason to question the validity of the model?

f. What conclusions can you reach concerning the effect of tamping on the time of separation?

15.47 The owners of a chain of ice cream stores have the business objective of improving the forecast of daily sales so that staffing shortages can be minimized during the summer season. As a starting point, the owners decide to develop a simple linear regression model to predict daily sales based on atmospheric temperature. They select a sample of 21 consecutive days and store the results in **IceCream** . (Hint: Determine which are the independent and dependent variables.)

a. Assuming a linear relationship, use the least-squares method to compute the regression coefficients b_0 and b_1.

b. Predict the sales for a day in which the temperature is 83°F.

c. Plot the residuals versus the time period.

d. Compute the Durbin-Watson statistic. At the 0.05 level of significance, is there evidence of positive autocorrelation among the residuals?

e. Based on the results of (c) and (d), is there reason to question the validity of the model?

f. What conclusions can you reach concerning the relationship between sales and atmospheric temperature?

Section 15.7

15.48 You are testing the null hypothesis that there is no linear relationship between two variables, X and Y. From your sample of $n = 10$, you determine that $r = 0.80$.

a. What is the value of the t test statistic t_{STAT}?

b. At the $\alpha = 0.05$ level of significance, what are the critical values?

c. Based on your answers to (a) and (b), what statistical decision should you make?

15.49 You are testing the null hypothesis that there is no linear relationship between two variables, X and Y. From your sample of $n = 18$, you determine that $b_1 = +4.5$ and $S_{b_1} = 1.5$.

a. What is the value of t_{STAT}?

b. At the $\alpha = 0.05$ level of significance, what are the critical values?

c. Based on your answers to (a) and (b), what statistical decision should you make?

d. Construct a 95% confidence interval estimate of the population slope, β_1.

15.50 You are testing the null hypothesis that there is no linear relationship between two variables, X and Y. From your sample of $n = 20$, you determine that $SSR = 60$ and $SSE = 40$.

a. What is the value of F_{STAT}?

b. At the $\alpha = 0.05$ level of significance, what is the critical value?

c. Based on your answers to (a) and (b), what statistical decision should you make?

d. Compute the correlation coefficient by first computing r^2 and assuming that b_1 is negative.

e. At the 0.05 level of significance, is there a significant correlation between X and Y?

15.51 In Problem 15.13 on page 306, you used the percentage of alcohol to predict wine quality. The data are stored in **VinhoVerde** . From the results of that problem, $b_1 = 0.5624$ and $S_{b_1} = 0.1127$.

a. At the 0.05 level of significance, is there evidence of a linear relationship between the percentage of alcohol and wine quality?

b. Construct a 95% confidence interval estimate of the population slope, β_1.

15.52 In Problem 15.14 on page 306, you used the summated rating of a restaurant to predict the cost of a meal. The data are stored in **Restaurants** . Using the results of that problem, $b_1 = 1.4963$ and $S_{b_1} = 0.1379$.

a. At the 0.05 level of significance, is there evidence of a linear relationship between the summated rating of a restaurant and the cost of a meal?

b. Construct a 95% confidence interval estimate of the population slope, β_1.

15.53 In Problem 15.15 on page 307, the owner of a moving company wanted to predict labor hours, based on the number of cubic feet moved. The data are stored in **Moving** . Use the results of that problem.

a. At the 0.05 level of significance, is there evidence of a linear relationship between the number of cubic feet moved and labor hours?

b. Construct a 95% confidence interval estimate of the population slope, β_1.

15.54 In Problem 15.16 on page 307, you used the plate gap in the bag-sealing equipment to predict the tear rating of a bag of coffee. The data are stored in **Starbucks** . Use the results of that problem.

a. At the 0.05 level of significance, is there evidence of a linear relationship between the plate gap of the bag-sealing machine and the tear rating of a bag of coffee?

b. Construct a 95% confidence interval estimate of the population slope, β_1.

15.55 In Problem 15.17 on page 307, you used annual revenues to predict the value of a baseball franchise. The data are stored in **BBValues** . Use the results of that problem.

a. At the 0.05 level of significance, is there evidence of a linear relationship between annual revenue and franchise value?

b. Construct a 95% confidence interval estimate of the population slope, β_1.

15.56 In Problem 15.18 on page 307, an agent for a real estate company wanted to predict the monthly rent for one-bedroom apartments, based on the size of the apartment. The data are stored in `RentSilverSpring`. Use the results of that problem.
a. At the 0.05 level of significance, is there evidence of a linear relationship between the size of the apartment and the monthly rent?
b. Construct a 95% confidence interval estimate of the population slope, β_1.

15.57 In Problem 15.19 on page 307, you used box office gross to predict DVD revenue. The data are stored in `Movie`. Use the results of that problem.
a. At the 0.05 level of significance, is there evidence of a linear relationship between box office gross and DVD revenue?
b. Construct a 95% confidence interval estimate of the population slope, β_1.

15.58 The volatility of a stock is often measured by its beta value. You can estimate the beta value of a stock by developing a simple linear regression model, using the percentage weekly change in the stock as the dependent variable and the percentage weekly change in a market index as the independent variable. The S&P 500 Index is a common index to use. For example, if you wanted to estimate the beta value for Disney, you could use the following model, which is sometimes referred to as a *market model*:

$$(\% \text{ weekly change in Disney}) = \beta_0$$
$$+ \beta_1 (\% \text{ weekly change in S \& P 500 index}) + \varepsilon$$

The least-squares regression estimate of the slope b_1 is the estimate of the beta value for Disney. A stock with a beta value of 1.0 tends to move the same as the overall market. A stock with a beta value of 1.5 tends to move 50% more than the overall market, and a stock with a beta value of 0.6 tends to move only 60% as much as the overall market. Stocks with negative beta values tend to move in the opposite direction of the overall market. The following table gives some beta values for some widely held stocks as of June 8, 2014:

Company	Ticker Symbol	Beta
Apple	AAPL	0.74
Disney	DIS	1.32
Dr. Pepper Snapple Group	DPS	0.22
Marriott	MAR	1.34
Microsoft	MSFT	0.68
Procter & Gamble	PG	0.40

Source: Data extracted from finance.yahoo.com, June 8, 2014.

a. For each of the six companies, interpret the beta value.
b. How can investors use the beta value as a guide for investing?

15.59 Index funds are mutual funds that try to mimic the movement of leading indexes, such as the S&P 500 or the Russell 2000. The beta values (as described in Problem 15.49) for these funds are therefore approximately 1.0, and the estimated market models for these funds are approximately

$$(\% \text{ weekly change in index fund}) = 0.0 + 1.0$$
$$(\% \text{ weekly change in the index})$$

Leveraged index funds are designed to magnify the movement of major indexes. Direxion Funds is a leading provider of leveraged index and other alternative-class mutual fund products for investment advisors and sophisticated investors. Two of the company's funds are shown in the following table:

Name	Ticker Symbol	Description
Daily Small Cap Bull 3x Fund	TNA	300% of the Russell 2000 Index
Monthly S&P Bear 2x Fund	DXSSX	200% of the S&P 500 Index

Source: Data extracted from **www.direxionfunds.com**.

The estimated market models for these funds are approximately

$$(\% \text{ weekly change in TNA}) = 0.0 + 3.0$$
$$(\% \text{ weekly change in the Russell 2000})$$
$$(\% \text{ weekly change in DXSSX}) = 0.0 + 2.0$$
$$(\% \text{ weekly change in the S\&P 500 Index})$$

Thus, if the Russell 2000 Index gains 10% over a period of time, the leveraged mutual fund TNA gains approximately 30%. On the downside, if the same index loses 20%, TNA loses approximately 60%.
a. The objective of the Direxion Funds Bull 3x Fund, SPXL, is 300% of the performance of the S&P 500 Index. What is its approximate market model?
b. If the S&P 500 Index gains 10% in a year, what return do you expect SPXL to have?
c. If the S&P 500 Index loses 20% in a year, what return do you expect SPXL to have?
d. What type of investors should be attracted to leveraged index funds? What type of investors should stay away from these funds?

15.60 The file `Cereals` contains the calories and sugar, in grams, in one serving of seven breakfast cereals:

Cereal	Calories	Sugar
Kellogg's All Bran	80	6
Kellogg's Corn Flakes	100	2
Wheaties	100	4
Nature's Path Organic Multigrain Flakes	110	4
Kellogg's Rice Krispies	130	4
Post Shredded Wheat Vanilla Almond	190	11
Kellogg's Mini Wheats	200	10

a. Compute and interpret the coefficient of correlation, r.
b. At the 0.05 level of significance, is there a significant linear relationship between calories and sugar?

15.61 Movie companies need to predict the gross receipts of an individual movie once the movie has debuted. The following results (stored in `PotterMovies`) are the first weekend gross, the U.S. gross, and the worldwide gross (in $millions) of the eight Harry Potter movies that debuted from 2001 to 2011:

Title	First Weekend	U.S. Gross	Worldwide Gross
Sorcerer's Stone	90.295	317.558	976.458
Chamber of Secrets	88.357	261.988	878.988
Prisoner of Azkaban	93.687	249.539	795.539
Goblet of Fire	102.335	290.013	896.013
Order of the Phoenix	77.108	292.005	938.469
Half-Blood Prince	77.836	301.460	934.601
Deathly Hallows Part I	125.017	295.001	955.417
Deathly Hallows Part II	169.189	381.001	1,328.11

Source: Data extracted from **www.the-numbers.com/interactive/comp-Harry-Potter.php**.

a. Compute the coefficient of correlation between first weekend gross and U.S. gross, first weekend gross and worldwide gross, and U.S. gross and worldwide gross.
b. At the 0.05 level of significance, is there a significant linear relationship between first weekend gross and U.S. gross, first weekend gross and worldwide gross, and U.S. gross and worldwide gross?

15.62 College football is big business, with coaches' salaries, revenues, and expenses in millions of dollars. The file College Football contains the coaches' pay and revenue for college football at 105 of the 124 schools that are part of the Division I Football Bowl Subdivision. (Data extracted from "College Football Coaches Continue to See Salary Explosion," *USA Today*, November 20, 2012, p. 8C.)
a. Compute and interpret the coefficient of correlation, r.
b. At the 0.05 level of significance, is there a significant linear relationship between a coach's pay and revenue?

15.63 A survey by the Pew Research Center found that social networking is popular in many nations around the world. The file Global-SocialMedia contains the level of social media networking (measured as the percent of individuals polled who use social networking sites) and the GDP per capita based on purchasing power parity (PPP) for each of 24 selected countries. (Data extracted from "Emerging Nations Embrace Internet, Mobile Technology," **bit.ly/1hL6JKA**.)
a. Compute and interpret the coefficient of correlation, r.
b. At the 0.05 level of significance, is there a significant linear relationship between GDP and social media usage?
c. What conclusions can you reach about the relationship between GDP and social media usage?

Section 15.8

15.64 Based on a sample of $n = 20$, the least-squares method was used to develop the following prediction line: $\hat{Y}_i = 5 + 3X_i$. In addition,

$$S_{YX} = 1.0 \quad \overline{X} = 2 \quad \sum_{i=1}^{n}(X_i - \overline{X})^2 = 20$$

a. Construct a 95% confidence interval estimate of the population mean response for $X = 2$.
b. Construct a 95% prediction interval of an individual response for $X = 2$.

15.65 Based on a sample of $n = 20$, the least-squares method was used to develop the following prediction line: $\hat{Y}_i = 5 + 3X_i$. In addition,

$$S_{YX} = 1.0 \quad \overline{X} = 2 \quad \sum_{i=1}^{n}(X_i - \overline{X})^2 = 20$$

a. Construct a 95% confidence interval estimate of the population mean response for $X = 4$.
b. Construct a 95% prediction interval of an individual response for $X = 4$.
c. Compare the results of (a) and (b) with those of Problem 15.55 (a) and (b). Which intervals are wider? Why?

15.66 In Problem 15.14 on page 306, you used the summated rating of a restaurant to predict the cost of a meal. The data are stored in Restaurants . For these data, $S_{YX} = 9.094$ and $h_i = 0.046319$ when $X = 50$.
a. Construct a 95% confidence interval estimate of the mean cost of a meal for restaurants that have a summated rating of 50.
b. Construct a 95% prediction interval of the cost of a meal for an individual restaurant that has a summated rating of 50.
c. Explain the difference in the results in (a) and (b).

15.67 In Problem 15.13 on page 306, you used the percentage of alcohol to predict wine quality. The data are stored in VinhoVerde . For these data, $S_{YX} = 0.9369$ and $h_i = 0.024934$ when $X = 10$.
a. Construct a 95% confidence interval estimate of the mean wine quality rating for all wines that have 10% alcohol.
b. Construct a 95% prediction interval of the wine quality rating of an individual wine that has 10% alcohol.
c. Explain the difference in the results in (a) and (b).

15.68 In Problem 15.16 on page 307, you used the plate gap on the bag-sealing equipment to predict the tear rating of a bag of coffee. The data are stored in Starbucks .
a. Construct a 95% confidence interval estimate of the mean tear rating for all bags of coffee when the plate gap is 0.
b. Construct a 95% prediction interval of the tear rating for an individual bag of coffee when the plate gap is 0.
c. Why is the interval in (a) narrower than the interval in (b)?

15.69 In Problem 15.15 on page 307, the owner of a moving company wanted to predict labor hours based on the number of cubic feet moved. The data are stored in Moving .
a. Construct a 95% confidence interval estimate of the mean labor hours for all moves of 500 cubic feet.
b. Construct a 95% prediction interval of the labor hours of an individual move that has 500 cubic feet.
c. Why is the interval in (a) narrower than the interval in (b)?

15.70 In Problem 15.18 on page 307, an agent for a real estate company wanted to predict the monthly rent for one-bedroom apartments, based on the size of an apartment. The data are stored in RentSilverSpring .
a. Construct a 95% confidence interval estimate of the mean monthly rental for all one-bedroom apartments that are 800 square feet in size.
b. Construct a 95% prediction interval of the monthly rental for an individual one-bedroom apartment that is 800 square feet in size.
c. Explain the difference in the results in (a) and (b).

15.71 In Problem 15.17 on page 307, you predicted the value of a baseball franchise, based on current revenue. The data are stored in BBValues .
a. Construct a 95% confidence interval estimate of the mean value of all baseball franchises that generate $250 million of annual revenue.

b. Construct a 95% prediction interval of the value of an individual baseball franchise that generates $250 million of annual revenue.

c. Explain the difference in the results in (a) and (b).

15.72 In Problem 15.19 on page 307, you used box office gross to predict DVD revenue. The data are stored in [Movie]. The company is about to release a movie on DVD that had a box office gross of $100 million.

a. What is the predicted DVD revenue?

b. Which interval is more useful here, the confidence interval estimate of the mean or the prediction interval for an individual response? Explain.

c. Construct and interpret the interval you selected in (b).

Review

15.73 Can you use Twitter activity to forecast box office receipts on the opening weekend? The following data (stored in [Twitter-Movies]) indicate the Twitter activity ("want to see") and the receipts ($) per theater on the weekend a movie opened for seven movies:

Movie	Twitter Activity	Receipts ($)
The Devil Inside	219,509	14,763
The Dictator	6,405	5,796
Paranormal Activity 3	165,128	15,829
The Hunger Games	579,288	36,871
Bridesmaids	6,564	8,995
Red Tails	11,104	7,477
Act of Valor	9,152	8,054

Source: R. Dodes, "Twitter Goes to the Movies," *The Wall Street Journal*, August 3, 2012, pp. D1–D12.

a. Use the least-squares method to compute the regression coefficients b_0 and b_1.

b. Interpret the meaning of b_0 and b_1 in this problem.

c. Predict the mean receipts for a movie that has a Twitter activity of 100,000.

d. Should you use the model to predict the receipts for a movie that has a Twitter activity of 1,000,000? Why or why not?

e. Determine the coefficient of determination, r^2, and explain its meaning in this problem.

f. Perform a residual analysis. Is there any evidence of a pattern in the residuals? Explain.

g. At the 0.05 level of significance, is there evidence of a linear relationship between Twitter activity and receipts?

h. Construct a 95% confidence interval estimate of the mean receipts for a movie that has a Twitter activity of 100,000 and a 95% prediction interval of the receipts for a single movie that has a Twitter activity of 100,000.

i. Based on the results of (a)–(h), do you think that Twitter activity is a useful predictor of receipts on the first weekend a movie opens? What issues about these data might make you hesitant to use Twitter activity to predict receipts?

15.74 Management of a soft-drink bottling company has the business objective of developing a method for allocating delivery costs to customers. Although one cost clearly relates to travel time within a particular route, another variable cost reflects the time required to unload the cases of soft drink at the delivery point. To be-

gin, management decided to develop a regression model to predict delivery time based on the number of cases delivered. A sample of 20 deliveries within a territory was selected. The delivery times and the number of cases delivered were organized in the following table and stored in [Delivery].

Customer	Number of Cases	Delivery Time (minutes)	Customer	Number of Cases	Delivery Time (minutes)
1	52	32.1	11	161	43.0
2	64	34.8	12	184	49.4
3	73	36.2	13	202	57.2
4	85	37.8	14	218	56.8
5	95	37.8	15	243	60.6
6	103	39.7	16	254	61.2
7	116	38.5	17	267	58.2
8	121	41.9	18	275	63.1
9	143	44.2	19	287	65.6
10	157	47.1	20	298	67.3

a. Use the least-squares method to compute the regression coefficients b_0 and b_1.

b. Interpret the meaning of b_0 and b_1 in this problem.

c. Predict the mean delivery time for 150 cases of soft drink.

d. Should you use the model to predict the delivery time for a customer who is receiving 500 cases of soft drink? Why or why not?

e. Determine the coefficient of determination, r^2, and explain its meaning in this problem.

f. Perform a residual analysis. Is there any evidence of a pattern in the residuals? Explain.

g. At the 0.05 level of significance, is there evidence of a linear relationship between delivery time and the number of cases delivered?

h. Construct a 95% confidence interval estimate of the mean delivery time for 150 cases of soft drink and a 95% prediction interval of the delivery time for a single delivery of 150 cases of soft drink.

i. What conclusions can you reach from (a) through (h) about the relationship between the number of cases and delivery time?

15.75 Measuring the height of a California redwood tree is very difficult because these trees grow to heights of over 300 feet. People familiar with these trees understand that the height of a California redwood tree is related to other characteristics of the tree, including the diameter of the tree at the breast height of a person. The data in [Redwood] represent the height (in feet) and diameter (in inches) at the breast height of a person for a sample of 21 California redwood trees.

a. Assuming a linear relationship, use the least-squares method to compute the regression coefficients b_0 and b_1. State the regression equation that predicts the height of a tree based on the tree's diameter at breast height of a person.

b. Interpret the meaning of the slope in this equation.

c. Predict the mean height for a tree that has a breast height diameter of 25 inches.

d. Interpret the meaning of the coefficient of determination in this problem.

e. Perform a residual analysis on the results and determine the adequacy of the model.

f. Determine whether there is a significant relationship between the height of redwood trees and the breast height diameter at the 0.05 level of significance.

g. Construct a 95% confidence interval estimate of the population slope between the height of the redwood trees and breast height diameter.

h. What conclusions can you reach about the relationship of the diameter of the tree and its height?

15.76 You want to develop a model to predict the assessed value of homes based on their size. A sample of 30 single-family houses listed for sale in Silver Spring, Maryland, a suburb of Washington, DC, is selected to study the relationship between assessed value (in $thousands) and size (in thousands of square feet), and the data is collected and stored in **SilverSpring**. (Hint: First determine which are the independent and dependent variables.)

a. Construct a scatter plot and, assuming a linear relationship, use the least-squares method to compute the regression coefficients b_0 and b_1.

b. Interpret the meaning of the Y intercept, b_0, and the slope, b_1, in this problem.

c. Use the prediction line developed in (a) to predict the mean assessed value for a house whose size is 2,000 square feet.

d. Determine the coefficient of determination, r^2, and interpret its meaning in this problem.

e. Perform a residual analysis on your results and evaluate the regression assumptions.

f. At the 0.05 level of significance, is there evidence of a linear relationship between assessed value and size?

g. Construct a 95% confidence interval estimate of the population slope.

h. What conclusions can you reach about the relationship between the size of the house and its assessed value?

15.77 You want to develop a model to predict the taxes of houses, based on assessed value. A sample of 30 single-family houses listed for sale in Silver Spring, Maryland, a suburb of Washington, DC, is selected. The taxes (in $) and the assessed value of the houses (in $thousands) are recorded and stored in **SilverSpring**. (Hint: First determine which are the independent and dependent variables.)

a. Construct a scatter plot and, assuming a linear relationship, use the least-squares method to compute the regression coefficients b_0 and b_1.

b. Interpret the meaning of the Y intercept, b_0, and the slope, b_1, in this problem.

c. Use the prediction line developed in (a) to predict the mean taxes for a house whose assessed value is $400,000.

d. Determine the coefficient of determination, r^2, and interpret its meaning in this problem.

e. Perform a residual analysis on your results and evaluate the regression assumptions.

f. At the 0.05 level of significance, is there evidence of a linear relationship between taxes and assessed value?

g. What conclusions can you reach concerning the relationship between taxes and assessed value?

15.78 The director of graduate studies at a large college of business has the objective of predicting the grade point average (GPA) of students in an MBA program. The director begins by using the Graduate Management Admission Test (GMAT) score. A sample of 20 students who have completed two years in the program is selected and stored in **GPIGMAT**.

a. Construct a scatter plot and, assuming a linear relationship, use the least-squares method to compute the regression coefficients b_0 and b_1.

b. Interpret the meaning of the Y intercept, b_0, and the slope, b_1, in this problem.

c. Use the prediction line developed in (a) to predict the mean GPA for a student with a GMAT score of 600.

d. Determine the coefficient of determination, r^2, and interpret its meaning in this problem.

e. Perform a residual analysis on your results and evaluate the regression assumptions.

f. At the 0.05 level of significance, is there evidence of a linear relationship between GMAT score and GPA?

g. Construct a 95% confidence interval estimate of the mean GPA of students with a GMAT score of 600 and a 95% prediction interval of the GPA for a particular student with a GMAT score of 600.

h. Construct a 95% confidence interval estimate of the population slope.

i. What conclusions can you reach concerning the relationship between GMAT score and GPA?

15.79 An accountant for a large department store has the business objective of developing a model to predict the amount of time it takes to process invoices. Data are collected from the past 32 working days, and the number of invoices processed and completion time (in hours) are stored in **Invoice**. (Hint: First determine which are the independent and dependent variables.)

a. Assuming a linear relationship, use the least-squares method to compute the regression coefficients b_0 and b_1.

b. Interpret the meaning of the Y intercept, b_0, and the slope, b_1, in this problem.

c. Use the prediction line developed in (a) to predict the mean amount of time it would take to process 150 invoices.

d. Determine the coefficient of determination, r^2, and interpret its meaning.

e. Plot the residuals against the number of invoices processed and also against time.

f. Based on the plots in (e), does the model seem appropriate?

g. Based on the results in (e) and (f), what conclusions can you reach about the validity of the prediction made in (c)?

h. What conclusions can you reach about the relationship between the number of invoices and the completion time?

15.80 On January 28, 1986, the space shuttle *Challenger* exploded, and seven astronauts were killed. Prior to the launch, the predicted atmospheric temperature was for freezing weather at the launch site. Engineers for Morton Thiokol (the manufacturer of the rocket motor) prepared charts to make the case that the launch should not take place due to the cold weather. These arguments were rejected, and the launch tragically took place. Upon investigation after the tragedy, experts agreed that the disaster occurred because of leaky rubber O-rings that did not seal properly due to the cold temperature. Data indicating the atmospheric temperature at the time of 23 previous launches and the O-ring damage index are stored in **O-Ring**.

Note: Data from flight 4 is omitted due to unknown O-ring condition.

Sources: Data extracted from *Report of the Presidential Commission on the Space Shuttle Challenger Accident*, Washington, DC, 1986, Vol. II (H1–H3) and Vol. IV (664); and *Post-Challenger Evaluation of Space Shuttle Risk Assessment and Management*, Washington, DC, 1988, pp. 135–136.

a. Construct a scatter plot for the seven flights in which there was O-ring damage (O-ring damage index $\neq$ 0). What conclusions, if any, can you reach about the relationship between atmospheric temperature and O-ring damage?

b. Construct a scatter plot for all 23 flights.

c. Explain any differences in the interpretation of the relationship between atmospheric temperature and O-ring damage in (a) and (b).

d. Based on the scatter plot in (b), provide reasons why a prediction should not be made for an atmospheric temperature of 31°F, the temperature on the morning of the launch of the *Challenger*.

e. Although the assumption of a linear relationship may not be valid for the set of 23 flights, fit a simple linear regression model to predict O-ring damage, based on atmospheric temperature.

f. Include the prediction line found in (e) on the scatter plot developed in (b).

g. Based on the results in (f), do you think a linear model is appropriate for these data? Explain.

h. Perform a residual analysis. What conclusions do you reach?

15.81 A baseball analyst would like to study various team statistics for a recent season to determine which variables might be useful in predicting the number of wins achieved by teams during the season. He begins by using a team's earned run average (ERA), a measure of pitching performance, to predict the number of wins. He collects the team ERA and team wins for each of the 30 Major League Baseball teams and stores these data in Baseball . (Hint: First determine which are the independent and dependent variables.)

a. Assuming a linear relationship, use the least-squares method to compute the regression coefficients b_0 and b_1.

b. Interpret the meaning of the Y intercept, b_0, and the slope, b_1, in this problem.

c. Use the prediction line developed in (a) to predict the mean number of wins for a team with an ERA of 4.50.

d. Compute the coefficient of determination, r^2, and interpret its meaning.

e. Perform a residual analysis on your results and determine the adequacy of the fit of the model.

f. At the 0.05 level of significance, is there evidence of a linear relationship between the number of wins and the ERA?

g. Construct a 95% confidence interval estimate of the mean number of wins expected for teams with an ERA of 4.50.

h. Construct a 95% prediction interval of the number of wins for an individual team that has an ERA of 4.50.

i. Construct a 95% confidence interval estimate of the population slope.

j. The 30 teams constitute a population. In order to use statistical inference, as in (f) through (i), the data must be assumed to represent a random sample. What "population" would this sample be drawing conclusions about?

k. What other independent variables might you consider for inclusion in the model?

l. What conclusions can you reach concerning the relationship between ERA and wins?

15.82 Can you use the annual revenues generated by National Basketball Association (NBA) franchises to predict franchise

values? Figure 2.14 on page xxx shows a scatter plot of revenue with franchise value, and Figure 3.9 on page xxx, shows the correlation coefficient. Now, you want to develop a simple linear regression model to predict franchise values based on revenues. (Franchise values and revenues are stored in NBAValues .)

a. Assuming a linear relationship, use the least-squares method to compute the regression coefficients b_0 and b_1.

b. Interpret the meaning of the Y intercept, b_0, and the slope, b_1, in this problem.

c. Predict the mean value of an NBA franchise that generates $150 million of annual revenue.

d. Compute the coefficient of determination, r^2, and interpret its meaning.

e. Perform a residual analysis on your results and evaluate the regression assumptions.

f. At the 0.05 level of significance, is there evidence of a linear relationship between the annual revenues generated and the value of an NBA franchise?

g. Construct a 95% confidence interval estimate of the mean value of all NBA franchises that generate $150 million of annual revenue.

h. Construct a 95% prediction interval of the value of an individual NBA franchise that generates $150 million of annual revenue.

i. Compare the results of (a) through (h) to those of baseball franchises in Problems 15.8, 15.20, 15.30, 15.46, and 15.62 and European soccer teams in Problem 15.83.

15.83 In Problem 15.82 you used annual revenue to develop a model to predict the franchise value of National Basketball Association (NBA) teams. Can you also use the annual revenues generated by European soccer teams to predict franchise values? (European soccer team values and revenues are stored in SoccerValues2014 .)

a. Repeat Problem 15.82 (a) through (h) for the European soccer teams.

b. Compare the results of (a) to those of baseball franchises in Problems 15.8, 15.20, 15.30, 15.46, and 15.62 and NBA franchises in Problem 15.82.

15.84 During the fall harvest season in the United States, pumpkins are sold in large quantities at farm stands. Often, instead of weighing the pumpkins prior to sale, the farm stand operator will just place the pumpkin in the appropriate circular cutout on the counter. When asked why this was done, one farmer replied, "I can tell the weight of the pumpkin from its circumference." To determine whether this was really true, the circumference and weight of each pumpkin from a sample of 23 pumpkins were determined and the results stored in Pumpkin .

a. Assuming a linear relationship, use the least-squares method to compute the regression coefficients b_0 and b_1.

b. Interpret the meaning of the slope, b_1, in this problem.

c. Predict the mean weight for a pumpkin that is 60 centimeters in circumference.

d. Do you think it is a good idea for the farmer to sell pumpkins by circumference instead of weight? Explain.

e. Determine the coefficient of determination, r^2, and interpret its meaning.

f. Perform a residual analysis for these data and evaluate the regression assumptions.

g. At the 0.05 level of significance, is there evidence of a linear relationship between the circumference and weight of a pumpkin?

h. Construct a 95% confidence interval estimate of the population slope, β_1.

15.85 Refer to the discussion of beta values and market models in Problem 15.58 on page 311. The S&P 500 Index tracks the overall movement of the stock market by considering the stock prices of 500 large corporations. The file StockPrices2013 contains 2013 weekly data for the S&P 500 and three companies. The following variables are included:

WEEK—Week ending on date given
S&P—Weekly closing value for the S&P 500 Index
GE—Weekly closing stock price for General Electric
DISCA—Weekly closing stock price for Discovery Communications
GOOG—Weekly closing stock price for Google

Source: Data extracted from finance.yahoo.com, June 6, 2014.

a. Estimate the market model for GE. (Hint: Use the percentage change in the S&P 500 Index as the independent variable and the percentage change in GE's stock price as the dependent variable.)

b. Interpret the beta value for GE.

c. Repeat (a) and (b) for Discovery Communications.

d. Repeat (a) and (b) for Google.

e. Write a brief summary of your findings.

15.86 The file CEO-Compensation2013 includes the total compensation (in $millions) for CEOs of 200 Standard & Poor's 500 companies and the investment return in 2013. (Data extracted from "Millions by millions, CEO pay goes up," **usat. ly/1jhbypL**.)

a. Compute the correlation coefficient between compensation and the investment return in 2013.

b. At the 0.05 level of significance, is the correlation between compensation and the investment return in 2013 statistically significant?

c. Write a short summary of your findings in (a) and (b). Do the results surprise you?

REPORT WRITING EXERCISE

15.87 In Problems 15.8, 15.20, 15.30, 15.46, 15.62, 15.82, and 15.83, you developed regression models to predict franchise value of major league baseball, NBA basketball, and soccer teams. Now, write a report based on the models you developed. Append to your report all appropriate charts and statistical information.

CASES FOR CHAPTER 15

Managing Ashland MultiComm Services

To ensure that as many trial subscriptions to the *3-For-All* service as possible are converted to regular subscriptions, the marketing department works closely with the customer support department to accomplish a smooth initial process for the trial subscription customers. To assist in this effort, the marketing department needs to accurately forecast the monthly total of new regular subscriptions.

A team consisting of managers from the marketing and customer support departments was convened to develop a better method of forecasting new subscriptions. Previously, after examining new subscription data for the prior three months, a group of three managers would develop a subjective forecast of the number of new subscriptions. Livia Salvador, who was recently hired by the company to provide expertise in quantitative forecasting methods, suggested that the department look for factors that might help in predicting new subscriptions.

Members of the team found that the forecasts in the past year had been particularly inaccurate because in some months, much more time was spent on telemarketing than in other months. Livia collected data (stored in AMS12) for the number of new subscriptions and hours spent on telemarketing for each month for the past two years.

1. What criticism can you make concerning the method of forecasting that involved taking the new subscriptions data for the prior three months as the basis for future projections?

2. What factors other than number of telemarketing hours spent might be useful in predicting the number of new subscriptions? Explain.

3. **a.** Analyze the data and develop a regression model to predict the number of new subscriptions for a month, based on the number of hours spent on telemarketing for new subscriptions.

   b. If you expect to spend 1,200 hours on telemarketing per month, estimate the number of new subscriptions for the month. Indicate the assumptions on which this prediction is based. Do you think these assumptions are valid? Explain.

   c. What would be the danger of predicting the number of new subscriptions for a month in which 2,000 hours were spent on telemarketing?

Digital Case

Apply your knowledge of simple linear regression in this Digital Case, which extends the Sunflowers Apparel Using Statistics scenario from this chapter.

Leasing agents from the Triangle Mall Management Corporation have suggested that Sunflowers consider several locations in some of Triangle's newly renovated lifestyle malls that cater to shoppers with higher-than-mean disposable income. Although the locations are smaller than the typical Sunflowers location, the leasing agents argue that higher-than-mean disposable income in the surrounding community is a better predictor of higher sales than profiled customers. The leasing agents maintain that sample data from 14 Sunflowers stores prove that this is true.

Open **Triangle_Sunflower.pdf** and review the leasing agents' proposal and supporting documents. Then answer the following questions:

1. Should mean disposable income be used to predict sales based on the sample of 14 Sunflowers stores?

2. Should the management of Sunflowers accept the claims of Triangle's leasing agents? Why or why not?

3. Is it possible that the mean disposable income of the surrounding area is not an important factor in leasing new locations? Explain.

4. Are there any other factors not mentioned by the leasing agents that might be relevant to the store leasing decision?

Brynne Packaging

Brynne Packaging is a large packaging company, offering its customers the highest standards in innovative packaging solutions and reliable service. About 25% of the employees at Brynne Packaging are machine operators. The human resources department has suggested that the company consider using the Wesman Personnel Classification Test (WPCT), a measure of reasoning ability, to screen applicants for the machine operator job. In order to assess the WPCT as a predictor of future job performance, 25 recent applicants were tested using the WPCT; all were hired, regardless of their WPCT score. At a later time, supervisors were asked to rate the quality of the job performance of these 25 employees, using a 1-to-10 rating scale (where 1 = very low and 10 = very high). Factors considered in the ratings included the employee's output, defect rate, ability to implement continuous quality procedures, and contributions to team problem-solving efforts. The file BrynnePackaging contains the WPCT scores (WPCT) and job performance ratings (Ratings) for the 25 employees.

1. Assess the significance and importance of WPCT score as a predictor of job performance. Defend your answer.

2. Predict the mean job performance rating for all employees with a WPCT score of 6. Give a point prediction as well as a 95% confidence interval. Do you have any concerns using the regression model for predicting mean job performance rating given the WPCT score of 6?

3. Evaluate whether the assumptions of regression have been seriously violated.

CHAPTER 15 CASIO CALCULATOR GUIDE

CALCULATOR LESSON 18A

LESSON 18A – SIMPLE LINEAR REGRESSION

EXAMPLE 15.5

We will use the scenario "Forecasting Sales for a Clothing Store" to demonstrate how to perform simple linear regression on the calculator.

The sales for Sunflowers Apparel, a chain of apparel stores for women, have increased during the past 12 years as the chain has increased the number of its stores. Until now, Sunflowers senior managers selected sites based on subjective factors such as the availability of a good lease or the perception that a location seemed ideal for an apparel store. As the new director of planning, you need to develop a systematic approach to selecting new sites that will allow Sunflowers to make better-informed decisions for opening additional stores. This plan must be able to forecast annual sales for all potential stores under consideration. You believe that the size of the store significantly contributes to the success of a store, and you want to use this relationship in the decision-making process. You wish to predict annual sales based on the size of the store in square feet.

Table 15.8 summarizes the results of the 14 stores.

TABLE 15.8

Store	Square Feet (000)	Annual Sales (in millions of dollars)	Store	Square Feet (000)	Annual Sales (in millions of dollars)
1	1.7	3.7	8	1.1	2.7
2	1.6	3.9	9	3.2	5.5
3	2.8	6.7	10	1.5	2.9
4	5.6	9.5	11	5.2	10.7
5	1.3	3.4	12	4.6	7.6
6	2.2	5.6	13	5.8	11.8
7	1.3	3.7	14	3.0	4.1

The dependent variable, y, is the annual sales (in millions of dollars), and the independent variable, x, is the size of the store (in square feet).

1. Compute the regression coefficients – b_0 (intercept) and b_1 (slope)
To obtain the regression coefficients, use the calculator and follow these steps.

  a) From the **Main Menu** select **STAT** and press **EXE**.

  b) Enter the x values (square feet) in List 1 and the y values (annual sales) in List 2.

c) Now press **F2 (CALC)**, and then press **F6 (SET)**.
The first row will be highlighted. Use the Arrow key to highlight the third row (2 Var XList : List 1).

d) Now enter the following in response to the screen prompts.

2 Var XList : List 1 (F1)   *Note: You entered the x values in List 1.*

2 Var YLIst : List 2 (F2)   *Note: You entered the y values in List 2.*

2 Var Freq : 1

e) Now press **EXIT** to return to the display of the data.

f) Now press **F3 (REG)**, and then press **F1 (X)**.
The calculator will show the following results:

Linear Reg
a = 1.66986231
b = 0.96447365
r = 0.95088327
r^2 = 0.904179
y = $ax + b$

The values are put together to obtain the simple linear regression equation (the prediction line):

$$\hat{y} = 0.96447365 + 1.66986231x$$

The coefficient of determination, r^2, is 0.904179.

2. Hypothesis tests for the slope and correlation coefficient

At the 0.05 level of significance, is there evidence of a linear relationship between the size of the store and annual sales?

Solution:

We test for a linear relationship between the variables x and y by testing whether the population regression coefficient (slope), B, is different from zero.

$H_0: \beta_1 = 0$ (There is *not* a linear relationship.)

$H_a: \beta_1 \neq 0$ (There is a linear relationship.)

Note: Use the same data that you used for the x values (square feet) in List 1 and the y values (annual sales) in List 2.

From the **Main Menu** select

STAT F3(TEST) F2(t) F3(REG), and then enter the following items.

(Note: Only use the **EXE** key after a new data entry. Otherwise, use the cursor ▼ arrow. If you accidentally hit the wrong key, use **AC/ON** or **EXIT** to go back.)

1-Sample ZInterval

β & ρ	: $\neq$ (F1)0	▼
XList	: .List1 (F1)	**EXE**
YList	: .List2 (F2)	**EXE**
Freq	: 1 (F1)	**EXE**

Execute

Now press **EXE** or **F1**(Calc).

The calculator will show the following results:

LinearReg tTest

$\beta \neq 0$ & $\rho \neq 0$

t = 10.641

p = 1.8226E-07

df = 12

a = 0.96447

b = 1.6698

y = $a + bx$

Use the cursor ▼ arrow to scroll down for more results.

df = 12

a = 0.96447

b = 1.6698

s = 0.96637

r = 0.95088

r^2 = 0.90417

y = $a + bx$

Conclusion:

p-value = 0.00000018226 < 0.05 = α, hence we reject H_0.

There is sufficient evidence to conclude that there is a linear relationship between size of the store and annual sales.

3. Compute the prediction value

What is the average annual sales if the size of the store is 1.8 (000) square feet?

Note: You have to make sure that the information in this example (in **#1**) is still recorded in the calculator and the regression calculations have been performed before you can compute the prediction value.

From the **Main Menu** select

MENU   RUN   EXE, and then enter **1.8   OPTN**.

Use the following options on the bottom of the display.

Select   **STAT (F5)**   ŷ**(F2)**   **EXE**

The calculator will show the following result:

3.97022583

We interpret the value as follows:

$$\hat{y} = 0.96447365 + 1.66986231\,(1.8) = 3.97022583$$

We predict that the annual sales will be $3.97022583 (in millions of dollars) if the size of the store is 1.8 (000) square feet.

4. Compute the residual

To obtain the residuals, follow the following steps.

a. From the **Main Menu** select **STAT** and press **EXE**.

b. Enter the x values (square feet) in List 1 and the y values (annual sales) in List 2.

c. While the data lists is on display, press "SHIFT" key followed by the "MENU" key.

You will see the screen displayed:

Stat Wind	: Auto
Resid List	**: List 3** ← Bring the cursor to highlight on "Resid List"
List File	: File1
Sub Name	: On
Frac Result	: d/c
Func Type	: Y=
Graph Func	: On

Bring the cursor to highlight on "Resid List" and specify which list you would like to store your residual values.

After you have done with the setup, press "EXIT" key. Then run the linear regression.

CALCULATOR LESSON 18B

FX-9850GII CALCULATOR

EXAMPLE 15.6

LESSON 18B – SIMPLE LINEAR REGRESSION

We will use the scenario "Forecasting Sales for a Clothing Store" to demonstrate how to perform simple linear regression on the calculator.

The sales for Sunflowers Apparel, a chain of apparel stores for women, have increased during the past 12 years as the chain has increased the number of its stores. Until now, Sunflowers senior managers selected sites based on subjective factors such as the availability of a good lease or the perception that a location seemed ideal for an apparel store. As the new director of planning, you need to develop a systematic approach to selecting new sites that will allow Sunflowers to make better-informed decisions for opening additional stores. This plan must be able to forecast annual sales for all potential stores under consideration. You believe that the size of the store significantly contributes to the success of a store and you want to use this relationship in the decision-making process. You wish to predict annual sales based on the size of the store in square feet.

Table 15.9 summarizes the results of the 14 stores.

TABLE 15.9

Store	Square Feet (000)	Annual Sales (in millions of dollars)	Store	Square Feet (000)	Annual Sales (in millions of dollars)
1	1.7	3.7	8	1.1	2.7
2	1.6	3.9	9	3.2	5.5
3	2.8	6.7	10	1.5	2.9
4	5.6	9.5	11	5.2	10.7
5	1.3	3.4	12	4.6	7.6
6	2.2	5.6	13	5.8	11.8
7	1.3	3.7	14	3.0	4.1

The dependent variable, y, is the annual sales (in millions of dollars), and the independent variable, x, is the size of the store (in square feet).

1. Compute the regression coefficients – b_0 (intercept) and b_1 (slope)
To obtain the regression coefficients, use the calculator and follow these steps.

a) From the **Main Menu** select **STAT** and press **EXE.**

b) Enter the x values (square feet) in List 1 and the y values (annual sales) in List 2.

c) Now press **F2 (CALC)**, and then press **F6 (SET)**.
The first row will be highlighted. Use the Arrow key to highlight the third row (2 Var XList : List 1).

d) Now enter the following in response to the screen prompts.

2 Var XList   :   List 1 (F1)   *Note: You entered the x values in List 1.*

2 Var YLIst   :   List 2 (F2)   *Note: You entered the y values in List 2.*

2 Var Freq   :   1

e) Now press **EXIT** to return to the display of the data.

f) Now press **F3 (REG)**, and then press **F1 (X).**

g) At this point you have two options:
1. ax + b (corresponds to function key **F1**)
2. a + bx (corresponds to function key **F2**)
Select either one to change the linear regression equation.
Suppose you select **F1 (ax + b)**.
The calculator will show the following results:

Linear-Reg
a = 1.66986231
b = 0.96447365
r = 0.95088327
r^2 = 0.904179
y = $ax + b$

The values are put together to obtain the simple linear regression equation (the prediction line):

$\hat{y}$ = 0.96447365 + 1.66986231x

The coefficient of determination, r^2, is 0.904179.

2. Hypothesis tests for the slope and correlation coefficient

At the 0.05 level of significance, is there evidence of a linear relationship between the size of the store and annual sales?

Solution:

We test for a linear relationship between the variables x and y by testing whether the population regression coefficient (slope), B, is different from zero.

$H_0: \beta_1 = 0$ (There is *not* a linear relationship.)

$H_a: \beta_1 \neq 0$ (There is a linear relationship.)

Note: Use the same data that you used for the x values (square feet) in List 1 and the y values (annual sales) in List 2.

From the **Main Menu** select

STAT   F3(TEST)   F2(t)   F3(REG), and then enter the following items:

(Note: Only use the **EXE** key after a new data entry. Otherwise, use the cursor ▼ arrow. If you accidentally hit the wrong key, use **AC/^{ON}** or **EXIT** to go back.)

> **1-Sample ZInterval**
> $\beta \,\&\, \rho$: ≠(F1)0   ▼
> XList   : .List1 (F1)   **EXE**
> YList   : .List2 (F2)   **EXE**
> Freq   : 1 (F1)   **EXE**
> Save Res   : None
> **Execute**

Now press **EXE** or **F1**(Calc).

The calculator will show the following results:

> **LinearReg tTest**
> $\beta \neq 0 \,\&\, \rho \neq 0$
> t = 10.6411237
> p = 1.8226E-07
> df = 12
> a = 0.96447365
> b = 1.66986232

Use the cursor ▼ arrow to scroll down for more results.

> df = 12
> a = 0.96447365
> b = 1.66986232
> se = 0.96637967
> r = 0.95088327
> r^2 = 0.904179

Conclusion:

p-value = 0.00000018226 < 0.05 = α, hence we reject H_o.

There is sufficient evidence to conclude that there is a linear relationship between size of the store and annual sales.

3. Compute the prediction value

What is the average annual sales if the size of the store is 1.8 (000) square feet?

You have to make sure that the data (Table 15.1) is recorded in the calculator and the simple linear regression is performed prior to computing the prediction value.

To obtain predicted value for X=1.8, go to the main menu and select:

MENU RUN-MAT   EXE then enter **1.8 OPTN**

Use the following options at the bottom of the display.
Select   **STAT (F5)**   **ȳ(F2)**   **EXE**

The calculator will now show the result:
3.97022583

We interpret the value as follows:

ŷ =0.96447365 + 1.66986231 (1.8) = 3.97022583

We predict that the annual sales will be $3.97022583 (in millions of dollars) if the size of the store is 1.8 (000) square feet.

4. Compute the residuals

    a) From the **Main Menu** select **STAT** and press **EXE.**

    b) Enter the x values (square feet) in List 1 and the y values (annual sales) in List 2.

    c) While the data lists is on display, press "SHIFT" key followed by the "MENU" key.

You will see the screen displayed:

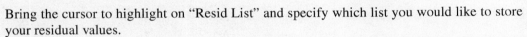

    Stat Wind : Auto
    Resid List : List 3
    List File   : File1
    Sub Name   : On
    Frac Result : d/c
    Func Type : Y=
    Graph Func : On

Bring the cursor to highlight on "Resid List" and specify which list you would like to store your residual values.

After you have done with the setup, press "EXIT" key. Then run the linear regression.

CHAPTER 15 SPSS GUIDE

SPSS—VERSION 16—SIMPLE LINEAR REGRESSION

We will use the scenario "Forecasting Sales for a Clothing Store" to demonstrate how to perform simple linear regression using SPSS.

The dependent variable, y, is the annual sales (in millions of dollars), and the independent variable, x, is the size of the store (in square feet). You wish to predict annual sales based on the size of the store in square feet.

A random sample of 14 stores was selected with the results shown in Table 15.10.

Table 15.10 summarizes the results of the 14 stores.

TABLE 15.10

Store	Square Feet (000)	Annual Sales (in millions of dollars)	Store	Square Feet (000)	Annual Sales (in millions of dollars)
1	1.7	3.7	8	1.1	2.7
2	1.6	3.9	9	3.2	5.5
3	2.8	6.7	10	1.5	2.9
4	5.6	9.5	11	5.2	10.7
5	1.3	3.4	12	4.6	7.6
6	2.2	5.6	13	5.8	11.8
7	1.3	3.7	14	3.0	4.1

Performing a simple linear regression on SPSS—Version 16

Step 1: Open the SPSS Data Editor.

Click **Cancel** to cancel the SPSS opening window.

FIGURE 15.25

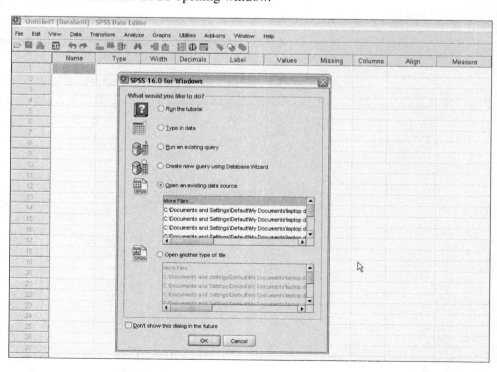

Step 2: Define the variables and give the variables a label.

Click **Variable View** (at the bottom of the window) to go to the variable view window to define the variables and fix the data at zero or one decimal places.

- Enter the variable name "size" and label it as "square feet (thousands)."

- Enter the variable name "sales" and label it as "Annual Sales (millions of dollars)."

FIGURE 15.26

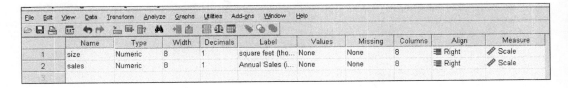

Step 3: Create a SPSS data file.

Click **Data View** to return to the data view window. Now, enter the raw data (in Table 15.8) into the appropriate columns of variables.

FIGURE 15.27

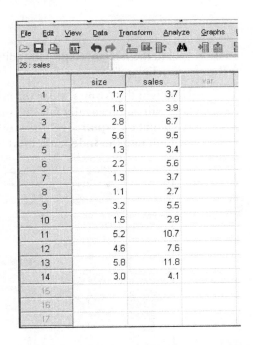

After you have entered all the data, save it as "sales.sav" (or any filename).

Step 3: Perform regression analysis.

Make the following menu selections:

Analyze   Regression   Linear

FIGURE 15.28

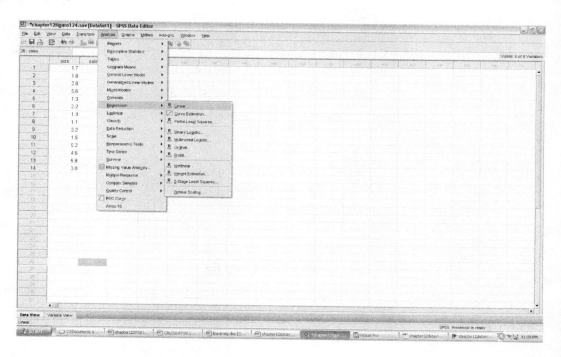

At this point, the **Linear Regression** dialog box will appear. Make these entries in the **Linear Regression** dialog box:

- Highlight the **Annual sales (or sales)** variable and click on the arrow key ( ). The variable will automatically fall into the **Dependent** box.
- Highlight the **square feet (or size)** variable and click on the arrow key ( ). The variable will fall into the **Independent(s)** box.

FIGURE 15.29

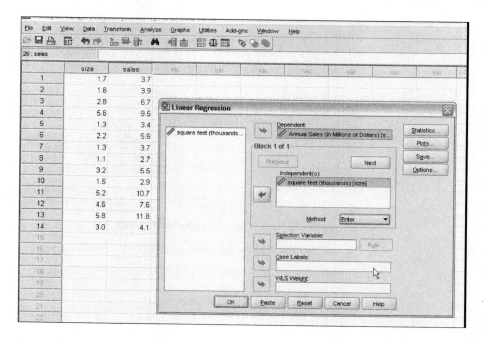

- ***Obtaining Predictions and Residuals.*** Click on the save button (note that the **Save** is a button on the pop-up menu and not the usual File save option) and the **save** dialog box will pop up. In the **save** dialog box, click on **Unstandardized** in the the **Predicted Values** box. Click on **Unstandardized** in the **Residuals** box. Click on **Mean** and **Individual** in the **Prediction Intervals** box. Click on **Continue** to return to the **Linear Regression** dialog box. Then click **OK**.

FIGURE 15.30

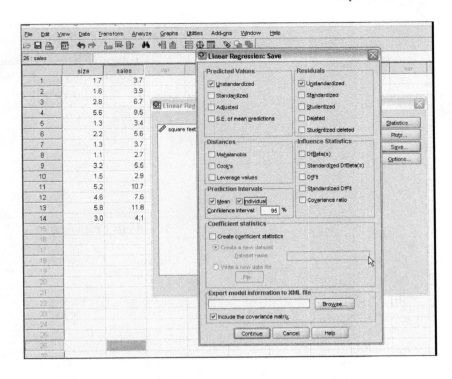

Step 3: Go to **SPSS Viewer** to obtain your SPSS results.

SPSS output:
Regression

FIGURE 15.31

Variables Entered/Removed[b]			
Model	**Variables Entered**	**Variables Removed**	**Method**
1	square feet (thousands)[a]		Enter

a. *Predictors: (constant), square feet (thousands)*
b. *Dependent Variable: Annual Sales (in millions of dollars)*

FIGURE 15.32

Model Summary				
Model	**R**	**R Square**	**Adjusted R Square**	**Std. Error of the Estimate**
1	.951[a]	.904	.896	.9664

a. *Predictors: (constant), square feet (thousands)*
b. *Dependent Variable: Annual Sales (in millions of dollars)*

FIGURE 15.33

ANOVA[b]					
Model	**Sum of Squares**	**df**	**Mean Square**	**F**	**Sig.**
1 Regression	105.748	1	105.748	113.234	.000[a]
Residual	11.207	12	.934		
Total	116.954	13			

a. *Predictors: (constant), square feet (thousands)*
b. *Dependent Variable: Annual Sales (in millions of dollars)*

FIGURE 15.34

	Coefficients[a]					
	Unstandardized Coefficients		Standardized Coefficients			
Model	B	Std. Error	Beta	t	Sig.
1 (Constant)	.964	.526		1.833	.092
square feet (thousands)	1.670	.157	.951	10.641	.000

a. Dependent Variable: Annual Sales (in millions of dollars)

FIGURE 15.35

Residuals Statistics[a]					
	Minimum	Maximum	Mean	Std. Deviation	N
Predicted Value	2.801	10.650	5.843	2.8521	14
Std. Predicted Value	−1.066	1.685	.000	1.000	14
Standard Error of Predicted Value	.259	.520	.356	.083	14
Adjusted Predicted Value	2.820	10.603	5.821	2.8263	14
Residual	−1.8741	1.1503	.0000	.9285	14
Std. Residual	−1.939	1.190	.000	.961	14
Stud. Residual	−2.013	1.413	.010	1.038	14
Deleted Residual	−2.0186	1.6200	.0215	1.0888	14
Stud. Deleted Residual	−2.368	1.481	−.009	1.104	14
Mahal. Distance	.002	2.840	.929	.886	14
Cook's Distance	.001	.407	.090	.113	14
Centred Leverage Value	.000	.218	.071	.068	14

a. Dependent Variable: Annual Sales (in millions of dollars)

Obtaining Predictions and Residuals

The confidence interval values and prediction interval values are displayed on the **SPSS Data Editor** under the variables PRE_1, RES_1, LMCI_1, UMCI_1, LICI_1, and UICI_1.

Notation:

PRE_1—Unstandardized Predicted (for Model 1)

RES_1—Unstandardized Residual (for Model 1)

LMCI_1—95% Lower Confidence Interval for y mean (for Model 1)

UMCI_1—95% Upper Confidence Interval for y mean (for Model 1)

LICI_1—95% Lower Confidence Interval for y individual (for Model 1)

UICI_1—5% Upper Confidence Interval for y individual (for Model 1)

FIGURE 15.36

	size	sales	PRE_1	RES_1	LMCI_1	UMCI_1	LICI_1	UICI_1
1	1.7	3.7	3.80324	-0.10324	3.10247	4.50401	1.58413	6.02235
2	1.6	3.9	3.63625	0.26375	2.91459	4.35792	1.41045	5.86205
3	2.8	6.7	5.64009	1.05991	5.07582	6.20435	3.46023	7.81995
4	5.6	9.5	10.31670	-0.81570	9.24060	11.39061	7.95164	12.67977
5	1.3	3.4	3.13529	0.26471	2.34535	3.92524	0.88643	5.38416
6	2.2	5.6	4.63817	0.96183	4.02375	5.25259	2.44479	6.83155
7	1.3	3.7	3.13529	0.56471	2.34535	3.92524	0.88643	5.38416
8	1.1	2.7	2.80132	-0.10132	1.96197	3.64067	0.53463	5.06801
9	3.2	5.5	6.30803	-0.80803	5.73729	6.87877	4.12649	8.48958
10	1.5	2.9	3.46927	-0.56927	2.72572	4.21282	1.23628	5.70226
11	5.2	10.7	9.64776	1.05224	8.68671	10.60881	7.33324	11.96228
12	4.6	7.6	8.64584	-1.04584	7.84206	9.44962	6.39208	10.89960
13	5.8	11.8	10.64968	1.15032	9.51594	11.78341	8.25829	13.04106
14	3.0	4.1	5.97406	-1.87406	5.41069	6.53744	3.79443	8.15369

16

Multiple Regression

CONTENTS

16.1 Developing a Multiple Regression Model

16.2 r^2, Adjusted r^2, and the Overall F Test

16.3 Residual Analysis for the Multiple Regression Model

16.4 Inferences Concerning the Population Regression Coefficients

16.5 Using Dummy Variables and Interaction Terms in Regression Models

USING STATISTICS: The Multiple Effects of OmniPower Bars, Revisited

CHAPTER 16 SPSS GUIDE

OBJECTIVES

Develop a multiple regression model

Interpret the regression coefficients

Determine which independent variables to include in a regression model

How to use categorical independent variables in a regression model

The Multiple Effects of OmniPower Bars

You are a marketing manager for OmniFoods, with oversight for nutrition bars and similar snack items. You seek to revive the sales of OmniPower, the company's primary product in this category. Originally marketed as a high-energy bar to runners, mountain climbers, and other athletes, OmniPower reached its greatest sales in an earlier time, when high-energy bars were most popular with consumers. Now, you seek to remarket the product as a nutrition bar to benefit from the booming market for such bars.

Because the marketplace already contains several successful nutrition bars, you need to develop an effective marketing strategy. In particular, you need to determine the effect that price and in-store promotional expenses (special in-store coupons, signs, and displays as well as the cost of free samples) will have on sales of OmniPower. Before marketing the bar nationwide, you plan to conduct a test-market study of OmniPower sales, using a sample of 34 stores in a supermarket chain.

How can you extend the linear regression methods discussed in Chapter 15 to incorporate the effects of price *and* promotion into the same model? How can you use this model to improve the success of the nationwide introduction of OmniPower?

Ariwasabi/Shutterstock

Chapter 15 discusses simple linear regression models that use *one* numerical independent variable, X, to predict the value of a numerical dependent variable, Y. Often you can make better predictions by using *more than one* independent variable. This chapter introduces you to **multiple regression models** that use two or more independent variables to predict the value of a dependent variable.

16.1 Developing a Multiple Regression Model

In the OmniPower Bars scenario, your business objective, to determine the effect that price and in-store promotional expenses will have on sales, calls for examining a multiple regression model in which the price of an OmniPower bar in cents (X_1) and the monthly budget for in-store promotional expenditures in dollars (X_2) are the independent variables and the number of OmniPower bars sold in a month (Y) is the dependent variable.

To develop this model, you collect data from a sample of 34 stores in a supermarket chain selected for a test-market study of OmniPower. You choose stores in a way to ensure that they all have approximately the same monthly sales volume. You organize and store the data collected in OmniPower . Table 16.1 presents these data.

TABLE 16.1

Monthly OmniPower Sales, Price, and Promotional Expenditures

Store	Sales	Price	Promotion	Store	Sales	Price	Promotion
1	4,141	59	200	18	2,730	79	400
2	3,842	59	200	19	2,618	79	400
3	3,056	59	200	20	4,421	79	400
4	3,519	59	200	21	4,113	79	600
5	4,226	59	400	22	3,746	79	600
6	4,630	59	400	23	3,532	79	600
7	3,507	59	400	24	3,825	79	600
8	3,754	59	400	25	1,096	99	200
9	5,000	59	600	26	761	99	200
10	5,120	59	600	27	2,088	99	200
11	4,011	59	600	28	820	99	200
12	5,015	59	600	29	2,114	99	400
13	1,916	79	200	30	1,882	99	400
14	675	79	200	31	2,159	99	400
15	3,636	79	200	32	1,602	99	400
16	3,224	79	200	33	3,354	99	600
17	2,295	79	400	34	2,927	99	600

When there are two independent variables in the multiple regression model, using a three-dimensional (3D) scatter plot can help suggest a starting point for analysis. Figure 16.1 on page 333 presents a 3D scatter plot of the OmniPower data. In this figure, points are plotted at a height equal to their sales and have drop lines down to their corresponding price and promotion expense values. Rotating 3D plots can sometimes reveal patterns. One rotated view (Figure 16.1 right) suggests a negative linear relationship between sales and price (sales decrease as price increases) and a positive linear relationship between sales and promotional expenses (sales increase as those expenses increase). These relationships are not easily seen in the original orientation of the scatter plot.

FIGURE 16.1

Original (left) and rotated (right) Minitab 3D scatter plot of the monthly OmniPower sales, price, and promotional expenses

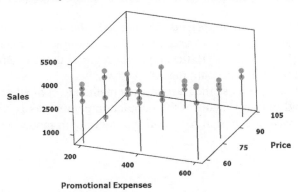

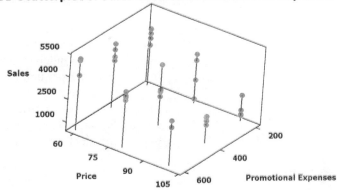

Excel does not include the capability to construct 3D scatter plots

Interpreting the Regression Coefficients

When there are several independent variables, you can extend the simple linear regression model of Equation (15.1) on page 265 by assuming a linear relationship between each independent variable and the dependent variable. For example, with k independent variables, the multiple regression model is expressed in Equation (16.1).

MULTIPLE REGRESSION MODEL WITH k INDEPENDENT VARIABLES

$$Y_i = \beta_0 + \beta_1 X_{1i} + \beta_2 X_{2i} + \beta_3 X_{3i} + \cdots + \beta_k X_{ki} + \varepsilon_i \qquad \textbf{(16.1)}$$

where

$\beta_0 = Y$ intercept

$\beta_1 = $ slope of Y with variable X_1, holding variables $X_2, X_3, \ldots, X_k$ constant

$\beta_2 = $ slope of Y with variable X_2, holding variables $X_1, X_3, \ldots, X_k$ constant

$\beta_3 = $ slope of Y with variable X_3, holding variables $X_1, X_2, \ldots, X_k$ constant

$\vdots$

$\beta_k = $ slope of Y with variable X_k holding variables $X_1, X_2, X_3, \ldots, X_{k-1}$ constant

$\varepsilon_i = $ random error in Y for observation i

Equation (16.2) defines the multiple regression model with two independent variables.

MULTIPLE REGRESSION MODEL WITH TWO INDEPENDENT VARIABLES

$$Y_i = \beta_0 + \beta_1 X_{1i} + \beta_2 X_{2i} + \varepsilon_i \qquad \textbf{(16.2)}$$

where

$\beta_0 = $ intercept

$\beta_1 = $ slope of Y with variable X_1, holding variable X_2 constant

$\beta_2 = $ slope of Y with variable X_2, holding variable X_1 constant

$\varepsilon_i = $ random error in Y for observation i

Compare the multiple regression model to the simple linear regression model [Equation (15.1) on page 283]:

$$Y_i = \beta_0 + \beta_1 X_i + \varepsilon_i$$

In the simple linear regression model, the slope, β_1, represents the change in the mean of Y per unit change in X and does not take into account any other variables. In the multiple regression model with two independent variables [Equation (16.2)], the slope, β_1, represents the change in the mean of Y per unit change in X_1, taking into account the effect of X_2.

As in the case of simple linear regression, you use the least-squares method to compute the sample regression coefficients b_0, b_1, and b_2 as estimates of the population parameters β_0, β_1, and β_2. Equation (16.3) defines the regression equation for a multiple regression model with two independent variables.

Student Tip

Because multiple regression computations are more complex than computations for simple linear regression, always use a computerized method to obtain multiple regression results.

MULTIPLE REGRESSION EQUATION WITH TWO INDEPENDENT VARIABLES

$$\hat{Y}_i = b_0 + b_1 X_{1i} + b_2 X_{2i} \tag{16.3}$$

Figure 16.2 shows the SPSS result for the OmniPower sales data multiple regression model. In these results, the b_0 coefficient is labeled constant by SPSS.

FIGURE 16.2

SPSS result for OmniPower sales multiple regression model

Regression

Model Summary

Model	R	R Square	Adjusted R Square	Std. Error of the Estimate
1	.870[a]	.758	.742	638.065

a. Predictors: (Constant), Promotion, Price

ANOVA[a]

Model		Sum of Squares	df	Mean Square	F	Sig.
1	Regression	39472730.77	2	19736365.39	48.477	.000[b]
	Residual	12620946.67	31	407127.312		
	Total	52093677.44	33			

a. Dependent Variable: Sales
b. Predictors: (Constant), Promotion, Price

Coefficients[a]

Model		Unstandardized Coefficients B	Std. Error	Standardized Coefficients Beta	t	Sig.	95.0% Confidence Interval for B Lower Bound	Upper Bound
1	(Constant)	5837.521	628.150		9.293	.000	4556.400	7118.642
	Price	-53.217	6.852	-.690	-7.766	.000	-67.193	-39.242
	Promotion	3.613	.685	.468	5.273	.000	2.216	5.011

a. Dependent Variable: Sales

From Figure 16.2, the computed values of the three regression coefficients are

$$b_0 = 5,837.521 \quad b_1 = -53.217 \quad b_2 = 3.613$$

Therefore, the multiple regression equation is

$$\hat{Y}_i = 5,837.521 - 53.217X_{1i} + 3.613X_{2i}$$

where

$\hat{Y}_i$ = predicted monthly sales of OmniPower bars for store i

X_{1i} = price of OmniPower bar (in cents) for store i

X_{2i} = monthly in-store promotional expenditures (in \$) for store i

The sample Y intercept ($b_0 = 5,837.521$) estimates the number of OmniPower bars sold in a month if the price is \$0.00 and the total amount spent on promotional expenditures is also \$0.00. Because these values of price and promotion are outside the range of price and promotion used in the test-market study, and because they make no sense in the context of the problem, the value of b_0 has little or no practical interpretation.

The slope of price with OmniPower sales ($b_1 = -53.217$) indicates that, for a given amount of monthly promotional expenditures, the predicted mean sales of OmniPower are estimated to decrease by 53.217 bars per month for each 1-cent increase in the price. The slope of monthly promotional expenditures with OmniPower sales ($b_2 = 3.613$) indicates that, for a given price, the predicted mean sales of OmniPower are estimated to increase by 3.6131 bars for each additional \$1 spent on promotions. These estimates allow you to better understand the likely effect that price and promotion decisions will have in the marketplace. For example, a 10-cent decrease in price is predicted to increase mean sales by 532.173 bars, with a fixed amount of monthly promotional expenditures. A \$100 increase in promotional expenditures is predicted to increase mean sales by 361.31 bars for a given price.

Regression coefficients in multiple regression are called **net regression coefficients**, and they estimate the predicted mean change in Y per unit change in a particular X, *holding constant the effect of the other X variables*. For example, in the study of OmniPower bar sales, for a store with a given amount of promotional expenditures, the mean sales are predicted to decrease by 53.217 bars per month for each 1-cent increase in the price of an OmniPower bar. Another way to interpret this "net effect" is to think of two stores with an equal amount of promotional expenditures. If the first store charges 1 cent more than the other store, the net effect of this difference is that the first store is predicted to sell a mean of 53.217 fewer bars per month than the second store. To interpret the net effect of promotional expenditures, you can consider two stores that are charging the same price. If the first store spends \$1 more on promotional expenditures, the net effect of this difference is that the first store is predicted to sell a mean of 3.613 more bars per month than the second store.

> **Student Tip**
> Remember that in multiple regression, the regression coefficients are conditional on holding constant the other independent variables. The slope of b_1 holds constant the effect of variable X_2. The slope of b_2 holds constant the effect of variable X_1.

Predicting the Dependent Variable Y

You can use the multiple regression equation to predict values of the dependent variable. For example, what are the predicted mean sales for a store charging 79 cents during a month in which promotional expenditures are \$400? Using the multiple regression equation,

$$\hat{Y}_i = 5,837.521 - 53.217X_{1i} + 3.613X_{2i}$$

with $X_{1i} = 79$ and $X_{2i} = 400$,

$$\hat{Y}_i = 5,837.521 - 53.217(79) + 3.613(400)$$
$$= 3,078.57$$

> **Student Tip**
> You should only predict within the range of the values of all the independent variables.

Thus, you predict that stores charging 79 cents and spending $400 in promotional expenditures will sell a mean of 3,078.57 OmniPower bars per month.

After you have developed the regression equation, done a residual analysis (see Section 16.3), and determined the significance of the overall fitted model (see Section 16.2), you can construct a confidence interval estimate of the mean value and a prediction interval for an individual value. Figure 16.3 presents Excel and Minitab results that compute a confidence interval estimate and a prediction interval for the OmniPower sales data.

Store	Sales	Price	Promotion	LMCI_1	UMCI_1	LICI_1	UICI_1
15	3636	79	200	2011.80629	2700.11930	1009.88085	3702.04475
16	3224	79	200	2011.80629	2700.11930	1009.88085	3702.04475
17	2295	79	400	2854.07145	3303.07736	1758.00843	4399.14038
18	2730	79	400	2854.07145	3303.07736	1758.00843	4399.14038
19	2618	79	400	2854.07145	3303.07736	1758.00843	4399.14038
20	4421	79	400	2854.07145	3303.07736	1758.00843	4399.14038
21	4113	79	600	3428.88999	4173.48204	2447.63614	5154.73588
22	3746	79	600	3428.88999	4173.48204	2447.63614	5154.73588
23	3632	79	600	3428.88999	4173.48204	2447.63614	5154.73588
24	3825	79	600	3428.88999	4173.48204	2447.63614	5154.73588
25	1096	99	200	853.97925	1729.25289	-81.34383	2664.57598
26	761	99	200	853.97925	1729.25289	-81.34383	2664.57598
27	2088	99	200	853.97925	1729.25289	-81.34383	2664.57598
28	820	99	200	853.97925	1729.25289	-81.34383	2664.57598
29	2114	99	400	1641.93165	2386.52370	660.67781	3367.77755
30	1882	99	400	1641.93165	2386.52370	660.67781	3367.77755
31	2159	99	400	1641.93165	2386.52370	660.67781	3367.77755
32	1602	99	400	1641.93165	2386.52370	660.67781	3367.77755
33	3354	99	600	2244.97796	3228.70061	1345.64538	4128.03319
34	2927	99	600	2244.97796	3228.70061	1345.64538	4128.03319
		79	400	2854.07145	3303.07736	1758.00843	4399.14038

The 95% confidence interval estimate of the mean OmniPower sales for all stores charging 79 cents and spending $400 in promotional expenditures is 2,854.07 to 3,303.08 bars. The prediction interval for an individual store is 1,758.01 to 4,399.14 bars.

16.2 r^2, Adjusted r^2, and the Overall F Test

This section discusses three methods you can use to evaluate the overall multiple regression model: the coefficient of multiple determination, r^2, the adjusted r^2, and the overall F test.

Coefficient of Multiple Determination

Recall from Section 15.3 that the coefficient of determination, r^2, measures the proportion of the variation in Y that is explained by the independent variable X in the simple linear regression model. In multiple regression, the **coefficient of multiple determination** represents the proportion of the variation in Y that is explained by all the independent variables. Equation (16.4) defines the coefficient of multiple determination for a multiple regression model with two or more independent variables.

COEFFICIENT OF MULTIPLE DETERMINATION

The coefficient of multiple determination is equal to the regression sum of squares (SSR) divided by the total sum of squares (SST).

$$r^2 = \frac{\text{Regression sum of squares}}{\text{Total sum of squares}} = \frac{SSR}{SST}$$

(16.4)

In the OmniPower example, from Figure 16.2 on page 334, $SSR = 39{,}472{,}730.77$ and $SST = 52{,}093{,}677.44$. Thus,

$$r^2 = \frac{SSR}{SST} = \frac{39{,}472{,}730.77}{52{,}093{,}677.44} = 0.7577$$

Student Tip
Remember that r^2 in multiple regression represents the proportion of the variation in the dependent variable Y that is explained by all the independent X variables included in the model.

The coefficient of multiple determination ($r^2 = 0.7577$) indicates that 75.77% of the variation in sales is explained by the variation in the price and in the promotional expenditures. The coefficient of multiple determination also appears in the Figure 16.2 results on page 334, labeled R Square in the Excel results and R-Sq in the Minitab results.

Adjusted r^2

When considering multiple regression models, some statisticians suggest that you should use the **adjusted r^2** to take into account both the number of independent variables in the model and the sample size. Reporting the adjusted r^2 is extremely important when you are comparing two or more regression models that predict the same dependent variable but have a different number of independent variables. Equation (16.5) defines the adjusted r^2.

ADJUSTED r^2

$$r^2_{\text{adj}} = 1 - \left[(1 - r^2)\frac{n-1}{n-k-1}\right] \tag{16.5}$$

where k is the number of independent variables in the regression equation.

Thus, for the OmniPower data, because $r^2 = 0.7577$, $n = 34$, and $k = 2$,

$$\begin{aligned} r^2_{\text{adj}} &= 1 - \left[(1 - 0.7577)\frac{34-1}{34-2-1}\right] \\ &= 1 - \left[(0.2423)\frac{33}{31}\right] \\ &= 1 - 0.2579 \\ &= 0.7421 \end{aligned}$$

Therefore, 74.21% of the variation in sales is explained by the multiple regression model—adjusted for the number of independent variables and sample size. The adjusted r^2 also appears in the Figure 16.2 results on page 334, labeled Adjusted R Square and R Sq(adj) in the results.

FIGURE 16.4
SPSS r^2 and adjusted r^2 result for the OmniPower sales data

Regression

Model Summary[b]

Model	R	R Square	Adjusted R Square	Std. Error of the Estimate
1	.870[a]	.758	.742	638.065

a. Predictors: (Constant), Promotion, Price

b. Dependent Variable: Sales

The Model Summary of the SPSS result shows the r^2 which is labelled as R Square and the adjusted r^2 which is labelled as Adjusted R Square.

Test for the Significance of the Overall Multiple Regression Model

You use the **overall F test** to determine whether there is a significant relationship between the dependent variable and the entire set of independent variables (the overall multiple regression model). Because there is more than one independent variable, you use the following null and alternative hypotheses:

H_0: $\beta_1 = \beta_2 = \cdots = \beta_k = 0$ (There is no linear relationship between the dependent variable and the independent variables.)

H_1: At least one $\beta_j \neq 0, j = 1, 2, \ldots, k$ (There is a linear relationship between the dependent variable and at least one of the independent variables.)

Equation (16.6) defines the overall F test statistic. Table 16.2 presents the ANOVA summary table.

OVERALL F TEST

The F_{STAT} test statistic is equal to the regression mean square (MSR) divided by the mean square error (MSE).

$$F_{STAT} = \frac{MSR}{MSE} \tag{16.6}$$

where

k = number of independent variables in the regression model

The F_{STAT} test statistic follows an F distribution with k and $n - k - 1$ degrees of freedom.

TABLE 16.2

ANOVA Summary Table for the Overall F Test

Source	Degrees of Freedom	Sum of Squares	Mean Squares (Variance)	F
Regression	k	SSR	$MSR = \dfrac{SSR}{k}$	$F_{STAT} = \dfrac{MSR}{MSE}$
Error	$n - k - 1$	SSE	$MSE = \dfrac{SSE}{n - k - 1}$	
Total	$n - 1$	SST		

FIGURE 16.4A

ANOVA Table from the SPSS Output

ANOVA[b]

Model	Sum of Squares	df	Mean Square	F	Sig.
1 Regression	39472730.773	2	19736365.387	48.477	.000[a]
Residual	12620946.668	31	407127.312		
Total	52093677.441	33			

a. Predictors: (Constant), Promotion, Price
b. Dependent Variable: Sales

Test statistics, F_{STAT} p-value

The decision rule is

Reject H_0 at the α level of significance if $F_{STAT} > F_{\alpha}$;
otherwise, do not reject H_0.

Using a 0.05 level of significance, the critical value of the F distribution with 2 and 31 degrees of freedom found in Table E.5 is approximately 3.32 (see Figure 16.4 on page 337). From Figure 16.2 on page 334, the F_{STAT} test statistic given in the ANOVA summary table is 48.4771. Because 48.4771 > 3.32, or because the p-value = 0.000 < 0.05, you reject H_0 and conclude that at least one of the independent variables (price and/or promotional expenditures) is related to sales.

FIGURE 16.5

Testing for the significance of a set of regression coefficients at the 0.05 level of significance, with 2 and 31 degrees of freedom

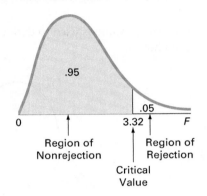

How to Find F Critical Value Using the Calculator

To find the F critical value, use the Casio Calculator fx-9750GII and follow the following calculator steps:

Note: Fx-9750G Plus does not have this option, therefore you have to use the Table G3 in the Appendix.

From the **Main Menu** select:

STAT   F5 (DIST)   **F4** (F)   **F3**(InvF)   then enter the following items:

Now key **EXE** or **F1**(CALC)

The calculator will now show the results:

The critical value is used to define the rejection and non-rejection regions as shown in the diagram below.

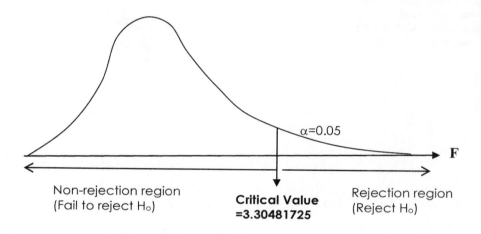

16.3 Residual Analysis for the Multiple Regression Model

In Section 15.5, you used residual analysis to evaluate the fit of the simple linear regression model. For the multiple regression model with two independent variables, you need to construct and analyze the following residual plots:

- Residuals versus $\hat{Y}_i$
- Residuals versus X_{1i}
- Residuals versus X_{2i}
- Residuals versus time

> **Student Tip**
>
> As is the case with simple linear regression, a residual plot that does not contain any apparent patterns will look like a random scattering of points.

The first residual plot examines the pattern of residuals versus the predicted values of Y. If the residuals show a pattern for the predicted values of Y, there is evidence of a possible curvilinear effect in at least one independent variable, a possible violation of the assumption of equal variance (see Figure 15.13 on page 285), and/or the need to transform the Y variable.

The second and third residual plots involve the independent variables. Patterns in the plot of the residuals versus an independent variable may indicate the existence of a curvilinear effect and, therefore, the need to add a curvilinear independent variable to the multiple regression model (see reference 7).

The fourth plot is used to investigate patterns in the residuals in order to validate the independence assumption when the data are collected in time order. Associated with this residual plot, as in Section 15.6, you can compute the Durbin-Watson statistic to determine the existence of positive autocorrelation among the residuals.

Figure 16.5 presents the residual plots for the OmniPower sales example. There is very little or no pattern in the relationship between the residuals and the predicted value of Y, the value of X_1 (price), or the value of X_2 (promotional expenditures). Thus, you can conclude that the multiple regression model is appropriate for predicting sales. There is no need to plot the residuals versus time because the data were not collected in time order.

FIGURE 16.6

Residual plots for the OmniPower sales data: residuals versus predicted Y, residuals versus price, and residuals versus promotional expenditures

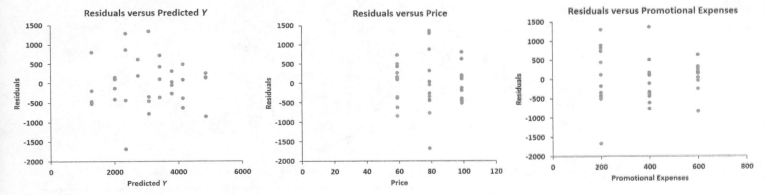

EXAMPLE 16.1

Use the Monthly OminiPower Data to Test the Assumptions for Multiple Regression

The variables used in the Monthly OmniPower data are Sales, Price and Promotional Expenditures data. The data is depicted in Table 16.1.

The dependent variable (denoted as Y) is Sales and

The independent variables (denoted as $X1$ and $X2$) are Price and Promotion respectively.

Test the Linearity Assumption

Construct the scatterplots of dependent variable against each independent variable to validate the linearity assumption. The two scatterplots are:

a. Scatterplot of Y against $X1$ as shown in Figure 16.6
b. Scatterplot of Y against $X2$ as shown in Figure 16.7

You can use SPSS to construct the scatterplots.

The linearity assumption requires you to verify if a linear relationship exists between the dependent variable and independent variable. You can visually see if the points in the scatterplot appear to fall in a straight line (i.e. no curvature). The scatterplot of sales against price shown in Figure 16.6 has a fairly straight line relationship with the responses. The scatterplot

FIGURE 16.7

A scatterplot of *Y* (sales) against *X1* (sales)

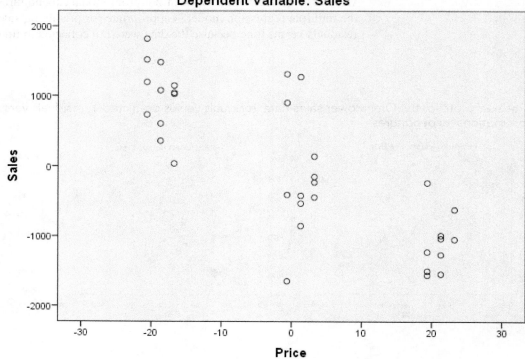

of sales and promotion shown in Figure 16.7 is also fairly linear. Studying the two scatter plots, you can conclude that the assumption of linearity is met.

FIGURE 16.8

A scatterplot of *Y* (sales) against *X2* (promotion)

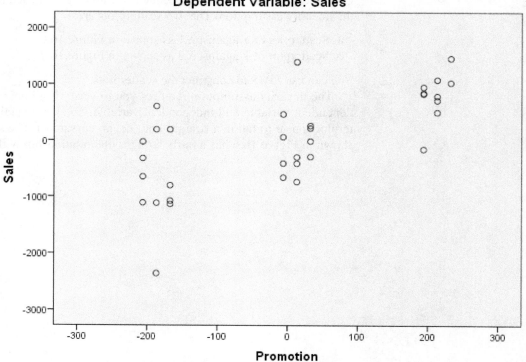

Test of Independence of Errors Assumption

As mentioned in Section 15.4, this assumption requires that the errors (ε_i) are independent of one another. To check this assumption, construct the following residual plots.

a. Residuals against time. This plot is applicable to the data that are collected in time order. For this example there is no need to plot the residuals against time since the data is not collected in time order.

b. Residuals against $X1$ as shown in Figure 16.8.

c. Residuals against $X2$ as shown in Figure 16.9.

The two residual plots containing the independent variables are used to investigate any curvature pattern in the residuals that may violate the independence assumptions. Observing residual plots in Figures 16.8 and 16.9, you notice that there is very little pattern in the relationship between the residuals and the independent variables, and therefore, the independence assumption is not violated.

Test of Equal Variance Assumption

The scatterplot of residuals against the predicted value allow you to check the equal variance assumption. The residual plot shown in Figure 16.10 is plotted with the predicted values and residuals in the unstandardized form. The other residual plot (Figure 16.11) is plotted with the standardized predicted values and standardized residuals. Both plots will give you the same results. It is common to use the standardized residual in the analysis because it is easy to identify outliers and unusual observations in your data set. For example, you can identify an outlier using the standardized residual values below −2 and above 2. In Figure 16.11, you see that there is one outlier with standardized value below −2 and two outliers with standardized value above 2.

FIGURE 16.9

A scatterplot of residual against price

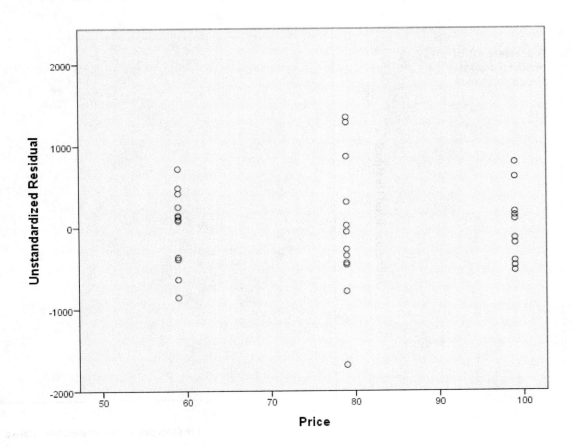

FIGURE 16.10

FIGURE 16.10

A scatterplot of residual against promotion

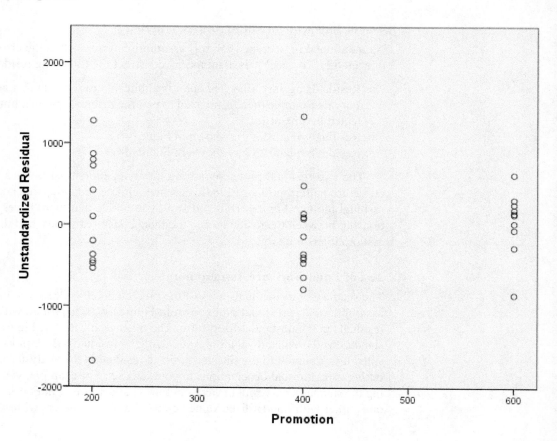

FIGURE 16.11

A scatterplot of residual against predicted value

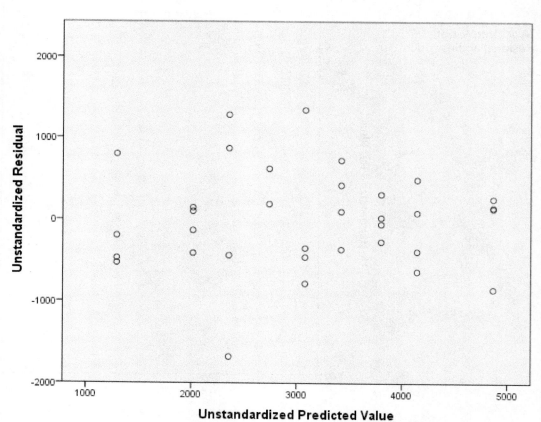

FIGURE 16.12

A scatterplot of
standardized residual
against standardized
predicted value

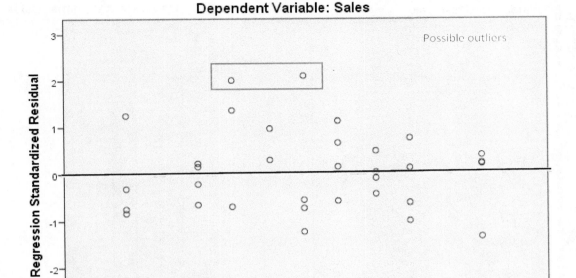

The scatterplot in Figure 16.11 should display a random pattern with points centered on the line of zero standardized residual value. The points should be evenly distributed around this line over the standardized predicted value. There is no obvious pattern in Figure 16.11 that would indicate the violation of the assumption of equal variance.

Test of Normality Assumption

To check this assumption, construct a histogram of standardized residual and a normal probability plot of standardized residual as shown in Figures 16.12 and 16.13 respectively.

The histogram of residuals in Figure 16.12 appears reasonably normal. The normal curve fitted in the histogram guide you in our examination. There is no concern that this assumption is violated.

Studying the normal probability plot (Figure 16.13), the points seemed to follow the straight line. It suggests that the normality assumption is met.

FIGURE 16.13

Histogram of standardized residuals

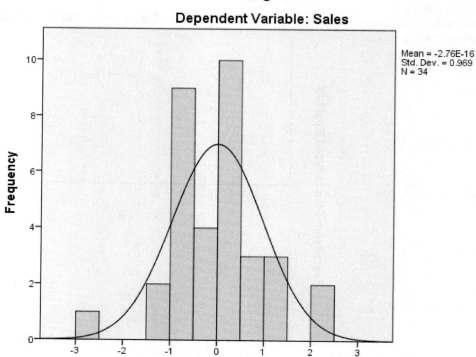

In summary, you just check the four assumptions of the regression model visually using scatterplots. You can conclude that all the four assumptions have been met and you can therefore use the regression model for inference and predictions.

FIGURE 16.14

A normal probability plot of standardized residuals

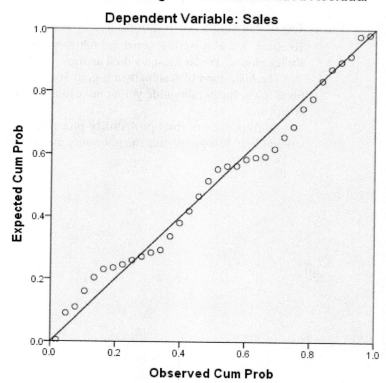

16.4 Inferences Concerning the Population Regression Coefficients

In Section 15.7, you tested the slope in a simple linear regression model to determine the significance of the relationship between X and Y. In addition, you constructed a confidence interval estimate of the population slope. This section extends those procedures to multiple regression.

Tests of Hypothesis

In a simple linear regression model, to test a hypothesis concerning the population slope, β_1, you used Equation (15.16) on page 289:

$$t_{STAT} = \frac{b_1 - \beta_1}{S_{b_1}}$$

Equation (16.7) generalizes this equation for multiple regression.

TESTING FOR THE SLOPE IN MULTIPLE REGRESSION

$$t_{STAT} = \frac{b_j - \beta_j}{S_{b_j}} \tag{16.7}$$

where

$\quad b_j$ = slope of variable j with Y, holding constant the effects of all other independent variables

$\quad S_{b_j}$ = standard error of the regression coefficient b_j

$\quad k$ = number of independent variables in the regression equation

$\quad \beta_j$ = hypothesized value of the population slope for variable j, holding constant the effects of all other independent variables

$\quad t_{STAT}$ = test statistic for a t distribution with $n - k - 1$ degrees of freedom

---

To determine whether variable X_2 (amount of promotional expenditures) has a significant effect on sales, taking into account the price of OmniPower bars, the null and alternative hypotheses are

$$H_0: \beta_2 = 0$$
$$H_1: \beta_2 \neq 0$$

From Equation (16.7) and Figure 16.2 on page 334,

$$t_{STAT} = \frac{b_2 - \beta_2}{S_{b_2}}$$
$$= \frac{3.6131 - 0}{0.6852} = 5.2728$$

FIGURE 16.14a

Coefficient table from the SPSS output

Coefficients[a]

Model		Unstandardized Coefficients		Standardized Coefficients			95.0% Confidence Interval for B	
		B	Std. Error	Beta	t	Sig.	Lower Bound	Upper Bound
1	(Constant)	5837.521	628.150		9.293	.000	4556.400	7118.642
	Price	−53.217	6.852	−.690	−7.766	.000	−67.193	−39.242
	Promotion	3.613	.685	.468	5.273	.000	2.216	5.011

a. Dependent Variable: Sales

Test statistics, t_{STAT} p-value

Confidence interval estimate of slope of sales with price, β_1.

If you select a level of significance of 0.05, the critical values of t for 31 degrees of freedom from Table E.3 are −2.0395 and +2.0395 (see Figure 16.6).

FIGURE 16.15

Testing for significance of a regression coefficient at the 0.05 level of significance, with 31 degrees of freedom

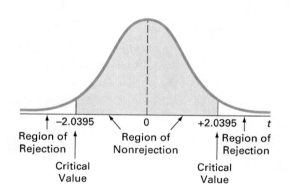

From Figure 16.2 on page 334, observe that the computed t_{STAT} test statistic is 5.2728. Because $t_{STAT} = 5.2728 > 2.0395$ or because the p-value is 0.0000, you reject H_0 and conclude that there is a significant relationship between the variable X_2 (promotional expenditures) and sales, taking into account the price, X_1. The extremely small p-value allows you to strongly reject the null hypothesis that there is no linear relationship between sales and promotional expenditures. Example 16.1 presents the test for the significance of β_1, the slope of sales with price.

How to Find t Critical Value Using Calculator

To find the t critical value, use the Casio Calculator fx-9750GII and follow the following calculator steps:

From the **Main Menu** select:

STAT **F5** (DIST) **F2** (t) **F3**(Invt)   then enter the following items:

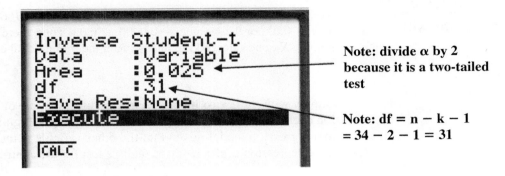

Now key **EXE** or **F1**(CALC)

The calculator will now show the results:

The critical values define the rejection and non-rejection regions.

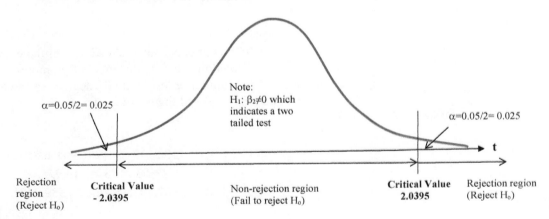

EXAMPLE 16.1

Testing for the Significance of the Slope of Sales with Price

At the 0.05 level of significance, is there evidence that the slope of sales with price is different from zero?

SOLUTION From Figure 16.2 on page 334, $t_{STAT} = -7.7664 < -2.0395$ (the critical value for $\alpha = 0.05$) or the p-value $= 0.0000 < 0.05$. Thus, there is a significant relationship between price, X_1, and sales, taking into account the promotional expenditures, X_2.

As shown with these two independent variables, the test of significance for a specific regression coefficient in multiple regression is a test for the significance of adding that variable into a regression model, given that the other variable is included. In other words, the t test for the regression coefficient is actually a test for the contribution of each independent variable.

Confidence Interval Estimation

Instead of testing the significance of a population slope, you may want to estimate the value of a population slope. Equation (16.8) defines the confidence interval estimate for a population slope in multiple regression.

CONFIDENCE INTERVAL ESTIMATE FOR THE SLOPE

$$b_j \pm t_{\alpha/2}S_{b_j} \qquad\qquad (16.8)$$

where

$t_{\alpha/2} =$ critical value corresponding to an upper-tail probability of $\alpha/2$ from the t distribution with $n - k - 1$ degrees of freedom (i.e., a cumulative area of $1 - \alpha/2$)

$k =$ number of independent variables

To construct a 95% confidence interval estimate of the population slope, β_1 (the effect of price, X_1, on sales, Y, holding constant the effect of promotional expenditures, X_2), the critical value of t at the 95% confidence level with 31 degrees of freedom is 2.0395 (see Table E.3). Then, using Equation (16.8) and Figure 16.2 on page 334,

$$b_1 \pm t_{\alpha/2}S_{b_1}$$
$$-53.2173 \pm (2.0395)(6.8522)$$
$$-53.2173 \pm 13.9752$$
$$-67.1925 \le \beta_1 \le -39.2421$$

Taking into account the effect of promotional expenditures, the estimated effect of a 1-cent increase in price is to reduce mean sales by approximately 39.2 to 67.2 bars. You have 95% confidence that this interval correctly estimates the relationship between these variables. From a hypothesis-testing viewpoint, because this confidence interval does not include 0, you conclude that the regression coefficient, β_1, has a significant effect.

Example 16.2 constructs and interprets a confidence interval estimate for the slope of sales with promotional expenditures.

EXAMPLE 16.2

Constructing a Confidence Interval Estimate for the Slope of Sales with Promotional Expenditures

Construct a 95% confidence interval estimate of the population slope of sales with promotional expenditures.

SOLUTION The critical value of t at the 95% confidence level, with 31 degrees of freedom, is 2.0395 (see Table E.3). Using Equation (16.8) and Figure 16.2 on page 334,

$$b_2 \pm t_{\alpha/2}S_{b_2}$$
$$3.6131 \pm (2.0395)(0.6852)$$
$$3.6131 \pm 1.3975$$
$$2.2156 \leq \beta_2 \leq 5.0106$$

Thus, taking into account the effect of price, the estimated effect of each additional dollar of promotional expenditures is to increase mean sales by approximately 2.22 to 5.01 bars. You have 95% confidence that this interval correctly estimates the relationship between these variables. From a hypothesis-testing viewpoint, because this confidence interval does not include 0, you can conclude that the regression coefficient, β_2, has a significant effect.

FIGURE 16.16

SPSS Confidence interval estimate for the slope of sales with promotional expenditures

Regression

Coefficients[a]

Model		Unstandardized Coefficients B	Std. Error	Standardized Coefficients Beta	t	Sig.	95.0% Confidence Interval for B Lower Bound	Upper Bound
1	(Constant)	5837.521	628.150		9.293	.000	4556.400	7118.642
	Price	-53.217	6.852	-.690	-7.766	.000	-67.193	-39.242
	Promotion	3.613	.685	.468	5.273	.000	2.216	5.011

a. Dependent Variable: Sales

16.5 Using Dummy Variables and Interaction Terms in Regression Models

The multiple regression models discussed in Sections 16.1 through 16.4 assumed that each independent variable is a numerical variable. For example, in Section 16.1, you used price and promotional expenditures, two numerical independent variables, to predict the monthly sales of OmniPower nutrition bars. However, for some models, you need to include the effect of a categorical independent variable. For example, to predict the monthly sales of the OmniPower bars, you might include the categorical variable end-cap location in the model to explore the possible effect on sales caused by displaying the OmniPower bars in the two different end-cap display locations, produce or beverage, used in the North Fork Beverages scenario in Chapter 12.

Dummy Variables

You use a **dummy variable** to include a categorical independent variable in a regression model. A dummy variable X_d recodes the categories of a categorical variable using the numeric values 0 and 1. In the special case of a categorical independent variable that has only two categories, you define one dummy variable, X_d, and use the values 0 and 1 to represent the two categories. For example, for the categorical variable end-cap location discussed in the Chapter 12 Using Statistics scenario, the dummy variable, X_d, would have these values:

$X_d = 0$ if the observation is in first category (produce end-cap)
$X_d = 1$ if the observation is in second category (beverage end-cap)

To illustrate using dummy variables in regression, consider the business problem that involves developing a model for predicting the assessed value ($thousands) of houses in Silver Spring, Maryland, based on house size (in thousands of square feet) and whether the house has a fireplace. To include the categorical variable for the presence of a fireplace, the dummy variable X_2 is defined as

$$X_2 = 0 \text{ if the house does not have a fireplace}$$
$$X_2 = 1 \text{ if the house has a fireplace}$$

Assuming that the slope of assessed value with the size of the house is the same for houses that have and do not have a fireplace, the multiple regression model is

$$Y_i = \beta_0 + \beta_1 X_{1i} + \beta_2 X_{2i} + \varepsilon_i$$

where

Y_i = assessed value, in thousands of dollars, for house i

β_0 = Y intercept

X_{1i} = house size, in thousands of square feet, for house i

β_1 = slope of assessed value with house size, holding constant the presence or absence of a fireplace

FIGURE 16.17
SPSS result for the regression model that includes size of house and presence of fireplace

Regression

Model Summary

Model	R	R Square	Adjusted R Square	Std. Error of the Estimate
1	.576[a]	.332	.283	61.8788

a. Predictors: (Constant), Fireplace Coded, Size(000 sq. ft.

ANOVA[a]

Model		Sum of Squares	df	Mean Square	F	Sig.
1	Regression	51462.396	2	25731.198	6.720	.004[b]
	Residual	103382.712	27	3828.989		
	Total	154845.108	29			

a. Dependent Variable: Assessed Value

b. Predictors: (Constant), Fireplace Coded, Size(000 sq. ft.

Coefficients[a]

Model		Unstandardized Coefficients		Standardized Coefficients	t	Sig.	95.0% Confidence Interval for B	
		B	Std. Error	Beta			Lower Bound	Upper Bound
1	(Constant)	269.418	33.570		8.026	.000	200.539	338.298
	Size(000 sq. ft.	49.821	14.133	.561	3.525	.002	20.824	78.819
	Fireplace Coded	12.162	27.035	.072	.450	.656	-43.309	67.634

a. Dependent Variable: Assessed Value

X_{2i} = dummy variable that represents the absence or presence of a fireplace for house i

β_2 = net effect of the presence of a fireplace on assessed value, holding constant the house size

ε_i = random error in Y for house i

Figure 16.7 presents the regression results for this model, using a sample of 30 Silver Spring houses listed for sale that was extracted from **trulia.com** and stored in SilverSpring . In these results, the dummy variable X_2 is labeled as Fireplace Coded.

From Figure 16.7, the regression equation is

$$\hat{Y}_i = 269.4185 + 49.8215X_{1i} + 12.1623X_{2i}$$

For houses without a fireplace, you substitute $X_2 = 0$ into the regression equation:

$$\begin{aligned} \hat{Y}_i &= 269.4185 + 49.8215X_{1i} + 12.1623X_{2i} \\ &= 269.4185 + 49.8215X_{1i} + 12.1623(0) \\ &= 269.4185 + 49.8215X_{1i} \end{aligned}$$

For houses with a fireplace, you substitute $X_2 = 1$ into the regression equation:

$$\begin{aligned} \hat{Y}_i &= 269.4185 + 49.8215X_{1i} + 12.1623X_{2i} \\ &= 269.4185 + 49.8215X_{1i} + 12.1623(1) \\ &= 281.5807 + 49.8215X_{1i} \end{aligned}$$

In this model, the regression coefficients are interpreted as follows:

- Holding constant whether a house has a fireplace, for each increase of 1.0 thousand square feet in house size, the predicted mean assessed value is estimated to increase by 49.8215 thousand dollars (i.e., $49,821.50).
- Holding constant the house size, the presence of a fireplace is estimated to increase the predicted mean assessed value of the house by 12.1623 thousand dollars (i.e., $12,162.30).

Student Tip
Remember that an independent variable does not always make a significant contribution to a regression model.

In Figure 16.7, the t_{STAT} test statistic for the slope of house size with assessed value is 3.5253, and the p-value is 0.015; the t_{STAT} test statistic for presence of a fireplace is 0.4499, and the p-value is 0.6564. Thus, using the 0.05 level of significance, since $0.0015 < 0.05$, the size of the house makes a significant contribution to the model. However, since $0.6564 > 0.05$, the presence of a fireplace does not make a significant contribution to the model. In addition, from Figure 16.7, observe that the coefficient of multiple determination indicates that 33.23% of the variation in assessed value is explained by variation in house size and whether the house has a fireplace. Thus, the variable fireplace does not make a significant contribution and should not be included in the model.

Interactions

In the regression models discussed so far, the effect an independent variable has on the dependent variable has been assumed to be independent of the other independent variables in the model. An **interaction** occurs if the effect of an independent variable on the dependent variable changes according to the *value* of a second independent variable. For example, it is possible that advertising will have a large effect on the sales of a product when the price of a product is low. However, if the price of the product is too high, increases in advertising will not dramatically change sales. In this case, price and advertising are said to interact. In other words, you cannot make general statements about the effect of advertising on sales. The effect that advertising has on sales is *dependent* on the price. You use an **interaction term** (sometimes referred to as a **cross-product term**) to model an interaction effect in a regression model.

To illustrate the concept of interaction and use of an interaction term, return to the example concerning the assessed values of homes discussed on pages 351–352. In the regression model, you assumed that the effect that house size has on the assessed value is independent of whether the house has a fireplace. In other words, you assumed that the slope of assessed value with house size is the same for all houses, regardless of whether the house contains a fireplace. If these two slopes are different, an interaction exists between the house size and the presence or absence of a fireplace.

To evaluate whether an interaction exists, you first define an interaction term that is the product of the independent variable X_1 (house size) and the dummy variable X_2 (Fireplace-Coded). You then test whether this interaction variable makes a significant contribution to the regression model. If the interaction is significant, you cannot use the original model for prediction. For these data you define the following:

$$X_3 = X_1 \times X_2$$

Figure 16.8 presents regression results for the model that includes the house size, X_1, the presence of a fireplace, X_2, and the interaction of X_1 and X_2 (defined as X_3 and labeled Size*Fireplace). To test for the existence of an interaction, you use the null hypothesis:

$$H_0: \beta_3 = 0$$

versus the alternative hypothesis:

$$H_1: \beta_3 \neq 0.$$

In Figure 16.8, the t_{STAT} test statistic for the interaction of size and fireplace is -0.7474. Because $t_{STAT} = -0.7474 > -2.201$ or the p-value $= 0.4615 > 0.05$, you do not reject the null hypothesis. Therefore, the interaction does not make a significant contribution to the model, given that house size and presence of a fireplace are already included. You can conclude that the slope of assessed value with size is the same for houses with fireplaces and houses without fireplaces.

> **Student Tip**
> The interaction between two independent variables can be significant even if one of the independent variables is not significant.

FIGURE 16.18

SPSS result for the regression model that includes house size, presence of fireplace, and interaction of house size and fireplace

Regression

Model Summary

Model	R	R Square	Adjusted R Square	Std. Error of the Estimate
1	.589[a]	.346	.271	62.3909

a. Predictors: (Constant), Size*Fireplace, Size(000 sq. ft., Fireplace Coded

ANOVA[a]

Model		Sum of Squares	df	Mean Square	F	Sig.
1	Regression	53636.854	3	17878.951	4.593	.010[b]
	Residual	101208.254	26	3892.625		
	Total	154845.108	29			

a. Dependent Variable: Assessed Value
b. Predictors: (Constant), Size*Fireplace, Size(000 sq. ft., Fireplace Coded

Coefficients[a]

Model		Unstandardized Coefficients B	Std. Error	Standardized Coefficients Beta	t	Sig.	95.0% Confidence Interval for B Lower Bound	Upper Bound
1	(Constant)	226.857	66.245		3.425	.002	90.688	363.027
	Size(000 sq. ft.	74.799	36.330	.842	2.059	.050	.122	149.476
	Fireplace Coded	63.803	74.276	.376	.859	.398	-88.874	216.479
	Size*Fireplace	-29.518	39.495	-.460	-.747	.462	-110.701	51.664

Multiple Regression Practice Questions

USING QUESTION 16.1

The data in the file (Redwood) include height, diameter at breast height of a person, and bark thickness for a sample of 21 California redwood trees. The data are shown in the table below.

Height	Diameter at Breast Height	Bark Thickness
122	20	1.1
193.5	36	2.8
166.5	18	2
82	10	1.2
133.5	21	2
156	29	1.4
172.5	51	1.8
81	11	1.1
148	26	2.5
113	12	1.5
84	13	1.4
164	40	2.3
203.3	52	2
174	30	2.5
159	22	3
205	42	2.6
223.5	45	4.3
195	54	4
232.5	39	2.2
190.5	36	3.5
100	8	1.4

The SPSS outputs are shown below:

Descriptive Statistics

	Mean	Std. Deviation	N
Height	157.083	46.3199	21
Diameter at breast height	29.29	14.792	21
Bark thickness	2.219	.9163	21

Model Summary[c]

Model	R	R Square	Adjusted R Square	Std. Error of the Estimate
1	.854[a]	.729	.715	24.7486
2	.886[b]	.786	.762	22.5982

a. Predictors: (Constant), Diameter at breast height
b. Predictors: (Constant), Diameter at breast height, Bark thickness
c. Dependent Variable: Height

ANOVA[a]

Model		Sum of Squares	df	Mean Square	F	Sig.
1	Regression	31273.267	1	31273.267	51.059	.000[b]
	Residual	11637.400	19	612.495		
	Total	42910.667	20			
2	Regression	33718.478	2	16859.239	33.013	.000[c]
	Residual	9192.189	18	510.677		
	Total	42910.667	20			

a. Dependent Variable: Height
b. Predictors: (Constant), Diameter at breast height
c. Predictors: (Constant), Diameter at breast height, Bark thickness

Coefficients[a]

Model		Unstandardized Coefficients B	Unstandardized Coefficients Std. Error	Standardized Coefficients Beta	t	Sig.	95.0% Confidence Interval for B Lower Bound	95.0% Confidence Interval for B Upper Bound
1	(Constant)	78.796	12.215		6.451	.000	53.230	104.362
	Diameter at breast height	2.673	.374	.854	7.146	.000	1.890	3.456
2	(Constant)	62.141	13.503		4.602	.000	33.772	90.510
	Diameter at breast height	2.057	.443	.657	4.645	.000	1.126	2.987
	Bark thickness	15.642	7.148	.309	2.188	.042	.624	30.660

a. Dependent Variable: Height

CHARTS

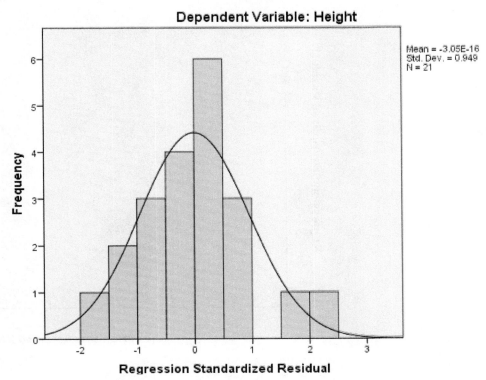

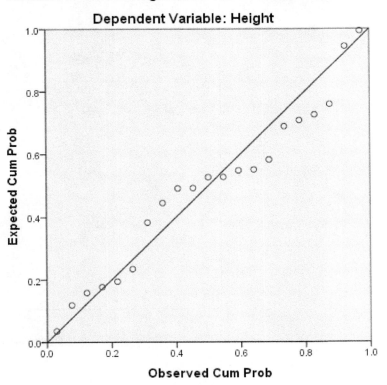

Scatterplot
Dependent Variable: Height

Partial Regression Plot
Dependent Variable: Height

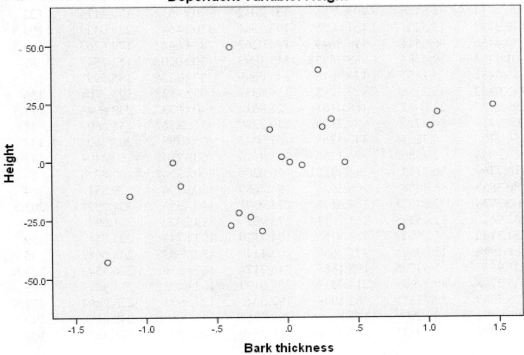

PRE_2	RES_2	LMCI_2	UMCI_2	LICI_2	UICI_2	Height	Diameter at Breast Height	Bark Thickness
120.4814	1.51864	103.7586	137.2042	70.14533	170.8174	122	20	1.1
179.9798	13.52017	167.6055	192.3541	130.9167	229.0429	193.5	36	2.8
130.4456	36.05444	116.8649	144.0262	81.0644	179.8267	166.5	18	2
101.4784	−19.4784	83.75755	119.1993	50.80206	152.1548	82	10	1.2
136.6157	−3.1157	124.5615	148.6699	87.63235	185.5991	133.5	21	2
143.6843	12.31568	127.7298	159.6389	93.59827	193.7704	156	29	1.4
195.1887	−22.6887	168.4161	221.9614	140.6833	249.6941	172.5	51	1.8
101.971	−20.971	84.21302	119.7289	51.28162	152.6603	81	11	1.1
154.7202	−6.72016	142.4363	167.0041	105.6798	203.7605	148	26	2.5
110.2844	2.71562	94.11167	126.4571	60.12842	160.4404	113	12	1.5
110.7769	−26.7769	94.93321	126.6206	60.72607	160.8278	84	13	1.4
180.3858	−16.3858	166.5026	194.2689	130.9206	229.851	164	40	2.3
200.3738	2.87621	174.8175	225.9301	146.4555	254.2921	203.3	52	2
162.947	11.05298	151.9011	173.993	114.202	211.692	174	30	2.5
154.3142	4.68579	134.5156	174.1129	102.8744	205.754	159	22	3
189.1918	15.80825	175.2686	203.1149	139.7153	238.6682	205	42	2.6
221.953	1.54705	195.1885	248.7174	167.4516	276.4543	223.5	45	4.3
235.7708	−40.7708	211.9219	259.6197	182.6405	288.9012	195	54	4
176.7649	55.73511	162.8949	190.6349	127.3034	226.2264	232.5	39	2.2
190.9291	−0.42909	171.863	209.9952	139.7668	242.0914	190.5	36	3.5
100.4934	−0.49335	82.03281	118.9539	49.55362	151.4331	100	8	1.4

Based on Model 2

PRE—Unstandardized Predicted

RES—Unstandardized Residual

LMCI—95% Lower Confidence Interval for y mean

UMCI—95% Upper Confidence Interval for y mean

LICI—95% Lower Confidence Interval for y individual

UICI—95% Upper Confidence Interval for y individual

Note: Independent variable, Y: height of a tree

Dependent variable, X1: diameter at breast height

Dependent variable, X2: thickness of the bark

Use the SPSS outputs to answer the following questions:

1. Are the regression assumptions valid for these data? Justify your answers with the appropriate charts.

2. State the multiple regression equation that predicts the height of a tree based on the tree's diameter at breast height and the thickness of the bark.

3. Interpret the meaning of the coefficients in this equation (corresponds to model 2 in the SPSS output).

4. At the 0.05 level of significance, is the linear model 2 useful for predicting the height of a tree?

5. Predict the height for a tree that has a breast height diameter of 25 inches and a bark thickness of 2 inches.

6. For model 2, what is the forecast error (or residual) of the height for a tree that has a breast height diameter of 25 inches and a bark thickness of 2 inches?

7. At the 0.05 level of significance, determine whether each independent variable makes a significant contribution to the regression model 2. Indicate the most appropriate regression model for this set of data.

8. Based on model 2, construct a 95% confidence interval estimate of the population slope for diameter at breast height and thickness of the bark.

9. Based on model 2, construct a 95% confidence interval estimate of the mean height for trees that have a breast-height diameter of 25 inches and a bark thickness of 2 inches.

10. Based on model 2, construct a 95% confidence interval estimate of the height for an individual tree that has a breast-height diameter of 25 inches and a bark thickness of 2 inches.

11. What is the coefficient of multiple determination for model 2? And interpret its meaning.

12. Of the two models given in the SPSS output, which model appears to be the more efficient? Why?

13. State the multiple regression equation for model 1.

14. At the 0.05 level of significance, is the linear model 1 useful for predicting the height of a tree?

USING QUESTION 16.2

Nassau County is located approximately 25 miles east of New York City. Data in the file (Glen Cove) include the appraised value, land area of the property in acres, house size (square feet), age, rooms, baths and garage for a sample of 30 single-family homes located in Glen Cove, a small city in Nassau County. The data are shown in the table below.

Address	Appraised Value	Land (acres)	House Size (square feet)	Age	Rooms	Baths	Garage
9 Sycamore Road	466.0	0.2297	2448	46	7	3.5	2
21 Jefferson St.	364.0	0.2192	1942	51	7	2.5	1
38 Hitching Post Lane	429.0	0.1630	2073	29	5	3	2
4 Poppy Lane	548.4	0.4608	2707	18	8	2.5	1
5 Daniel Drive	405.9	0.2549	2042	46	7	1.5	1
15 Francis Terrace	374.1	0.2290	2089	88	7	2	0
23 Guilfoy Street	315.0	0.1808	1433	48	7	2	0
17 Carlyle Drive	749.7	0.5015	2991	7	9	2.5	1
8 Craft Avenue	217.7	0.2229	1008	52	5	1	0
22 Beechwood Ct.	635.7	0.1300	3202	15	8	2.5	2
14 Fox Street	350.7	0.1763	2230	54	8	2	0
7 Raynham Road	455.0	0.4200	1848	48	7	2	1
2 Jerome Drive	356.2	0.2520	2100	46	6	2	0
7 Valentine Street	271.7	0.1148	1846	12	5	3	1
38 Jefferson Street	304.3	0.1693	1331	64	5	1	1
15 Inwood Road	288.4	0.1714	1344	52	8	1	0
29 Meadowfield Lane	396.7	0.3849	1822	44	6	2	1
13 Westland Drive	613.5	0.6545	2479	46	6	2.5	2
79 Valentine Street	314.1	0.1722	1605	52	6	3	0
13 Fairmont Place	363.5	0.1435	2080	78	11	2	0
1 Prestwick Terrace	364.3	0.2755	2410	71	6	1	1
11 Clement Street	305.1	0.1148	1753	97	8	2	0
7 Woodland Road	441.7	0.3636	1884	45	7	2	2
36 Elm Avenue	353.1	0.1474	2050	41	10	2	2
17 Duke Place	463.3	0.2281	2978	40	6	2.5	2
12 Prospect Avenue	320.0	0.4626	2132	82	7	1	0
1 Buckeye Road	332.8	0.1889	1551	54	6	2	0
30 Ann Street	276.6	0.1228	1129	44	5	1	0
26 Broadfield Place	397.0	0.1492	1674	34	7	2	1
16 Jackson Street	221.9	0.0852	1184	94	5	1	0

The SPSS outputs are shown below:

Descriptive Statistics

	Mean	Std. Deviation	N
Appraised Value	389.849	120.3881	30
Land (acres)	.246293	.1372620	30
House Size (square feet)	1978.83	550.875	30
Age	49.93	22.490	30
Rooms	6.83	1.487	30
Baths	2.000	.6948	30
Garage	.80	.805	30

Model Summary[e]

Model	R	R Square	Adjusted R Square	Std. Error of the Estimate
1	.828[a]	.686	.675	68.6650
2	.879[b]	.773	.756	59.4552
3	.911[c]	.830	.810	52.4795
4	.920[d]	.847	.807	52.8354

a. Predictors: (Constant), House Size (square feet)
b. Predictors: (Constant), House Size (square feet), Land (acres)
c. Predictors: (Constant), House Size (square feet), Land (acres), Age
d. Predictors: (Constant), Garage, Rooms, Land (acres), Baths, Age, House Size (square feet)
e. Dependent Variable: Appraised Value

ANOVA[a]

Model		Sum of Squares	df	Mean Square	F	Sig.
1	Regression	288288.833	1	288288.833	61.144	.000[b]
	Residual	132016.709	28	4714.882		
	Total	420305.542	29			
2	Regression	324862.616	2	162431.308	45.950	.000[c]
	Residual	95442.927	27	3534.923		
	Total	420305.542	29			
3	Regression	348699.010	3	116233.003	42.204	.000[d]
	Residual	71606.532	26	2754.097		
	Total	420305.542	29			
4	Regression	356099.115	6	59349.853	21.260	.000[e]
	Residual	64206.427	23	2791.584		
	Total	420305.542	29			

a. Dependent Variable: Appraised Value
b. Predictors: (Constant), House Size (square feet)
c. Predictors: (Constant), House Size (square feet), Land (acres)
d. Predictors: (Constant), House Size (square feet), Land (acres), Age
e. Predictors: (Constant), Garage, Rooms, Land (acres), Baths, Age, House Size (square feet)

Coefficients[a]

Model		Unstandardized Coefficients		Standardized Coefficients		
		B	Std. Error	Beta	t	Sig.
1	(Constant)	31.694	47.488		.667	.510
	House Size (square feet)	.181	.023	.828	7.819	.000
2	(Constant)	20.209	41.273		.490	.628
	House Size (square feet)	.151	.022	.693	6.862	.000
	Land (acres)	284.755	88.527	.325	3.217	.003
3	(Constant)	136.794	53.830		2.541	.017
	House Size (square feet)	.129	.021	.589	6.157	.000
	Land (acres)	276.088	78.196	.315	3.531	.002
	Age	−1.399	.476	−.261	−2.942	.007
4	(Constant)	83.064	68.789		1.208	.240
	Land (acres)	292.184	80.883	.333	3.612	.001
	House Size (square feet)	.101	.028	.460	3.597	.002
	Age	−1.253	.551	−.234	−2.273	.033
	Rooms	10.690	7.542	.132	1.417	.170
	Baths	6.279	18.476	.036	.340	.737
	Garage	15.971	16.754	.107	.953	.350

a. Dependent Variable: Appraised Value

CHARTS

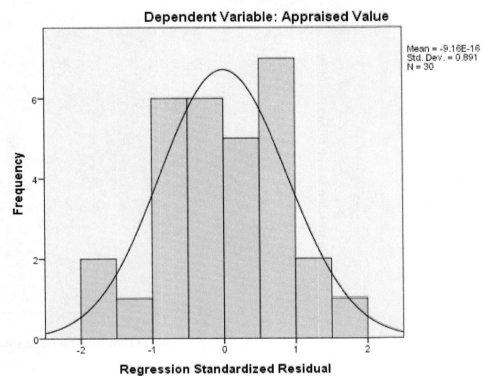

Histogram

Dependent Variable: Appraised Value

Mean = -9.16E-16
Std. Dev. = 0.891
N = 30

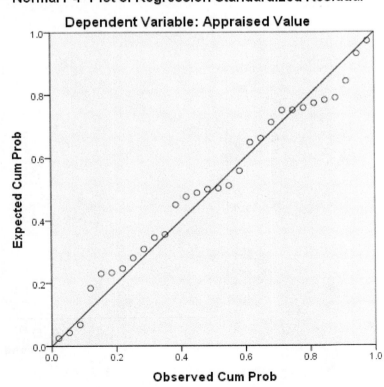

Normal P-P Plot of Regression Standardized Residual

Dependent Variable: Appraised Value

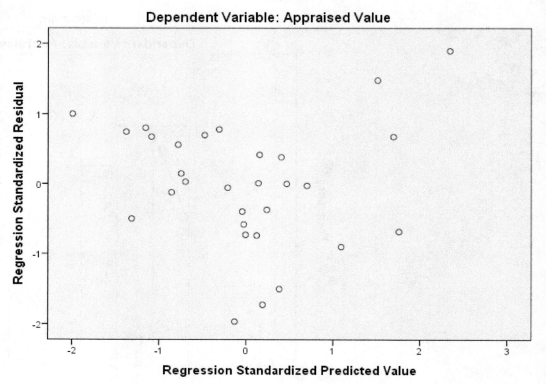

Scatterplot

Dependent Variable: Appraised Value

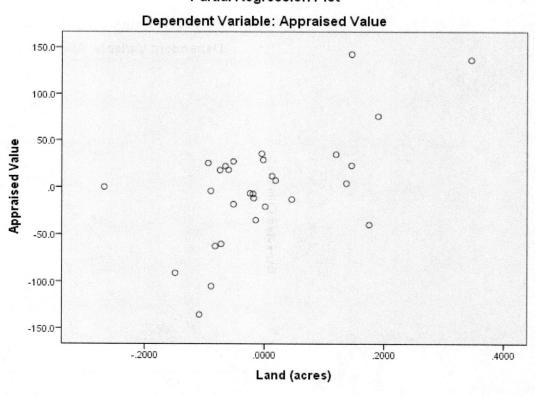

Partial Regression Plot

Dependent Variable: Appraised Value

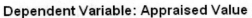

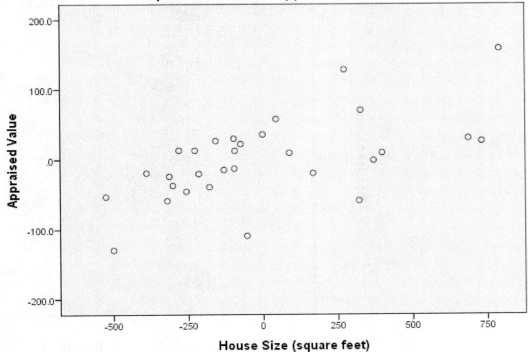

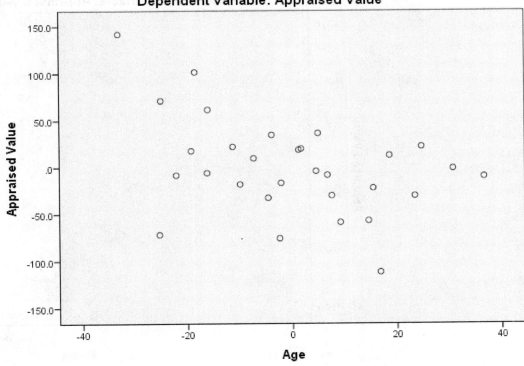

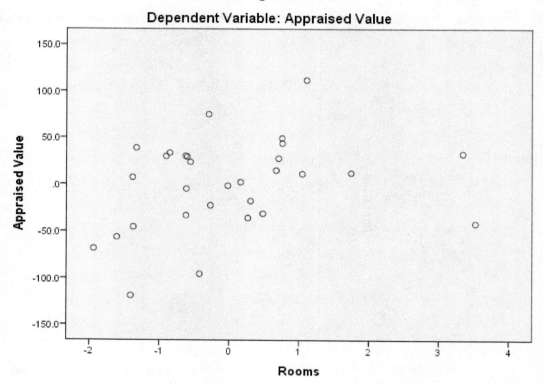

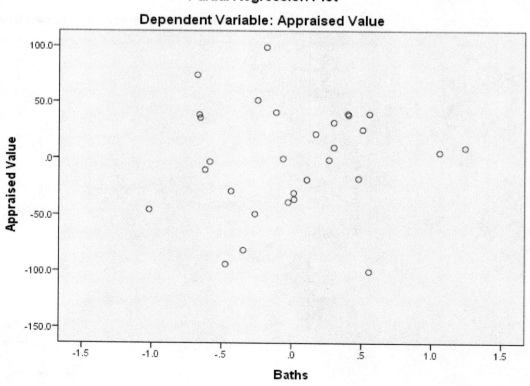

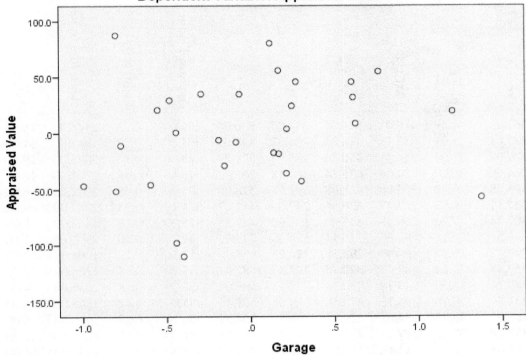

Partial Regression Plot

Dependent Variable: Appraised Value

Pre_4	Res_4	LMCI_4	UMCI_4	LICI_4	UICI_4	Appraised Value	Land (acres)	House Size (square feet)	Age	Rooms	Baths	Garage
467.49	−1.49	410.01	524.96	344.00	590.98	466.00	0.23	2448.00	46.00	7.00	3.50	2.00
385.01	−21.01	356.16	413.85	271.97	498.05	364.00	0.22	1942.00	51.00	7.00	2.50	1.00
407.07	21.93	354.41	459.73	285.75	528.39	429.00	0.16	2073.00	29.00	5.00	3.00	2.00
584.60	−36.20	534.05	635.14	464.18	705.02	548.40	0.46	2707.00	18.00	8.00	2.50	1.00
405.48	0.42	374.89	436.08	291.98	518.98	405.90	0.25	2042.00	46.00	7.00	1.50	1.00
337.17	36.93	287.37	386.96	217.06	457.27	374.10	0.23	2089.00	88.00	7.00	2.00	0.00
307.24	7.76	269.48	345.00	191.60	422.88	315.00	0.18	1433.00	48.00	7.00	2.00	0.00
649.53	100.21	582.66	716.41	521.40	777.67	749.70	0.50	2991.00	7.00	9.00	2.50	1.00
244.12	−26.42	194.90	293.35	124.25	363.99	217.70	0.22	1008.00	52.00	5.00	1.00	0.0
557.46	78.24	487.18	627.75	427.52	687.41	635.70	0.13	3202.00	15.00	8.00	2.50	2.00
389.26	−38.56	348.14	430.38	272.48	506.04	350.70	0.18	2230.00	54.00	8.00	2.00	0.00
434.84	20.16	395.13	474.56	318.55	551.13	455.00	0.42	1848.00	48.00	7.00	2.00	1.00
386.95	−30.75	344.02	429.87	269.52	504.37	356.20	0.25	2100.00	46.00	6.00	2.00	0.00
375.49	-103.79	317.05	433.93	251.55	499.43	271.70	0.11	1846.00	12.00	5.00	3.00	1.00
261.88	42.42	212.13	311.63	141.79	381.97	304.30	0.17	1331.00	64.00	5.00	1.00	1.00
294.94	−6.54	244.90	344.98	174.73	415.15	288.40	0.17	1344.00	52.00	8.00	1.00	0.00
416.30	−19.60	381.61	450.98	301.63	530.97	396.70	0.38	1822.00	44.00	6.00	2.00	1.00
577.76	35.74	505.91	649.60	446.96	708.55	613.50	0.65	2479.00	46.00	6.00	2.50	2.00
312.60	1.50	255.01	370.20	189.06	436.15	314.10	0.17	1605.00	52.00	6.00	3.00	0.00
366.57	−3.07	298.37	434.77	237.74	495.40	363.50	0.14	2080.00	78.00	11.00	2.00	0.00
403.35	−39.05	343.37	463.33	278.68	528.03	364.30	0.28	2410.00	71.00	6.00	1.00	1.00
269.41	35.69	213.38	325.45	146.59	392.24	305.10	0.11	1753.00	97.00	8.00	2.00	0.00
441.72	−0.02	389.80	493.63	320.72	562.72	441.70	0.36	1884.00	45.00	7.00	2.00	2.00
432.33	−79.23	359.85	504.80	301.18	563.47	353.10	0.15	2050.00	41.00	10.00	2.00	2.00
510.88	−47.58	452.22	569.54	386.83	634.92	463.30	0.23	2978.00	40.00	6.00	2.50	2.00
410.99	−90.99	352.48	469.49	287.01	534.96	320.00	0.46	2132.00	82.00	7.00	1.00	0.00
303.27	29.57	269.65	336.88	188.91	417.62	332.80	0.19	1551.00	54.00	6.00	2.00	0.00
237.07	39.53	184.51	289.64	115.79	358.36	276.60	0.12	1129.00	44.00	5.00	1.00	0.00
355.77	41.23	319.85	391.69	240.72	470.82	397.00	0.15	1674.00	34.00	7.00	2.00	1.00
168.94	52.96	114.99	222.89	47.06	290.83	221.90	0.09	1184.00	94.00	5.00	1.00	0.00

Based on Model 4
PRE—Unstandardized Predicted
RES—Unstandardized Residual
LMCI—95% Lower Confidence Interval for y mean
UMCI—95% Upper Confidence Interval for y mean
LICI—95% Lower Confidence Interval for y individual
UICI—95% Upper Confidence Interval for y individual

Note: Independent variable: the appraised value
Dependent variables: land area of the property in acres, house size (square feet), age, rooms, baths and garage

Use the SPSS outputs to answer the following questions:

1. Are the regression assumptions valid for these data? Justify your answers with the appropriate charts.

2. State the multiple regression equation for model 1.

3. State the multiple regression equation for model 2.

4. State the multiple regression equation for model 3.

5. State the multiple regression equation for model 4.

6. Of the four models given in the SPSS outputs, which model appears to be the most efficient? Why?

7. At the 0.05 level of significance, is the linear model 1 useful for predicting the appraised value of a single-family home?

8. At the 0.05 level of significance, is the linear model 2 useful for predicting the appraised value of a single-family home?

9. At the 0.05 level of significance, is the linear model 3 useful for predicting the appraised value of a single-family home?

10. At the 0.05 level of significance, is the linear model 4 useful for predicting the appraised value of a single-family home?

11. Use model 4 to predict the appraised value of a single-family home that has a land area of 0.2297 acres, house size of 2448 square feet, age of 46 years, 7 rooms, 3.5 baths and 2 garages.

12. For model 4, what is the forecast error (or residual) of appraised value of a single-family home that has a land area of 0.2297 acres, house size of 2448 square feet, age of 46 years, 7 rooms, 3.5 baths and 2 garages?

13. At the 0.05 level of significance, determine whether each independent variable makes a significant contribution to the regression model 4. Indicate the most appropriate regression model for this set of data.

14. Based on model 4, construct a 95% confidence interval estimate of the mean appraised value of a single-family home that has a land area of 0.2297 acres, house size of 2448 square feet, age of 46 years, 7 rooms, 3.5 baths and 2 garages.

15. Based on model 4, construct a 95% confidence interval estimate of the appraised value of a single-family home that has a land area of 0.2297 acres, house size of 2448 square feet, age of 46 years, 7 rooms, 3.5 baths and 2 garages.

16. What is the coefficient of multiple determination for model 4? And interpret its meaning.

Many factors determine the attendance at Major League Baseball games. These factors can include when the game is played, the weather, the opponent, and whether the team is having a good season. In an effort to increase ticket sales, ball clubs run promotions such as free concerts after the game or giveaways of team hats or bobbleheads of star players (T.C. Boyd and T.C. Krehbiel, "An Analysis of the Effects of Specific Promotion Types on Attendance at Major League Baseball Games," *American Journal of Business,* 2006, 21, pp. 21–32).

The data file (**Phillies**) include the following variables for a recent season:

Attendance—Paid attendance for each Philadelphia Phillies home game

Temp—High temperature for the day

Win—Team's winning percentage at the time of the game

OpWin—opponent team's winning percentage at the time of the game

Weekend—Dummy variable, 1 if game played on Friday, Saturday, or Sunday; 0 otherwise

Promotion—Dummy variable, 1 if a promotion was held; 0 if no promotion was held

A regression analysis using attendance as the dependent variable and the other five variables as independent variables was performed and the SPSS results were provided.

The data are shown in the table below.

Attendance	Temp	Win	OpWin	Weekend	Promotion
18,591	48	531	469	1	1
18,073	49	531	469	1	1
14,502	67	500	500	0	0
13,020	75	429	571	0	0
14,542	66	500	500	0	0
14,111	65	556	444	0	0
13,366	57	500	556	1	0
15,606	73	455	600	1	0
19,195	78	417	636	1	1
12,138	57	368	474	0	0
12,250	61	400	450	0	0
12,249	62	381	476	0	0
15,257	65	325	434	1	0
16,205	66	345	414	1	0
32,411	71	367	400	1	1
12,321	82	387	467	0	0
13,216	77	406	452	0	0
12,476	89	424	438	0	0
20,504	77	441	647	1	0
32,634	89	457	629	1	1
21,114	79	444	639	1	1
21,090	60	409	545	0	0
22,640	67	422	533	0	0
26,405	74	435	522	0	0
15,455	91	404	491	1	0
16,601	89	396	500	1	0
19,223	85	407	491	1	1
14,942	78	418	491	0	0
13,039	91	411	500	0	0
16,888	63	444	469	1	0
20,634	70	438	477	1	0

(continued)

Attendance	Temp	Win	OpWin	Weekend	Promotion
41,079	81	446	470	1	1
17,424	81	439	493	0	0
21,905	82	433	500	0	1
22,132	85	441	493	0	1
17,039	84	435	556	1	0
18,759	86	441	548	1	0
38,158	88	437	554	1	1
18,422	90	456	500	0	0
20,826	95	463	494	0	0
50,396	97	457	500	0	1
12,303	99	463	518	1	0
44,143	88	458	524	1	1
15,228	86	452	529	1	0
17,393	86	453	529	1	1
23,541	93	467	429	0	0
27,672	92	473	424	0	1
20,422	69	470	629	1	0
23,570	73	468	635	1	0
25,012	83	458	643	1	0
27,330	94	471	552	0	0
22,595	95	467	557	0	0
20,380	94	472	551	0	0
17,076	86	477	556	1	0
23,506	82	481	551	1	0
28,186	84	477	555	1	1
20,259	86	473	558	0	0
14,046	99	470	359	0	0
14,509	99	475	356	0	0
14,289	93	479	353	0	0
31,117	93	483	559	1	0
20,242	95	488	555	1	1
58,493	96	484	558	1	1
16,126	86	496	500	0	0
13,821	74	500	496	0	0
14,268	67	496	500	0	0
18,335	80	504	464	1	0
21,747	85	500	468	1	1
24,047	86	496	471	1	1
13,514	93	493	475	0	0
14,345	91	490	486	0	1
14,345	91	487	489	0	1
12,247	82	483	487	0	0
13,167	77	486	490	0	0
13,718	84	486	438	1	0
16,621	85	486	442	1	0
23,054	81	490	439	1	1
15,807	80	500	630	0	0
14,516	77	503	626	0	0

The SPSS outputs are shown below:

Model Summary[b]

Model	R	R Square	Adjusted R Square	Std. Error of the Estimate
1	.345[a]	.119	.084	8296.787

a. *Predictors: (Constant), OpWin, Temp, Win*
b. *Dependent Variable: Attendance*

ANOVA[a]

Model		Sum of Squares	df	Mean Square	F	Sig.
1	Regression	699691116.010	3	233230372.003	3.388	.022[b]
	Residual	5162750420.369	75	68836672.272		
	Total	5862441536.380	78			

a. *Dependent Variable: Attendance*
b. *Predictors: (Constant), OpWin, Temp, Win*

Coefficients[a]

Model		Unstandardized Coefficients		Standardized Coefficients			95.0% Confidence Interval for B	
		B	Std. Error	Beta	t	Sig.	Lower Bound	Upper Bound
1	(Constant)	−8820.597	13031.698		−.677	.501	−3478.071	17139.877
	Temp	203.665	79.116	.281	2.574	.012	46.058	361.272
	Win	−3.001	22.404	−.015	−.134	.894	−47.632	41.630
	OpWin	27.249	14.089	.211	1.934	.057	−.817	55.316

a. *Dependent Variable: Attendance*

CHARTS

Histogram
Dependent Variable: Attendance

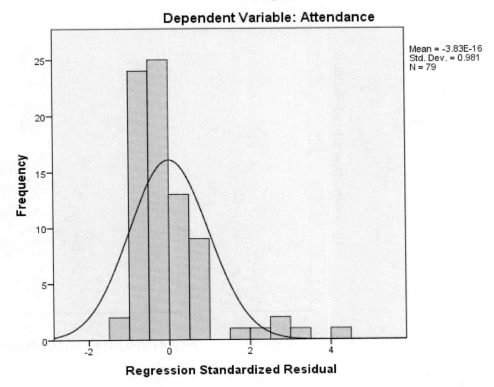

Mean = -3.83E-16
Std. Dev. = 0.981
N = 79

Normal P-P Plot of Regression Standardized Residual
Dependent Variable: Attendance

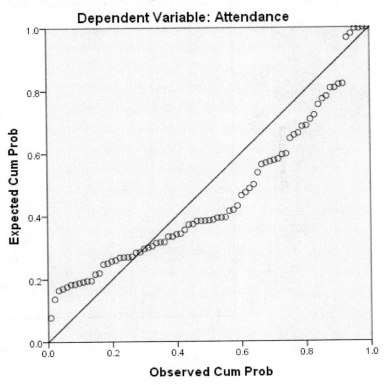

Scatterplot

Dependent Variable: Attendance

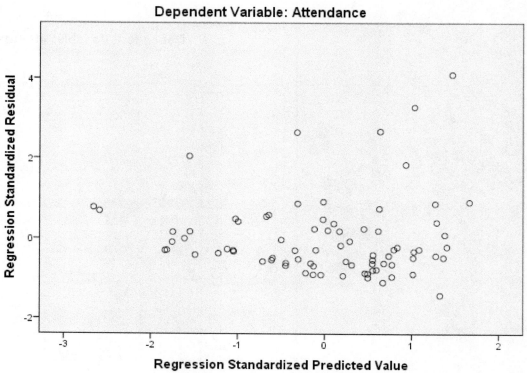

Partial Regression Plot

Dependent Variable: Attendance

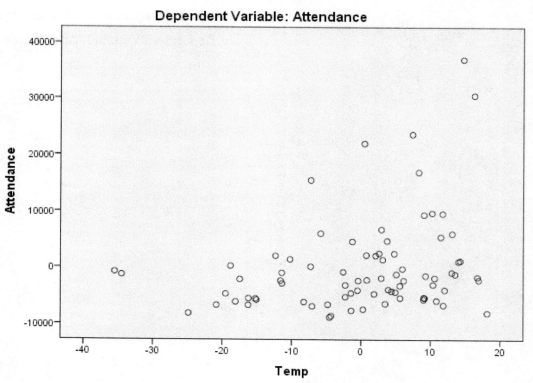

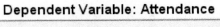

Partial Regression Plot

Dependent Variable: Attendance

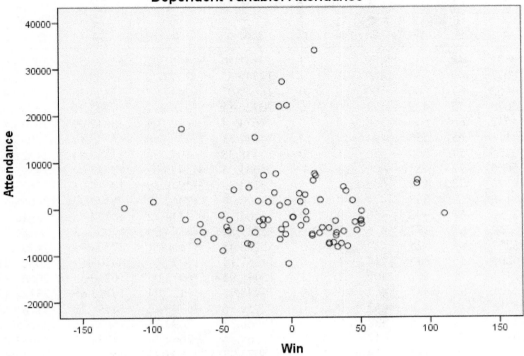

Partial Regression Plot

Dependent Variable: Attendance

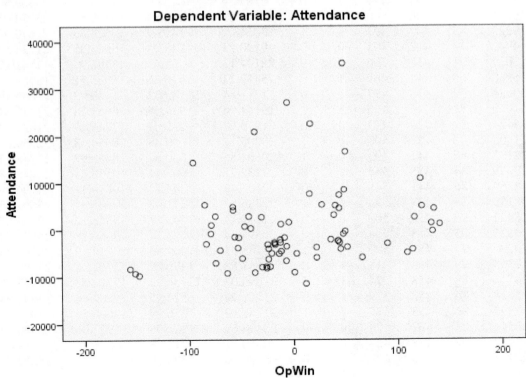

Attendance	Temp	Win	OpWin	Weekend	Promotion	PRE_1	RES_1	LMCI_1	UMCI_1	LICI_1	UICI_1
18591	48	531	469	1	1	12141.66	6449.337	5237.852	19045.47	−5770.31	30053.64
18073	49	531	469	1	1	12345.33	5727.672	5568.641	19122.01	−5518.04	30208.69
14502	67	500	500	0	0	16949.07	−2447.07	13327.16	20570.97	28.82554	33869.31
13020	75	429	571	0	0	20726.17	−7706.17	17745.44	23706.91	3931.498	37520.85
14542	66	500	500	0	0	16745.4	−2203.4	13017.09	20473.72	−197.936	33688.74
14111	65	556	444	0	0	14847.71	−736.706	8743.11	20952.3	−2771.67	32467.08
13366	57	500	556	1	0	16438.38	−3072.38	11553.84	21322.92	−796.327	33673.09
15606	73	455	600	1	0	21031.05	−5425.05	17667.04	24395.06	4164.128	37897.96
19195	78	417	636	1	1	23144.39	−3949.39	18614.91	27673.88	6006.931	40281.85
12138	57	368	474	0	0	14600.09	−2462.09	9144.693	20055.48	−2805.02	32005.19
12250	61	400	450	0	0	14664.72	−2414.72	10224.55	19104.9	−2449.35	31778.8
12249	62	381	476	0	0	15633.89	−3384.89	11006.03	20261.76	−1529.83	32797.62
15257	65	325	434	1	0	15268.48	−11.4811	8739.099	21797.86	−2502.54	33039.5
16205	66	345	414	1	0	14867.14	1337.864	8910.457	20823.81	−2701.54	32435.81
32411	71	367	400	1	1	15437.94	16973.06	10210.35	20665.54	−1897.11	32773
12321	82	387	467	0	0	19443.94	−7122.94	15723.66	23164.23	2502.372	36385.52
13216	77	406	452	0	0	17959.86	−4743.86	14738.23	21181.48	1120.759	34798.95
12476	89	424	438	0	0	19968.33	−7492.33	16670.78	23265.87	3114.539	36822.11
20504	77	441	647	1	0	23168.44	−2664.44	18734.67	27602.21	6056.03	40280.86
32634	89	457	629	1	1	25073.92	7560.084	20963.96	29183.88	8042.53	42105.3
21114	79	444	639	1	1	23348.77	−2234.77	19159.38	27538.17	6298.044	40399.5
21090	60	409	545	0	0	17022.74	4067.262	12765.25	21280.23	−44.8505	34090.33
22640	67	422	533	0	0	18082.39	4557.614	14883.07	21281.7	1247.542	34917.23
26405	74	435	522	0	0	19169.28	7235.717	16841.41	21497.16	2478.108	35860.46
15455	91	404	491	1	0	21879.9	−6424.9	18353.4	25406.39	4979.821	38779.97
16601	89	396	500	1	0	21741.82	−5140.82	18109.59	25374.05	4819.366	38664.27
19223	85	407	491	1	1	20648.9	−1425.9	17626.83	23670.98	3846.84	37450.96
14942	78	418	491	0	0	19190.23	−4248.23	16645.95	21734.51	2467.503	35912.96
13039	91	411	500	0	0	22104.13	−9065.13	18798.07	25410.2	5248.675	38959.59
16888	63	444	469	1	0	15457.74	1430.26	11925.51	18989.97	−1443.53	32359.01
20634	70	438	477	1	0	17119.4	3514.602	14405.3	19833.49	369.9905	33868.81
41079	81	446	470	1	1	19144.96	21934.04	16967.28	21322.64	2474.067	35815.85
17424	81	439	493	0	0	19792.7	−2368.7	17746.17	21839.24	3138.435	36446.97
21905	82	433	500	0	1	20205.12	1699.88	18050.63	22359.61	3537.242	36873
22132	85	441	493	0	1	20601.36	1530.64	18453.97	22748.75	3934.399	37268.32
17039	84	435	556	1	0	22132.41	−5093.41	19516.44	24748.38	5398.625	38866.2
18759	86	441	548	1	0	22303.74	−3544.74	19810.49	24796.99	5588.698	39018.78
38158	88	437	554	1	1	22886.57	15271.43	20105.81	25667.33	6126.232	39646.91
18422	90	456	500	0	0	21765.41	−3343.41	19388.12	24142.7	5067.275	38463.55
20826	95	463	494	0	0	22599.24	−1773.24	19666.58	25531.89	5813.027	39385.44
50396	97	457	500	0	1	23188.07	27207.93	20014.89	26361.24	6358.173	40017.96
12303	99	463	518	1	0	24067.88	−11764.9	20635.8	27499.96	7187.255	40948.51
44143	88	458	524	1	1	22006.07	22136.93	19772.33	24239.8	5327.76	38684.37
15228	86	452	529	1	0	21752.99	−6524.99	19602.64	23903.34	5085.647	38420.33
17393	86	453	529	1	1	21749.99	−4356.99	19606.55	23893.43	5083.535	38416.44
23541	93	467	429	0	0	20408.69	3132.309	16927.06	23890.33	3517.921	37299.46
27672	92	473	424	0	1	20050.77	7621.228	16506.84	23594.7	3147.051	36954.49
20422	69	470	629	1	0	20961.6	−539.599	16710.43	25212.77	3895.588	38027.61

(continued)

Attendance	Temp	Win	OpWin	Weekend	Promotion	PRE_1	RES_1	LMCI_1	UMCI_1	LICI_1	UICI_1
23570	73	468	635	1	0	21945.76	1624.242	17789.67	26101.84	4903.183	38988.33
25012	83	458	643	1	0	24230.42	781.5843	20002.43	28458.4	7170.163	41290.67
27330	94	471	552	0	0	23952.02	3377.976	20876.04	27028.01	7140.183	40763.87
22595	95	467	557	0	0	24303.94	−1708.94	21071.59	27536.29	7462.789	41145.09
20380	94	472	551	0	0	23921.77	−3541.77	20852.53	26991.02	7111.163	40732.38
17076	86	477	556	1	0	22413.69	−5337.69	19878.9	24948.49	5692.404	39134.98
23506	82	481	551	1	0	21450.78	2055.218	19036.72	23864.84	4747.368	38154.2
28186	84	477	555	1	1	21979.11	6206.886	19536.17	24422.06	5271.501	38686.73
20259	86	473	558	0	0	22480.2	−2221.2	19958.22	25002.18	5760.845	39199.55
14046	99	470	359	0	0	19714.22	−5668.22	14327.28	25101.16	2330.453	37097.99
14509	99	475	356	0	0	19617.47	−5108.47	14132.39	25102.54	2203.039	37031.9
14289	93	479	353	0	0	18301.73	−4012.73	13093.07	23510.38	972.3726	35631.08
31117	93	483	559	1	0	23903.09	7213.909	20751.17	27055.01	7077.19	40728.99
20242	95	488	555	1	1	24186.42	−3944.42	20824.84	27548	7319.984	41052.85
58493	96	484	558	1	1	24483.84	34009.16	21034.75	27932.92	7599.745	41367.93
16126	86	496	500	0	0	20830.71	−4704.71	18173.49	23487.92	4090.422	37570.99
13821	74	500	496	0	0	18265.72	−4444.72	15240.25	21291.2	1463.051	35068.4
14268	67	496	500	0	0	16961.07	−2693.07	13446.56	20475.58	63.49248	33858.65
18335	80	504	464	1	0	18603.73	−268.73	15415.88	21791.58	1771.062	35436.4
21747	85	500	468	1	1	19743.06	2003.942	16728.85	22757.26	2942.41	36543.71
24047	86	496	471	1	1	20040.48	4006.525	17149.34	22931.61	3261.471	36819.48
13514	93	493	475	0	0	21584.13	−8070.13	18390.41	24777.86	4750.35	38417.91
14345	91	490	486	0	1	21485.55	−7140.55	18607.34	24363.75	4708.767	38262.33
14345	91	487	489	0	1	21576.3	−7231.3	18779.47	24373.13	4813.287	38339.31
12247	82	483	487	0	0	19700.82	−7453.82	17385.88	22015.76	3011.444	36390.2
13167	77	486	490	0	0	18755.24	−5588.24	16272.1	21238.38	2041.702	35468.78
13718	84	486	438	1	0	18763.93	−5045.93	15650.42	21877.44	1945.179	35582.68
16621	85	486	442	1	0	19076.59	−2455.59	16018.14	22135.04	2267.948	35885.23
23054	81	490	439	1	1	18168.18	4885.823	14990.63	21345.73	1337.456	34998.9
15807	80	500	630	0	0	23139.13	−7332.13	18948.46	27329.8	6088.088	40190.17
14516	77	503	626	0	0	22410.13	−7894.13	18195.43	26624.84	5353.168	39467.1

Based on Model 1

PRE—Unstandardized Predicted

RES—Unstandardized Residual

LMCI—95% Lower Confidence Interval for y mean

UMCI—95% Upper Confidence Interval for y mean

LICI—95% Lower Confidence Interval for y individual

UICI—95% Upper Confidence Interval for y individual

Note: Independent variable: Attendance
Dependent variables: Temp, Win, OpWin, Weekend, and Promotion

Use the SPSS results to answer the following questions:

1. Are the regression assumptions valid for these data? Justify your answers with the appropriate charts.

2. Interpret the regression coefficients in (1).

3. State the multiple regression equation.

4. Predict the attendance for a Philadelphia Phillies home game that is held when the high temperature of the day is 48 (Temp=48), the team's winning percentage at the time of the game is 531 (Win=531), the opponent team's winning percentage at the time of the game is 469 (OpWin=469) and the game is played on Friday, Saturday or Sunday (Weekend=1), and promotion is being held (Promotion=1).

5. What is the forecast error (or residual) of attendance for a Philadelphia Phillies home game that is held when the high temperature of the day is 48 (Temp=48), the team's winning percentage at the time of the game is 531 (Win=531), the opponent team's winning percentage at the time of the game is 469 (OpWin=469) and the game is played on Friday, Saturday or Sunday (Weekend=1), and promotion is being held (Promotion=1)?

6. At the 0.05 level of significance, is the linear regression model useful for predicting the attendance for a Philadelphia Phillies home game?

7. At the 0.05 level of significance, determine which independent variables significantly influenced attendance?

8. What is the coefficient of multiple determination? And interpret its meaning.

9. Construct a 95% confidence interval estimate of the population slope between attendance and temperature of the day (Temp).

10. Construct a 95% confidence interval estimate of the population slope between attendance and the team's winning percentage at the time of the game (Win).

11. Construct a 95% confidence interval estimate of the population slope between attendance and the opponent team's winning percentage at the time of the game (OpWin).

12. Construct a 95% confidence interval estimate of the mean attendance for a Philadelphia Phillies home game that is held when the high temperature of the day is 48 (Temp=48), the team's winning percentage at the time of the game is 531 (Win=531), the opponent team's winning percentage at the time of the game is 469 (OpWin=469) and the game is played on Friday, Saturday or Sunday (Weekend=1), and promotion is being held (Promotion=1).

13. Based on model 4, construct a 95% confidence interval estimate of the Philadelphia Phillies home game that is held when the high temperature of the day is 48 (Temp=48), the team's winning percentage at the time of the game is 531 (Win=531), the opponent team's winning percentage at the time of the game is 469 (OpWin=469) and the game is played on Friday, Saturday or Sunday (Weekend=1), and promotion is being held (Promotion=1).

USING STATISTICS

The Multiple Effects of OmniPower Bars, Revisited

Ariwasabi/Shutterstock

In the Using Statistics scenario, you were a marketing manager for OmniFoods, responsible for nutrition bars and similar snack items. You needed to determine the effect that price and in-store promotions would have on sales of OmniPower nutrition bars in order to develop an effective marketing strategy. A sample of 34 stores in a supermarket chain was selected for a test-market study. The stores charged between 59 and 99 cents per bar and were given an in-store promotion budget between $200 and $600.

At the end of the one-month test-market study, you performed a multiple regression analysis on the data. Two independent variables were considered: the price of an OmniPower bar and the monthly budget for in-store promotional expenditures. The dependent variable was the number of OmniPower bars sold in a month. The coefficient of determination indicated that 75.8% of the variation in sales was explained by knowing the price charged and the amount spent on in-store promotions. The model indicated that the predicted sales of OmniPower are estimated to decrease by 532 bars per month for each 10-cent increase in the price, and the predicted sales are estimated to increase by 361 bars for each additional $100 spent on promotions.

After studying the relative effects of price and promotion, OmniFoods needs to set price and promotion standards for a nationwide introduction (obviously, lower prices and higher promotion budgets lead to more sales, but they do so at a lower profit margin). You determined that if stores spend $400 a month for in-store promotions and charge 79 cents, the 95% confidence interval estimate of the mean monthly sales is 2,854 to 3,303 bars. OmniFoods can multiply the lower and upper bounds of this confidence interval by the number of stores included in the nationwide introduction to estimate total monthly sales. For example, if 1,000 stores are in the nationwide introduction, then total monthly sales should be between 2.854 million and 3.308 million bars.

SUMMARY

Figure 16.9 presents a roadmap of this chapter. In this chapter, you learned how to develop and fit multiple regression models that use two or more independent variables to predict the value of a dependent variable. You also learned how to include categorical independent variables and interaction terms in regression models.

REFERENCES

1. Andrews, D. F., and D. Pregibon. "Finding the Outliers that Matter." *Journal of the Royal Statistical Society* 40 (Ser. B., 1978): 85–93.
2. Atkinson, A. C. "Robust and Diagnostic Regression Analysis." *Communications in Statistics* 11 (1982): 2559–2572.
3. Belsley, D. A., E. Kuh, and R. Welsch. *Regression Diagnostics: Identifying Influential Data and Sources of Collinearity.* New York: Wiley, 1980.
4. Cook, R. D., and S. Weisberg. *Residuals and Influence in Regression.* New York: Chapman and Hall, 1982.
5. Hosmer, D. W., and S. Lemeshow. *Applied Logistic Regression*, 3rd ed. New York: Wiley, 2013.
6. Hoaglin, D. C., and R. Welsch. "The Hat Matrix in Regression and ANOVA," *The American Statistician*, 32, (1978), 17–22.
7. Kutner, M., C. Nachtsheim, J. Neter, and W. Li. *Applied Linear Statistical Models*, 5th ed. New York: McGraw-Hill/Irwin, 2005.
8. *Microsoft Excel 2013*. Redmond, WA: Microsoft Corp., 2012.
9. *Minitab Release 16*. State College, PA: Minitab, Inc., 2010.

FIGURE 16.19
Roadmap for multiple regression

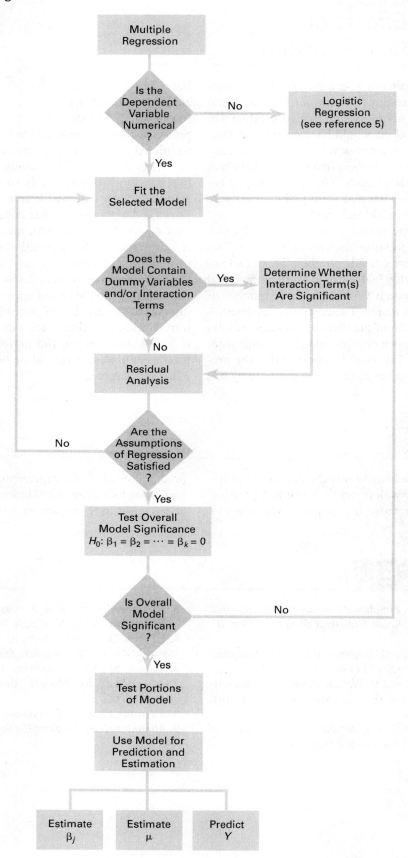

FIGURE 16.19
Roadmap for multiple regression

KEY EQUATIONS

Multiple Regression Model with k Independent Variables

$$Y_i = \beta_0 + \beta_1 X_{1i} + \beta_2 X_{2i} + \beta_3 X_{3i} + \cdots + \beta_k X_{ki} + \varepsilon_i \tag{16.1}$$

Multiple Regression Model with Two Independent Variables

$$Y_i = \beta_0 + \beta_1 X_{1i} + \beta_2 X_{2i} + \varepsilon_i \tag{16.2}$$

Multiple Regression Equation with Two Independent Variables

$$\hat{Y}_i = b_0 + b_1 X_{1i} + b_2 X_{2i} \tag{16.3}$$

Coefficient of Multiple Determination

$$r^2 = \frac{\text{Regression sum of squares}}{\text{Total sum of squares}} = \frac{SSR}{SST} \tag{16.4}$$

Adjusted r^2

$$r^2_{\text{adj}} = 1 - \left[(1 - r^2) \frac{n-1}{n-k-1} \right] \tag{16.5}$$

Overall F Test

$$F_{STAT} = \frac{MSR}{MSE} \tag{16.6}$$

Testing for the Slope in Multiple Regression

$$t_{STAT} = \frac{b_j - \beta_j}{S_{b_j}} \tag{16.7}$$

Confidence Interval Estimate for the Slope

$$b_j \pm t_{\alpha/2} S_{b_j} \tag{16.8}$$

KEY TERMS

adjusted r^2 337
coefficient of multiple determination 336
cross-product term 353

dummy variable 351
interaction 353
interaction term 353

multiple regression model 332
net regression coefficient 335
overall F test 338

CHECKING YOUR UNDERSTANDING

16.1 What is the difference between r^2 and adjusted r^2?

16.2 How does the interpretation of the regression coefficients differ in multiple regression and simple linear regression?

16.3 Why and how do you use dummy variables?

16.4 How can you evaluate whether the slope of the dependent variable with an independent variable is the same for each level of the dummy variable?

16.5 Under what circumstances do you include an interaction term in a regression model?

16.6 When a dummy variable is included in a regression model that has one numerical independent variable, what assumption do you need to make concerning the slope between the dependent variable, Y, and the numerical independent variable, X?

PROBLEMS

Section 16.1

16.7 For this problem, use the following multiple regression equation:

$$\hat{Y}_i = 10 + 5X_{1i} + 3X_{2i}$$

a. Interpret the meaning of the slopes.
b. Interpret the meaning of the Y intercept.

16.8 For this problem, use the following multiple regression equation:

$$\hat{Y}_i = 50 - 2X_{1i} + 7X_{2i}$$

a. Interpret the meaning of the slopes.
b. Interpret the meaning of the Y intercept.

16.9 A small business analyst seeks to determine which variables should be used to predict small-business mean annual revenue for U.S. metropolitan areas. The analyst decides to consider the independent variables age, the mean age (in months) of small businesses in the metropolitan area; and BizAnalyzer, the mean BizAnalyzer score of small businesses in the metropolitan area. (The BizAnalyzer score measures on a scale of 1 to 100 the level of risk that the small businesses in the metropolitan area present to potential lenders.) The dependent variable, revenue, is mean annual revenue. Using data collected from a sample of 25 metropolitan areas, the regression results are:

Variable	Coefficients	Standard Error	t Statistic	p-Value
Intercept	−680.2357	1,313.5154	−0.52	0.6097
Age	1.7454	7.8519	0.22	0.8261
BizAnalyzer	20.5265	29.1859	0.70	0.4885

a. State the multiple regression equation.
b. Interpret the meaning of the slopes, b_1 and b_2, in this problem.
c. What conclusions can you reach concerning mean annual revenue?

16.10 Profitability remains a challenge for banks and thrifts with less than $2 billion of assets. The business problem facing a bank analyst relates to the factors that affect return on assets (ROA), an indicator of how profitable a company is relative to its total assets. Data collected from a sample of 200 community banks and stored in CommunityBanks include the ROA (%), the efficiency ratio (%), as a measure of bank productivity (the lower the efficiency ratio, the better), and total risk-based capital (%), as a measure of capital adequacy. (Data extracted from "Rising Tide: The Top 200 Community Banks," **bit.ly/1ldN8gC**.)
a. State the multiple regression equation.
b. Interpret the meaning of the slopes, b_1 and b_2, in this problem.
c. Predict the mean ROA when the efficiency ratio is 60% and the total risk-based capital is 15%.
d. Construct a 95% confidence interval estimate for the mean ROA when the efficiency ratio is 60% and the total risk-based capital is 15%.
e. Construct a 95% prediction interval for the ROA for a particular community bank when the efficiency ratio is 60% and the total risk-based capital is 15%.
f. Explain why the interval in (d) is narrower than the interval in (e).
g. What conclusions can you reach concerning ROA?

16.11 The production of wine is a multibillion-dollar worldwide industry. In an attempt to develop a model of wine quality as judged by wine experts, data was collected from red wine variants of Portuguese "Vinho Verde" wine. A sample of 50 wines is stored in VinhoVerde. (Data extracted from P. Cortez, A. Cerdeira, F. Almeida, T. Matos, and J. Reis, "Modeling Wine Preferences by Data Mining from Physiochemical Properties," *Decision Support Systems*, 47, 2009, pp. 547–553 and **bit.ly/9xKlEa**.) Develop a multiple linear regression model to predict wine quality, measured on a scale from 0 (very bad) to 10 (excellent) based on alcohol content (%) and the amount of chlorides.
a. State the multiple regression equation.
b. Interpret the meaning of the slopes, b_1 and b_2, in this problem.
c. Explain why the regression coefficient, b_0, has no practical meaning in the context of this problem.
d. Predict the mean wine quality rating for wines that have 10% alcohol and chlorides of 0.08.
e. Construct a 95% confidence interval estimate for the mean wine quality rating for wines that have 10% alcohol and chlorides of 0.08.
f. Construct a 95% prediction interval for the wine quality rating for an individual wine that has 10% alcohol and chlorides of 0.08.
g. What conclusions can you reach concerning this regression model?

16.12 The business problem facing a human resource manager is to assess the impact of factors on full-time job growth. Specifically, the human resource manager is interested in the impact of total worldwide revenues and full-time voluntary turnover on the number of full-time jobs added in a year. Data were collected from a sample of 96 "best companies to work for." The total number of full-time jobs added in the past year, total worldwide revenue (in $millions) and the full-time voluntary turnover (%) are recorded and stored in BestCompanies. (Data extracted from *Best Companies to Work For 2014,* available at **fortune.com/best-companies/google-1/**.)
a. State the multiple regression equation.
b. Interpret the meaning of the slopes, b_1 and b_2, in this problem.
c. Interpret the meaning of the regression coefficient, b_0.
d. What conclusions can you reach concerning full-time jobs added?

16.13 The business problem facing the director of broadcasting operations for a television station was the issue of standby hours (i.e., hours in which unionized graphic artists at the station are paid but are not actually involved in any activity) and what factors were related to standby hours. The study included the following variables:

Standby hours (Y)—Total number of standby hours in a week
Total staff present (X_1)—Weekly total of people-days
Remote hours (X_2)—Total number of hours worked by employees at locations away from the central plant

Data were collected for 26 weeks; these data are organized and stored in Standby.
a. State the multiple regression equation.
b. Interpret the meaning of the slopes, b_1 and b_2, in this problem.
c. Explain why the regression coefficient, b_0, has no practical meaning in the context of this problem.
d. Predict the mean standby hours for a week in which the total staff present have 310 people-days and the remote hours total 400.
e. Construct a 95% confidence interval estimate for the mean standby hours for weeks in which the total staff present have 310 people-days and remote hours total 400.
f. Construct a 95% prediction interval for the standby hours for a single week in which the total staff present have 310 people-days and the remote hours total 400.
g. What conclusions can you reach concerning standby hours?

16.14 Nassau County is located approximately 25 miles east of New York City. The data organized and stored in GlenCove include the fair market value (in $thousands), land area of the property in acres, and age, in years, for a sample of 30 single-family homes located in Glen Cove, a small city in Nassau County. Develop a multiple linear regression model to predict the fair market value based on land area of the property and age, in years.
a. State the multiple regression equation.
b. Interpret the meaning of the slopes, b_1 and b_2, in this problem.
c. Explain why the regression coefficient, b_0, has no practical meaning in the context of this problem.
d. Predict the mean fair market value for a house that has a land area of 0.25 acre and is 55 years old.
e. Construct a 95% confidence interval estimate for the mean fair market value for houses that have a land area of 0.25 acre and are 55 years old.
f. Construct a 95% prediction interval estimate for the fair market value for an individual house that has a land area of 0.25 acre and is 55 years old.

Section 16.2

16.15 The following ANOVA summary table is for a multiple regression model with two independent variables:

Source	Degrees of Freedom	Sum of Squares	Mean Squares	F
Regression	2	60		
Error	18	120		
Total	20	180		

a. Determine the regression mean square (*MSR*) and the mean square error (*MSE*).
b. Compute the overall F_{STAT} test statistic.
c. Determine whether there is a significant relationship between *Y* and the two independent variables at the 0.05 level of significance.
d. Compute the coefficient of multiple determination, r^2, and interpret its meaning.
e. Compute the adjusted r^2.

16.16 The following ANOVA summary table is for a multiple regression model with two independent variables:

Source	Degrees of Freedom	Sum of Squares	Mean Squares	F
Regression	2	30		
Error	10	120		
Total	12	150		

a. Determine the regression mean square (*MSR*) and the mean square error (*MSE*).
b. Compute the overall F_{STAT} test statistic.
c. Determine whether there is a significant relationship between *Y* and the two independent variables at the 0.05 level of significance.
d. Compute the coefficient of multiple determination, r^2, and interpret its meaning.
e. Compute the adjusted r^2.

16.17 A financial analyst engaged in business valuation obtained financial data on 53 drug companies (Industry Group SIC 3 code: 283). The file **BusinessValuation** contains the following variables:

COMPANY—Drug Company name
PB fye—Price-to-book-value ratio (fiscal year ending)
ROE—Return on equity
SGROWTH—Growth (GS5)

a. Develop a regression model to predict price-to-book-value ratio based on return on equity.
b. Develop a regression model to predict price-to-book-value ratio based on growth.
c. Develop a regression model to predict price-to-book-value ratio based on return on equity and growth.
d. Compute and interpret the adjusted r^2 for each of the three models.
e. Which of these three models do you think is the best predictor of price-to-book-value ratio?

16.18 In Problem 16.9 on page 383, you predicted the mean annual revenue for U.S. metropolitan areas, based on the mean age (Age) and mean BizAnalyzer score (BizAnalyzer) for a sample of 25 small business metropolitan areas. The regression analysis resulted in the following ANOVA summary table:

Source	Degrees of Freedom	Sum of Squares	Mean Squares	F	p-Value
Regression	2	96,655.1	48,327.6	0.6531	0.5302
Error	22	1,627,941.1	73,997.3		
Total	24	1,724,596.2			

a. Determine whether there is a significant relationship between mean annual revenue and the two independent variables at the 0.05 level of significance.
b. Interpret the meaning of the *p*-value.
c. Compute the coefficient of multiple determination, r^2, and interpret its meaning.

16.19 In Problem 16.11 on page 384, you used the percentage of alcohol and chlorides to predict wine quality (stored in **VinhoVerde**). Use the results from that problem to do the following:
a. Determine whether there is a significant relationship between wine quality and the two independent variables (percentage of alcohol and chlorides) at the 0.05 level of significance.
b. Interpret the meaning of the *p*-value.
c. Compute the coefficient of multiple determination, r^2, and interpret its meaning.
d. Compute the adjusted r^2.

16.20 In Problem 16.10 on page 384, you used efficiency ratio and total risk-based capital to predict ROA at a community bank (stored in **CommunityBanks**). Using the results from that problem,
a. determine whether there is a significant relationship between ROA and the two independent variables (used efficiency ratio and total risk-based capital) at the 0.05 level of significance.
b. interpret the meaning of the *p*-value.
c. compute the coefficient of multiple determination, r^2, and interpret its meaning.
d. compute the adjusted r^2.

16.21 In Problem 16.13 on page 384, you used the total staff present and remote hours to predict standby hours (stored in **Standby**). Using the results from that problem,
a. determine whether there is a significant relationship between standby hours and the two independent variables (total staff present and remote hours) at the 0.05 level of significance.
b. interpret the meaning of the *p*-value.
c. compute the coefficient of multiple determination, r^2, and interpret its meaning.
d. compute the adjusted r^2.

16.22 In Problem 16.12 on page 384, you used the total worldwide revenue ($millions), and full-time voluntary turnover (%) data stored in **BestCompanies** to predict the number of full-time jobs added. Using the results from that problem,
a. determine whether there is a significant relationship at the 0.05 level of significance between the number of full-time jobs added and the two independent variables, total worldwide revenue ($millions) and full-time voluntary turnover (%).
b. interpret the meaning of the *p*-value.
c. compute the coefficient of multiple determination, r^2, and interpret its meaning.
d. compute the adjusted r^2.

16.23 In Problem 16.14 on page 384, you used the land area of a property and the age of a house to predict the fair market value (stored in GlenCove). Using the results from that problem,

a. determine whether there is a significant relationship between fair market value and the two independent variables (land area of a property and age of a house) at the 0.05 level of significance.

b. interpret the meaning of the p-value.

c. compute the coefficient of multiple determination, r^2, and interpret its meaning.

d. compute the adjusted r^2.

Section 16.3

16.24 In Problem 16.10 on page 384, you used the efficiency ratio and total risk-based capital data stored in CommunityBanks to predict ROA at a community bank.

a. Plot the residuals versus $\hat{Y}_i$.

b. Plot the residuals versus X_{1i}.

c. Plot the residuals versus X_{2i}.

d. Plot the residuals versus time.

e. In the residual plots created in (a) through (d), is there any evidence of a violation of the regression assumptions? Explain.

16.25 In Problem 16.11 on page 384, you used the percentage of alcohol and chlorides to predict wine quality (stored in VinhoVerde).

a. Plot the residuals versus $\hat{Y}_i$

b. Plot the residuals versus X_{1i}.

c. Plot the residuals versus X_{2i}.

d. In the residual plots created in (a) through (c), is there any evidence of a violation of the regression assumptions? Explain.

e. Should you compute the Durbin-Watson statistic for these data? Explain.

16.26 In Problem 16.12 on page 384, you used the total worldwide revenue ($millions) and full-time voluntary turnover (%) stored in BestCompanies to predict the number of full-time jobs added.

a. Perform a residual analysis on your results.

b. If appropriate, perform the Durbin-Watson test, using $\alpha = 0.05$.

c. Are the regression assumptions valid for these data?

16.27 In Problem 16.13 on page 384, you used the total staff present and remote hours to predict standby hours (stored in Standby).

a. Perform a residual analysis on your results.

b. If appropriate, perform the Durbin-Watson test, using $\alpha = 0.05$.

c. Are the regression assumptions valid for these data?

16.28 In Problem 16.14 on page 384, you used the land area of a property and the age of a house to predict the fair market value (stored in GlenCove).

a. Perform a residual analysis on your results.

b. If appropriate, perform the Durbin-Watson test, using $\alpha = 0.05$.

c. Are the regression assumptions valid for these data?

Section 16.4

16.29 Use the following information from a multiple regression model:

$$n = 25 \quad b_1 = 5 \quad b_2 = 10 \quad S_{b_1} = 2 \quad S_{b_2} = 8$$

a. Which variable has the largest slope, in units of a t statistic?

b. Construct a 95% confidence interval estimate of the population slope, β_1.

c. At the 0.05 level of significance, determine whether each independent variable makes a significant contribution to the regression model. On the basis of these results, indicate the independent variables to include in this model.

16.30 Use the following information from a multiple regression model:

$$n = 20 \quad b_1 = 4 \quad b_2 = 3 \quad S_{b_1} = 1.2 \quad S_{b_2} = 0.8$$

a. Which variable has the largest slope, in units of a t statistic?

b. Construct a 95% confidence interval estimate of the population slope, β_1.

c. At the 0.05 level of significance, determine whether each independent variable makes a significant contribution to the regression model. On the basis of these results, indicate the independent variables to include in this model.

16.31 In Problem 16.9 on page 383, you predicted the mean annual revenue for metropolitan areas in the United States, based on the mean age (Age) and mean BizAnalyzer score (BizAnalyzer) for a sample of 25 small business metropolitan areas. Use the following results:

Variable	Coefficient	Standard Error	t Statistic	p-Value
Intercept	$- 680.2357$	1,313.5154	-0.52	0.6097
Age	1.74539	7.85185	0.22	0.8261
BizAnalyzer	20.5265	29.18594	0.70	0.4885

a. Construct a 95% confidence interval estimate of the population slope between mean revenue and mean age.

b. At the 0.05 level of significance, determine whether each independent variable makes a significant contribution to the regression model. On the basis of these results, indicate the independent variables to include in this model.

16.32 In Problem 16.10 on page 384, you used efficiency ratio and total risk-based capital stored in CommunityBanks to predict ROA at a community bank. Using the results from that problem,

a. construct a 95% confidence interval estimate of the population slope between ROA and efficiency ratio.

b. at the 0.05 level of significance, determine whether each independent variable makes a significant contribution to the regression model. On the basis of these results, indicate the independent variables to include in this model.

16.33 In Problem 16.11 on page 384, you used the percentage of alcohol and chlorides to predict wine quality (stored in VinhoVerde). Using the results from that problem,

a. construct a 95% confidence interval estimate of the population slope between wine quality and the percentage of alcohol.

b. at the 0.05 level of significance, determine whether each independent variable makes a significant contribution to the regression model. On the basis of these results, indicate the independent variables to include in this model.

16.34 In Problem 16.10 on page 384, you used the total world-wide revenue ($millions) and full-time voluntary turnover (%) data stored in **BestCompanies** to predict the number of full-time jobs added. Using the results from that problem,

a. construct a 95% confidence interval estimate of the population slope between the number of full-time jobs added and total worldwide revenue.
b. at the 0.05 level of significance, determine whether each independent variable makes a significant contribution to the regression model. On the basis of these results, indicate the independent variables to include in this model.

16.35 In Problem 16.11 on page 384, you used the total number of staff present and remote hours to predict standby hours (stored in **Standby**). Using the results from that problem,

a. construct a 95% confidence interval estimate of the population slope between standby hours and total number of staff present.
b. at the 0.05 level of significance, determine whether each independent variable makes a significant contribution to the regression model. On the basis of these results, indicate the independent variables to include in this model.

16.36 In Problem 16.12 on page 384, you used land area of a property and age of a house to predict the fair market value (stored in **GlenCove**). Using the results from that problem,

a. construct a 95% confidence interval estimate of the population slope between fair market value and land area of a property.
b. at the 0.05 level of significance, determine whether each independent variable makes a significant contribution to the regression model. On the basis of these results, indicate the independent variables to include in this model.

Section 16.5

16.37 Suppose X_1 is a numerical variable and X_2 is a dummy variable with two categories and the regression equation for a sample of $n = 20$ is

$$\hat{Y}_i = 6 + 4X_{1i} + 2X_{2i}$$

a. Interpret the regression coefficient associated with variable X_1.
b. Interpret the regression coefficient associated with variable X_2.

16.38 Suppose that in Problem 16.37, t_{STAT} for testing the contribution of X_2 is 3.27. At the 0.05 level of significance, is there evidence that X_2 makes a significant contribution to the model?

16.39 The chair of the accounting department plans to develop a regression model to predict the grade point average in accounting for those students who are graduating and have completed the accounting major, based on a student's SAT score and whether the student received a grade of B or higher in the introductory statistics course (0 = no and 1 = yes).

a. Explain the steps involved in developing a regression model for these data. Be sure to indicate the particular models you need to evaluate and compare.
b. Suppose the regression coefficient for the variable whether the student received a grade of B or higher in the introductory statistics course is +0.30. How do you interpret this result?

16.40 A real estate association in a suburban community would like to study the relationship between the size of a single-family house (as measured by the number of rooms) and the selling price of the house (in $thousands). Two different neighborhoods are included in the study, one on the east side of the community ($=0$) and the other on the west side ($=1$). A random sample of 20 houses was selected, with the results stored in **Neighbor** . For (a) through (j), do not include an interaction term.

a. State the multiple regression equation that predicts the selling price, based on the number of rooms and the neighborhood.
b. Interpret the regression coefficients in (a).
c. Predict the mean selling price for a house with nine rooms that is located in an east-side neighborhood. Construct a 95% confidence interval estimate and a 95% prediction interval.
d. Perform a residual analysis on the results and determine whether the regression assumptions are valid.
e. Is there a significant relationship between selling price and the two independent variables (rooms and neighborhood) at the 0.05 level of significance?
f. At the 0.05 level of significance, determine whether each independent variable makes a contribution to the regression model. Indicate the most appropriate regression model for this set of data.
g. Construct and interpret a 95% confidence interval estimate of the population slope for the relationship between selling price and number of rooms.
h. Construct and interpret a 95% confidence interval estimate of the population slope for the relationship between selling price and neighborhood.
i. Compute and interpret the adjusted r^2.
j. What assumption do you need to make about the slope of selling price with number of rooms?
k. Add an interaction term to the model and, at the 0.05 level of significance, determine whether it makes a significant contribution to the model.
l. On the basis of the results of (f) and (k), which model is most appropriate? Explain.
m. What conclusions can the real estate association reach about the effect of the number of rooms and neighborhood on the selling price of homes?

16.41 In Problem 16.11 on page 384, you developed a multiple regression model to predict wine quality for red wines. Now, you wish to determine whether there is an effect on wine quality due to whether the wine is white (0) or red (1). These data are organized and stored in **RedandWhite** . Develop a multiple regression model to predict wine quality based on the percentage of alcohol and the type of wine.

For (a) through (l), do not include an interaction term.
a. State the multiple regression equation that predicts wine quality based on the percentage of alcohol and the type of wine.
b. Interpret the regression coefficients in (a).
c. Predict the mean quality for a red wine that has 10% alcohol. Construct a 95% confidence interval estimate and a 95% prediction interval.
d. Perform a residual analysis on the results and determine whether the regression assumptions are valid.
e. Is there a significant relationship between wine quality and the two independent variables (percentage of alcohol and the type of wine) at the 0.05 level of significance?
f. At the 0.05 level of significance, determine whether each independent variable makes a contribution to the regression model. Indicate the most appropriate regression model for this set of data.

g. Construct and interpret 95% confidence interval estimates of the population slope for the relationship between wine quality and the percentage of alcohol and between wine quality and the type of wine.

h. Compare the slope in (b) with the slope for the simple linear regression model of Problem 15.13 on page 306. Explain the difference in the results.

i. Compute and interpret the meaning of the coefficient of multiple determination, r^2.

j. Compute and interpret the adjusted r^2.

k. Compare r^2 with the r^2 value computed in Problem 15.26 (a) on page 308.

l. What assumption about the slope of type of wine with wine quality do you need to make in this problem?

m. Add an interaction term to the model and, at the 0.05 level of significance, determine whether it makes a significant contribution to the model.

n. On the basis of the results of (f) and (m), which model is most appropriate? Explain.

o. What conclusions can you reach concerning the effect of alcohol percentage and type of wine on wine quality?

16.42 In mining engineering, holes are often drilled through rock, using drill bits. As a drill hole gets deeper, additional rods are added to the drill bit to enable additional drilling to take place. It is expected that drilling time increases with depth. This increased drilling time could be caused by several factors, including the mass of the drill rods that are strung together. The business problem relates to whether drilling is faster using dry drilling holes or wet drilling holes. Using dry drilling holes involves forcing compressed air down the drill rods to flush the cuttings and drive the hammer. Using wet drilling holes involves forcing water rather than air down the hole. Data have been collected from a sample of 50 drill holes that contains measurements of the time to drill each additional 5 feet (in minutes), the depth (in feet), and whether the hole was a dry drilling hole or a wet drilling hole. The data are organized and stored in **Drill**. (Data extracted from R. Penner and D. G. Watts, "Mining Information," *The American Statistician*, 45, 1991, pp. 4–9.) Develop a model to predict additional drilling time, based on depth and type of drilling hole (dry or wet). For (a) through (j) do not include an interaction term.

a. State the multiple regression equation.

b. Interpret the regression coefficients in (a).

c. Predict the mean additional drilling time for a dry drilling hole at a depth of 100 feet. Construct a 95% confidence interval estimate and a 95% prediction interval.

d. Perform a residual analysis on the results and determine whether the regression assumptions are valid.

e. Is there a significant relationship between additional drilling time and the two independent variables (depth and type of drilling hole) at the 0.05 level of significance?

f. At the 0.05 level of significance, determine whether each independent variable makes a contribution to the regression model. Indicate the most appropriate regression model for this set of data.

g. Construct a 95% confidence interval estimate of the population slope for the relationship between additional drilling time and depth.

h. Construct a 95% confidence interval estimate of the population slope for the relationship between additional drilling time and the type of hole drilled.

i. Compute and interpret the adjusted r^2.

j. What assumption do you need to make about the slope of additional drilling time with depth?

k. Add an interaction term to the model and, at the 0.05 level of significance, determine whether it makes a significant contribution to the model.

l. On the basis of the results of (f) and (k), which model is most appropriate? Explain.

m. What conclusions can you reach concerning the effect of depth and type of drilling hole on drilling time?

16.43 The owner of a moving company typically has his most experienced manager predict the total number of labor hours that will be required to complete an upcoming move. This approach has proved useful in the past, but the owner has the business objective of developing a more accurate method of predicting labor hours. In a preliminary effort to provide a more accurate method, the owner has decided to use the number of cubic feet moved and whether there is an elevator in the apartment building as the independent variables and has collected data for 36 moves in which the origin and destination were within the borough of Manhattan in New York City and the travel time was an insignificant portion of the hours worked. The data are organized and stored in **Moving**. For (a) through (j), do not include an interaction term.

a. State the multiple regression equation for predicting labor hours, using the number of cubic feet moved and whether there is an elevator.

b. Interpret the regression coefficients in (a).

c. Predict the mean labor hours for moving 500 cubic feet in an apartment building that has an elevator and construct a 95% confidence interval estimate and a 95% prediction interval.

d. Perform a residual analysis on the results and determine whether the regression assumptions are valid.

e. Is there a significant relationship between labor hours and the two independent variables (cubic feet moved and whether there is an elevator in the apartment building) at the 0.05 level of significance?

f. At the 0.05 level of significance, determine whether each independent variable makes a contribution to the regression model. Indicate the most appropriate regression model for this set of data.

g. Construct a 95% confidence interval estimate of the population slope for the relationship between labor hours and cubic feet moved.

h. Construct a 95% confidence interval estimate for the relationship between labor hours and the presence of an elevator.

i. Compute and interpret the adjusted r^2.

j. What assumption do you need to make about the slope of labor hours with cubic feet moved?

k. Add an interaction term to the model, and at the 0.05 level of significance, determine whether it makes a significant contribution to the model.

l. On the basis of the results of (f) and (k), which model is most appropriate? Explain.

m. What conclusions can you reach concerning the effect of the number of cubic feet moved and whether there is an elevator on labor hours?

16.44 In Problem 16.10 on page 384, you used efficiency ratio and total risk-based capital stored in **CommunityBanks** to predict ROA at a community bank. Develop a regression model to predict

ROA that includes efficiency ratio, total risk-based capital, and the interaction of efficiency ratio and total risk-based capital.

a. At the 0.05 level of significance, is there evidence that the interaction term makes a significant contribution to the model?

b. Which regression model is more appropriate, the one used in (a) or the one used in Problem 16.10? Explain.

16.45 Zagat's publishes restaurant ratings for various locations in the United States. The file **Restaurants** contains the Zagat rating for food, décor, service, and cost per person for a sample of 50 restaurants located in a city and 50 restaurants located in a suburb. (Data extracted from *Zagat Survey 2013, New York City Restaurants*; and *Zagat Survey 2012–2013, Long Island Restaurants*.) Develop a regression model to predict the cost per person, based on a variable that represents the sum of the ratings for food, décor, and service and a dummy variable concerning location (city versus suburban). For (a) through (l), do not include an interaction term.

a. State the multiple regression equation.

b. Interpret the regression coefficients in (a).

c. Predict the mean cost at a restaurant with a summated rating of 60 that is located in a city and construct a 95% confidence interval estimate and a 95% prediction interval.

d. Perform a residual analysis on the results and determine whether the regression assumptions are satisfied.

e. Is there a significant relationship between price and the two independent variables (summated rating and location) at the 0.05 level of significance?

f. At the 0.05 level of significance, determine whether each independent variable makes a contribution to the regression model. Indicate the most appropriate regression model for this set of data.

g. Construct a 95% confidence interval estimate of the population slope for the relationship between cost and summated rating.

h. Compare the slope in (b) with the slope for the simple linear regression model of Problem 15.14 on page 306. Explain the difference in the results.

i. Compute and interpret the meaning of the coefficient of multiple determination.

j. Compute and interpret the adjusted r^2.

k. Compare r^2 with the r^2 value computed in Problem 15.16 (b) on page 307.

l. What assumption about the slope of cost with summated rating do you need to make in this problem?

m. Add an interaction term to the model and, at the 0.05 level of significance, determine whether it makes a significant contribution to the model.

n. On the basis of the results of (f) and (m), which model is most appropriate? Explain.

o. What conclusions can you reach about the effect of the summated rating and the location of the restaurant on the cost of a meal?

16.46 In Problem 16.12 on page 384, you used the total worldwide revenue ($millions) and full-time voluntary turnover (%) data stored in **BestCompanies** to predict number of full-time jobs added. Develop a regression model to predict the number of full-time jobs added that includes full-time voluntary turnover, total worldwide revenue, and the interaction of full-time voluntary turnover and total worldwide revenue.

a. At the 0.05 level of significance, is there evidence that the interaction term makes a significant contribution to the model?

b. Which regression model is more appropriate, the one used in this problem or the one used in Problem 16.12? Explain.

16.47 In Problem 16.11 on page 384, the percentage of alcohol and chlorides were used to predict the quality of red wines (stored in **VinhoVerde**). Develop a regression model that includes the percentage of alcohol, the chlorides, and the interaction of the percentage of alcohol and the chlorides to predict wine quality.

a. At the 0.05 level of significance, is there evidence that the interaction term makes a significant contribution to the model?

b. Which regression model is more appropriate, the one used in this problem or the one used in Problem 16.11? Explain.

16.48 In Problem 16.13 on page 384, you used the total staff present and remote hours to predict standby hours stored in **Standby**. Develop a regression model to predict standby hours that includes total staff present, remote hours, and the interaction of total staff present and remote hours.

a. At the 0.05 level of significance, is there evidence that the interaction term makes a significant contribution to the model?

b. Which regression model is more appropriate, the one used in this problem or the one used in Problem 16.13? Explain.

Review

16.49 Increasing customer satisfaction typically results in increased purchase behavior. For many products, there is more than one measure of customer satisfaction. In many, purchase behavior can increase dramatically with an increase in just one of the customer satisfaction measures. Gunst and Barry ("One Way to Moderate Ceiling Effects," *Quality Progress*, October 2003, pp. 83–85) consider a product with two satisfaction measures, X_1 and X_2, that range from the lowest level of satisfaction, 1, to the highest level of satisfaction, 7. The dependent variable, Y, is a measure of purchase behavior, with the highest value generating the most sales. Consider the regression equation:

$$\hat{Y}_i = -3.888 + 1.449X_{1i} + 1.462X_{2i} - 0.190X_{1i}X_{2i}$$

Suppose that X_1 is the perceived quality of the product and X_2 is the perceived value of the product. (Note: If the customer thinks the product is overpriced, he or she perceives it to be of low value and vice versa.)

a. What is the predicted purchase behavior when $X_1 = 2$ and $X_2 = 2$?

b. What is the predicted purchase behavior when $X_1 = 2$ and $X_2 = 7$?

c. What is the predicted purchase behavior when $X_1 = 7$ and $X_2 = 2$?

d. What is the predicted purchase behavior when $X_1 = 7$ and $X_2 = 7$?

e. What is the regression equation when $X_2 = 2$? What is the slope for X_1 now?

f. What is the regression equation when $X_2 = 7$? What is the slope for X_1 now?

g. What is the regression equation when $X_1 = 2$? What is the slope for X_2 now?

h. What is the regression equation when $X_1 = 7$? What is the slope for X_2 now?

i. Discuss the implications of (a) through (h) in the context of increasing sales for this product with two customer satisfaction measures.

16.50 The owner of a moving company typically has his most experienced manager predict the total number of labor hours that will be required to complete an upcoming move. This approach has proved useful in the past, but the owner has the business objective of developing a more accurate method of predicting labor hours. In a preliminary effort to provide a more accurate method, the owner has decided to use the number of cubic feet moved and the number of pieces of large furniture as the independent variables and has collected data for 36 moves in which the origin and destination were within the borough of Manhattan in New York City and the travel time was an insignificant portion of the hours worked. The data are organized and stored in Moving .

a. State the multiple regression equation.
b. Interpret the meaning of the slopes in this equation.
c. Predict the mean labor hours for moving 500 cubic feet with two large pieces of furniture.
d. Perform a residual analysis on your results and determine whether the regression assumptions are valid.
e. Determine whether there is a significant relationship between labor hours and the two independent variables (the number of cubic feet moved and the number of pieces of large furniture) at the 0.05 level of significance.
f. Determine the p-value in (e) and interpret its meaning.
g. Interpret the meaning of the coefficient of multiple determination in this problem.
h. Determine the adjusted r^2.
i. At the 0.05 level of significance, determine whether each independent variable makes a significant contribution to the regression model. Indicate the most appropriate regression model for this set of data.
j. Determine the p-values in (i) and interpret their meaning.
k. Construct a 95% confidence interval estimate of the population slope between labor hours and the number of cubic feet moved. How does the interpretation of the slope here differ from that in Problem 15.53 on page 310?
l. What conclusions can you reach concerning labor hours?

16.51 Professional basketball has truly become a sport that generates interest among fans around the world. More and more players come from outside the United States to play in the National Basketball Association (NBA). You want to develop a regression model to predict the number of wins achieved by each NBA team, based on field goal (shots made) percentage and three-point field goal percentage for the team. The data are stored in NBA .
a. State the multiple regression equation.
b. Interpret the meaning of the slopes in this equation.
c. Predict the mean number of wins for a team that has a field goal percentage of 45% and a three-point field goal percentage of 37%.
d. Perform a residual analysis on your results and determine whether the regression assumptions are valid.
e. Is there a significant relationship between number of wins and the two independent variables (field goal percentage and three-point field goal percentage for the team) at the 0.05 level of significance?
f. Determine the p-value in (e) and interpret its meaning.
g. Interpret the meaning of the coefficient of multiple determination in this problem.
h. Determine the adjusted r^2.

i. At the 0.05 level of significance, determine whether each independent variable makes a significant contribution to the regression model. Indicate the most appropriate regression model for this set of data.
j. Determine the p-values in (i) and interpret their meaning.
k. What conclusions can you reach concerning field goal percentage and three-point field goal percentage in predicting the number of wins?

16.52 A sample of 30 houses recently listed for sale in Silver Spring, Maryland, was selected with the objective of developing a model to predict the assessed value (in $thousands), using the size of the house (in thousands of square feet) and age (in years). The results are stored in Silver Spring .
a. Fit a multiple regression model.
b. Interpret the meaning of the slopes in this model.
c. Predict the mean assessed value for a house that has 2,000 square feet and is 55 years old.
d. Perform a residual analysis on your results and determine whether the regression assumptions are valid.
e. Determine whether there is a significant relationship between assessed value and the two independent variables (house size and age) at the 0.05 level of significance.
f. Determine the p-value in (e) and interpret its meaning.
g. Interpret the meaning of the coefficient of multiple determination in this problem.
h. Determine the adjusted r^2.
i. At the 0.05 level of significance, determine whether each independent variable makes a significant contribution to the regression model. Indicate the most appropriate regression model for this set of data.
j. Determine the p-values in (i) and interpret their meaning.
k. Construct a 95% confidence interval estimate of the population slope between assessed value and the size of the house. How does the interpretation of the slope here differ from that in Problem 15.76 on page 314?
l. What conclusions can you reach about the assessed value?

16.53 Measuring the height of a California redwood tree is very difficult because these trees grow to heights over 300 feet. People familiar with these trees understand that the height of a California redwood tree is related to other characteristics of the tree, including the diameter of the tree at the breast height of a person (in inches) and the thickness of the bark of the tree (in inches). The file Redwood contains the height, diameter at breast height of a person, and bark thickness for a sample of 21 California redwood trees.
a. State the multiple regression equation that predicts the height of a tree, based on the tree's diameter at breast height and the thickness of the bark.
b. Interpret the meaning of the slopes in this equation.
c. Predict the mean height for a tree that has a breast height diameter of 25 inches and a bark thickness of 2 inches.
d. Interpret the meaning of the coefficient of multiple determination in this problem.
e. Perform a residual analysis on the results and determine whether the regression assumptions are valid.
f. Determine whether there is a significant relationship between the height of redwood trees and the two independent variables (breast-height diameter and bark thickness) at the 0.05 level of significance.

g. Construct a 95% confidence interval estimate of the population slope between the height of redwood trees and breast-height diameter and between the height of redwood trees and the bark thickness.

h. At the 0.05 level of significance, determine whether each independent variable makes a significant contribution to the regression model. Indicate the independent variables to include in this model.

i. Construct a 95% confidence interval estimate of the mean height for trees that have a breast-height diameter of 25 inches and a bark thickness of 2 inches, along with a prediction interval for an individual tree.

j. What conclusions can you reach concerning the effect of the diameter of the tree and the thickness of the bark on the height of the tree?

16.54 A sample of 30 houses recently listed for sale in Silver Spring, Maryland, was selected with the objective of developing a model to predict the taxes (in $) based on the assessed value of houses (in $thousands) and the age of the houses (in years) (stored in SilverSpring):

a. State the multiple regression equation.

b. Interpret the meaning of the slopes in this equation.

c. Predict the mean taxes for a house that has an assessed value of $400,000 and is 50 years old.

d. Perform a residual analysis on the results and determine whether the regression assumptions are valid.

e. Determine whether there is a significant relationship between taxes and the two independent variables (assessed value and age) at the 0.05 level of significance.

f. Determine the p-value in (e) and interpret its meaning.

g. Interpret the meaning of the coefficient of multiple determination in this problem.

h. Determine the adjusted r^2.

i. At the 0.05 level of significance, determine whether each independent variable makes a significant contribution to the regression model. Indicate the most appropriate regression model for this set of data.

j. Determine the p-values in (i) and interpret their meaning.

k. Construct a 95% confidence interval estimate of the population slope between taxes and assessed value. How does the interpretation of the slope here differ from that of Problem 15.77 on page 314?

l. The real estate assessor's office has been publicly quoted as saying that the age of a house has no bearing on its taxes. Based on your answers to (a) through (k), do you agree with this statement? Explain.

16.55 A baseball analytics specialist wants to determine which variables are important in predicting a team's wins in a given season. He has collected data related to wins, earned run average (ERA), and runs scored per game in a recent season (stored in Baseball). Develop a model to predict the number of wins based on ERA and runs scored per game.

a. State the multiple regression equation.

b. Interpret the meaning of the slopes in this equation.

c. Predict the mean number of wins for a team that has an ERA of 4.00 and has scored 4.0 runs per game.

d. Perform a residual analysis on the results and determine whether the regression assumptions are valid.

e. Is there a significant relationship between the number of wins and the two independent variables (ERA and runs scored per game) at the 0.05 level of significance?

f. Determine the p-value in (e) and interpret its meaning.

g. Interpret the meaning of the coefficient of multiple determination in this problem.

h. Determine the adjusted r^2.

i. At the 0.05 level of significance, determine whether each independent variable makes a significant contribution to the regression model. Indicate the most appropriate regression model for this set of data.

j. Determine the p-values in (i) and interpret their meaning.

k. Construct a 95% confidence interval estimate of the population slope between wins and ERA.

l. Which is more important in predicting wins—pitching, as measured by ERA, or offense, as measured by runs scored per game? Explain.

16.56 Referring to Problem 16.55, suppose that in addition to using ERA to predict the number of wins, the analytics specialist wants to include the league (0 = American, 1 = National) as an independent variable. Develop a model to predict wins based on ERA and league. For (a) through (j), do not include an interaction term.

a. State the multiple regression equation.

b. Interpret the slopes in (a).

c. Predict the mean number of wins for a team with an ERA of 4.00 in the American League. Construct a 95% confidence interval estimate for all teams and a 95% prediction interval for an individual team.

d. Perform a residual analysis on the results and determine whether the regression assumptions are valid.

e. Is there a significant relationship between wins and the two independent variables (ERA and league) at the 0.05 level of significance?

f. At the 0.05 level of significance, determine whether each independent variable makes a contribution to the regression model. Indicate the most appropriate regression model for this set of data.

g. Construct a 95% confidence interval estimate of the population slope for the relationship between wins and ERA.

h. Construct a 95% confidence interval estimate of the population slope for the relationship between wins and league.

i. Compute and interpret the adjusted r^2.

j. What assumption do you have to make about the slope of wins with ERA?

k. Add an interaction term to the model and, at the 0.05 level of significance, determine whether it makes a significant contribution to the model.

l. On the basis of the results of (f) and (k), which model is most appropriate? Explain.

16.57 You are a real estate broker who wants to compare property values in Glen Cove and Roslyn (which are located approximately 8 miles apart). In order to do so, you will analyze the data in GCRoslyn , a file that includes samples of houses from Glen Cove and Roslyn. Making sure to include the dummy variable for location (Glen Cove or Roslyn), develop a regression model to predict fair market value, based on the land area of a property, the age of a house, and location. Be sure to determine whether any interaction terms need to be included in the model.

16.58 The list of Best Small Companies in America features a group with strong earnings growth across industries. A business analyst wishes to determine the relationship between earnings per share growth (%) and sales growth (%) and return on equity (%). Data were collected on 100 small companies and stored in SmallBusinesses . (Data extracted from "America's Best Small Companies," **forbes.com/best-small-companies/list/**.)

Develop a multiple regression model that uses sales growth and return on equity to predict earnings per share growth. Be sure to perform a thorough residual analysis.

16.59 Starbucks Coffee Co. uses a data-based approach to improving the quality and customer satisfaction of its products. When survey data indicated that Starbucks needed to improve its package-sealing process, an experiment was conducted to determine the factors in the bag-sealing equipment that might be affecting the ease of opening the bag without tearing the inner liner of the bag. (Data extracted from L. Johnson and S. Burrows, "For Starbucks, It's in the Bag," *Quality Progress*, March 2011, pp. 17–23.) Among the factors that could affect the rating of the ability of the bag to resist tears were the viscosity, pressure, and plate gap on the bag-sealing equipment. Data were collected on 19 bags in which the plate gap was varied. The results are stored in Starbucks . Develop a multiple regression model that uses the viscosity, pressure, and plate gap on the bag-sealing equipment to predict the tear rating of the bag. Be sure to perform a thorough residual analysis. Do you think that you need to use all three independent variables in the model? Explain.

16.60 An experiment was conducted to study the extrusion process of biodegradable packaging foam. Among the factors considered for their effect on the unit density (mg/ml) were the die temperature (145°C versus 155°C) and the die diameter (3 mm versus 4 mm). The results were stored in PackagingFoam3 . (Data extracted from W. Y. Koh, K. M. Eskridge, and M. A. Hanna, "Supersaturated Split-Plot Designs," *Journal of Quality Technology*, 45, January 2013, pp. 61–72.) Develop a multiple regression model that uses die temperature and die diameter to predict the unit density (mg/ml). Be sure to perform a thorough residual analysis. Do you think that you need to use both independent variables in the model? Explain.

16.61 Referring to Problem 16.60, instead of predicting the unit density, you now wish to predict the foam diameter from results stored in PackagingFoam4 . Develop a multiple regression model that uses die temperature and die diameter to predict the foam diameter (mg/ml). Be sure to perform a thorough residual analysis. Do you think that you need to use both independent variables in the model? Explain.

CASES FOR CHAPTER 16

Managing Ashland MultiComm Services

In its continuing study of the *3-For-All* subscription solicitation process, a marketing department team wants to test the effects of two types of structured sales presentations (personal formal and personal informal) and the number of hours spent on telemarketing on the number of new subscriptions. The staff has recorded these data for the past 24 weeks in AMS16 .

Analyze these data and develop a multiple regression model to predict the number of new subscriptions for a week, based on the number of hours spent on telemarketing and the sales presentation type. Write a report, giving detailed findings concerning the regression model used.

Digital Case

Apply your knowledge of multiple regression models in this Digital Case, which extends the OmniFoods Using Statistics scenario from this chapter.

To ensure a successful test marketing of its OmniPower energy bars, the OmniFoods marketing department has contracted with In-Store Placements Group (ISPG), a merchandising consulting firm. ISPG will work with the grocery store chain that is conducting the test-market study. Using the same 34-store sample used in the test-market study, ISPG claims that the choice of shelf location and the presence of in-store OmniPower coupon dispensers both increase sales of the energy bars.

Open **Omni_ISPGMemo.pdf** to review the ISPG claims and supporting data. Then answer the following questions:

1. Are the supporting data consistent with ISPG's claims? Perform an appropriate statistical analysis to confirm (or discredit) the stated relationship between sales and the two independent variables of product shelf location and the presence of in-store OmniPower coupon dispensers.

2. If you were advising OmniFoods, would you recommend using a specific shelf location and in-store coupon dispensers to sell OmniPower bars?

3. What additional data would you advise collecting in order to determine the effectiveness of the sales promotion techniques used by ISPG?

CHAPTER 16 SPSS GUIDE

SPSS—VERSION 16—MULTIPLE REGRESSION

Suppose the professor wanted to develop a model to predict the students' marks at the end of the QMS 202 course as measured in percentage based on how frequently they missed class, number of problems solved, total hours spent studying, and how frequently they sought help from the teaching assistant.

The dependent variable, Y, is the final QMS 202 marks (in percentage). Three independent variables are the following:

- Number of lectures missed during the semester (X_1)
- Total number of problems solved (X_2)
- Total hours spent per week studying for QMS 202 (X_3)
- Total number of times the student sought the teaching assistant's help (X_4)

A random sample of 35 students who enrolled in the QMS 202 course was selected with the results shown in Table 16.4.

TABLE 16.3

Data for Multiple Regression Model to Predict QMS202 Marks

Student	y = QMS 202 Marks	X1 = Number of lectures missed during the semester	X2 = Total number of problems solved	X3 = Total hours spent studying for QMS 202	X4 = Total number of times the student sought the teaching assistant's help
1	90	0	100	24.2	11
2	60	5	20	5.3	2
3	45	9	5	1.2	0
4	85	1	50	11.5	5
5	72	3	45	8.6	6
6	96	1	110	22.3	12
7	50	6	10	3.5	4
8	65	3	34	7.8	5
9	87	2	78	10.4	11
10	88	1	77	11.6	10
11	78	2	50	9.2	8
12	73	3	49	10.3	10
13	59	5	22	6.4	4
14	49	7	6	2.6	0
15	94	0	110	25.4	12
16	55	4	21	4.5	5
17	52	5	20	5.8	3
18	63	3	40	8.9	4

(continued)

19	51	6	20	4.0	3
20	93	1	107	19.1	12
21	50	7	15	3.3	5
22	65	4	30	6.4	4
23	87	1	80	11.6	12
24	88	0	87	12.2	11
25	78	1	55	10.1	9
26	73	4	51	14.2	11
27	56	6	30	5.5	3
28	44	9	3	1.6	0
29	95	0	115	23.8	12
30	56	7	27	3.9	4
31	52	6	24	3.4	5
32	63	5	46	5.5	2
33	56	8	23	3.7	1
34	98	0	150	23.8	12
35	71	1	48	3.9	6

Performing a multiple regression on SPSS—Version 16

Step 1: Open the SPSS Data Editor.

Click **cancel** to cancel the SPSS opening window.

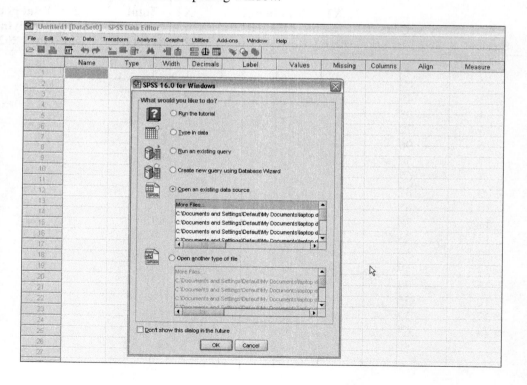

Step 2: Define the variables and give the variables a label.

Click **Variable View** (at the bottom of the window) to go to the variable view window to define the variables and fix the data at zero or one decimal places.

- Give variable name—"student" to trace the respondent's responses if there is a data entry error.
- Give variable name—"y" and label it as "QMS 202 Marks."
- Give variable name—"x1" and label it as "Number of lectures missed during the semester."
- Give variable name—"x2" and label it as "Total number of problems solved."
- Give variable name—"x3" and label it as "Total hours spent studying for QMS 202."
- Give variable name—"x4" and label it as "Total number of times the student seeks the teaching assistant's help."

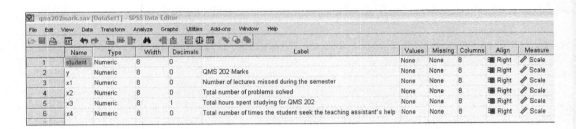

Step 3: Create an SPSS data file.

Click **Data View** to return to the data view window. Now, enter the raw data (in Table 16.4) into the appropriate columns of variables.

	student	y	x1	x2	x3	x4
1	1	90	0	100	24.2	11
2	2	60	5	20	5.3	2
3	3	45	9	5	1.2	0
4	4	85	1	50	11.5	5
5	5	72	3	45	8.6	6
6	6	96	1	110	22.3	12
7	7	50	6	10	3.5	4
8	8	65	3	34	7.8	5
9	9	87	2	78	10.4	11
10	10	88	1	77	11.6	10
11	11	78	2	50	9.2	8
12	12	73	3	49	10.3	10
13	13	59	5	22	6.4	4
14	14	49	7	6	2.6	0
15	15	94	0	110	25.4	12
16	16	55	4	21	4.5	5
17	17	52	5	20	5.8	3
18	18	63	3	40	8.9	4
19	19	51	6	20	4.0	3
20	20	93	1	107	19.1	12
21	21	50	7	15	3.3	5
22	22	65	4	30	6.4	4
23	23	87	1	80	11.6	12
24	24	88	0	87	12.2	11
25	25	78	1	55	10.1	9
26	26	73	4	51	14.2	11
27	27	56	6	30	5.5	3
28	28	44	9	3	1.6	0
29	29	95	0	115	23.8	12
30	30	56	7	27	3.9	4
31	31	52	6	24	3.4	5

After you have entered all the data, save the file as "qms202mark.sav" (or any filename).

Step 4: Perform regression analysis.

Make the following menu selections:

Analyze → Regression → Linear

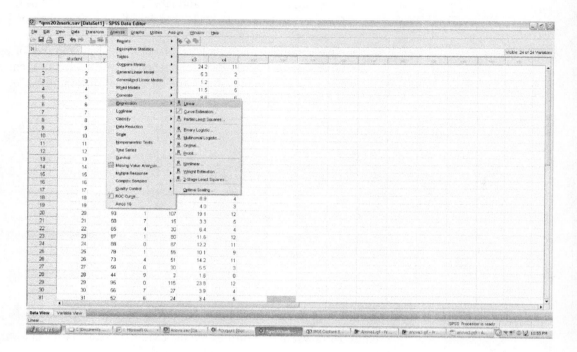

At this point, the **Linear Regression** dialog box will appear. Make these entries in the **Linear Regression** dialog box:

- Highlight the **QMS 202 Marks** variable and click the arrow key. The variable will automatically fall into the **Dependent** box (→).
- Highlight each x_1, x_2, x_3, and x_4 variable and click the arrow key. The variable will fall into the **Independent(s)** box (→).
- Click the **Enter** button next to the **Method.** Select **stepwise** as the method to develop several multiple regression models.

Note: The **Stepwise** method uses a step-by-step algorithm that starts building a regression model with one independent variable. At each step the algorithm checks to see if any of the variables (already included in the model) can be removed and adds a variable (not yet included in the model) by examining the fit of the model. The algorithm stops when there are no more significant independent variables to be considered.

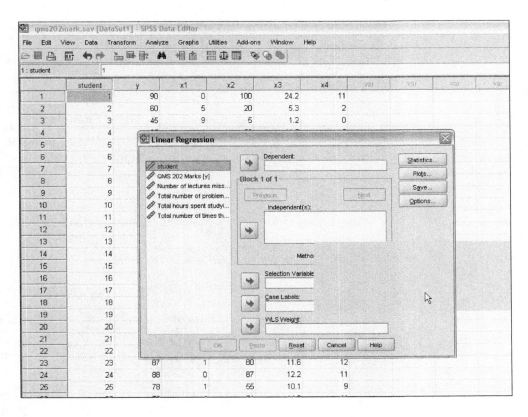

- *Obtaining Predictions and Residuals*   Click the save button (note that **Save** is a button on the pop-up menu and is not the usual File save option) and the **save** dialog box will pop up. In the **save** dialog box, click on **Unstandardized** in the the **Predicted Values** box. Click on **Unstandardized** in the **Residuals** box. Click on **Mean** and **Individual** in the **Prediction Intervals** box. Click on **Continue** to return to the **Linear Regression** dialog box. Then click **OK.**

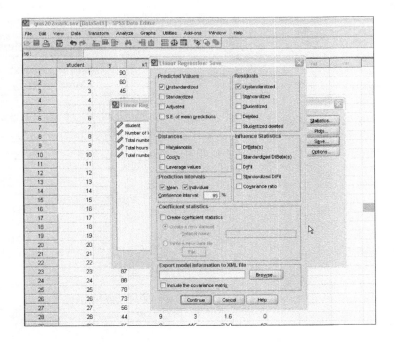

Step 5: Go to SPSS Viewer to obtain your SPSS results.

SPSS output:
Regression

Model Summary[c]

Model	R	R Square	Adjusted R Square	Std. Error of the Estimate
1	.948[a]	.898	.895	5.541
2	.975[b]	.952	.949	3.874

a. Predictors: (Constant), Total number of problems solved
b. Predictors: (Constant), Total number of problems solved, Number of lectures missed during the semester
c. Dependent Variable: QMS 202 Marks

ANOVA[c]

	Model	Sum of Squares	df	Mean Square	F	Sig.
1	Regression	8906.850	1	8906.850	290.062	.000[a]
	Residual	1013.322	33	30.707		
	Total	9920.171	34			
2	Regression	9439.916	2	4719.958	314.497	.000[b]
	Residual	480.255	32	15.008		
	Total	9920.171	34			

a. Predictors: (Constant), Total number of problems solved
b. Predictors: (Constant), Total number of problems solved, Number of lectures missed during the semester
c. Dependent Variable: QMS 202 Marks

Coefficients[a]

	Model	Unstandardized Coefficients		Standardized Coefficients		
		B	Std. Error	Beta	t	Sig.
1	(Constant)	47.864	1.584		30.208	.000
	Total number of problems solved	.433	.025	.948	17.031	.000
2	(Constant)	66.176	3.266		20.261	.000
	Total number of problems solved	.262	.034	.574	7.781	.000
	Number of lectures missed during the semester	−2.703	.454	−.440	−5.960	.000

a. Dependent Variable: QMS 202 Marks

Obtaining Predictions and Residuals

The confidence interval values and prediction interval values are displayed on the **SPSS Data Editor** under the variables PRE_1, RES_1, LMCI_1, UMCI_1, LICI_1 and UICI_1.

Notation:

PRE_1—Unstandardized Predicted (for Model 1)

RES_1—Unstandardized Residual (for Model 1)

LMCI_1—95% Lower Confidence Interval for y mean (for Model 1)

UMCI_1—95% Upper Confidence Interval for y mean (for Model 1)

LICI_1—95% Lower Confidence Interval for y individual (for Model 1)

UICI_1—5% Upper Confidence Interval for y individual (for Model 1)

*qns202mark.sav [DataSet1] - SPSS Data Editor

	student	y	x1	x2	x3	x4	PRE_1	RES_1	LMCI_1	UMCI_1	LICI_1	UICI_1
1	1	90	0	100	24.2	11	92.42439	-2.42439	90.14242	94.70635	84.20995	100.63882
2	2	60	5	20	5.3	2	57.90953	2.09047	56.12041	59.69865	49.81814	66.00091
3	3	45	9	5	1.2	0	43.15942	1.84058	40.00047	46.31836	34.65951	51.65933
4	4	85	1	50	11.5	5	76.59692	8.40308	73.83760	79.35623	68.23729	84.95654
5	5	72	3	45	8.6	6	69.87807	2.12193	68.27996	71.47619	61.82677	77.92938
6	6	96	1	110	22.3	12	92.34603	3.65397	89.57978	95.11228	83.98411	100.70795
7	7	50	6	10	3.5	4	52.58147	-2.58147	50.60136	54.56157	44.44572	60.71721
8	8	65	3	34	7.6	5	66.99074	-1.99074	64.89777	69.08370	58.82679	75.15468
9	9	87	2	78	10.4	11	81.24329	5.75671	79.56637	82.92022	73.17598	89.31061
10	10	88	1	77	11.6	10	83.68402	4.31598	81.83363	85.53440	75.57887	91.78917
11	11	78	2	50	9.2	8	73.89371	4.10629	71.89270	75.89472	65.75295	82.03457
12	12	73	3	49	10.3	10	70.92801	2.07199	69.45388	72.40215	62.90040	78.95563
13	13	59	5	22	6.4	4	58.43450	0.56550	56.71665	60.15234	50.35857	66.51042
14	14	49	7	6	2.6	0	48.82832	0.17168	46.66977	50.98687	40.64731	57.00933
15	15	94	0	110	25.4	12	95.04924	-1.04924	92.50056	97.59792	86.75675	103.34172
16	16	55	4	21	4.5	5	60.87522	-5.87522	58.70999	63.04045	52.69245	69.05799
17	17	52	6	20	5.8	3	57.90953	-5.90953	56.12041	59.69865	49.81814	66.00091
18	18	63	3	40	8.9	4	68.96565	-5.96565	66.76493	70.36636	60.47169	76.65960
19	19	51	6	20	4.0	3	55.20632	-4.20632	53.42214	56.99050	47.11603	63.29661
20	20	93	1	107	19.1	12	91.55857	1.44143	88.94270	94.17445	83.24519	99.87196
21	21	50	7	15	3.3	5	51.19068	-1.19068	49.04963	53.33174	43.01428	59.36709
22	22	65	4	30	6.4	4	63.23759	1.76241	61.51281	64.96237	55.16019	71.31499
23	23	87	1	80	11.6	12	84.47147	2.52853	82.63208	86.31086	76.36882	92.57412
24	24	88	0	87	12.2	11	89.01208	-1.01208	86.78951	91.23565	80.81367	97.21048
25	25	78	1	55	10.1	9	77.90934	0.09066	75.39568	80.42301	69.62755	86.19113
26	26	73	4	51	14.2	11	68.74978	4.25022	67.35271	70.14685	60.73595	76.76360
27	27	56	6	30	5.5	3	57.83117	-1.83117	55.98994	59.67241	49.72810	65.93424
28	28	44	9	3	1.6	0	42.63445	1.36555	39.52208	45.74682	34.16173	51.11716
29	29	95	0	115	23.8	12	96.36166	-1.36166	93.62413	99.09920	88.00920	104.71413
30	30	56	7	27	3.9	4	54.34051	1.65949	51.95856	56.72246	46.09774	62.59328
31	31	52	6	24	3.4	5	56.25626	-4.25626	54.48067	58.03185	48.16786	64.34466

Data View / Variable View

Appendices

A. BASIC MATH CONCEPTS AND SYMBOLS

A.1 Rules for Arithmetic Operations
A.2 Rules for Algebra: Exponents and Square Roots
A.3 Rules for Logarithms
A.4 Summation Notation
A.5 Statistical Symbols
A.6 Greek Alphabet

B. ONLINE RESOURCES

B.1 About the Online Resources for This Book
B.2 Accessing the Online Resources
B.3 Details of Downloadable Files
B.4 PHStat

C. TABLES

C.1 Table of Random Numbers
C.2 The Cumulative Standardized Normal Distribution
C.3 Critical Values of t
C.4 Critical Values of χ^2
C.5 Critical Values of F
C.6 Critical Values of the Studentized Range, Q
C.7 Critical Values, d_L and d_U, of the Durbin-Watson Statistic, D
C.8 Control Chart Factors
C.9 The Standardized Normal Distribution

SELF-TEST SOLUTIONS AND ANSWERS TO SELECTED EVEN-NUMBERED PROBLEMS

APPENDIX A Basic Math Concepts and Symbols

A.1 Rules for Arithmetic Operations

RULE	EXAMPLE
1. $a + b = c$ and $b + a = c$	$2 + 1 = 3$ and $1 + 2 = 3$
2. $a + (b + c) = (a + b) + c$	$5 + (7 + 4) = (5 + 7) + 4 = 16$
3. $a - b = c$ but $b - a \neq c$	$9 - 7 = 2$ but $7 - 9 \neq 2$
4. $(a)(b) = (b)(a)$	$(7)(6) = (6)(7) = 42$
5. $(a)(b + c) = ab + ac$	$(2)(3 + 5) = (2)(3) + (2)(5) = 16$
6. $a \div b \neq b \div a$	$12 \div 3 \neq 3 \div 12$
7. $\dfrac{a + b}{c} = \dfrac{a}{c} + \dfrac{b}{c}$	$\dfrac{7 + 3}{2} = \dfrac{7}{2} + \dfrac{3}{2} = 5$
8. $\dfrac{a}{b + c} \neq \dfrac{a}{b} + \dfrac{a}{c}$	$\dfrac{3}{4 + 5} \neq \dfrac{3}{4} + \dfrac{3}{5}$
9. $\dfrac{1}{a} + \dfrac{1}{b} = \dfrac{b + a}{ab}$	$\dfrac{1}{3} + \dfrac{1}{5} = \dfrac{5 + 3}{(3)(5)} = \dfrac{8}{15}$
10. $\left(\dfrac{a}{b}\right)\left(\dfrac{c}{d}\right) = \left(\dfrac{ac}{bd}\right)$	$\left(\dfrac{2}{3}\right)\left(\dfrac{6}{7}\right) = \left(\dfrac{(2)(6)}{(3)(7)}\right) = \dfrac{12}{21}$
11. $\dfrac{a}{b} \div \dfrac{c}{d} = \dfrac{ad}{bc}$	$\dfrac{5}{8} \div \dfrac{3}{7} = \left(\dfrac{(5)(7)}{(8)(3)}\right) = \dfrac{35}{24}$

A.2 Rules for Algebra: Exponents and Square Roots

RULE	EXAMPLE
1. $(X^a)(X^b) = X^{a+b}$	$(4^2)(4^3) = 4^5$
2. $(X^a)^b = X^{ab}$	$(2^2)^3 = 2^6$
3. $(X^a / X^b) = X^{a-b}$	$\dfrac{3^5}{3^3} = 3^2$
4. $\dfrac{X^a}{X^a} = X^0 = 1$	$\dfrac{3^4}{3^4} = 3^0 = 1$
5. $\sqrt{XY} = \sqrt{X}\sqrt{Y}$	$\sqrt{(25)(4)} = \sqrt{25}\sqrt{4} = 10$
6. $\sqrt{\dfrac{X}{Y}} = \dfrac{\sqrt{X}}{\sqrt{Y}}$	$\sqrt{\dfrac{16}{100}} = \dfrac{\sqrt{16}}{\sqrt{100}} = 0.40$

A.3 Rules for Logarithms

Base 10

Log is the symbol used for base-10 logarithms:

RULE	EXAMPLE
1. $\log(10^a) = a$	$\log(100) = \log(10^2) = 2$
2. If $\log(a) = b$, then $a = 10^b$	If $\log(a) = 2$, then $a = 10^2 = 100$
3. $\log(ab) = \log(a) + \log(b)$	$\log(100) = \log[(10)(10)] = \log(10) + \log(10)$ $= 1 + 1 = 2$
4. $\log(a^b) = (b)\log(a)$	$\log(1{,}000) = \log(10^3) = (3)\log(10) = (3)(1) = 3$
5. $\log(a/b) = \log(a) - \log(b)$	$\log(100) = \log(1{,}000/10) = \log(1{,}000) - \log(10)$ $= 3 - 1 = 2$

EXAMPLE

Take the base-10 logarithm of each side of the following equation:

$$Y = \beta_0 \beta_1^X \varepsilon$$

SOLUTION: Apply rules 3 and 4:

$$\log(Y) = \log(\beta_0 \beta_1^X \varepsilon)$$
$$= \log(\beta_0) + \log(\beta_1^X) + \log(\varepsilon)$$
$$= \log(\beta_0) + X\log(\beta_1) + \log(\varepsilon)$$

Base e

ln is the symbol used for base e logarithms, commonly referred to as natural logarithms. e is Euler's number, and $e \cong 2.718282$:

RULE	EXAMPLE
1. $\ln(e^a) = a$	$\ln(7.389056) = \ln(e^2) = 2$
2. If $\ln(a) = b$, then $a = e^b$	If $\ln(a) = 2$, then $a = e^2 = 7.389056$
3. $\ln(ab) = \ln(a) + \ln(b)$	$\ln(100) = \ln[(10)(10)]$ $= \ln(10) + \ln(10) = 2.302585 + 2.302585 = 4.605170$
4. $\ln(a^b) = (b)\ln(a)$	$\ln(1{,}000) = \ln(10^3) = 3\ln(10) = 3(2.302585) = 6.907755$
5. $\ln(a/b) = \ln(a) - \ln(b)$	$\ln(100) = \ln(1{,}000/10) = \ln(1{,}000) - \ln(10)$ $= 6.907755 - 2.302585 = 4.605170$

EXAMPLE

Take the base e logarithm of each side of the following equation:

$$Y = \beta_0 \beta_1^X \varepsilon$$

SOLUTION: Apply rules 3 and 4:

$$\begin{aligned} \ln(Y) &= \ln(\beta_0 \beta_1^X \varepsilon) \\ &= \ln(\beta_0) + \ln(\beta_1^X) + \ln(\varepsilon) \\ &= \ln(\beta_0) + X \ln(\beta_1) + \ln(\varepsilon) \end{aligned}$$

A.4 Summation Notation

The symbol Σ, the Greek capital letter sigma, represents "taking the sum of." Consider a set of n values for variable X. The expression $\sum_{i=1}^{n} X_i$ means to take the sum of the n values for variable X. Thus:

$$\sum_{i=1}^{n} X_i = X_1 + X_2 + X_3 + \cdots + X_n$$

The following problem illustrates the use of the symbol Σ. Consider five values of a variable X: $X_1 = 2, X_2 = 0, X_3 = -1, X_4 = 5$, and $X_5 = 7$. Thus:

$$\sum_{i=1}^{5} X_i = X_1 + X_2 + X_3 + X_4 + X_5 = 2 + 0 + (-1) + 5 + 7 = 13$$

In statistics, the squared values of a variable are often summed. Thus:

$$\sum_{i=1}^{n} X_i^2 = X_1^2 + X_2^2 + X_3^2 + \cdots + X_n^2$$

and, in the example above:

$$\begin{aligned} \sum_{i=1}^{5} X_i^2 &= X_1^2 + X_2^2 + X_3^2 + X_4^2 + X_5^2 \\ &= 2^2 + 0^2 + (-1)^2 + 5^2 + 7^2 \\ &= 4 + 0 + 1 + 25 + 49 \\ &= 79 \end{aligned}$$

$\sum_{i=1}^{n} X_i^2$, the summation of the squares, is *not* the same as $\left(\sum_{i=1}^{n} X_i \right)^2$, the square of the sum:

$$\sum_{i=1}^{n} X_i^2 \neq \left(\sum_{i=1}^{n} X_i \right)^2$$

In the example given above, the summation of squares is equal to 79. This is not equal to the square of the sum, which is $13^2 = 169$.

Another frequently used operation involves the summation of the product. Consider two variables, X and Y, each having n values. Then:

$$\sum_{i=1}^{n} X_i Y_i = X_1 Y_1 + X_2 Y_2 + X_3 Y_3 + \cdots + X_n Y_n$$

Continuing with the previous example, suppose there is a second variable, Y, whose five values are $Y_1 = 1$, $Y_2 = 3$, $Y_3 = -2$, $Y_4 = 4$, and $Y_5 = 3$. Then,

$$\sum_{i=1}^{n} X_i Y_i = X_1 Y_1 + X_2 Y_2 + X_3 Y_3 + X_4 Y_4 + X_5 Y_5$$
$$= (2)(1) + (0)(3) + (-1)(-2) + (5)(4) + (7)(3)$$
$$= 2 + 0 + 2 + 20 + 21$$
$$= 45$$

In computing $\sum_{i=1}^{n} X_i Y_i$, you need to realize that the first value of X is multiplied by the first value of Y, the second value of X is multiplied by the second value of Y, and so on. These products are then summed in order to compute the desired result. However, the summation of products is *not* equal to the product of the individual sums:

$$\sum_{i=1}^{n} X_i Y_i \neq \left(\sum_{i=1}^{n} X_i \right) \left(\sum_{i=1}^{n} Y_i \right)$$

In this example,

$$\sum_{i=1}^{5} X_i = 13$$

and

$$\sum_{i=1}^{5} Y_i = 1 + 3 + (-2) + 4 + 3 = 9$$

so that

$$\left(\sum_{i=1}^{5} X_i \right) \left(\sum_{i=1}^{5} Y_i \right) = (13)(9) = 117$$

However,

$$\sum_{i=1}^{5} X_i Y_i = 45$$

The following table summarizes these results:

VALUE	X_i	Y_i	$X_i Y_i$
1	2	1	2
2	0	3	0
3	-1	-2	2
4	5	4	20
5	7	3	21
	$\sum_{i=1}^{5} X_i = 13$	$\sum_{i=1}^{5} Y_i = 9$	$\sum_{i=1}^{5} X_i Y_i = 45$

Rule 1 The summation of the values of two variables is equal to the sum of the values of each summed variable:

$$\sum_{i=1}^{n} (X_i + Y_i) = \sum_{i=1}^{n} X_i + \sum_{i=1}^{n} Y_i$$

Thus,

$$\sum_{i=1}^{5} (X_i + Y_i) = (2 + 1) + (0 + 3) + (-1 + (-2)) + (5 + 4) + (7 + 3)$$

$$= 3 + 3 + (-3) + 9 + 10$$

$$= 22$$

$$\sum_{i=1}^{5} X_i + \sum_{i=1}^{5} Y_i = 13 + 9 = 22$$

Rule 2   The summation of a difference between the values of two variables is equal to the difference between the summed values of the variables:

$$\sum_{i=1}^{n} (X_i - Y_i) = \sum_{i=1}^{n} X_i - \sum_{i=1}^{n} Y_i$$

Thus,

$$\sum_{i=1}^{5} (X_i - Y_i) = (2 - 1) + (0 - 3) + (-1 - (-2)) + (5 - 4) + (7 - 3)$$

$$= 1 + (-3) + 1 + 1 + 4$$

$$= 4$$

$$\sum_{i=1}^{5} X_i - \sum_{i=1}^{5} Y_i = 13 - 9 = 4$$

Rule 3   The sum of a constant times a variable is equal to that constant times the sum of the values of the variable:

$$\sum_{i=1}^{n} cX_i = c \sum_{i=1}^{n} X_i$$

where c is a constant. Thus, if $c = 2$,

$$\sum_{i=1}^{5} cX_i = \sum_{i=1}^{5} 2X_i = (2)(2) + (2)(0) + (2)(-1) + (2)(5) + (2)(7)$$

$$= 4 + 0 + (-2) + 10 + 14$$

$$= 26$$

$$c \sum_{i=1}^{5} X_i = 2 \sum_{i=1}^{5} X_i = (2)(13) = 26$$

Rule 4   A constant summed n times will be equal to n times the value of the constant.

$$\sum_{i=1}^{n} c = nc$$

where c is a constant. Thus, if the constant $c = 2$ is summed 5 times,

$$\sum_{i=1}^{5} c = 2 + 2 + 2 + 2 + 2 = 10$$

$$nc = (5)(2) = 10$$

EXAMPLE

Suppose there are six values for the variables X and Y, such that $X_1 = 2, X_2 = 1, X_3 = 5, X_4 = -3, X_5 = 1, X_6 = -2$ and $Y_1 = 4, Y_2 = 0, Y_3 = -1, Y_4 = 2, Y_5 = 7,$ and $Y_6 = -3$. Compute each of the following:

(a) $\sum_{i=1}^{6} X_i$ **(b)** $\sum_{i=1}^{6} Y_i$

(continued)

(c) $\displaystyle\sum_{i=1}^{6} X_i^2$

(d) $\displaystyle\sum_{i=1}^{6} Y_i^2$

(e) $\displaystyle\sum_{i=1}^{6} X_i Y_i$

(f) $\displaystyle\sum_{i=1}^{6} (X_i + Y_i)$

(g) $\displaystyle\sum_{i=1}^{6} (X_i - Y_i)$

(h) $\displaystyle\sum_{i=1}^{6} (X_i - 3Y_i + 2X_i^2)$

(i) $\displaystyle\sum_{i=1}^{6} (cX_i)$, where $c = -1$

(j) $\displaystyle\sum_{i=1}^{6} (X_i - 3Y_i + c)$, where $c = +3$

Answers

(a) 4   **(b)** 9   **(c)** 44   **(d)** 79   **(e)** 10   **(f)** (13)   **(g)** -5 **(h)** 65   **(i)** -4 **(j)** -5

REFERENCES

1. Bashaw, W. L. *Mathematics for Statistics.* New York: Wiley, 1969.
2. Lanzer, P. *Basic Math: Fractions, Decimals, Percents.* Hicksville, NY: Video Aided Instruction, 2006.
3. Levine, D. and A. Brandwein *The MBA Primer: Business Statistics*, 3rd ed. Cincinnati, OH: Cengage Publishing, 2011.
4. Levine, D. *Statistics.* Hicksville, NY: Video Aided Instruction, 2006.
5. Shane, H. *Algebra 1.* Hicksville, NY: Video Aided Instruction, 2006.

A.5 Statistical Symbols

$+$	add	$\times$	multiply
$-$	subtract	$\div$	divide
$=$	equal to	$\neq$	not equal to
$\cong$	approximately equal to	$<$	less than
$>$	greater than	$\leq$	less than or equal to
$\geq$	greater than or equal to		

A.6 Greek Alphabet

GREEK LETTER		LETTER NAME	ENGLISH EQUIVALENT	GREEK LETTER		LETTER NAME	ENGLISH EQUIVALENT
A	α	Alpha	a	N	ν	Nu	n
B	β	Beta	b	Ξ	ξ	Xi	x
Γ	γ	Gamma	g	O	o	Omicron	ŏ
Δ	δ	Delta	d	Π	π	Pi	p
E	ε	Epsilon	ĕ	P	ρ	Rho	r
Z	ζ	Zeta	z	Σ	σ	Sigma	s
H	η	Eta	ē	T	τ	Tau	t
Θ	θ	Theta	th	Y	υ	Upsilon	u
I	ι	Iota	i	Φ	ϕ	Phi	ph
K	κ	Kappa	k	X	χ	Chi	ch
Λ	λ	Lambda	l	Ψ	ψ	Psi	ps
M	μ	Mu	m	Ω	ω	Omega	ō

B.1 About the Online Resources for This Book

Online resources support your study of business statistics and your use of this book. Online resources are available from the student download web page or MyStatLab course for this book. Some resources are packaged as a zip archive files. The online resources for this book are:

- **Excel and Minitab Data files** The files that contain the data used in chapter examples, named in problems, or used in the end-of-chapter cases. Section B.3 includes a complete listing of these files and their contents.
- **Excel Guide Workbooks** Excel workbooks that contain templates or model solutions for applying Excel to a particular statistical method. Section B.3 includes a complete listing of these files.
- **Files for the Digital Cases** The set of PDF files that support the end-of-chapter Digital Cases. Some of the Digital Case PDF files contain attached files as well.
- **Online Topics** The set of PDF format files that present additional statistical topics. This set includes the full text of two chapters, "Statistical Applications in Quality Management" and "Decision Making."
- **Short Takes** The set of PDF files that extend the discussion of specific concepts or further document the results presented in the book.
- **Visual Explorations Workbooks** The workbooks that interactively demonstrate various key statistical concepts. See *Visual Explorations* in Section B.3 for additional information.

If you plan to use PHStat, the Pearson Education statistics add-in for Microsoft Excel, see Section B.4.

B.2 Accessing the Online Resources

Online resources for this book are available either on the student download page for this book or inside the MyStatLab course for this book (see Section B.3). To access resources from the student download page for this book:

1. Visit **www.pearsonhighered.com/levine**.
2. In that web page, find the entries for this book, *Business Statistics: A First Course*, seventh edition, and click the student download page link.
3. In the download page, click the link for the desired items. Most items will cause the web browser to prompt

you to save the (zip archive) that you can save and later unzip. Some download links may require an access code (see Section B.2).

To access resources from the MyStatLab course for this book, log into the course and in the left panel of the course page for this book, click **Tools for Success**. On that page, click the link for one of the online resource categories listed in Section B.1.

Using MyStatLab requires an access code. An access code may have been packaged with this book. If your book did not come with an access code, you can obtain one at **mypearson.com**.

B.3 Details of Downloadable Files

Data Files

Throughout this book, the names of data workbooks appear in a special inverted color typeface—for example, Retirement Funds. Data files are stored as worksheets in both the **.xlsx** Excel workbook and the **.mtw** Minitab worksheet file formats. (For files that contain more than one worksheet, Minitab versions are stored as **.mpj** Minitab project files.)

In the following alphabetical list, the variables for each data file are presented in the order of their appearance, starting with first column (A in Excel and C1 in Minitab). Chapter references indicate the chapter or chapters that use the data file in an example or problem. A trailing (E) notes a file exclusive to Excel. A trailing (M) notes a file exclusive to Minitab.

311CALLCENTER Day and abandonment rate (%) (Chapter 4)

ACCOUNTINGPARTNERS Firm and number of partners (Chapter 4)

ACCOUNTINGPARTNERS2 Region and number of partners (Chapter 12)

ACCOUNTINGPARTNERS4 Region and number of partners (Chapter 13)

ADINDEX Respondent, cola A Adindex, and cola B Adindex (Chapter 12)

AMS2-1 Types of errors and frequency, types of errors and cost, types of wrong billing errors and cost (as three separate worksheets) (Chapter 2)

AMS2-2 Days and number of calls (Chapter 2)

AMS10 Rate willing to pay ($) (Chapter 10)

AMS11 Upload speed (Chapter 11)

AMS12-1 Update times for email interface 1 and email interface 2 (Chapter 12)

AMS12-2 Update times for system 1, system 2, and system 3 (Chapter 12)

AMS12 Number of hours spent telemarketing and number of new subscriptions (Chapter 15)

AMS13 Week, number of new subscriptions, hours spent telemarketing, and type of presentation (formal or informal) (Chapter 16)

ANSCOMBE Data sets A, B, C, and D, each with 11 pairs of *X* and *Y* values (Chapter 15)

AUTOMAKER1 Automaker and number of complaints (Chapter 2)

AUTOMAKER2 Category and number of complaints (Chapter 2)

BANK1 Waiting time (in minutes) of 15 customers at a bank located in a commercial district (Chapters 4, 11, and 12)

BANK2 Waiting time (in minutes) of 15 customers at a bank located in a residential area (Chapters 4 and 12)

BASEBALL Team, E.R.A, runs scored per game, league (0 = American, 1 = National), wins (Chapters 15 and 16)

BBCOST2012 Team and fan cost index (Chapter 2)

BESTFUNDS1 Fund type (short-term or long-term), 1-year return, and 3-year return (Chapter 13)

BESTFUNDS2 Fund type (short-term, long-term, or world), 1-year return, and 3-year return (Chapter 13)

BESTFUNDS3 Fund type (small, mid-cap, or large), 1-year return, and 3-year return (Chapter 13)

BOOKPRICES Author, title, bookstore price, and online price ($) (Chapter 12)

BRANDZTECHFIN Brand, brand value in 2014 ($millions), % change in brand value from 2013, region, and sector (Chapter 12)

BRYNNEPACKAGING WPCT score and rating (Chapter 15)

BULBS Manufacturer (1 = A, 2 = B) and length of life (hours) (Chapter 13)

BUSINESSVALUATION Drug company name, price to book value ratio, return on equity (ROE), and growth% (Chapter 16)

CARDIOGOODFITNESS Product purchased (TM195, TM498, TM798), age in years, gender (Male or Female), education in years, relationship status (Single or Partnered), average number of times the customer plans to use the treadmill each week, self-rated fitness on a 1-to-5 ordinal scale (1 = poor to 5 = excellent), annual household income ($), and average number of miles the customer expects to walk/run each week (Chapters 2, 4, 7, 10, 12, and 14)

CATFOOD Ounces eaten of kidney, shrimp, chicken liver, salmon, and beef cat food (Chapter 12)

CDRATE Bank, 1-year CD rate, and 5-year CD rate (Chapters 3, 4, 7, and 10)

CEO-COMPENSATION Company, CEO compensation ($millions), and return in 2012 (Chapter 3)

CEO-COMPENSATION 2013 Company, CEO compensation ($millions), and return in 2013 ($millions) (Chapter 15)

CEREALS Cereal, calories, carbohydrates, and sugar (Chapters 2, 4, and 15)

CIGARETTETAX State and cigarette tax ($) (Chapters 3 and 4)

COFFEE Expert and rating of coffees by brand A, B, C, and D (Chapter 12)

COFFEESALES Coffee sales at $0.59, $0.69, $0.79, and $0.89 (Chapter 12)

COLA Beverage end-cap sales and produce end-cap sales (Chapter 12)

COLLEGE FOOTBALL Head coach, school, conference, school pay of head coach, other pay, total pay, max bonus, and football net revenue (Chapters 2, 4, and 15)

COMMUNITYBANKS Institution, location, return on investment (ROI%), efficiency ratio (%), total risk based capital (%) (Chapter 16)

CONCRETE1 Sample number and compressive strength after two days and seven days (Chapter 12)

CONGESTION City, annual time waiting in traffic (hours), and cost of waiting in traffic ($) (Chapter 4)

CREDIT SCORES City, state, and average credit score (Chapter 4)

CURRENCY Year, coded year, and exchange rates (against the U.S. dollar) for the Canadian dollar, Japanese yen, and English pound sterling (Chapter 3)

DELIVERY Customer, number of cases, and delivery time (Chapter 15)

DOINGBUSINESS Region, country name, 2012 GDP per capita, Internet users 2011 (per 100 people), and mobile cellular subscriptions 2011 (per 100 people) (Chapter 2)

DOMESTICBEER Brand, alcohol percentage, calories, and carbohydrates (Chapters 3, 4, and 7)

DOWDOGS Stock and one-year return (Chapter 4)

DOWMARKETCAP Company and market capitalization ($billions) (Chapters 4 and 7)

DOWNLOADSPEED Country and download speed in Mbps (Chapter 4)

DRILL Depth, time to drill additional 5 feet, and type of hole (dry or wet) (Chapter 16)

DRINK Amount of soft drink filled in 2-liter bottles (Chapters 3 and 11)

ENERGY State and per capita kilowatt hour use (Chapter 4)

ERWAITING Emergency room waiting time (in minutes) at the main facility and at satellite 1, satellite 2, and satellite 3 (Chapter 13)

ESPRESSO Tamp (inches) and time (seconds) (Chapter 15)

FASTFOOD Amount spent on fast food ($) (Chapters 2, 10, and 11)

FASTFOODCHAIN Mean sales per unit for burger, chicken, sandwich, and pizza segments (Chapter 13)

FIFTEENWEEKS Week number, number of customers, and sales ($thousands) over a period of 15 consecutive weeks (Chapter 15)

FIVEYEARCDRATE Five-year CD rates in New York and Los Angeles (Chapter 12)

FORCE Force required to break an insulator (Chapters 4, 10, and 11)

FOREIGNMARKET Country, level of development (Emerging or Developed), and time required to start a business (days) (Chapter 12)

FOREIGNMARKET2 Country, region, cost to export container (US$), cost to import container (US$) (Chapter 13)

FURNITURE Days between receipt and resolution of complaints regarding purchased furniture (Chapters 3, 4, 10, and 11)

GCROSLYN Address, location (Glen Cove or Roslyn), fair market value ($thousands), property size (acres), age, house size (sq. ft.), number of rooms, number of bathrooms, and number of cars that can be parked in the garage (Chapter 16)

GLENCOVE Address, fair market value ($thousands), property size (acres), age, house size (sq. ft.), number of rooms, number of bathrooms, and number of cars that can be parked in the garage (Chapter 16)

GLOBALSOCIALMEDIA Country, GDP, and social media usage (%) (Chapter 3, and 12)

GOLFBALL Distance for designs 1, 2, 3, and 4 (Chapter 13)

GPIGMAT GMAT scores and GPA (Chapter 15)

GRADSURVEY ID, gender (Female or Male), age (as of last birthday), graduate major (Accounting, CIS, Economics/Finance, International Business, Management, Retailing/Marketing, or Other), current graduate GPA, undergraduate major (Biological Sciences, Business, Engineering, or Other), undergraduate GPA, current employment status (Full-Time, Part-Time, or Unemployed), number of different full-time jobs held in the past 10 years, expected salary upon completion of MBA ($thousands), amount spent for books and supplies this semester ($), advisory rating, type of computer owned (Desktop or Laptop), text messages per week, wealth accumulated to feel rich (Chapters 1, 2, 4, 5, 7, 10, 13, and 14)

GRANULE Granule loss in Boston and Vermont shingles (Chapters 4, 10, and 11)

HOTELAWAY nationality and price (US$) (Chapter 4)

HOTELPRICES City and average price (US$) of a hotel room at a 2-star price, 3-star price, and 4-star hotel (Chapters 3 and 4)

ICECREAM Daily temperature (in degrees Fahrenheit) and sales ($thousands) for 21 days (Chapter 15)

INSURANCE Processing time in days for insurance policies (Chapters 4, 10, and 11)

INSURANCECLAIMS Claims, buildup (0 = buildup not indicated, 1 = buildup indicated), excess payment ($) (Chapter 10)

INTERNETMOBILETIME Time spent per day accessing the Internet via mobile device (minutes) (Chapter 11)

INTERNETMOBILETIME2 Gender (F or M), time spent per day accessing the Internet via mobile device (minutes) (Chapter 12)

INVOICES Amount recorded (in dollars) from sales invoices (Chapter 11)

LUGGAGE Delivery time (in minutes) for luggage in Wing A and Wing B of a hotel (Chapter 13)

MARKET PENETRATION Country and Facebook penetration (in percentage) (Chapters 4 and 10)

MOBILE ELECTRONICS In-aisle sales, front sales, kiosk sales, and expert area sales (Chapter 13) (E)

MOBILE ELECTRONICS STACKED Stacked version of Mobile Electronics (Chapter 13) (M)

MOISTURE Moisture content of Boston shingles and Vermont shingles (Chapter 11)

MOTIVATION Factor, mean rating by global employees, and mean rating by U.S. employees (Chapter 12)

MOVIE Title, box office gross ($millions), and DVD revenue ($millions) (Chapter 15)

MOVING Labor hours, cubic feet, number of large pieces of furniture, and availability of an elevator (Chapters 15 and 16)

MYELOMA Patient, before transplant measurement, after transplant measurement (Chapter 12)

NATURAL GAS Month, wellhead price ($/thousands cu. ft.), and residential price ($/thousands cu. ft.) (Chapter 3)

NBA Team, team code, wins, field goal %, three-point field goal % (Chapter 16)

NBACOST2013 Team, fan cost index ($) (Chapter 7)

NBAVALUES Team, team code, annual revenue ($millions), and value ($millions) and 1-year change in value (%) (Chapters 4, and 15)

NEEDS Need and frequency (Chapter 2)

NEIGHBOR Selling price ($thousands), number of rooms, neighborhood location (0 = east, 1 = west) (Chapter 16)

OIL&GASOLINE Week, price of a gallon of gasoline ($), and price of oil per barrel, ($) (Chapter 15)

OMNIPOWER Bars sold, price (cents), and promotion expenses ($) (Chapter 16)

ORDER Time in minutes to fill orders for a population of 200 (Chapter 10)

PACKAGINGFOAM3 Die temperature, die diameter, and foam density (Chapter 16)

PACKAGINGFOAM4 Die temperature, die diameter, and foam diameter (Chapter 16)

PALLET Weight of Boston shingles and weight of Vermont shingles (Chapters 3, 10, 11, and 13)

PEN Ad and product rating (Chapter 13)

PHONE Time (in minutes) to clear telephone line problems and location (1 = I, 2 = II) (Chapter 12)

PIZZATIME Time period, delivery time for local restaurant, and delivery time for national chain (Chapter 12)

POTTERMOVIES Title, first weekend gross ($millions), U.S. gross ($millions), and worldwide gross ($millions) (Chapters 4, and 15)

PROPERTYTAXES State and property taxes per capita ($) (Chapters 4, and 7)

PROTEIN Type of food, calories (in grams), protein, percentage of calories from fat, percentage of calories from saturated fat, and cholesterol (mg) (Chapters 3 and 4)

PUMPKIN Circumference and weight of pumpkins (Chapter 15)

RADIOSHACK State and number of stores (Chapters 4)

REDANDWHITE Fixed acidity, volatile acidity, citric acid, residual sugar, chlorides, free sulfur dioxide, total sulfur dioxide, density, pH, sulphates, alcohol, wine type coded (0 = White, 1 = Red), wine type (Red or White), quality (Chapter 16)

REDWOOD Height (ft.), breast height diameter (in.), and bark thickness (in.) (Chapters 15 and 16)

RENTSILVERSPRING Apartment size (sq. ft.) and monthly rental cost ($) (Chapter 15)

RESTAURANTS Location (City or Suburban), food rating, decor rating, service rating, summated rating, coded location (0 = City, 1 = Suburban), and cost of a meal (Chapters 3, 4, 13, 15, and 16)

RETIREMENT FUNDS Fund number, market cap (Small, Mid-Cap, or Large), type (Growth or Value), assets ($millions), turnover ratio, beta (measure of the volatility of a stock), standard deviation (measure of returns relative to 36-month average), risk (Low, Average, or High), 1-year return, 3-year return, 5-year return, 10-year return,

expense ratio, star rating (Chapters 2, 4, 5, 7, 10, 13, and 14)

SEDANS Miles per gallon for 2014 midsized sedans (Chapters 4 and 10)

SILVERSPRING Address, asking price ($000), assessed value ($000), taxes ($), size (thousands sq. ft.) fireplace coded (0 = no, 1 = yes), number of bedrooms, number of bathrooms, age (years), fireplace (No or Yes) (Chapters 15 and 16)

SITESELECTION Store number, profiled customers, and sales ($millions) (Chapter 15)

SMALLBUSINESSES Company, earnings per share growth (%), sales growth (%), and return on equity (%) (Chapter 16)

SMARTPHONES Price ($) (Chapter 4)

SMARTPHONE SALES Type and market share percentage for the years 2011 through 2013 (Chapter 2)

SOCCERVALUES2014 Team, revenues ($millions), and value ($millions) (Chapter 15)

STANDBY Standby hours, total staff present, remote hours, Dubner hours, and total labor hours (Chapter 16)

STARBUCKS Tear, viscosity, pressure, plate gap (Chapters 15 and 16)

STEEL Error in actual length and specified length (Chapters 7, 10, and 11)

STOCKPRICES2013 Date, S&P 500 value, and closing weekly stock price for GE, Discovery Communications, and Google (Chapter 15)

STUDYTIME Gender and study time in hours (Chapter 10)

SUV Miles per gallon for 2014 small SUVs (Chapters 4, 7, and 10)

TABLE_5.1 X and P(X) (Chapter 6) (M)

TABLETS Battery life (hours) for WiFi-only and 3G/4G/WiFi tablets (Chapter 12)

TARGETWALMART Shopping item, Target price ($), and Walmart price ($) (Chapter 12)

TEABAGS Weight of tea bags in ounces (Chapters 4, 10, and 11)

TELECOM Provider, TV rating, and Phone rating (Chapter 12)

THREE-HOTEL SURVEY Choose again? (No or Yes) and Golden Palm, Palm Royale, and Palm Princess tallies (Chapter 15) (M)

TIMES Get-ready times (Chapter 4)

TROUGH Width of trough (Chapters 4, 10, and 11)

TWITTERMOVIES Movie, Twitter activity, and receipts ($) (Chapter 15)

TWO-HOTEL SURVEY Choose again? (No or Yes) and Beachcomber and Windsurfer tallies (Chapter 15) (M)

UNDERGRADSURVEY ID, gender (Female or Male), age (as of last birthday), class designation (Sophomore, Junior, or Senior), major (Accounting, CIS, Economics/

Finance, International Business, Management, Retail/ Marketing, Other, or Undecided), graduate school intention (No, Yes, or Undecided), cumulative GPA, current employment status (Full-Time, Part-Time, or Unemployed), expected starting salary ($thousands), number of social networking sites registered for, satisfaction with student advisement services on campus, amount spent on books and supplies this semester, type of computer preferred (Desktop, Laptop, or Tablet), text messages per week, wealth accumulated to feel rich (Chapters 1, 2, 4, 5, 7, 10, 12, and 14)

UTILITY Utilities charges ($) for 50 one-bedroom apartments (Chapter 7)

VB Time to complete program (Chapter 12)

VINHOVERDE Fixed acidity, volatile acidity, citric acid, residual sugar, chlorides, free sulfur dioxide, total sulfur dioxide, density, pH, sulphates, alcohol, and quality (Chapters 15 and 16)

WAIT Waiting time and seating time (Chapter 7)

WARECOST Distribution cost ($thousands), sales ($thousands), and number of orders (Chapter 15)

Excel Guide Workbooks

Excel Guide workbooks contain templates or model solutions for applying Excel to a particular statistical method. Chapter examples and the *In-Depth Excel* instructions of the Excel Guides feature worksheets from these workbooks and PHStat constructs many of the worksheets from these workbooks for you.

Workbooks are stored in the **.xlsx** Excel workbook format. Most contain a **COMPUTE worksheet** (often shown in this book) that presents results as well as a **COMPUTE_ FORMULAS worksheet** that allows you to examine all of the formulas used in the worksheet. The Excel Guide workbooks (with the number of the chapter in which each is first mentioned) are:

Recoded (1)	**NPP (7)**
Random (1)	**SDS (8)**
Data Cleaning (1)	**CIE sigma known (10)**
Summary Table (2)	**CIE sigma unknown (10)**
Contingency Table (2)	**CIE Proportion (10)**
Distributions (2)	**Sample Size Mean (10)**
Pareto (2)	**Sample Size Proportion (10)**
Stem-and-leaf (2)	**Z Mean workbook (11)**
Histogram (2)	**T mean workbook (11)**
Polygons (3)	**Z Proportion (11)**
Scatter Plot (3)	**Pooled-Variance T (12)**
Time Series (3)	**Separate-Variance T (12)**
Descriptive(4)	**Paired T (12)**
Quartiles (4)	**F Two Variances (12)**
Boxplot (4)	**Z Two Proportions (13)**
Parameters (4)	**One-Way ANOVA (13)**
Covariance (4)	**Levene (13)**
Probabilities (5)	**Chi-Square (14)**
Bayes (5)	**Chi-Square Worksheets (14)**
Discrete Variable (6)	**Simple Linear Regression (15)**
Binomial (6)	
Poisson (6)	**Package Delivery (15)**
Normal (7)	**Multiple Regression (16)**

Digital Cases, Online Topics, and Short Takes

These files use the Portable Document Format (PDF) that are best viewed using the latest version of Adobe Reader (**get.adobe.com/reader/**).

Visual Explorations

Visual Explorations are workbooks that interactively demonstrate various key statistical concepts. Three workbooks are add-in workbooks that are stored in the **.xlam** Excel add-in format. Using these add-in workbooks with Microsoft Windows Excels requires the security settings discussed in Appendix Section D.3. The Visual Explorations workbooks are:

VE-Normal Distribution (add-in)
VE-Sampling Distribution (add-in)
VE-Simple Linear Regression (add-in)
VE-Variability

B.4 PHStat

PHStat is the Pearson Education statistics add-in for Microsoft Excel that simplifies the task of using Excel as you learn business statistics. PHStat comes packaged as a zip file archive that you download and unzip to the folder of your choice. The archive contains:

PHStat.xlam, the actual add-in workbook that is further discussed in Appendix Sections D.2 and G.1, and these four supporting files:

PHStat readme.pdf Explains the technical requirements, and setup and troubleshooting procedures for PHStat (PDF format).

PHStatHelp.chm The integrated help system for users of Microsoft Windows Excel.

PHStatHelp.pdf The help system as a PDF format file.

PHStatHelp.epub The help system in Open Publication Structure eBook format.

PHStat is available for download with an access code. If your book was packaged with an access code, download PHStat from **www.pearsonhighered.com/phstat**. Click the download link and follow the instructions for entering the access code. If your book was not packaged with an access code, visit **myPearsonStore.com** to purchase a PHStat access code.

TABLE C.1

Table of Random
Numbers

	Column							
Row	**00000** **12345**	**00001** **67890**	**11111** **12345**	**11112** **67890**	**22222** **12345**	**22223** **67890**	**33333** **12345**	**33334** **67890**
01	49280	88924	35779	00283	81163	07275	89863	02348
02	61870	41657	07468	08612	98083	97349	20775	45091
03	43898	65923	25078	86129	78496	97653	91550	08078
04	62993	93912	30454	84598	56095	20664	12872	64647
05	33850	58555	51438	85507	71865	79488	76783	31708
06	97340	03364	88472	04334	63919	36394	11095	92470
07	70543	29776	10087	10072	55980	64688	68239	20461
08	89382	93809	00796	95945	34101	81277	66090	88872
09	37818	72142	67140	50785	22380	16703	53362	44940
10	60430	22834	14130	96593	23298	56203	92671	15925
11	82975	66158	84731	19436	55790	69229	28661	13675
12	30987	71938	40355	54324	08401	26299	49420	59208
13	55700	24586	93247	32596	11865	63397	44251	43189
14	14756	23997	78643	75912	83832	32768	18928	57070
15	32166	53251	70654	92827	63491	04233	33825	69662
16	23236	73751	31888	81718	06546	83246	47651	04877
17	45794	26926	15130	82455	78305	55058	52551	47182
18	09893	20505	14225	68514	47427	56788	96297	78822
19	54382	74598	91499	14523	68479	27686	46162	83554
20	94750	89923	37089	20048	80336	94598	26940	36858
21	70297	34135	53140	33340	42050	82341	44104	82949
22	85157	47954	32979	26575	57600	40881	12250	73742
23	11100	02340	12860	74697	96644	89439	28707	25815
24	36871	50775	30592	57143	17381	68856	25853	35041
25	23913	48357	63308	16090	51690	54607	72407	55538
26	79348	36085	27973	65157	07456	22255	25626	57054
27	92074	54641	53673	54421	18130	60103	69593	49464
28	06873	21440	75593	41373	49502	17972	82578	16364
29	12478	37622	99659	31065	83613	69889	58869	29571
30	57175	55564	65411	42547	70457	03426	72937	83792
31	91616	11075	80103	07831	59309	13276	26710	73000
32	78025	73539	14621	39044	47450	03197	12787	47709
33	27587	67228	80145	10175	12822	86687	65530	49325
34	16690	20427	04251	64477	73709	73945	92396	68263
35	70183	58065	65489	31833	82093	16747	10386	59293
36	90730	35385	15679	99742	50866	78028	75573	67257
37	10934	93242	13431	24590	02770	48582	00906	58595
38	82462	30166	79613	47416	13389	80268	05085	96666
39	27463	10433	07606	16285	93699	60912	94532	95632
40	02979	52997	09079	92709	90110	47506	53693	49892
41	46888	69929	75233	52507	32097	37594	10067	67327
42	53638	83161	08289	12639	08141	12640	28437	09268
43	82433	61427	17239	89160	19666	08814	37841	12847
44	35766	31672	50082	22795	66948	65581	84393	15890
45	10853	42581	08792	13257	61973	24450	52351	16602
46	20341	27398	72906	63955	17276	10646	74692	48438
47	54458	90542	77563	51839	52901	53355	83281	19177
48	26337	66530	16687	35179	46560	00123	44546	79896
49	34314	23729	85264	05575	96855	23820	11091	79821
50	28603	10708	68933	34189	92166	15181	66628	58599

TABLE C.1

Table of Random
Numbers (*continued*)

Row	00000 12345	00001 67890	11111 12345	11112 67890	22222 12345	22223 67890	33333 12345	33334 67890
51	66194	28926	99547	16625	45515	67953	12108	57846
52	78240	43195	24837	32511	70880	22070	52622	61881
53	00833	88000	67299	68215	11274	55624	32991	17436
54	12111	86683	61270	58036	64192	90611	15145	01748
55	47189	99951	05755	03834	43782	90599	40282	51417
56	76396	72486	62423	27618	84184	78922	73561	52818
57	46409	17469	32483	09083	76175	19985	26309	91536
58	74626	22111	87286	46772	42243	68046	44250	42439
59	34450	81974	93723	49023	58432	67083	36876	93391
60	36327	72135	33005	28701	34710	49359	50693	89311
61	74185	77536	84825	09934	99103	09325	67389	45869
62	12296	41623	62873	37943	25584	09609	63360	47270
63	90822	60280	88925	99610	42772	60561	76873	04117
64	72121	79152	96591	90305	10189	79778	68016	13747
65	95268	41377	25684	08151	61816	58555	54305	86189
66	92603	09091	75884	93424	72586	88903	30061	14457
67	18813	90291	05275	01223	79607	95426	34900	09778
68	38840	26903	28624	67157	51986	42865	14508	49315
69	05959	33836	53758	16562	41081	38012	41230	20528
70	85141	21155	99212	32685	51403	31926	69813	58781
71	75047	59643	31074	38172	03718	32119	69506	67143
72	30752	95260	68032	62871	58781	34143	68790	69766
73	22986	82575	42187	62295	84295	30634	66562	31442
74	99439	86692	90348	66036	48399	73451	26698	39437
75	20389	93029	11881	71685	65452	89047	63669	02656
76	39249	05173	68256	36359	20250	68686	05947	09335
77	96777	33605	29481	20063	09398	01843	35139	61344
78	04860	32918	10798	50492	52655	33359	94713	28393
79	41613	42375	00403	03656	77580	87772	86877	57085
80	17930	00794	53836	53692	67135	98102	61912	11246
81	24649	31845	25736	75231	83808	98917	93829	99430
82	79899	34061	54308	59358	56462	58166	97302	86828
83	76801	49594	81002	30397	52728	15101	72070	33706
84	36239	63636	38140	65731	39788	06872	38971	53363
85	07392	64449	17886	63632	53995	17574	22247	62607
86	67133	04181	33874	98835	67453	59734	76381	63455
87	77759	31504	32832	70861	15152	29733	75371	39174
88	85992	72268	42920	20810	29361	51423	90306	73574
89	79553	75952	54116	65553	47139	60579	09165	85490
90	41101	17336	48951	53674	17880	45260	08575	49321
91	36191	17095	32123	91576	84221	78902	82010	30847
92	62329	63898	23268	74283	26091	68409	69704	82267
93	14751	13151	93115	01437	56945	89661	67680	79790
94	48462	59278	44185	29616	76537	19589	83139	28454
95	29435	88105	59651	44391	74588	55114	80834	85686
96	28340	29285	12965	14821	80425	16602	44653	70467
97	02167	58940	27149	80242	10587	79786	34959	75339
98	17864	00991	39557	54981	23588	81914	37609	13128
99	79675	80605	60059	35862	00254	36546	21545	78179
100	72335	82037	92003	34100	29879	46613	89720	13274

Source: Partially extracted from the Rand Corporation, *A Million Random Digits with 100,000 Normal Deviates*
(Glencoe, IL, The Free Press, 1955).

TABLE C.2

The Cumulative Standardized Normal Distribution

Entry represents area under the cumulative standardized
normal distribution from $-\infty$ to Z

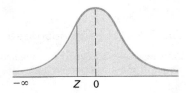

					Cumulative Probabilities					
Z	0.00	0.01	0.02	0.03	0.04	0.05	0.06	0.07	0.08	0.09
−6.0	0.000000001									
−5.5	0.000000019									
−5.0	0.000000287									
−4.5	0.000003398									
−4.0	0.000031671									
−3.9	0.00005	0.00005	0.00004	0.00004	0.00004	0.00004	0.00004	0.00004	0.00003	0.00003
−3.8	0.00007	0.00007	0.00007	0.00006	0.00006	0.00006	0.00006	0.00005	0.00005	0.00005
−3.7	0.00011	0.00010	0.00010	0.00010	0.00009	0.00009	0.00008	0.00008	0.00008	0.00008
−3.6	0.00016	0.00015	0.00015	0.00014	0.00014	0.00013	0.00013	0.00012	0.00012	0.00011
−3.5	0.00023	0.00022	0.00022	0.00021	0.00020	0.00019	0.00019	0.00018	0.00017	0.00017
−3.4	0.00034	0.00032	0.00031	0.00030	0.00029	0.00028	0.00027	0.00026	0.00025	0.00024
−3.3	0.00048	0.00047	0.00045	0.00043	0.00042	0.00040	0.00039	0.00038	0.00036	0.00035
−3.2	0.00069	0.00066	0.00064	0.00062	0.00060	0.00058	0.00056	0.00054	0.00052	0.00050
−3.1	0.00097	0.00094	0.00090	0.00087	0.00084	0.00082	0.00079	0.00076	0.00074	0.00071
−3.0	0.00135	0.00131	0.00126	0.00122	0.00118	0.00114	0.00111	0.00107	0.00103	0.00100
−2.9	0.0019	0.0018	0.0018	0.0017	0.0016	0.0016	0.0015	0.0015	0.0014	0.0014
−2.8	0.0026	0.0025	0.0024	0.0023	0.0023	0.0022	0.0021	0.0021	0.0020	0.0019
−2.7	0.0035	0.0034	0.0033	0.0032	0.0031	0.0030	0.0029	0.0028	0.0027	0.0026
−2.6	0.0047	0.0045	0.0044	0.0043	0.0041	0.0040	0.0039	0.0038	0.0037	0.0036
−2.5	0.0062	0.0060	0.0059	0.0057	0.0055	0.0054	0.0052	0.0051	0.0049	0.0048
−2.4	0.0082	0.0080	0.0078	0.0075	0.0073	0.0071	0.0069	0.0068	0.0066	0.0064
−2.3	0.0107	0.0104	0.0102	0.0099	0.0096	0.0094	0.0091	0.0089	0.0087	0.0084
−2.2	0.0139	0.0136	0.0132	0.0129	0.0125	0.0122	0.0119	0.0116	0.0113	0.0110
−2.1	0.0179	0.0174	0.0170	0.0166	0.0162	0.0158	0.0154	0.0150	0.0146	0.0143
−2.0	0.0228	0.0222	0.0217	0.0212	0.0207	0.0202	0.0197	0.0192	0.0188	0.0183
−1.9	0.0287	0.0281	0.0274	0.0268	0.0262	0.0256	0.0250	0.0244	0.0239	0.0233
−1.8	0.0359	0.0351	0.0344	0.0336	0.0329	0.0322	0.0314	0.0307	0.0301	0.0294
−1.7	0.0446	0.0436	0.0427	0.0418	0.0409	0.0401	0.0392	0.0384	0.0375	0.0367
−1.6	0.0548	0.0537	0.0526	0.0516	0.0505	0.0495	0.0485	0.0475	0.0465	0.0455
−1.5	0.0668	0.0655	0.0643	0.0630	0.0618	0.0606	0.0594	0.0582	0.0571	0.0559
−1.4	0.0808	0.0793	0.0778	0.0764	0.0749	0.0735	0.0721	0.0708	0.0694	0.0681
−1.3	0.0968	0.0951	0.0934	0.0918	0.0901	0.0885	0.0869	0.0853	0.0838	0.0823
−1.2	0.1151	0.1131	0.1112	0.1093	0.1075	0.1056	0.1038	0.1020	0.1003	0.0985
−1.1	0.1357	0.1335	0.1314	0.1292	0.1271	0.1251	0.1230	0.1210	0.1190	0.1170
−1.0	0.1587	0.1562	0.1539	0.1515	0.1492	0.1469	0.1446	0.1423	0.1401	0.1379
−0.9	0.1841	0.1814	0.1788	0.1762	0.1736	0.1711	0.1685	0.1660	0.1635	0.1611
−0.8	0.2119	0.2090	0.2061	0.2033	0.2005	0.1977	0.1949	0.1922	0.1894	0.1867
−0.7	0.2420	0.2388	0.2358	0.2327	0.2296	0.2266	0.2236	0.2206	0.2177	0.2148
−0.6	0.2743	0.2709	0.2676	0.2643	0.2611	0.2578	0.2546	0.2514	0.2482	0.2451
−0.5	0.3085	0.3050	0.3015	0.2981	0.2946	0.2912	0.2877	0.2843	0.2810	0.2776
−0.4	0.3446	0.3409	0.3372	0.3336	0.3300	0.3264	0.3228	0.3192	0.3156	0.3121
−0.3	0.3821	0.3783	0.3745	0.3707	0.3669	0.3632	0.3594	0.3557	0.3520	0.3483
−0.2	0.4207	0.4168	0.4129	0.4090	0.4052	0.4013	0.3974	0.3936	0.3897	0.3859
−0.1	0.4602	0.4562	0.4522	0.4483	0.4443	0.4404	0.4364	0.4325	0.4286	0.4247
−0.0	0.5000	0.4960	0.4920	0.4880	0.4840	0.4801	0.4761	0.4721	0.4681	0.4641

TABLE C.2

The Cumulative Standardized Normal Distribution (*continued*)

Entry represents area under the cumulative standardized
normal distribution from $-\infty$ to Z

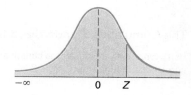

					Cumulative Probabilities					
Z	0.00	0.01	0.02	0.03	0.04	0.05	0.06	0.07	0.08	0.09
0.0	0.5000	0.5040	0.5080	0.5120	0.5160	0.5199	0.5239	0.5279	0.5319	0.5359
0.1	0.5398	0.5438	0.5478	0.5517	0.5557	0.5596	0.5636	0.5675	0.5714	0.5753
0.2	0.5793	0.5832	0.5871	0.5910	0.5948	0.5987	0.6026	0.6064	0.6103	0.6141
0.3	0.6179	0.6217	0.6255	0.6293	0.6331	0.6368	0.6406	0.6443	0.6480	0.6517
0.4	0.6554	0.6591	0.6628	0.6664	0.6700	0.6736	0.6772	0.6808	0.6844	0.6879
0.5	0.6915	0.6950	0.6985	0.7019	0.7054	0.7088	0.7123	0.7157	0.7190	0.7224
0.6	0.7257	0.7291	0.7324	0.7357	0.7389	0.7422	0.7454	0.7486	0.7518	0.7549
0.7	0.7580	0.7612	0.7642	0.7673	0.7704	0.7734	0.7764	0.7794	0.7823	0.7852
0.8	0.7881	0.7910	0.7939	0.7967	0.7995	0.8023	0.8051	0.8078	0.8106	0.8133
0.9	0.8159	0.8186	0.8212	0.8238	0.8264	0.8289	0.8315	0.8340	0.8365	0.8389
1.0	0.8413	0.8438	0.8461	0.8485	0.8508	0.8531	0.8554	0.8577	0.8599	0.8621
1.1	0.8643	0.8665	0.8686	0.8708	0.8729	0.8749	0.8770	0.8790	0.8810	0.8830
1.2	0.8849	0.8869	0.8888	0.8907	0.8925	0.8944	0.8962	0.8980	0.8997	0.9015
1.3	0.9032	0.9049	0.9066	0.9082	0.9099	0.9115	0.9131	0.9147	0.9162	0.9177
1.4	0.9192	0.9207	0.9222	0.9236	0.9251	0.9265	0.9279	0.9292	0.9306	0.9319
1.5	0.9332	0.9345	0.9357	0.9370	0.9382	0.9394	0.9406	0.9418	0.9429	0.9441
1.6	0.9452	0.9463	0.9474	0.9484	0.9495	0.9505	0.9515	0.9525	0.9535	0.9545
1.7	0.9554	0.9564	0.9573	0.9582	0.9591	0.9599	0.9608	0.9616	0.9625	0.9633
1.8	0.9641	0.9649	0.9656	0.9664	0.9671	0.9678	0.9686	0.9693	0.9699	0.9706
1.9	0.9713	0.9719	0.9726	0.9732	0.9738	0.9744	0.9750	0.9756	0.9761	0.9767
2.0	0.9772	0.9778	0.9783	0.9788	0.9793	0.9798	0.9803	0.9808	0.9812	0.9817
2.1	0.9821	0.9826	0.9830	0.9834	0.9838	0.9842	0.9846	0.9850	0.9854	0.9857
2.2	0.9861	0.9864	0.9868	0.9871	0.9875	0.9878	0.9881	0.9884	0.9887	0.9890
2.3	0.9893	0.9896	0.9898	0.9901	0.9904	0.9906	0.9909	0.9911	0.9913	0.9916
2.4	0.9918	0.9920	0.9922	0.9925	0.9927	0.9929	0.9931	0.9932	0.9934	0.9936
2.5	0.9938	0.9940	0.9941	0.9943	0.9945	0.9946	0.9948	0.9949	0.9951	0.9952
2.6	0.9953	0.9955	0.9956	0.9957	0.9959	0.9960	0.9961	0.9962	0.9963	0.9964
2.7	0.9965	0.9966	0.9967	0.9968	0.9969	0.9970	0.9971	0.9972	0.9973	0.9974
2.8	0.9974	0.9975	0.9976	0.9977	0.9977	0.9978	0.9979	0.9979	0.9980	0.9981
2.9	0.9981	0.9982	0.9982	0.9983	0.9984	0.9984	0.9985	0.9985	0.9986	0.9986
3.0	0.99865	0.99869	0.99874	0.99878	0.99882	0.99886	0.99889	0.99893	0.99897	0.99900
3.1	0.99903	0.99906	0.99910	0.99913	0.99916	0.99918	0.99921	0.99924	0.99926	0.99929
3.2	0.99931	0.99934	0.99936	0.99938	0.99940	0.99942	0.99944	0.99946	0.99948	0.99950
3.3	0.99952	0.99953	0.99955	0.99957	0.99958	0.99960	0.99961	0.99962	0.99964	0.99965
3.4	0.99966	0.99968	0.99969	0.99970	0.99971	0.99972	0.99973	0.99974	0.99975	0.99976
3.5	0.99977	0.99978	0.99978	0.99979	0.99980	0.99981	0.99981	0.99982	0.99983	0.99983
3.6	0.99984	0.99985	0.99985	0.99986	0.99986	0.99987	0.99987	0.99988	0.99988	0.99989
3.7	0.99989	0.99990	0.99990	0.99990	0.99991	0.99991	0.99992	0.99992	0.99992	0.99992
3.8	0.99993	0.99993	0.99993	0.99994	0.99994	0.99994	0.99994	0.99995	0.99995	0.99995
3.9	0.99995	0.99995	0.99996	0.99996	0.99996	0.99996	0.99996	0.99996	0.99997	0.99997
4.0	0.999968329									
4.5	0.999996602									
5.0	0.999999713									
5.5	0.999999981									
6.0	0.999999999									

TABLE C.3

Critical Values of t

For a particular number of degrees of freedom, entry represents the critical value of t corresponding to the cumulative probability $(1 - \alpha)$ and a specified upper-tail area (α).

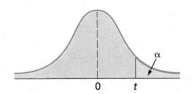

Degrees of Freedom	Cumulative Probabilities					
	0.75	0.90	0.95	0.975	0.99	0.995
	Upper-Tail Areas					
	0.25	0.10	0.05	0.025	0.01	0.005
1	1.0000	3.0777	6.3138	12.7062	31.8207	63.6574
2	0.8165	1.8856	2.9200	4.3027	6.9646	9.9248
3	0.7649	1.6377	2.3534	3.1824	4.5407	5.8409
4	0.7407	1.5332	2.1318	2.7764	3.7469	4.6041
5	0.7267	1.4759	2.0150	2.5706	3.3649	4.0322
6	0.7176	1.4398	1.9432	2.4469	3.1427	3.7074
7	0.7111	1.4149	1.8946	2.3646	2.9980	3.4995
8	0.7064	1.3968	1.8595	2.3060	2.8965	3.3554
9	0.7027	1.3830	1.8331	2.2622	2.8214	3.2498
10	0.6998	1.3722	1.8125	2.2281	2.7638	3.1693
11	0.6974	1.3634	1.7959	2.2010	2.7181	3.1058
12	0.6955	1.3562	1.7823	2.1788	2.6810	3.0545
13	0.6938	1.3502	1.7709	2.1604	2.6503	3.0123
14	0.6924	1.3450	1.7613	2.1448	2.6245	2.9768
15	0.6912	1.3406	1.7531	2.1315	2.6025	2.9467
16	0.6901	1.3368	1.7459	2.1199	2.5835	2.9208
17	0.6892	1.3334	1.7396	2.1098	2.5669	2.8982
18	0.6884	1.3304	1.7341	2.1009	2.5524	2.8784
19	0.6876	1.3277	1.7291	2.0930	2.5395	2.8609
20	0.6870	1.3253	1.7247	2.0860	2.5280	2.8453
21	0.6864	1.3232	1.7207	2.0796	2.5177	2.8314
22	0.6858	1.3212	1.7171	2.0739	2.5083	2.8188
23	0.6853	1.3195	1.7139	2.0687	2.4999	2.8073
24	0.6848	1.3178	1.7109	2.0639	2.4922	2.7969
25	0.6844	1.3163	1.7081	2.0595	2.4851	2.7874
26	0.6840	1.3150	1.7056	2.0555	2.4786	2.7787
27	0.6837	1.3137	1.7033	2.0518	2.4727	2.7707
28	0.6834	1.3125	1.7011	2.0484	2.4671	2.7633
29	0.6830	1.3114	1.6991	2.0452	2.4620	2.7564
30	0.6828	1.3104	1.6973	2.0423	2.4573	2.7500
31	0.6825	1.3095	1.6955	2.0395	2.4528	2.7440
32	0.6822	1.3086	1.6939	2.0369	2.4487	2.7385
33	0.6820	1.3077	1.6924	2.0345	2.4448	2.7333
34	0.6818	1.3070	1.6909	2.0322	2.4411	2.7284
35	0.6816	1.3062	1.6896	2.0301	2.4377	2.7238
36	0.6814	1.3055	1.6883	2.0281	2.4345	2.7195
37	0.6812	1.3049	1.6871	2.0262	2.4314	2.7154
38	0.6810	1.3042	1.6860	2.0244	2.4286	2.7116
39	0.6808	1.3036	1.6849	2.0227	2.4258	2.7079
40	0.6807	1.3031	1.6839	2.0211	2.4233	2.7045
41	0.6805	1.3025	1.6829	2.0195	2.4208	2.7012
42	0.6804	1.3020	1.6820	2.0181	2.4185	2.6981
43	0.6802	1.3016	1.6811	2.0167	2.4163	2.6951
44	0.6801	1.3011	1.6802	2.0154	2.4141	2.6923
45	0.6800	1.3006	1.6794	2.0141	2.4121	2.6896
46	0.6799	1.3002	1.6787	2.0129	2.4102	2.6870
47	0.6797	1.2998	1.6779	2.0117	2.4083	2.6846
48	0.6796	1.2994	1.6772	2.0106	2.4066	2.6822
49	0.6795	1.2991	1.6766	2.0096	2.4049	2.6800
50	0.6794	1.2987	1.6759	2.0086	2.4033	2.6778

TABLE C.3

Critical Values of t (continued)

For a particular number of degrees of freedom, entry represents the critical value of t corresponding to the cumulative probability $(1 - \alpha)$ and a specified upper-tail area (α).

Degrees of Freedom	Cumulative Probabilities					
	0.75	0.90	0.95	0.975	0.99	0.995
	Upper-Tail Areas					
	0.25	0.10	0.05	0.025	0.01	0.005
51	0.6793	1.2984	1.6753	2.0076	2.4017	2.6757
52	0.6792	1.2980	1.6747	2.0066	2.4002	2.6737
53	0.6791	1.2977	1.6741	2.0057	2.3988	2.6718
54	0.6791	1.2974	1.6736	2.0049	2.3974	2.6700
55	0.6790	1.2971	1.6730	2.0040	2.3961	2.6682
56	0.6789	1.2969	1.6725	2.0032	2.3948	2.6665
57	0.6788	1.2966	1.6720	2.0025	2.3936	2.6649
58	0.6787	1.2963	1.6716	2.0017	2.3924	2.6633
59	0.6787	1.2961	1.6711	2.0010	2.3912	2.6618
60	0.6786	1.2958	1.6706	2.0003	2.3901	2.6603
61	0.6785	1.2956	1.6702	1.9996	2.3890	2.6589
62	0.6785	1.2954	1.6698	1.9990	2.3880	2.6575
63	0.6784	1.2951	1.6694	1.9983	2.3870	2.6561
64	0.6783	1.2949	1.6690	1.9977	2.3860	2.6549
65	0.6783	1.2947	1.6686	1.9971	2.3851	2.6536
66	0.6782	1.2945	1.6683	1.9966	2.3842	2.6524
67	0.6782	1.2943	1.6679	1.9960	2.3833	2.6512
68	0.6781	1.2941	1.6676	1.9955	2.3824	2.6501
69	0.6781	1.2939	1.6672	1.9949	2.3816	2.6490
70	0.6780	1.2938	1.6669	1.9944	2.3808	2.6479
71	0.6780	1.2936	1.6666	1.9939	2.3800	2.6469
72	0.6779	1.2934	1.6663	1.9935	2.3793	2.6459
73	0.6779	1.2933	1.6660	1.9930	2.3785	2.6449
74	0.6778	1.2931	1.6657	1.9925	2.3778	2.6439
75	0.6778	1.2929	1.6654	1.9921	2.3771	2.6430
76	0.6777	1.2928	1.6652	1.9917	2.3764	2.6421
77	0.6777	1.2926	1.6649	1.9913	2.3758	2.6412
78	0.6776	1.2925	1.6646	1.9908	2.3751	2.6403
79	0.6776	1.2924	1.6644	1.9905	2.3745	2.6395
80	0.6776	1.2922	1.6641	1.9901	2.3739	2.6387
81	0.6775	1.2921	1.6639	1.9897	2.3733	2.6379
82	0.6775	1.2920	1.6636	1.9893	2.3727	2.6371
83	0.6775	1.2918	1.6634	1.9890	2.3721	2.6364
84	0.6774	1.2917	1.6632	1.9886	2.3716	2.6356
85	0.6774	1.2916	1.6630	1.9883	2.3710	2.6349
86	0.6774	1.2915	1.6628	1.9879	2.3705	2.6342
87	0.6773	1.2914	1.6626	1.9876	2.3700	2.6335
88	0.6773	1.2912	1.6624	1.9873	2.3695	2.6329
89	0.6773	1.2911	1.6622	1.9870	2.3690	2.6322
90	0.6772	1.2910	1.6620	1.9867	2.3685	2.6316
91	0.6772	1.2909	1.6618	1.9864	2.3680	2.6309
92	0.6772	1.2908	1.6616	1.9861	2.3676	2.6303
93	0.6771	1.2907	1.6614	1.9858	2.3671	2.6297
94	0.6771	1.2906	1.6612	1.9855	2.3667	2.6291
95	0.6771	1.2905	1.6611	1.9853	2.3662	2.6286
96	0.6771	1.2904	1.6609	1.9850	2.3658	2.6280
97	0.6770	1.2903	1.6607	1.9847	2.3654	2.6275
98	0.6770	1.2902	1.6606	1.9845	2.3650	2.6269
99	0.6770	1.2902	1.6604	1.9842	2.3646	2.6264
100	0.6770	1.2901	1.6602	1.9840	2.3642	2.6259
110	0.6767	1.2893	1.6588	1.9818	2.3607	2.6213
120	0.6765	1.2886	1.6577	1.9799	2.3578	2.6174
∞	0.6745	1.2816	1.6449	1.9600	2.3263	2.5758

TABLE C.4

Critical Values of χ^2

For a particular number of degrees of freedom, entry represents the critical value of χ^2 corresponding to the cumulative probability $(1 - \alpha)$ and a specified upper-tail area (α).

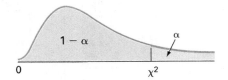

$1 - \alpha$ α

0 χ^2

	Cumulative Probabilities											
	0.005	0.01	0.025	0.05	0.10	0.25	0.75	0.90	0.95	0.975	0.99	0.995
Degrees of Freedom	Upper-Tail Areas (α)											
	0.995	0.99	0.975	0.95	0.90	0.75	0.25	0.10	0.05	0.025	0.01	0.005
1			0.001	0.004	0.016	0.102	1.323	2.706	3.841	5.024	6.635	7.879
2	0.010	0.020	0.051	0.103	0.211	0.575	2.773	4.605	5.991	7.378	9.210	10.597
3	0.072	0.115	0.216	0.352	0.584	1.213	4.108	6.251	7.815	9.348	11.345	12.838
4	0.207	0.297	0.484	0.711	1.064	1.923	5.385	7.779	9.488	11.143	13.277	14.860
5	0.412	0.554	0.831	1.145	1.610	2.675	6.626	9.236	11.071	12.833	15.086	16.750
6	0.676	0.872	1.237	1.635	2.204	3.455	7.841	10.645	12.592	14.449	16.812	18.548
7	0.989	1.239	1.690	2.167	2.833	4.255	9.037	12.017	14.067	16.013	18.475	20.278
8	1.344	1.646	2.180	2.733	3.490	5.071	10.219	13.362	15.507	17.535	20.090	21.955
9	1.735	2.088	2.700	3.325	4.168	5.899	11.389	14.684	16.919	19.023	21.666	23.589
10	2.156	2.558	3.247	3.940	4.865	6.737	12.549	15.987	18.307	20.483	23.209	25.188
11	2.603	3.053	3.816	4.575	5.578	7.584	13.701	17.275	19.675	21.920	24.725	26.757
12	3.074	3.571	4.404	5.226	6.304	8.438	14.845	18.549	21.026	23.337	26.217	28.299
13	3.565	4.107	5.009	5.892	7.042	9.299	15.984	19.812	22.362	24.736	27.688	29.819
14	4.075	4.660	5.629	6.571	7.790	10.165	17.117	21.064	23.685	26.119	29.141	31.319
15	4.601	5.229	6.262	7.261	8.547	11.037	18.245	22.307	24.996	27.488	30.578	32.801
16	5.142	5.812	6.908	7.962	9.312	11.912	19.369	23.542	26.296	28.845	32.000	34.267
17	5.697	6.408	7.564	8.672	10.085	12.792	20.489	24.769	27.587	30.191	33.409	35.718
18	6.265	7.015	8.231	9.390	10.865	13.675	21.605	25.989	28.869	31.526	34.805	37.156
19	6.844	7.633	8.907	10.117	11.651	14.562	22.718	27.204	30.144	32.852	36.191	38.582
20	7.434	8.260	9.591	10.851	12.443	15.452	23.828	28.412	31.410	34.170	37.566	39.997
21	8.034	8.897	10.283	11.591	13.240	16.344	24.935	29.615	32.671	35.479	38.932	41.401
22	8.643	9.542	10.982	12.338	14.042	17.240	26.039	30.813	33.924	36.781	40.289	42.796
23	9.260	10.196	11.689	13.091	14.848	18.137	27.141	32.007	35.172	38.076	41.638	44.181
24	9.886	10.856	12.401	13.848	15.659	19.037	28.241	33.196	36.415	39.364	42.980	45.559
25	10.520	11.524	13.120	14.611	16.473	19.939	29.339	34.382	37.652	40.646	44.314	46.928
26	11.160	12.198	13.844	15.379	17.292	20.843	30.435	35.563	38.885	41.923	45.642	48.290
27	11.808	12.879	14.573	16.151	18.114	21.749	31.528	36.741	40.113	43.194	46.963	49.645
28	12.461	13.565	15.308	16.928	18.939	22.657	32.620	37.916	41.337	44.461	48.278	50.993
29	13.121	14.257	16.047	17.708	19.768	23.567	33.711	39.087	42.557	45.722	49.588	52.336
30	13.787	14.954	16.791	18.493	20.599	24.478	34.800	40.256	43.773	46.979	50.892	53.672

For larger values of degrees of freedom (df) the expression $Z = \sqrt{2\chi^2} - \sqrt{2(df) - 1}$ may be used and the resulting upper-tail area can be found from the cumulative standardized normal distribution (Table C.2).

TABLE C.5

Critical Values of F

For a particular combination of numerator and denominator degrees of freedom, entry represents the critical values of F corresponding to the cumulative probability $(1 - \alpha)$ and a specified upper-tail area (α).

$\alpha = 0.05$

Cumulative Probabilities = 0.95

Upper-Tail Areas = 0.05

Numerator, df_1

Denominator, df_2	1	2	3	4	5	6	7	8	9	10	12	15	20	24	30	40	60	120	∞
1	161.40	199.50	215.70	224.60	230.20	234.00	236.80	238.90	240.50	241.90	243.90	245.90	248.00	249.10	250.10	251.10	252.20	253.30	254.30
2	18.51	19.00	19.16	19.25	19.30	19.33	19.35	19.37	19.38	19.40	19.41	19.43	19.45	19.45	19.46	19.47	19.48	19.49	19.50
3	10.13	9.55	9.28	9.12	9.01	8.94	8.89	8.85	8.81	8.79	8.74	8.70	8.66	8.64	8.62	8.59	8.57	8.55	8.53
4	7.71	6.94	6.59	6.39	6.26	6.16	6.09	6.04	6.00	5.96	5.91	5.86	5.80	5.77	5.75	5.72	5.69	5.66	5.63
5	6.61	5.79	5.41	5.19	5.05	4.95	4.88	4.82	4.77	4.74	4.68	4.62	4.56	4.53	4.50	4.46	4.43	4.40	4.36
6	5.99	5.14	4.76	4.53	4.39	4.28	4.21	4.15	4.10	4.06	4.00	3.94	3.87	3.84	3.81	3.77	3.74	3.70	3.67
7	5.59	4.74	4.35	4.12	3.97	3.87	3.79	3.73	3.68	3.64	3.57	3.51	3.44	3.41	3.38	3.34	3.30	3.27	3.23
8	5.32	4.46	4.07	3.84	3.69	3.58	3.50	3.44	3.39	3.35	3.28	3.22	3.15	3.12	3.08	3.04	3.01	2.97	2.93
9	5.12	4.26	3.86	3.63	3.48	3.37	3.29	3.23	3.18	3.14	3.07	3.01	2.94	2.90	2.86	2.83	2.79	2.75	2.71
10	4.96	4.10	3.71	3.48	3.33	3.22	3.14	3.07	3.02	2.98	2.91	2.85	2.77	2.74	2.70	2.66	2.62	2.58	2.54
11	4.84	3.98	3.59	3.36	3.20	3.09	3.01	2.95	2.90	2.85	2.79	2.72	2.65	2.61	2.57	2.53	2.49	2.45	2.40
12	4.75	3.89	3.49	3.26	3.11	3.00	2.91	2.85	2.80	2.75	2.69	2.62	2.54	2.51	2.47	2.43	2.38	2.34	2.30
13	4.67	3.81	3.41	3.18	3.03	2.92	2.83	2.77	2.71	2.67	2.60	2.53	2.46	2.42	2.38	2.34	2.30	2.25	2.21
14	4.60	3.74	3.34	3.11	2.96	2.85	2.76	2.70	2.65	2.60	2.53	2.46	2.39	2.35	2.31	2.27	2.22	2.18	2.13
15	4.54	3.68	3.29	3.06	2.90	2.79	2.71	2.64	2.59	2.54	2.48	2.40	2.33	2.29	2.25	2.20	2.16	2.11	2.07
16	4.49	3.63	3.24	3.01	2.85	2.74	2.66	2.59	2.54	2.49	2.42	2.35	2.28	2.24	2.19	2.15	2.11	2.06	2.01
17	4.45	3.59	3.20	2.96	2.81	2.70	2.61	2.55	2.49	2.45	2.38	2.31	2.23	2.19	2.15	2.10	2.06	2.01	1.96
18	4.41	3.55	3.16	2.93	2.77	2.66	2.58	2.51	2.46	2.41	2.34	2.27	2.19	2.15	2.11	2.06	2.02	1.97	1.92
19	4.38	3.52	3.13	2.90	2.74	2.63	2.54	2.48	2.42	2.38	2.31	2.23	2.16	2.11	2.07	2.03	1.98	1.93	1.88
20	4.35	3.49	3.10	2.87	2.71	2.60	2.51	2.45	2.39	2.35	2.28	2.20	2.12	2.08	2.04	1.99	1.95	1.90	1.84
21	4.32	3.47	3.07	2.84	2.68	2.57	2.49	2.42	2.37	2.32	2.25	2.18	2.10	2.05	2.01	1.96	1.92	1.87	1.81
22	4.30	3.44	3.05	2.82	2.66	2.55	2.46	2.40	2.34	2.30	2.23	2.15	2.07	2.03	1.98	1.91	1.89	1.84	1.78
23	4.28	3.42	3.03	2.80	2.64	2.53	2.44	2.37	2.32	2.27	2.20	2.13	2.05	2.01	1.96	1.91	1.86	1.81	1.76
24	4.26	3.40	3.01	2.78	2.62	2.51	2.42	2.36	2.30	2.25	2.18	2.11	2.03	1.98	1.94	1.89	1.84	1.79	1.73
25	4.24	3.39	2.99	2.76	2.60	2.49	2.40	2.34	2.28	2.24	2.16	2.09	2.01	1.96	1.92	1.87	1.82	1.77	1.71
26	4.23	3.37	2.98	2.74	2.59	2.47	2.39	2.32	2.27	2.22	2.15	2.07	1.99	1.95	1.90	1.85	1.80	1.75	1.69
27	4.21	3.35	2.96	2.73	2.57	2.46	2.37	2.31	2.25	2.20	2.13	2.06	1.97	1.93	1.88	1.84	1.79	1.73	1.67
28	4.20	3.34	2.95	2.71	2.56	2.45	2.36	2.29	2.24	2.19	2.12	2.04	1.96	1.91	1.87	1.82	1.77	1.71	1.65
29	4.18	3.33	2.93	2.70	2.55	2.43	2.35	2.28	2.22	2.18	2.10	2.03	1.94	1.90	1.85	1.81	1.75	1.70	1.64
30	4.17	3.32	2.92	2.69	2.53	2.42	2.33	2.27	2.21	2.16	2.09	2.01	1.93	1.89	1.84	1.79	1.74	1.68	1.62
40	4.08	3.23	2.84	2.61	2.45	2.34	2.25	2.18	2.12	2.08	2.00	1.92	1.84	1.79	1.74	1.69	1.64	1.58	1.51
60	4.00	3.15	2.76	2.53	2.37	2.25	2.17	2.10	2.04	1.99	1.92	1.84	1.75	1.70	1.65	1.59	1.53	1.47	1.39
120	3.92	3.07	2.68	2.45	2.29	2.17	2.09	2.02	1.96	1.91	1.83	1.75	1.66	1.61	1.55	1.50	1.43	1.35	1.25
∞	3.84	3.00	2.60	2.37	2.21	2.10	2.01	1.94	1.88	1.83	1.75	1.67	1.57	1.52	1.46	1.39	1.32	1.22	1.00

(continued)

TABLE C.5

Critical Values of F (continued)

For a particular combination of numerator and denominator degrees of freedom, entry represents the critical values of F corresponding to the cumulative probability $(1 - \alpha)$ and a specified upper-tail area (α).

α = 0.025

Cumulative Probabilities = 0.975

Upper-Tail Areas = 0.025

Numerator, df_1

Denominator, df_2	1	2	3	4	5	6	7	8	9	10	12	15	20	24	30	40	60	120	∞
1	647.80	799.50	864.20	899.60	921.80	937.10	948.20	956.70	963.30	968.60	976.70	984.90	993.10	997.20	1,001.00	1,006.00	1,010.00	1,014.00	1,018.00
2	38.51	39.00	39.17	39.25	39.30	39.33	39.36	39.39	39.39	39.40	39.41	39.43	39.45	39.46	39.46	39.47	39.48	39.49	39.50
3	17.44	16.04	15.44	15.10	14.88	14.73	14.62	14.54	14.47	14.42	14.34	14.25	14.17	14.12	14.08	14.04	13.99	13.95	13.90
4	12.22	10.65	9.98	9.60	9.36	9.20	9.07	8.98	8.90	8.84	8.75	8.66	8.56	8.51	8.46	8.41	8.36	8.31	8.26
5	10.01	8.43	7.76	7.39	7.15	6.98	6.85	6.76	6.68	6.62	6.52	6.43	6.33	6.28	6.23	6.18	6.12	6.07	6.02
6	8.81	7.26	6.60	6.23	5.99	5.82	5.70	5.60	5.52	5.46	5.37	5.27	5.17	5.12	5.07	5.01	4.96	4.90	4.85
7	8.07	6.54	5.89	5.52	5.29	5.12	4.99	4.90	4.82	4.76	4.67	4.57	4.47	4.42	4.36	4.31	4.25	4.20	4.14
8	7.57	6.06	5.42	5.05	4.82	4.65	4.53	4.43	4.36	4.30	4.20	4.10	4.00	3.95	3.89	3.84	3.78	3.73	3.67
9	7.21	5.71	5.08	4.72	4.48	4.32	4.20	4.10	4.03	3.96	3.87	3.77	3.67	3.61	3.56	3.51	3.45	3.39	3.33
10	6.94	5.46	4.83	4.47	4.24	4.07	3.95	3.85	3.78	3.72	3.62	3.52	3.42	3.37	3.31	3.26	3.20	3.14	3.08
11	6.72	5.26	4.63	4.28	4.04	3.88	3.76	3.66	3.59	3.53	3.43	3.33	3.23	3.17	3.12	3.06	3.00	2.94	2.88
12	6.55	5.10	4.47	4.12	3.89	3.73	3.61	3.51	3.44	3.37	3.28	3.18	3.07	3.02	2.96	2.91	2.85	2.79	2.72
13	6.41	4.97	4.35	4.00	3.77	3.60	3.48	3.39	3.31	3.25	3.15	3.05	2.95	2.89	2.84	2.78	2.72	2.66	2.60
14	6.30	4.86	4.24	3.89	3.66	3.50	3.38	3.29	3.21	3.15	3.05	2.95	2.84	2.79	2.73	2.67	2.61	2.55	2.49
15	6.20	4.77	4.15	3.80	3.58	3.41	3.29	3.20	3.12	3.06	2.96	2.86	2.76	2.70	2.64	2.59	2.52	2.46	2.40
16	6.12	4.69	4.08	3.73	3.50	3.34	3.22	3.12	3.05	2.99	2.89	2.79	2.68	2.63	2.57	2.51	2.45	2.38	2.32
17	6.04	4.62	4.01	3.66	3.44	3.28	3.16	3.06	2.98	2.92	2.82	2.72	2.62	2.56	2.50	2.44	2.38	2.32	2.25
18	5.98	4.56	3.95	3.61	3.38	3.22	3.10	3.01	2.93	2.87	2.77	2.67	2.56	2.50	2.44	2.38	2.32	2.26	2.19
19	5.92	4.51	3.90	3.56	3.33	3.17	3.05	2.96	2.88	2.82	2.72	2.62	2.51	2.45	2.39	2.33	2.27	2.20	2.13
20	5.87	4.46	3.86	3.51	3.29	3.13	3.01	2.91	2.84	2.77	2.68	2.57	2.46	2.41	2.35	2.29	2.22	2.16	2.09
21	5.83	4.42	3.82	3.48	3.25	3.09	2.97	2.87	2.80	2.73	2.64	2.53	2.42	2.37	2.31	2.25	2.18	2.11	2.04
22	5.79	4.38	3.78	3.44	3.22	3.05	2.93	2.84	2.76	2.70	2.60	2.50	2.39	2.33	2.27	2.21	2.14	2.08	2.00
23	5.75	4.35	3.75	3.41	3.18	3.02	2.90	2.81	2.73	2.67	2.57	2.47	2.36	2.30	2.24	2.18	2.11	2.04	1.97
24	5.72	4.32	3.72	3.38	3.15	2.99	2.87	2.78	2.70	2.64	2.54	2.44	2.33	2.27	2.21	2.15	2.08	2.01	1.94
25	5.69	4.29	3.69	3.35	3.13	2.97	2.85	2.75	2.68	2.61	2.51	2.41	2.30	2.24	2.18	2.12	2.05	1.98	1.91
26	5.66	4.27	3.67	3.33	3.10	2.94	2.82	2.73	2.65	2.59	2.49	2.39	2.28	2.22	2.16	2.09	2.03	1.95	1.88
27	5.63	4.24	3.65	3.31	3.08	2.92	2.80	2.71	2.63	2.57	2.47	2.36	2.25	2.19	2.13	2.07	2.00	1.93	1.85
28	5.61	4.22	3.63	3.29	3.06	2.90	2.78	2.69	2.61	2.55	2.45	2.34	2.23	2.17	2.11	2.05	1.98	1.91	1.83
29	5.59	4.20	3.61	3.27	3.04	2.88	2.76	2.67	2.59	2.53	2.43	2.32	2.21	2.15	2.09	2.03	1.96	1.89	1.81
30	5.57	4.18	3.59	3.25	3.03	2.87	2.75	2.65	2.57	2.51	2.41	2.31	2.20	2.14	2.07	2.01	1.94	1.87	1.79
40	5.42	4.05	3.46	3.13	2.90	2.74	2.62	2.53	2.45	2.39	2.29	2.18	2.07	2.01	1.94	1.88	1.80	1.72	1.64
60	5.29	3.93	3.34	3.01	2.79	2.63	2.51	2.41	2.33	2.27	2.17	2.06	1.94	1.88	1.82	1.74	1.67	1.58	1.48
120	5.15	3.80	3.23	2.89	2.67	2.52	2.39	2.30	2.22	2.16	2.05	1.94	1.82	1.76	1.69	1.61	1.53	1.43	1.31
∞	5.02	3.69	3.12	2.79	2.57	2.41	2.29	2.19	2.11	2.05	1.94	1.83	1.71	1.64	1.57	1.48	1.39	1.27	1.00

TABLE C.5

Critical Values of F (continued)

For a particular combination of numerator and denominator degrees of freedom, entry represents the critical values of F corresponding to the cumulative probability $(1 - \alpha)$ and a specified upper-tail area (α).

Cumulative Probabilities = 0.99

Upper-Tail Areas = 0.01

Denominator, df_2	Numerator, df_1																		
	1	2	3	4	5	6	7	8	9	10	12	15	20	24	30	40	60	120	∞
1	4,052.00	4,999.50	5,403.00	5,625.00	5,764.00	5,859.00	5,928.00	5,982.00	6,022.00	6,056.00	6,106.00	6,157.00	6,209.00	6,235.00	6,261.00	6,287.00	6,313.00	6,339.00	6,366.00
2	98.50	99.00	99.17	99.25	99.30	99.33	99.36	99.37	99.39	99.40	99.42	99.43	44.45	99.46	99.47	99.47	99.48	99.49	99.50
3	34.12	30.82	29.46	28.71	28.24	27.91	27.67	27.49	27.35	27.23	27.05	26.87	26.69	26.60	26.50	26.41	26.32	26.22	26.13
4	21.20	18.00	16.69	15.98	15.52	15.21	14.98	14.80	14.66	14.55	14.37	14.20	14.02	13.93	13.84	13.75	13.65	13.56	13.46
5	16.26	13.27	12.06	11.39	10.97	10.67	10.46	10.29	10.16	10.05	9.89	9.72	9.55	9.47	9.38	9.29	9.20	9.11	9.02
6	13.75	10.92	9.78	9.15	8.75	8.47	8.26	8.10	7.98	7.87	7.72	7.56	7.40	7.31	7.23	7.14	7.06	6.97	6.88
7	12.25	9.55	8.45	7.85	7.46	7.19	6.99	6.84	6.72	6.62	6.47	6.31	6.16	6.07	5.99	5.91	5.82	5.74	5.65
8	11.26	8.65	7.59	7.01	6.63	6.37	6.18	6.03	5.91	5.81	5.67	5.52	5.36	5.28	5.20	5.12	5.03	4.95	4.86
9	10.56	8.02	6.99	6.42	6.06	5.80	5.61	5.47	5.35	5.26	5.11	4.96	4.81	4.73	4.65	4.57	4.48	4.40	4.31
10	10.04	7.56	6.55	5.99	5.64	5.39	5.20	5.06	4.94	4.85	4.71	4.56	4.41	4.33	4.25	4.17	4.08	4.00	3.91
11	9.65	7.21	6.22	5.67	5.32	5.07	4.89	4.74	4.63	4.54	4.40	4.25	4.10	4.02	3.94	3.86	3.78	3.69	3.60
12	9.33	6.93	5.95	5.41	5.06	4.82	4.64	4.50	4.39	4.30	4.16	4.01	3.86	3.78	3.70	3.62	3.54	3.45	3.36
13	9.07	6.70	5.74	5.21	4.86	4.62	4.44	4.30	4.19	4.10	3.96	3.82	3.66	3.59	3.51	3.43	3.34	3.25	3.17
14	8.86	6.51	5.56	5.04	4.69	4.46	4.28	4.14	4.03	3.94	3.80	3.66	3.51	3.43	3.35	3.27	3.18	3.09	3.00
15	8.68	6.36	5.42	4.89	4.56	4.32	4.14	4.00	3.89	3.80	3.67	3.52	3.37	3.29	3.21	3.13	3.05	2.96	2.87
16	8.53	6.23	5.29	4.77	4.44	4.20	4.03	3.89	3.78	3.69	3.55	3.41	3.26	3.18	3.10	3.02	2.93	2.81	2.75
17	8.40	6.11	5.18	4.67	4.34	4.10	3.93	3.79	3.68	3.59	3.46	3.31	3.16	3.08	3.00	2.92	2.83	2.75	2.65
18	8.29	6.01	5.09	4.58	4.25	4.01	3.84	3.71	3.60	3.51	3.37	3.23	3.08	3.00	2.92	2.84	2.75	2.66	2.57
19	8.18	5.93	5.01	4.50	4.17	3.94	3.77	3.63	3.52	3.43	3.30	3.15	3.00	2.92	2.84	2.76	2.67	2.58	2.49
20	8.10	5.85	4.94	4.43	4.10	3.87	3.70	3.56	3.46	3.37	3.23	3.09	2.94	2.86	2.78	2.69	2.61	2.52	2.42
21	8.02	5.78	4.87	4.37	4.04	3.81	3.64	3.51	3.40	3.31	3.17	3.03	2.88	2.80	2.72	2.64	2.55	2.46	2.36
22	7.95	5.72	4.82	4.31	3.99	3.76	3.59	3.45	3.35	3.26	3.12	2.98	2.83	2.75	2.67	2.58	2.50	2.40	2.31
23	7.88	5.66	4.76	4.26	3.94	3.71	3.54	3.41	3.30	3.21	3.07	2.93	2.78	2.70	2.62	2.54	2.45	2.35	2.26
24	7.82	5.61	4.72	4.22	3.90	3.67	3.50	3.36	3.26	3.17	3.03	2.89	2.74	2.66	2.58	2.49	2.40	2.31	2.21
25	7.77	5.57	4.68	4.18	3.85	3.63	3.46	3.32	3.22	3.13	2.99	2.85	2.70	2.62	2.54	2.45	2.36	2.27	2.17
26	7.72	5.53	4.64	4.14	3.82	3.59	3.42	3.29	3.18	3.09	2.96	2.81	2.66	2.58	2.50	2.42	2.33	2.23	2.13
27	7.68	5.49	4.60	4.11	3.78	3.56	3.39	3.26	3.15	3.06	2.93	2.78	2.63	2.55	2.47	2.38	2.29	2.20	2.10
28	7.64	5.45	4.57	4.07	3.75	3.53	3.36	3.23	3.12	3.03	2.90	2.75	2.60	2.52	2.44	2.35	2.26	2.17	2.06
29	7.60	5.42	4.54	4.04	3.73	3.50	3.33	3.20	3.09	3.00	2.87	2.73	2.57	2.49	2.41	2.33	2.23	2.14	2.03
30	7.56	5.39	4.51	4.02	3.70	3.47	3.30	3.17	3.07	2.98	2.84	2.70	2.55	2.47	2.39	2.30	2.21	2.11	2.01
40	7.31	5.18	4.31	3.83	3.51	3.29	3.12	2.99	2.89	2.80	2.66	2.52	2.37	2.29	2.20	2.11	2.02	1.92	1.80
60	7.08	4.98	4.13	3.65	3.34	3.12	2.95	2.82	2.72	2.63	2.50	2.35	2.20	2.12	2.03	1.94	1.84	1.73	1.60
120	6.85	4.79	3.95	3.48	3.17	2.96	2.79	2.66	2.56	2.47	2.34	2.19	2.03	1.95	1.86	1.76	1.66	1.53	1.38
∞	6.63	4.61	3.78	3.32	3.02	2.80	2.64	2.51	2.41	2.32	2.18	2.04	1.88	1.79	1.70	1.59	1.47	1.32	1.00

$\alpha = 0.01$

F

(continued)

α = 0.005

F

TABLE C.5

Critical Values of F (continued)

For a particular combination of numerator and denominator degrees of freedom, entry represents the critical values of F corresponding to the cumulative probability $(1 - \alpha)$ and a specified upper-tail area (α).

Cumulative Probabilities = 0.995

Upper – Tail Areas = 0.005

Numerator, df_1

Denominator, df_2	1	2	3	4	5	6	7	8	9	10	12	15	20	24	30	40	60	120	∞
1	16,211.00	20,000.00	21,615.00	22,500.00	23,056.00	23,437.00	23,715.00	23,925.00	24,091.00	24,224.00	24,426.00	24,630.00	24,836.00	24,910.00	25,044.00	25,148.00	25,253.00	25,359.00	25,465.00
2	198.50	199.00	199.20	199.20	199.30	199.30	199.40	199.40	199.40	199.40	199.40	199.40	199.40	199.50	199.50	199.50	199.50	199.50	199.50
3	55.55	49.80	47.47	46.19	45.39	44.84	44.43	44.13	43.88	43.69	43.39	43.08	42.78	42.62	42.47	42.31	42.15	41.99	41.83
4	31.33	26.28	24.26	23.15	22.46	21.97	21.62	21.35	21.14	20.97	20.70	20.44	20.17	20.03	19.89	19.75	19.61	19.47	19.32
5	22.78	18.31	16.53	15.56	14.94	14.51	14.20	13.96	13.77	13.62	13.38	13.15	12.90	12.78	12.66	12.53	12.40	12.27	12.11
6	18.63	14.54	12.92	12.03	11.46	11.07	10.79	10.57	10.39	10.25	10.03	9.81	9.59	9.47	9.36	9.24	9.12	9.00	8.88
7	16.24	12.40	10.88	10.05	9.52	9.16	8.89	8.68	8.51	8.38	8.18	7.97	7.75	7.65	7.53	7.42	7.31	7.19	7.08
8	14.69	11.04	9.60	8.81	8.30	7.95	7.69	7.50	7.34	7.21	7.01	6.81	6.61	6.50	6.40	6.29	6.18	6.06	5.95
9	13.61	10.11	8.72	7.96	7.47	7.13	6.88	6.69	6.54	6.42	6.23	6.03	5.83	5.73	5.62	5.52	5.41	5.30	5.19
10	12.83	9.43	8.08	7.34	6.87	6.54	6.30	6.12	5.97	5.85	5.66	5.47	5.27	5.17	5.07	4.97	4.86	4.75	4.61
11	12.23	8.91	7.60	6.88	6.42	6.10	5.86	5.68	5.54	5.42	5.24	5.05	4.86	4.75	4.65	4.55	4.44	4.34	4.23
12	11.75	8.51	7.23	6.52	6.07	5.76	5.52	5.35	5.20	5.09	4.91	4.72	4.53	4.43	4.33	4.23	4.12	4.01	3.90
13	11.37	8.19	6.93	6.23	5.79	5.48	5.25	5.08	4.94	4.82	4.64	4.46	4.27	4.17	4.07	3.97	3.87	3.76	3.65
14	11.06	7.92	6.68	6.00	5.56	5.26	5.03	4.86	4.72	4.60	4.43	4.25	4.06	3.96	3.86	3.76	3.66	3.55	3.41
15	10.80	7.70	6.48	5.80	5.37	5.07	4.85	4.67	4.54	4.42	4.25	4.07	3.88	3.79	3.69	3.58	3.48	3.37	3.26
16	10.58	7.51	6.30	5.64	5.21	4.91	4.69	4.52	4.38	4.27	4.10	3.92	3.73	3.64	3.54	3.44	3.33	3.22	3.11
17	10.38	7.35	6.16	5.50	5.07	4.78	4.56	4.39	4.25	4.14	3.97	3.79	3.61	3.51	3.41	3.31	3.21	3.10	2.98
18	10.22	7.21	6.03	5.37	4.96	4.66	4.44	4.28	4.14	4.03	3.86	3.68	3.50	3.40	3.30	3.20	3.10	2.99	2.87
19	10.07	7.09	5.92	5.27	4.85	4.56	4.34	4.18	4.04	3.93	3.76	3.59	3.40	3.31	3.21	3.11	3.00	2.89	2.78
20	9.94	6.99	5.82	5.17	4.76	4.47	4.26	4.09	3.96	3.85	3.68	3.50	3.32	3.22	3.12	3.02	2.92	2.81	2.69
21	9.83	6.89	5.73	5.09	4.68	4.39	4.18	4.02	3.88	3.77	3.60	3.43	3.24	3.15	3.05	2.95	2.84	2.73	2.61
22	9.73	6.81	5.65	5.02	4.61	4.32	4.11	3.94	3.81	3.70	3.54	3.36	3.18	3.08	2.98	2.88	2.77	2.66	2.55
23	9.63	6.73	5.58	4.95	4.54	4.26	4.05	3.88	3.75	3.64	3.47	3.30	3.12	3.02	2.92	2.82	2.71	2.60	2.48
24	9.55	6.66	5.52	4.89	4.49	4.20	3.99	3.83	3.69	3.59	3.42	3.25	3.06	2.97	2.87	2.77	2.66	2.55	2.43
25	9.48	6.60	5.46	4.84	4.43	4.15	3.94	3.78	3.64	3.54	3.37	3.20	3.01	2.92	2.82	2.72	2.61	2.50	2.38
26	9.41	6.54	5.41	4.79	4.38	4.10	3.89	3.73	3.60	3.49	3.33	3.15	2.97	2.87	2.77	2.67	2.56	2.45	2.33
27	9.34	6.49	5.36	4.74	4.34	4.06	3.85	3.69	3.56	3.45	3.28	3.11	2.93	2.83	2.73	2.63	2.52	2.41	2.29
28	9.28	6.44	5.32	4.70	4.30	4.02	3.81	3.65	3.52	3.41	3.25	3.07	2.89	2.79	2.69	2.59	2.48	2.37	2.25
29	9.23	6.40	5.28	4.66	4.26	3.98	3.77	3.61	3.48	3.38	3.21	3.04	2.86	2.76	2.66	2.56	2.45	2.33	2.21
30	9.18	6.35	5.24	4.62	4.23	3.95	3.74	3.58	3.45	3.34	3.18	3.01	2.82	2.73	2.63	2.52	2.42	2.30	2.18
40	8.83	6.07	4.98	4.37	3.99	3.71	3.51	3.35	3.22	3.12	2.95	2.78	2.60	2.50	2.40	2.30	2.18	2.06	1.93
60	8.49	5.79	4.73	4.14	3.76	3.49	3.29	3.13	3.01	2.90	2.74	2.57	2.39	2.29	2.19	2.08	1.96	1.83	1.69
120	8.18	5.54	4.50	3.92	3.55	3.28	3.09	2.93	2.81	2.71	2.54	2.37	2.19	2.09	1.98	1.87	1.75	1.61	1.43
∞	7.88	5.30	4.28	3.72	3.35	3.09	2.90	2.74	2.62	2.52	2.36	2.19	2.00	1.90	1.79	1.67	1.53	1.36	1.00

TABLE C.6

Critical Values of the Studentized Range, Q

Upper 5% Points ($\alpha = 0.05$)

Denominator, df	Numerator, df																		
	2	3	4	5	6	7	8	9	10	11	12	13	14	15	16	17	18	19	20
1	18.00	27.00	32.80	37.10	40.40	43.10	45.40	47.40	49.10	50.60	52.00	53.20	54.30	55.40	56.30	57.20	58.00	58.80	59.60
2	6.09	8.30	9.80	10.90	11.70	12.40	13.00	13.50	14.00	14.40	14.70	15.10	15.40	15.70	15.90	16.10	16.40	16.60	16.80
3	4.50	5.91	6.82	7.50	8.04	8.48	8.85	9.18	9.46	9.72	9.95	10.15	10.35	10.52	10.69	10.84	10.98	11.11	11.24
4	3.93	5.04	5.76	6.29	6.71	7.05	7.35	7.60	7.83	8.03	8.21	8.37	8.52	8.66	8.79	8.91	9.03	9.13	9.23
5	3.64	4.60	5.22	5.67	6.03	6.33	6.58	6.80	6.99	7.17	7.32	7.47	7.60	7.72	7.83	7.93	8.03	8.12	8.21
6	3.46	4.34	4.90	5.31	5.63	5.89	6.12	6.32	6.49	6.65	6.79	6.92	7.03	7.14	7.24	7.34	7.43	7.51	7.59
7	3.34	4.16	4.68	5.06	5.36	5.61	5.82	6.00	6.16	6.30	6.43	6.55	6.66	6.76	6.85	6.94	7.02	7.09	7.17
8	3.26	4.04	4.53	4.89	5.17	5.40	5.60	5.77	5.92	6.05	6.18	6.29	6.39	6.48	6.57	6.65	6.73	6.80	6.87
9	3.20	3.95	4.42	4.76	5.02	5.24	5.43	5.60	5.74	5.87	5.98	6.09	6.19	6.28	6.36	6.44	6.51	6.58	6.64
10	3.15	3.88	4.33	4.65	4.91	5.12	5.30	5.46	5.60	5.72	5.83	5.93	6.03	6.11	6.20	6.27	6.34	6.40	6.47
11	3.11	3.82	4.26	4.57	4.82	5.03	5.20	5.35	5.49	5.61	5.71	5.81	5.90	5.99	6.06	6.14	6.20	6.26	6.33
12	3.08	3.77	4.20	4.51	4.75	4.95	5.12	5.27	5.40	5.51	5.62	5.71	5.80	5.88	5.95	6.03	6.09	6.15	6.21
13	3.06	3.73	4.15	4.45	4.69	4.88	5.05	5.19	5.32	5.43	5.53	5.63	5.71	5.79	5.86	5.93	6.00	6.05	6.11
14	3.03	3.70	4.11	4.41	4.64	4.83	4.99	5.13	5.25	5.36	5.46	5.55	5.64	5.72	5.79	5.85	5.92	5.97	6.03
15	3.01	3.67	4.08	4.37	4.60	4.78	4.94	5.08	5.20	5.31	5.40	5.49	5.58	5.65	5.72	5.79	5.85	5.90	5.96
16	3.00	3.65	4.05	4.33	4.56	4.74	4.90	5.03	5.15	5.26	5.35	5.44	5.52	5.59	5.66	5.72	5.79	5.84	5.90
17	2.98	3.63	4.02	4.30	4.52	4.71	4.86	4.99	5.11	5.21	5.31	5.39	5.47	5.55	5.61	5.68	5.74	5.79	5.84
18	2.97	3.61	4.00	4.28	4.49	4.67	4.82	4.96	5.07	5.17	5.27	5.35	5.43	5.50	5.57	5.63	5.69	5.74	5.79
19	2.96	3.59	3.98	4.25	4.47	4.65	4.79	4.92	5.04	5.14	5.23	5.32	5.39	5.46	5.53	5.59	5.65	5.70	5.75
20	2.95	3.58	3.96	4.23	4.45	4.62	4.77	4.90	5.01	5.11	5.20	5.28	5.36	5.43	5.49	5.55	5.61	5.66	5.71
24	2.92	3.53	3.90	4.17	4.37	4.54	4.68	4.81	4.92	5.01	5.10	5.18	5.25	5.32	5.38	5.44	5.50	5.54	5.59
30	2.89	3.49	3.84	4.10	4.30	4.46	4.60	4.72	4.83	4.92	5.00	5.08	5.15	5.21	5.27	5.33	5.38	5.43	5.48
40	2.86	3.44	3.79	4.04	4.23	4.39	4.52	4.63	4.74	4.82	4.91	4.98	5.05	5.11	5.16	5.22	5.27	5.31	5.36
60	2.83	3.40	3.74	3.98	4.16	4.31	4.44	4.55	4.65	4.73	4.81	4.88	4.94	5.00	5.06	5.11	5.16	5.20	5.24
120	2.80	3.36	3.69	3.92	4.10	4.24	4.36	4.48	4.56	4.64	4.72	4.78	4.84	4.90	4.95	5.00	5.05	5.09	5.13
∞	2.77	3.31	3.63	3.86	4.03	4.17	4.29	4.39	4.47	4.55	4.62	4.68	4.74	4.80	4.85	4.89	4.93	4.97	5.01

TABLE C.6

Critical Values of the Studentized Range, Q (continued)

Upper 1% Points ($\alpha = 0.01$)

Denominator, df	Numerator, df																		
	2	3	4	5	6	7	8	9	10	11	12	13	14	15	16	17	18	19	20
1	90.03	135.00	164.30	185.60	202.20	215.80	227.20	237.00	245.60	253.20	260.00	266.20	271.80	277.00	281.80	286.30	290.40	294.30	298.00
2	14.04	19.02	22.29	24.72	26.63	28.20	29.53	30.68	31.69	32.59	33.40	34.13	34.81	35.43	36.00	36.53	37.03	37.50	37.95
3	8.26	10.62	12.17	13.33	14.24	15.00	15.64	16.20	16.69	17.13	17.53	17.89	18.22	18.52	18.81	19.07	19.32	19.55	19.77
4	6.51	8.12	9.17	9.96	10.58	11.10	11.55	11.93	12.27	12.57	12.84	13.09	13.32	13.53	13.73	13.91	14.08	14.24	14.40
5	5.70	6.98	7.80	8.42	8.91	9.32	9.67	9.97	10.24	10.48	10.70	10.89	11.08	11.24	11.40	11.55	11.68	11.81	11.93
6	5.24	6.33	7.03	7.56	7.97	8.32	8.61	8.87	9.10	9.30	9.49	9.65	9.81	9.95	10.08	10.21	10.32	10.43	10.54
7	4.95	5.92	6.54	7.01	7.37	7.68	7.94	8.17	8.37	8.55	8.71	8.86	9.00	9.12	9.24	9.35	9.46	9.55	9.65
8	4.75	5.64	6.20	6.63	6.96	7.24	7.47	7.68	7.86	8.03	8.18	8.31	8.44	8.55	8.66	8.76	8.85	8.94	9.03
9	4.60	5.43	5.96	6.35	6.66	6.92	7.13	7.32	7.50	7.65	7.78	7.91	8.03	8.13	8.23	8.33	8.41	8.50	8.57
10	4.48	5.27	5.77	6.14	6.43	6.67	6.87	7.06	7.21	7.36	7.49	7.60	7.71	7.81	7.91	7.99	8.08	8.15	8.23
11	4.39	5.15	5.62	5.97	6.25	6.48	6.67	6.84	6.99	7.13	7.25	7.36	7.47	7.56	7.65	7.73	7.81	7.88	7.95
12	4.32	5.04	5.50	5.84	6.10	6.32	6.51	6.67	6.81	6.94	7.06	7.17	7.26	7.36	7.44	7.52	7.59	7.66	7.73
13	4.26	4.96	5.40	5.73	5.98	6.19	6.37	6.53	6.67	6.79	6.90	7.01	7.10	7.19	7.27	7.35	7.42	7.49	7.55
14	4.21	4.90	5.32	5.63	5.88	6.09	6.26	6.41	6.54	6.66	6.77	6.87	6.96	7.05	7.13	7.20	7.27	7.33	7.40
15	4.17	4.84	5.25	5.56	5.80	5.99	6.16	6.31	6.44	6.56	6.66	6.76	6.85	6.93	7.00	7.07	7.14	7.20	7.26
16	4.13	4.79	5.19	5.49	5.72	5.92	6.08	6.22	6.35	6.46	6.56	6.66	6.74	6.82	6.90	6.97	7.03	7.09	7.15
17	4.10	4.74	5.14	5.43	5.66	5.85	6.01	6.15	6.27	6.38	6.48	6.57	6.66	6.73	6.81	6.87	6.94	7.00	7.05
18	4.07	4.70	5.09	5.38	5.60	5.79	5.94	6.08	6.20	6.31	6.41	6.50	6.58	6.66	6.73	6.79	6.85	6.91	6.97
19	4.05	4.67	5.05	5.33	5.55	5.74	5.89	6.02	6.14	6.25	6.34	6.43	6.51	6.59	6.65	6.72	6.78	6.84	6.89
20	4.02	4.64	5.02	5.29	5.51	5.69	5.84	5.97	6.09	6.19	6.29	6.37	6.45	6.52	6.59	6.65	6.71	6.77	6.82
24	3.96	4.55	4.91	5.17	5.37	5.54	5.69	5.81	5.92	6.02	6.11	6.19	6.26	6.33	6.39	6.45	6.51	6.56	6.61
30	3.89	4.46	4.80	5.05	5.24	5.40	5.54	5.65	5.76	5.85	5.93	6.01	6.08	6.14	6.20	6.26	6.31	6.36	6.41
40	3.83	4.37	4.70	4.93	5.11	5.27	5.39	5.50	5.60	5.69	5.76	5.84	5.90	5.96	6.02	6.07	6.12	6.17	6.21
60	3.76	4.28	4.60	4.82	4.99	5.13	5.25	5.36	5.45	5.53	5.60	5.67	5.73	5.79	5.84	5.89	5.93	5.97	6.02
120	3.70	4.20	4.50	4.71	4.87	5.01	5.12	5.21	5.30	5.38	5.44	5.51	5.56	5.61	5.66	5.71	5.75	5.79	5.83
∞	3.64	4.12	4.40	4.60	4.76	4.88	4.99	5.08	5.16	5.23	5.29	5.35	5.40	5.45	5.49	5.54	5.57	5.61	5.65

Source: Extracted from H. L. Harter and D. S. Clemm, "The Probability Integrals of the Range and of the Studentized Range—Probability Integral, Percentage Points, and Moments of the Range," *Wright Air Development Technical Report 58–484*, Vol. 1, 1959.

TABLE C.7

Critical Values, d_L and d_U of the Durbin-Watson Statistic, D (Critical Values Are One-Sided)[a]

| | $\alpha = 0.05$ | | | | | | | | | | $\alpha = 0.01$ | | | | | | | | | |
| | k = 1 | | k = 2 | | k = 3 | | k = 4 | | k = 5 | | k = 1 | | k = 2 | | k = 3 | | k = 4 | | k = 5 | |
n	d_L	d_U	d_L	d_U	d_L	d_U	d_L	d_U	d_L	d_U	d_L	d_U	d_L	d_U	d_L	d_U	d_L	d_U	d_L	d_U
15	1.08	1.36	.95	1.54	.82	1.75	.69	1.97	.56	2.21	.81	1.07	.70	1.25	.59	1.46	.49	1.70	.39	1.96
16	1.10	1.37	.98	1.54	.86	1.73	.74	1.93	.62	2.15	.84	1.09	.74	1.25	.63	1.44	.53	1.66	.44	1.90
17	1.13	1.38	1.02	1.54	.90	1.71	.78	1.90	.67	2.10	.87	1.10	.77	1.25	.67	1.43	.57	1.63	.48	1.85
18	1.16	1.39	1.05	1.53	.93	1.69	.82	1.87	.71	2.06	.90	1.12	.80	1.26	.71	1.42	.61	1.60	.52	1.80
19	1.18	1.40	1.08	1.53	.97	1.68	.86	1.85	.75	2.02	.93	1.13	.83	1.26	.74	1.41	.65	1.58	.56	1.77
20	1.20	1.41	1.10	1.54	1.00	1.68	.90	1.83	.79	1.99	.95	1.15	.86	1.27	.77	1.41	.68	1.57	.60	1.74
21	1.22	1.42	1.13	1.54	1.03	1.67	.93	1.81	.83	1.96	.97	1.16	.89	1.27	.80	1.41	.72	1.55	.63	1.71
22	1.24	1.43	1.15	1.54	1.05	1.66	.96	1.80	.86	1.94	1.00	1.17	.91	1.28	.83	1.40	.75	1.54	.66	1.69
23	1.26	1.44	1.17	1.54	1.08	1.66	.99	1.79	.90	1.92	1.02	1.19	.94	1.29	.86	1.40	.77	1.53	.70	1.67
24	1.27	1.45	1.19	1.55	1.10	1.66	1.01	1.78	.93	1.90	1.04	1.20	.96	1.30	.88	1.41	.80	1.53	.72	1.66
25	1.29	1.45	1.21	1.55	1.12	1.66	1.04	1.77	.95	1.89	1.05	1.21	.98	1.30	.90	1.41	.83	1.52	.75	1.65
26	1.30	1.46	1.22	1.55	1.14	1.65	1.06	1.76	.98	1.88	1.07	1.22	1.00	1.31	.93	1.41	.85	1.52	.78	1.64
27	1.32	1.47	1.24	1.56	1.16	1.65	1.08	1.76	1.01	1.86	1.09	1.23	1.02	1.32	.95	1.41	.88	1.51	.81	1.63
28	1.33	1.48	1.26	1.56	1.18	1.65	1.10	1.75	1.03	1.85	1.10	1.24	1.04	1.32	.97	1.41	.90	1.51	.83	1.62
29	1.34	1.48	1.27	1.56	1.20	1.65	1.12	1.74	1.05	1.84	1.12	1.25	1.05	1.33	.99	1.42	.92	1.51	.85	1.61
30	1.35	1.49	1.28	1.57	1.21	1.65	1.14	1.74	1.07	1.83	1.13	1.26	1.07	1.34	1.01	1.42	.94	1.51	.88	1.61
31	1.36	1.50	1.30	1.57	1.23	1.65	1.16	1.74	1.09	1.83	1.15	1.27	1.08	1.34	1.02	1.42	.96	1.51	.90	1.60
32	1.37	1.50	1.31	1.57	1.24	1.65	1.18	1.73	1.11	1.82	1.16	1.28	1.10	1.35	1.04	1.43	.98	1.51	.92	1.60
33	1.38	1.51	1.32	1.58	1.26	1.65	1.19	1.73	1.13	1.81	1.17	1.29	1.11	1.36	1.05	1.43	1.00	1.51	.94	1.59
34	1.39	1.51	1.33	1.58	1.27	1.65	1.21	1.73	1.15	1.81	1.18	1.30	1.13	1.36	1.07	1.43	1.01	1.51	.95	1.59
35	1.40	1.52	1.34	1.58	1.28	1.65	1.22	1.73	1.16	1.80	1.19	1.31	1.14	1.37	1.08	1.44	1.03	1.51	.97	1.59
36	1.41	1.52	1.35	1.59	1.29	1.65	1.24	1.73	1.18	1.80	1.21	1.32	1.15	1.38	1.10	1.44	1.04	1.51	.99	1.59
37	1.42	1.53	1.36	1.59	1.31	1.66	1.25	1.72	1.19	1.80	1.22	1.32	1.16	1.38	1.11	1.45	1.06	1.51	1.00	1.59
38	1.43	1.54	1.37	1.59	1.32	1.66	1.26	1.72	1.21	1.79	1.23	1.33	1.18	1.39	1.12	1.45	1.07	1.52	1.02	1.58
39	1.43	1.54	1.38	1.60	1.33	1.66	1.27	1.72	1.22	1.79	1.24	1.34	1.19	1.39	1.14	1.45	1.09	1.52	1.03	1.58
40	1.44	1.54	1.39	1.60	1.34	1.66	1.29	1.72	1.23	1.79	1.25	1.34	1.20	1.40	1.15	1.46	1.10	1.52	1.05	1.58
45	1.48	1.57	1.43	1.62	1.38	1.67	1.34	1.72	1.29	1.78	1.29	1.38	1.24	1.42	1.20	1.48	1.16	1.53	1.11	1.58
50	1.50	1.59	1.46	1.63	1.42	1.67	1.38	1.72	1.34	1.77	1.32	1.40	1.28	1.45	1.24	1.49	1.20	1.54	1.16	1.59
55	1.53	1.60	1.49	1.64	1.45	1.68	1.41	1.72	1.38	1.77	1.36	1.43	1.32	1.47	1.28	1.51	1.25	1.55	1.21	1.59
60	1.55	1.62	1.51	1.65	1.48	1.69	1.44	1.73	1.41	1.77	1.38	1.45	1.35	1.48	1.32	1.52	1.28	1.56	1.25	1.60
65	1.57	1.63	1.54	1.66	1.50	1.70	1.47	1.73	1.44	1.77	1.41	1.47	1.38	1.50	1.35	1.53	1.31	1.57	1.28	1.61
70	1.58	1.64	1.55	1.67	1.52	1.70	1.49	1.74	1.46	1.77	1.43	1.49	1.40	1.52	1.37	1.55	1.34	1.58	1.31	1.61
75	1.60	1.65	1.57	1.68	1.54	1.71	1.51	1.74	1.49	1.77	1.45	1.50	1.42	1.53	1.39	1.56	1.37	1.59	1.34	1.62
80	1.61	1.66	1.59	1.69	1.56	1.72	1.53	1.74	1.51	1.77	1.47	1.52	1.44	1.54	1.42	1.57	1.39	1.60	1.36	1.62
85	1.62	1.67	1.60	1.70	1.57	1.72	1.55	1.75	1.52	1.77	1.48	1.53	1.46	1.55	1.43	1.58	1.41	1.60	1.39	1.63
90	1.63	1.68	1.61	1.70	1.59	1.73	1.57	1.75	1.54	1.78	1.50	1.54	1.47	1.56	1.45	1.59	1.43	1.61	1.41	1.64
95	1.64	1.69	1.62	1.71	1.60	1.73	1.58	1.75	1.56	1.78	1.51	1.55	1.49	1.57	1.47	1.60	1.45	1.62	1.42	1.64
100	1.65	1.69	1.63	1.72	1.61	1.74	1.59	1.76	1.57	1.78	1.52	1.56	1.50	1.58	1.48	1.60	1.46	1.63	1.44	1.65

[a] n = number of observations; k = number of independent variables.

Source: Computed from TSP 4.5 based on R. W. Farebrother, "A Remark on Algorithms AS106, AS153, and AS155: The Distribution of a Linear Combination of Chi-Square Random Variables," *Journal of the Royal Statistical Society*, Series C (Applied Statistics), 29 (1984): 323–333.

TABLE C.8

Control Chart Factors

Number of Observations in Sample/Subgroup (n)	d_2	d_3	D_3	D_4	A_2
2	1.128	0.853	0	3.267	1.880
3	1.693	0.888	0	2.575	1.023
4	2.059	0.880	0	2.282	0.729
5	2.326	0.864	0	2.114	0.577
6	2.534	0.848	0	2.004	0.483
7	2.704	0.833	0.076	1.924	0.419
8	2.847	0.820	0.136	1.864	0.373
9	2.970	0.808	0.184	1.816	0.337
10	3.078	0.797	0.223	1.777	0.308
11	3.173	0.787	0.256	1.744	0.285
12	3.258	0.778	0.283	1.717	0.266
13	3.336	0.770	0.307	1.693	0.249
14	3.407	0.763	0.328	1.672	0.235
15	3.472	0.756	0.347	1.653	0.223
16	3.532	0.750	0.363	1.637	0.212
17	3.588	0.744	0.378	1.622	0.203
18	3.640	0.739	0.391	1.609	0.194
19	3.689	0.733	0.404	1.596	0.187
20	3.735	0.729	0.415	1.585	0.180
21	3.778	0.724	0.425	1.575	0.173
22	3.819	0.720	0.435	1.565	0.167
23	3.858	0.716	0.443	1.557	0.162
24	3.895	0.712	0.452	1.548	0.157
25	3.931	0.708	0.459	1.541	0.153

Source: Reprinted from *ASTM-STP 15D* by kind permission of the American Society for Testing and Materials. Copyright ASTM International, 100 Barr Harbor Drive, Conshohocken, PA 19428.

TABLE C.9

The Standardized Normal Distribution

Entry represents area under the standardized normal
distribution from the mean to Z

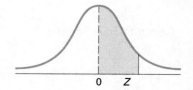

Z	.00	.01	.02	.03	.04	.05	.06	.07	.08	.09
0.0	.0000	.0040	.0080	.0120	.0160	.0199	.0239	.0279	.0319	.0359
0.1	.0398	.0438	.0478	.0517	.0557	.0596	.0636	.0675	.0714	.0753
0.2	.0793	.0832	.0871	.0910	.0948	.0987	.1026	.1064	.1103	.1141
0.3	.1179	.1217	.1255	.1293	.1331	.1368	.1406	.1443	.1480	.1517
0.4	.1554	.1591	.1628	.1664	.1700	.1736	.1772	.1808	.1844	.1879
0.5	.1915	.1950	.1985	.2019	.2054	.2088	.2123	.2157	.2190	.2224
0.6	.2257	.2291	.2324	.2357	.2389	.2422	.2454	.2486	.2518	.2549
0.7	.2580	.2612	.2642	.2673	.2704	.2734	.2764	.2794	.2823	.2852
0.8	.2881	.2910	.2939	.2967	.2995	.3023	.3051	.3078	.3106	.3133
0.9	.3159	.3186	.3212	.3238	.3264	.3289	.3315	.3340	.3365	.3389
1.0	.3413	.3438	.3461	.3485	.3508	.3531	.3554	.3577	.3599	.3621
1.1	.3643	.3665	.3686	.3708	.3729	.3749	.3770	.3790	.3810	.3830
1.2	.3849	.3869	.3888	.3907	.3925	.3944	.3962	.3980	.3997	.4015
1.3	.4032	.4049	.4066	.4082	.4099	.4115	.4131	.4147	.4162	.4177
1.4	.4192	.4207	.4222	.4236	.4251	.4265	.4279	.4292	.4306	.4319
1.5	.4332	.4345	.4357	.4370	.4382	.4394	.4406	.4418	.4429	.4441
1.6	.4452	.4463	.4474	.4484	.4495	.4505	.4515	.4525	.4535	.4545
1.7	.4554	.4564	.4573	.4582	.4591	.4599	.4608	.4616	.4625	.4633
1.8	.4641	.4649	.4656	.4664	.4671	.4678	.4686	.4693	.4699	.4706
1.9	.4713	.4719	.4726	.4732	.4738	.4744	.4750	.4756	.4761	.4767
2.0	.4772	.4778	.4783	.4788	.4793	.4798	.4803	.4808	.4812	.4817
2.1	.4821	.4826	.4830	.4834	.4838	.4842	.4846	.4850	.4854	.4857
2.2	.4861	.4864	.4868	.4871	.4875	.4878	.4881	.4884	.4887	.4890
2.3	.4893	.4896	.4898	.4901	.4904	.4906	.4909	.4911	.4913	.4916
2.4	.4918	.4920	.4922	.4925	.4927	.4929	.4931	.4932	.4934	.4936
2.5	.4938	.4940	.4941	.4943	.4945	.4946	.4948	.4949	.4951	.4952
2.6	.4953	.4955	.4956	.4957	.4959	.4960	.4961	.4962	.4963	.4964
2.7	.4965	.4966	.4967	.4968	.4969	.4970	.4971	.4972	.4973	.4974
2.8	.4974	.4975	.4976	.4977	.4977	.4978	.4979	.4979	.4980	.4981
2.9	.4981	.4982	.4982	.4983	.4984	.4984	.4985	.4985	.4986	.4986
3.0	.49865	.49869	.49874	.49878	.49882	.49886	.49889	.49893	.49897	.49900
3.1	.49903	.49906	.49910	.49913	.49916	.49918	.49921	.49924	.49926	.49929
3.2	.49931	.49934	.49936	.49938	.49940	.49942	.49944	.49946	.49948	.49950
3.3	.49952	.49953	.49955	.49957	.49958	.49960	.49961	.49962	.49964	.49965
3.4	.49966	.49968	.49969	.49970	.49971	.49972	.49973	.49974	.49975	.49976
3.5	.49977	.49978	.49978	.49979	.49980	.49981	.49981	.49982	.49983	.49983
3.6	.49984	.49985	.49985	.49986	.49986	.49987	.49987	.49988	.49988	.49989
3.7	.49989	.49990	.49990	.49990	.49991	.49991	.49992	.49992	.49992	.49992
3.8	.49993	.49993	.49993	.49994	.49994	.49994	.49994	.49995	.49995	.49995
3.9	.49995	.49995	.49996	.49996	.49996	.49996	.49996	.49996	.49997	.49997

Self-Test Solutions and Answers to Selected Problems

The following sections present worked-out solutions to Self-Test Problems and brief answers to most of the problems in the text. For more detailed solutions, including explanations and interpretations, see the *Student Solutions Manual*.

CHAPTER 10

Section 10.1

10.6 $114.68 \le \mu \le 135.32$.

10.8 Yes, it is true because 5% of intervals will not include the population mean.

10.10 (a) You would compute the mean first because you need the mean to compute the standard deviation. If you had a sample, you would compute the sample mean. If you had the population mean, you would compute the population standard deviation. **(b)** If you have a sample, you are computing the sample standard deviation, not the population standard deviation needed in Equation (10.1). If you have a population and have computed the population mean and population standard deviation, you don't need a confidence interval estimate of the population mean because you already know the mean.

10.12 Equation (10.1) assumes that you know the population standard deviation. Because you are selecting a sample of 100 from the population, you are computing a sample standard deviation, not the population standard deviation.

10.14 (a) $\bar{X} \pm Z \cdot \dfrac{\sigma}{\sqrt{n}} = 7,500 \pm 1.96 \cdot \dfrac{1,000}{\sqrt{64}}$; $7,255 \le \mu \le 7,745$.
(b) No, since the confidence interval does not include 8,000 hours the manufacturer cannot support a claim that the bulbs have a mean of 8,000 hours. **(c)** No. Because σ is known and $n = 64$, from the Central Limit Theorem, you know that the sampling distribution of $\bar{X}$ is approximately normal. **(d)** The confidence interval is narrower, based on a population standard deviation of 800 hours rather than the original standard deviation of 1,000 hours. $\bar{X} \pm Z \times \dfrac{\sigma}{\sqrt{n}} = 7,500 \pm 1.96 \times \dfrac{800}{\sqrt{64}}$, $7,304 \le \mu \le 7,696$. No, since the confidence interval does not include 8,000 the manufacturer cannot support a claim that the bulbs have a mean life of 8,000 hours.

Section 10.2

10.16 (a) 2.2622. **(b)** 3.2498. **(c)** 2.0395. **(d)** 1.9977. **(e)** 1.7531.

10.18 $-0.12 \le \mu \le 11.84$, $2.00 \le \mu \le 6.00$. The presence of the outlier increases the sample mean and greatly inflates the sample standard deviation.

10.20 (a) $75 \pm (2.0049)(9)/\sqrt{55}$; $72.57 \le \mu \le 77.43$. **(b)** You can be 95% confident that the population mean amount of one-time gift is between \$72.57 and \$77.43.

10.22 (a) $6.31 \le \mu \le 7.87$. **(b)** You can be 95% confident that the population mean amount spent for lunch at a fast-food restaurant is between \$6.31 and \$7.87.

10.24 (a) $22.09 \le \mu \le 23.61$. **(b)** You can be 95% confident that the population mean miles per gallon of 2014 small SUVs is between 22.09 and 23.61. **(c)** Because the 95% confidence interval for population mean miles per gallon of 2014 small SUVs does not overlap with that for the population mean miles per gallon of 2014 family sedans, you can conclude that the population mean miles per gallon of 2014 small SUVs is lower than that of 2014 family sedans.

10.26 (a) $31.12 \le \mu \le 54.96$. **(b)** The number of days is approximately normally distributed. **(c)** No, the outliers skew the data. **(d)** Because the sample size is fairly large, at $n = 50$, the use of the t distribution is appropriate.

10.28 (a) $31.23 \le \mu \le 47.59$. **(b)** That the population distribution is normally distributed. **(c)** The boxplot and the skewness and kurtosis statistics indicate an approximately normal distribution although the normal probability plot does not clearly show that.

Section 10.3

10.30 $0.19 \le \pi \le 0.31$.

10.32 (a) $p = \dfrac{X}{n} = \dfrac{135}{500} = 0.27, p \pm Z\sqrt{\dfrac{p(1-p)}{n}} = 0.27 \pm 2.58\sqrt{\dfrac{0.27(0.73)}{500}}$; $0.2189 \le \pi \le 0.3211$. **(b)** The manager in charge of promotional programs can infer that the proportion of households that would upgrade to an improved cellphone if it were made available at a substantially reduced cost is somewhere between 0.22 and 0.32, with 99% confidence.

10.34 (a) $0.2328 \le \pi \le 0.2872$. **(b)** No, you cannot because the interval estimate includes 0.25 (25%). **(c)** $0.2514 \le \pi \le 0.2686$. Yes, you can, because the interval is above 0.25 (25%). **(d)** The larger the sample size, the narrower the confidence interval, holding everything else constant.

10.36 (a) $0.4393 \le \pi \le 0.5024$. **(b)** $0.2811 \le \pi \le 0.3397$. **(c)** More people use Facebook to see photos and videos than keeping up with news and current events.

Section 10.4

10.38 $n = 35$.

10.40 $n = 1,041$.

10.42 (a) $n = \dfrac{Z^2\sigma^2}{e^2} = \dfrac{(1.96)^2(400)^2}{50^2} = 245.86$. Use $n = 246$.

(b) $n = \dfrac{Z^2\sigma^2}{e^2} = \dfrac{(1.96)^2(400)^2}{25^2} = 983.41$. Use $n = 984$.

10.44 $n = 97$.

10.46 (a) $n = 107$. **(b)** $n = 62$.

10.48 (a) $n = 246$. **(b)** $n = 385$. **(c)** $n = 554$. **(d)** When there is more variability in the population, a larger sample is needed to accurately estimate the mean.

10.50 (a) $0.2198 \le \pi \le 0.3202$. **(b)** $0.1639 \le \pi \le 0.2561$. **(c)** $0.0661 \le \pi \le 0.1339$. **(d) (a)** $n = 1,893$, **(b)** $n = 1,594$, **(c)** $n = 865$.

10.52 (a) If you conducted a follow-up study to estimate the population proportion of financial institutions that use churn rate to gauge the effectiveness of their marketing efforts, you would use $\pi = 0.68$ in the sample size formula because it is based on past information on the proportion. **(b)** $n = 929$.

Review

10.54 (a)

Cellphone: $p = 0.9006; 0.8821 \le \pi \le 0.9191$.
Smartphone: $p = 0.5805; 0.5500 \le \pi \le 0.6110$.
E-reader: $p = 0.3201; 0.2913 \le \pi \le 0.3489$.
Tablet computer: $p = 0.4205; 0.3900 \le \pi \le 0.4510$.

(b) Most adults have a cellphone. Many adults have a smartphone. Some adults have an e reader or a tablet computer.

10.56 (a) $39.88 \le \mu \le 42.12$. **(b)** $0.6158 \le \pi \le 0.8842$. **(c)** $n = 25$. **(d)** $n = 267$. **(e)** If a single sample were to be selected for both purposes, the larger of the two sample sizes ($n = 267$) should be used.

10.58 (a) $3.19 \le \mu \le 9.21$. **(b)** $0.3242 \le \pi \le 0.7158$. **(c)** $n = 110$. **(d)** $n = 121$. **(e)** If a single sample were to be selected for both purposes, the larger of the two sample sizes ($n = 121$) should be used.

10.60 (a) $0.2459 \le \pi \le 0.3741$. **(b)** $3.22 \le \mu \le \$3.78$. **(c)** $\$17,581.68 \le \mu \le \$18,418.32$.

10.62 (a) $\$36.66 \le \mu \le \$40.42$. **(b)** $0.2027 \le \pi \le 0.3973$. **(c)** $n = 110$. **(d)** $n = 423$. **(e)** If a single sample were to be selected for both purposes, the larger of the two sample sizes ($n = 423$) should be used.

10.64 (a) $0.4643 \le \pi \le 0.6690$. **(b)** $\$136.28 \le \mu \le \$502.21$.

10.66 (a) $8.41 \le \mu \le 8.43$. **(b)** With 95% confidence, the population mean width of troughs is somewhere between 8.41 and 8.43 inches. **(c)** The assumption is valid as the width of the troughs is approximately normally distributed.

10.68 (a) $0.2425 \le \mu \le 0.2856$. **(b)** $0.1975 \le \mu \le 0.2385$. **(c)** The amounts of granule loss for both brands are skewed to the right, but the sample sizes are large enough. **(d)** Because the two confidence intervals do not overlap, you can conclude that the mean granule loss of Boston shingles is higher than that of Vermont shingles.

CHAPTER 11

Section 11.1

11.10 Because $Z_{STAT} = +2.21 > 1.96$, reject H_0.

11.12 Reject H_0 if $Z_{STAT} < -2.58$ or if $Z_{STAT} > 2.58$.

11.14 p-value $= 0.0456$.

11.16 p-value $= 0.1676$.

11.18 H_0: Defendant is guilty; H_1: Defendant is innocent. A Type I error would be not convicting a guilty person. A Type II error would be convicting an innocent person.

11.20 H_0: $\mu = 20$ minutes. 20 minutes is adequate travel time between classes. H_1: $\mu \ne 20$ minutes. 20 minutes is not adequate travel time between classes.

11.22 (a) $Z_{STAT} = \dfrac{7,250 - 7,500}{\dfrac{1,000}{\sqrt{64}}} = -2.0$. Because $Z_{STAT} = -2.00$ < -1.96, reject H_0. **(b)** p-value $= 0.0456$. **(c)** $7,005 \le \mu \le 7,495$. **(d)** The conclusions are the same.

11.24 (a) Because $-2.58 < Z_{STAT} = -1.7678 < 2.58$, do not reject H_0. **(b)** p-value $= 0.0771$. **(c)** $0.9877 \le \mu \le 1.0023$. **(d)** The conclusions are the same.

Section 11.2

11.26 $t_{STAT} = 2.00$.

11.28 ± 2.1315.

11.30 No, you should not use a t test because the original population is left-skewed, and the sample size is not large enough for the t test to be valid.

11.32 (a) $t_{STAT} = (3.57 - 3.70)/0.8/\sqrt{64} = -1.30$. Because $-1.9983 < t_{STAT} = -1.30 < 1.9983$ and p-value $= 0.1984 > 0.05$, there is no evidence that the population mean waiting time is different from 3.7 minutes. **(b)** Because $n = 64$, the sampling distribution of the t test statistic is approximately normal. In general, the t test is appropriate for this sample size except for the case where the population is extremely skewed or bimodal.

11.34 (a) $-1.9842 < t_{STAT} = 1.4545 < 1.9842$. There is no evidence that the population mean savings for all showroomers is different from $50. **(b)** p-value $= 0.1490 > 0.05$. The probability of getting a t_{STAT} statistic greater than $+1.4545$ or less than -1.4545, given that the null hypothesis is true, is 0.1490.

11.36 (a) Because $-2.1448 < t_{STAT} = 1.6344 < 2.1448$, do not reject H_0. There is not enough evidence to conclude that the mean amount spent for lunch at a fast-food restaurant, is different from $6.50. **(b)** The p-value is 0.1245. If the population mean is $6.50, the probability of observing a sample of nine customers that will result in a sample mean farther away from the hypothesized value than this sample is 0.1245. **(c)** The distribution of the amount spent is normally distributed. **(d)** With a sample size of 15, it is difficult to evaluate the assumption of normality. However, the distribution may be fairly symmetric because the mean and the median are close in value. Also, the boxplot appears only slightly skewed so the normality assumption does not appear to be seriously violated.

11.38 (a) Because $-2.0096 < t_{STAT} = 0.114 < 2.0096$, do not reject H_0. There is no evidence that the mean amount is different from 2 liters. **(b)** p-value $= 0.9095$. **(d)** Yes, the data appear to have met the normality assumption. **(e)** The amount of fill is decreasing over time so the values are not independent. Therefore, the t test is invalid.

11.40 (a) Because $t_{STAT} = -5.9355 < -2.0106$, reject H_0. There is enough evidence to conclude that mean widths of the troughs is different from 8.46 inches. **(b)** The population distribution is normal. **(c)** Although the distribution of the widths is left-skewed, the large sample size means that the validity of the *t* test is not seriously affected. The large sample size allows you to use the *t* distribution.

11.42 **(a)** Because $-2.68 < t_{STAT} = 0.094 < 2.68$, do not reject H_0. There is no evidence that the mean amount is different from 5.5 grams. **(b)** $5.462 \leq \mu \leq 5.542$. **(c)** The conclusions are the same.

Section 11.3

11.44 *p*-value $= 0.0228$.

11.46 *p*-value $= 0.0838$.

11.48 *p*-value $= 0.9162$.

11.50 $t_{STAT} = 2.7638$.

11.52 $t_{STAT} = -2.5280$.

11.54 **(a)** $t_{STAT} = 2.7273 > 1.6604$. There is evidence that the population mean bus miles is greater than 3,900 miles. **(b)** *p*-value $= 0.0038 < 0.05$. The probability of getting a t_{STAT} statistic greater than 2.7273 given that the null hypothesis is true, is 0.0038.

11.56 **(a)** $t_{STAT} = (23.05 - 25)/16.83/\sqrt{355} = -2.1831$. Because $t_{STAT} = -2.1831 > -2.3369$, do not reject H_0. *p*-value $= 0.0148 > 0.01$, do not reject H_0. **(b)** The probability of getting a sample mean of 23.05 minutes or less if the population mean is 25 minutes is 0.0148.

11.58 **(a)** $t_{STAT} = 4.1201 > 2.3974$. There is evidence that the population mean one-time gift donation is greater than $70. **(b)** The probability of getting a sample mean of $75 or more if the population mean is $70 is 0.0001.

Section 11.4

11.60 $p = 0.22$.

11.62 Do not reject H_0.

11.64 **(a)** $Z_{STAT} = 1.3311$, *p*-value $= 0.0916$. Because $Z_{STAT} = 1.3311 < 1.645$ or $0.0916 > 0.05$, do not reject H_0. There is no evidence to show that more than 17% of students at your university use the Mozilla Firefox web browser. **(b)** $Z_{STAT} = 2.6622$, *p*-value $= 0.0039$. Because $Z_{STAT} = 2.6622 > 1.645$, reject H_0. There is evidence to show that more than 17% of students at your university use the Mozilla Firefox web browser. **(c)** The sample size had a major effect on being able to reject the null hypothesis. **(d)** You would be very unlikely to reject the null hypothesis with a sample of 20.

11.66 $H_0: \pi = 0.52; H_1: \pi \neq 0.52$. Decision rule: If $Z_{STAT} > 1.96$ or $Z_{STAT} < -1.96$, reject H_0.

$$p = \frac{543}{935} = 0.5807$$

Test statistic:

$$Z_{STAT} = \frac{p - \pi}{\sqrt{\dfrac{\pi(1 - \pi)}{n}}} = \frac{0.5807 - 0.52}{\sqrt{\dfrac{0.52(1 - 0.52)}{935}}} = 3.7181.$$

Because $Z_{STAT} = 3.7181 > 1.96$ or *p*-value $= 0.0002 < 0.05$, reject H_0 and conclude that there is evidence that the proportion of all LinkedIn members who engaged in professional networking within the last month is different from 52%.

11.68 **(a)** $H_0: \pi \geq 0.37$. The proportion who respond that the organization has a coherent business strategy that they stick to and effectively communicate is greater than or equal to 0.37. $H_1: \pi < 0.37$. The proportion who respond that the organization has a coherent business strategy that they stick to and effectively communicate is less than 0.37. **(b)** $Z_{STAT} = -0.6214 > -1.645$; *p*-value $= 0.2672$. Because $Z_{STAT} = -0.6214 > -1.645$ or *p*-value $= 0.2672 > 0.05$, do not reject H_0. There is insufficient evidence that the proportion who respond that the organization has a coherent business strategy that they stick to and effectively communicate is less than 0.37.

Review

11.70 **(a)** Concluding that a firm will go bankrupt when it will not. **(b)** Concluding that a firm will not go bankrupt when it will go bankrupt. **(c)** Type I. **(d)** If the revised model results in more moderate or large *Z* scores, the probability of committing a Type I error will increase. Many more of the firms will be predicted to go bankrupt than will go bankrupt. On the other hand, the revised model that results in more moderate or large *Z* scores will lower the probability of committing a Type II error because few firms will be predicted to go bankrupt than will actually go bankrupt.

11.72 **(a)** Because $t_{STAT} = 3.3197 > 2.0010$, reject H_0. **(b)** *p*-value $= 0.0015$. **(c)** Because $Z_{STAT} = 0.2582 < 1.645$, do not reject H_0. **(d)** Because $-2.0010 < t_{STAT} = -1.1066 < 2.0010$, do not reject H_0. **(e)** Because $Z_{STAT} = 2.3238 > 1.645$, reject H_0.

11.74 **(a)** Because $t_{STAT} = -1.69 > -1.7613$, do not reject H_0. **(b)** The data are from a population that is normally distributed. **(d)** With the exception of one extreme value, the data are approximately normally distributed. **(e)** There is insufficient evidence to state that the waiting time is less than five minutes.

11.76 **(a)** Because $t_{STAT} = -1.47 > -1.6896$, do not reject H_0. **(b)** *p*-value $= 0.0748$. If the null hypothesis is true, the probability of obtaining a t_{STAT} of -1.47 or more extreme is 0.0748. **(c)** Because $t_{STAT} = -3.10 < -1.6973$, reject H_0. **(d)** *p*-value $= 0.0021$. If the null hypothesis is true, the probability of obtaining a t_{STAT} of -3.10 or more extreme is 0.0021. **(e)** The data in the population are assumed to be normally distributed. **(g)** Both boxplots suggest that the data are skewed slightly to the right, more so for the Boston shingles. However, the very large sample sizes mean that the results of the *t* test are relatively insensitive to the departure from normality.

11.78 **(a)** $t_{STAT} = -3.2912$, reject H_0. **(b)** *p*-value $= 0.0012$. **(c)** $t_{STAT} = -7.9075$, reject H_0. **(d)** *p*-value $= 0.0000$. **(e)** Because of the large sample sizes, you do not need to be concerned with the normality assumption.

CHAPTER 12

Section 12.1

12.13 **(a)** $t = 3.8959$. **(b)** $df = 21$. **(c)** 2.5177. **(d)** Because $t_{STAT} = t_{STAT} = 3.8959 > 2.5177$, reject H_0.

12.15 $3.73 \leq \mu_1 - \mu_2 \leq 12.27$.

12.17 Because $t_{STAT} = 2.6762 < 2.9979$ or *p*-value $= 0.0158 > 0.01$, do not reject H_0. There is no evidence of a difference in the means of the two populations.

12.19 (a) Because $t_{STAT} = 2.8990 > 1.6620$ or p-value $= 0.0024 < 0.05$, reject H_0. There is evidence that the mean amount of Walker Crisps eaten by children who watched a commercial featuring a long-standing sports celebrity endorser is higher than for those who watched a commercial for an alternative food snack. **(b)** $3.4616 \leq \mu_1 - \mu_2 \leq 18.5384$. **(c)** The results cannot be compared because (a) is a one-tail test and (b) is a confidence interval that is comparable only to the results of a two-tail test.

12.21 (a) $H_0: \mu_1 = \mu_2$, where Populations: $1 =$ Southeast, $2 =$ Gulf Coast. $H_1: \mu_1 \neq \mu_2$. Decision rule: $df = 28$. If $t_{STAT} < -2.0484$ or $t_{STAT} > 2.0484$, reject H_0.

Test statistic:

$$S_p^2 = \frac{(n_1 - 1)(S_1^2) + (n_2 - 1)(S_2^2)}{(n_1 - 1) + (n_2 - 1)}$$

$$= \frac{(12)(42.5927^2) + (16)(36.1970^2)}{12 + 16} = 1,526.1865$$

$$t_{STAT} = \frac{(\bar{X}_1 - \bar{X}_2) - (\mu_1 - \mu_2)}{\sqrt{S_p^2 \left(\frac{1}{n_1} + \frac{1}{n_2}\right)}}$$

$$= \frac{(43.1538 - 29.7059) - 0}{\sqrt{1,526.1865\left(\frac{1}{13} + \frac{1}{17}\right)}} = 0.9343.$$

Decision: Because $-2.0484 < t_{STAT} = 0.9343 < 2.0484$, do not reject H_0. There is not enough evidence to conclude that the mean number of partners between the Southeast and Gulf Coast is different. **(b)** p-value $= 0.3581$. **(c)** In order to use the pooled-variance t test, you need to assume that the populations are normally distributed with equal variances.

12.23 (a) Because $t_{STAT} = -4.1343 < -2.0484$, reject H_0. **(b)** p-value $= 0.0003$. **(c)** The populations of waiting times are approximately normally distributed. **(d)** $-4.2292 \leq \mu_1 - \mu_2 \leq -1.4268$.

12.25 (a) Because $t_{STAT} = -1.4458 > -2.0484$, do not reject H_0. There is insufficient evidence of a difference in the mean time to start a business between developed and emerging countries. **(b)** p-value $= 0.1593$. The probability that two samples have a mean difference of 10.0667 or more is 0.1593 if there is no difference in the mean time to start a business between developed and emerging countries. **(c)** You need to assume that the population distribution of the time to start a business of both developed and emerging countries is normally distributed. **(d)** $-24.3286 \leq \mu_1 - \mu_2 \leq 4.1953$.

12.27 (a) Because $t_{STAT} = -2.1554 < -2.0017$ or p-value $= 0.0353 < 0.05$, reject H_0. There is evidence of a difference in the mean time per day accessing the Internet via a mobile device between males and females. **(b)** You must assume that each of the two independent populations is normally distributed.

Section 12.2

12.29 $df = 19$.

12.31 (a) $t_{STAT} = (-1.5566)/(1.424)/\sqrt{9} = -3.2772$. Because $t_{STAT} = -3.2772 < -2.306$ or p-value $= 0.0112 < 0.05$, reject H_0. There is enough evidence of a difference in the mean summated ratings between the two brands. **(b)** You must assume that the distribution of the differences between the two ratings is approximately normal. **(c)** p-value $= 0.0112$. The probability of obtaining a mean difference in ratings that results in a test statistic that deviates from 0 by 3.2772 or more

in either direction is 0.0112 if there is no difference in the mean summated ratings between the two brands. **(d)** $-2.6501 \leq \mu_D \leq -0.4610$. You are 95% confident that the mean difference in summated ratings between brand A and brand B is somewhere between -2.6501 and -0.4610.

12.33 (a) Because $t_{STAT} = 1.7948 > 1.6939$ reject H_0. There is evidence to conclude that the mean at Super Target is higher than at Walmart. **(b)** You must assume that the distribution of the differences between the prices is approximately normal. **(c)** p-value $= 0.0411$. The likelihood that you will obtain a t_{STAT} statistic greater than 1.7948 if the mean price at Super Target is not greater than Walmart is 0.0411.

12.35 (a) Because $t_{STAT} = 1.8425 < 1.943$, do not reject H_0. There is not enough evidence to conclude that the mean bone marrow microvessel density is higher before the stem cell transplant than after the stem cell transplant. **(b)** p-value $= 0.0575$. The probability that the t statistic for the mean difference in microvessel density is 1.8425 or more is 5.75% if the mean density is not higher before the stem cell transplant than after the stem cell transplant. **(c)** $-28.26 \leq \mu_D \leq 200.55$. You are 95% confident that the mean difference in bone marrow microvessel density before and after the stem cell transplant is somewhere between -28.26 and 200.55. **(d)** That the distribution of the difference before and after the stem cell transplant is normally distributed.

12.37 (a) Because $t_{STAT} = -9.3721 < -2.4258$, reject H_0. There is evidence that the mean strength is lower at two days than at seven days. **(b)** The population of differences in strength is approximately normally distributed. **(c)** $p = 0.000$.

Section 12.3

12.39 (a) Because $-2.58 \leq Z_{STAT} = -0.58 \leq 2.58$, do not reject H_0. **(b)** $-0.273 \leq \pi_1 - \pi_2 \leq 0.173$.

12.41 (a) $H_0: \pi_1 \leq \pi_2$. $H_1: \pi_1 > \pi_2$. Populations: $1 =$ social media recommendation, $2 =$ web browsing. **(b)** Because $Z_{STAT} = 1.5507 < 1.6449$ or p-value $= 0.0605 > 0.05$, do not reject H_0. There is insufficient evidence to conclude that the population proportion of those who recalled the brand is greater for those who had a social media recommendation than for those who did web browsing. **(c)** No, the result in (b) makes it inappropriate to claim that the population proportion of those who recalled the brand is greater for those who had a social media recommendation than for those who did web browsing.

12.43 (a) $H_0: \pi_1 = \pi_2$. $H_1: \pi_1 \neq \pi_2$. Decision rule: If $|Z_{STAT}| > 2.58$, reject H_0.

Test statistic: $\bar{p} = \frac{X_1 + X_2}{n_1 + n_2} = \frac{930 + 230}{1,000 + 1,000} = 0.58$

$$Z_{STAT} = \frac{(p_1 - p_2) - (\pi_1 - \pi_2)}{\sqrt{\bar{p}(1 - \bar{p})\left(\frac{1}{n_1} + \frac{1}{n_2}\right)}} = \frac{(0.93 - 0.23) - 0}{\sqrt{0.58(1 - 0.58)\left(\frac{1}{1,000} + \frac{1}{1,000}\right)}}.$$

$Z_{STAT} = 31.7135 > 2.58$, reject H_0. There is evidence of a difference in the proportion of Superbanked and Unbanked with respect to the proportion that use credit cards. **(b)** p-value $= 0.0001$. The probability of obtaining a difference in proportions that gives rise to a test statistic below -31.7135 or above $+31.7135$ is 0.0000 if there is no difference in the proportion of Superbanked and Unbanked who use credit cards. **(c)** $0.6599 \leq (\pi_1 - \pi_2) \leq 0.7401$. You are 99% confident that the difference in the proportion of Superbanked and Unbanked who use credit cards is between 0.6599 and 0.7401.

12.45 (a) Because $Z_{STAT} = 4.4662 > 1.96$, reject H_0. There is evidence of a difference in the proportion of co-browsing organizations and non-co-browsing organizations that use skills-based routing to match the caller with the *right* agent. **(b)** p-value $= 0.0000$. The probability of obtaining a difference in proportions that is 0.2586 or more in either direction is 0.0000 if there is no difference between the proportion of co-browsing organizations and non-co-browsing organizations that use skills-based routing to match the caller with the *right* agent.

Section 12.4

12.47 (a) 2.20. **(b)** 2.57. **(c)** 3.50.

12.49 (a) Population B: $S^2 = 25$. **(b)** 1.5625.

12.51 $df_{\text{numerator}} = 24$, $df_{\text{denominator}} = 24$.

12.53 Because $F_{STAT} = 1.2109 < 2.27$, do not reject H_0.

12.55 (a) Because $F_{STAT} = 1.2995 < 3.18$, do not reject H_0. **(b)** Because $F_{STAT} = 1.2995 < 2.62$, do not reject H_0.

12.57 (a) $H_0: \sigma_1^2 = \sigma_2^2$. $H_1: \sigma_1^2 \neq \sigma_2^2$.

Decision rule: If $F_{STAT} > 2.8890$, reject H_0.

Test statistic: $F_{STAT} = \dfrac{S_1^2}{S_2^2} = \dfrac{(42.5927)^2}{(36.1970)^2} = 1.3846$.

Decision: Because $F_{STAT} = 1.3846 < 2.8890$, do not reject H_0. There is insufficient evidence to conclude that the two population variances are different. **(b)** p-value $= 0.5346$. **(c)** The test assumes that each of the two populations is normally distributed. **(d)** Based on (a) and (b), a pooled-variance t test should be used.

12.59 (a) Because $F_{STAT} = 1.9078 < 5.4098$ or p-value $= 0.4417 > 0.05$, do not reject H_0. There is no evidence of a difference in the variability of the battery life between the two types of tablets. **(b)** p-value $= 0.4417$. The probability of obtaining a sample that yields a test statistic more extreme than 1.9078 is 0.4417 if there is no difference in the two population variances. **(c)** The test assumes that each of the two populations are normally distributed. The boxplots appear left-skewed especially the 3G/4G/WiFi tablets. The skewness and kurtosis statistics for the 3G/4G/WiFi tablets are very different from 0. Thus, the 3G/4G/WiFi tablets appear to be substantially different from a normal distribution. **(d)** Based on (a) and (b), a pooled-variance t test should be used. However, because of the skewness and kurtosis in the 3G/4G/WiFi tablets, the validity of either a pooled-variance or separate-variance t test is in doubt.

12.61 Because $F_{STAT} = 1.2908 < 4.8232$, or p-value $= 0.75 > 0.05$, do not reject H_0. There is insufficient evidence of a difference in the variance of the yield in the two cities.

CHAPTER 13

Section 13.1

13.13 (a) $SSW = 150$. **(b)** $MSA = 15$. **(c)** $MSW = 5$. **(d)** $F_{STAT} = 3$.

13.15 (a) 2. **(b)** 18. **(c)** 20.

13.17 (a) Reject H_0 if $F_{STAT} > 2.95$; otherwise, do not reject H_0. **(b)** Because $F_{STAT} = 4 > 2.95$, reject H_0. **(c)** The table does not have 28 degrees of freedom in the denominator, so use the next larger critical value, $Q_\alpha = 3.90$. **(d)** Critical range $= 6.166$.

13.19 (a) $H_0: \mu_A = \mu_B = \mu_C = \mu_D$ and H_1: At least one mean is different.

$$MSA = \frac{SSA}{c-1} = \frac{8,812,582.2}{3} = 2,937,527.4.$$

$$MSW = \frac{SSW}{n-c} = \frac{17,231,437.4}{36} = 478,651.0389.$$

$$F_{STAT} = \frac{MSA}{MSW} = \frac{2,937,527.4}{478,651.0389} = 6.1371.$$

$$F_{0.05,3,36} = 2.8663.$$

Because the p-value is 0.0018 and $F_{STAT} = 6.1371 > 2.8663$, reject H_0. There is sufficient evidence of a difference in the mean import cost across the four global regions. **(b)** Critical range $= Q_\alpha \sqrt{\dfrac{MSW}{2}\left(\dfrac{1}{n_j} + \dfrac{1}{n_{j'}}\right)}$

$$= 3.79 \sqrt{\frac{478,651.0389}{2}\left(\frac{1}{10} + \frac{1}{10}\right)} = 829.2.$$

From the Tukey-Kramer procedure, there is a difference in the mean import cost between the East Asia and Pacific region and each of the other regions. None of the other regions are different. **(c)** ANOVA output for Levene's test for homogeneity of variance:

$$MSA = \frac{SSA}{c-1} = \frac{1,620,045}{3} = 540,015$$

$$MSW = \frac{SSW}{n-c} = \frac{9,545,488.5}{36} = 265,152.4583$$

$$F_{STAT} = \frac{MSA}{MSW} = \frac{540,015}{265,152.4583} = 2.0366$$

$$F_{0.05,3,36} = 2.8663$$

Because p-value $= 0.1261 > 0.05$ and $F_{STAT} = 2.0366 < 2.8663$, do not reject H_0. There is insufficient evidence to conclude that the variances in the import cost are different. **(d)** From the results in (a) and (b), the mean import cost for the East Asia and Pacific region is lower than for the other regions.

13.21 (a) Because $F_{STAT} = 12.56 > 2.76$, reject H_0. **(b)** Critical range $= 4.67$. Advertisements A and B are different from Advertisements C and D. Advertisement E is only different from Advertisement D. **(c)** Because $F_{STAT} = 1.927 < 2.76$, do not reject H_0. There is no evidence of a significant difference in the variation in the ratings among the five advertisements. **(d)** The advertisements underselling the pen's characteristics had the highest mean ratings, and the advertisements overselling the pen's characteristics had the lowest mean ratings. Therefore, use an advertisement that undersells the pen's characteristics and avoid advertisements that oversell the pen's characteristics.

13.23 (a)

Source	Degrees of Freedom	Sum of Squares	Mean Squares	F
Among groups	2	1.879	0.9395	8.7558
Within groups	297	31.865	0.1073	
Total	299	33.744		

(b) Since $F_{STAT} = 8.7558 > 3.00$, reject H_0. There is evidence of a difference in the mean soft-skill score of the different groups. **(c)** Group 1 versus group 2: $0.072 <$ Critical range $= 0.1092$; group 1 versus group 3: $0.181 > 0.1056$; group 2 versus group 3: $0.109 < 0.1108$. There is evidence of a difference in the mean soft-skill score between those who had no coursework in leadership and those who had a degree in leadership.

13.25 (a) Because $F_{STAT} = 53.03 > 2.92$, reject H_0. **(b)** Critical range $= 5.27$ (using 30 degrees of freedom). Designs 3 and 4 are different from designs 1 and 2. Designs 1 and 2 are different from each other. **(c)** The assumptions are that the samples are randomly and independently selected (or randomly assigned), the original populations of distances are approximately normally distributed, and the variances are equal. **(d)** Because $F_{STAT} = 2.093 < 2.92$, do not reject H_0. There is sufficient evidence of a difference in the variation in the distance among the four designs. **(e)** The manager should choose design 3 or 4.

Review

13.26 (a) Because $F_{STAT} = 1.0041 < 1.6195$, or p-value $= 0.9501 > 0.05$, do not reject H_0. There is not enough evidence of a difference in the variance of the salary of Black Belts and Green Belts. **(b)** The pooled-variance t test. **(c)** Because $t_{STAT} = 5.1766 > 1.6541$ or p-value $= 0.0000 < 0.05$, reject H_0. There is evidence that the mean salary of Black Belts is greater than the mean salary of Green Belts.

13.28 (a) Because $F_{STAT} = 1.5625 < F_\alpha = 1.6854$, do not reject H_0. There is not enough evidence to conclude that there is a difference between the variances in the talking time per month between women and men. **(b)** It is more appropriate to use a pooled-variance t test. Using the pooled-variance t test, because $t_{STAT} = 11.1196 > 2.6009$, reject H_0. There is enough evidence of a difference in the mean talking time per month between women and men. **(c)** Because $F_{STAT} = 1.44 < 1.6854$, do not reject H_0. There is not enough evidence to conclude that there is a difference between the variances in the number of text messages sent per month between women and men. **(d)** Using the pooled-variance t test, because $t_{STAT} = 8.2456 > 2.6009$, reject H_0. There is enough evidence of a difference in the mean number of text messages sent per month between women and men.

13.30 (a) Because $t_{STAT} = 3.3282 > 1.8595$, reject H_0. There is enough evidence to conclude that the introductory computer students required more than a mean of 10 minutes to write and run a program in VB.NET **(b)** Because $t_{STAT} = 1.3636 < 1.8595$, do not reject H_0. There is not enough evidence to conclude that the introductory computer students required more than a mean of 10 minutes to write and run a program in VB.NET **(c)** Although the mean time necessary to complete the assignment increased from 12 to 16 minutes as a result of the increase in one data value, the standard deviation went from 1.8 to 13.2, which reduced the value of t statistic. **(d)** Because $F_{STAT} = 1.2308 < 3.8549$, do not reject H_0. There is not enough evidence to conclude that the population variances are different for the Introduction to Computers students and computer majors. Hence, the pooled-variance t test is a valid test to determine whether computer majors can write a VB.NET program in less time than introductory students, assuming that the distributions of the time needed to write a VB.NET program for both the Introduction to Computers students and the computer majors are approximately normally distributed. Because $t_{STAT} = 4.0666 > 1.7341$, reject H_0. There is enough evidence that the mean time is higher for Introduction to Computers students than for computer majors. **(e)** p-value $= 0.000362$. If the true population mean amount of time needed for Introduction to Computer students to write a VB.NET program is no more than 10 minutes, the probability of observing a sample mean greater than the 12 minutes in the current sample is 0.0362%. Hence, at a 5% level of significance, you can conclude that the population mean amount of time needed for Introduction to Computer students to write a VB.NET program is more than 10 minutes. As illustrated in (d), in which there is not enough evidence to conclude that the population variances are different for the Introduction to Computers students and computer majors, the pooled-variance t test performed is a valid test to determine whether computer majors can write a VB.NET program in less time than introductory students, assuming that the distribution of the time needed to write a VB.NET program for both the Introduction to Computers students and the computer majors are approximately normally distributed.

13.32 From the boxplot and the summary statistics, both distributions are approximately normally distributed. $F_{STAT} = 1.056 < 1.89$. There is insufficient evidence to conclude that the two population variances are significantly different at the 5% level of significance. $t_{STAT} = -5.084 < -1.99$. At the 5% level of significance, there is sufficient evidence to reject the null hypothesis of no difference in the mean life of the bulbs between the two manufacturers. You can conclude that there is a significant difference in the mean life of the bulbs between the two manufacturers.

13.34 (a) Because $Z_{STAT} = -3.6911 < -1.96$, reject H_0. There is enough evidence to conclude that there is a difference in the proportion of men and women who order dessert. **(b)** Because $Z_{STAT} = 6.0873 > 1.96$, reject H_0. There is enough evidence to conclude that there is a difference in the proportion of people who order dessert based on whether they ordered a beef entree.

13.36 The normal probability plots suggest that the two populations are not normally distributed. An F test is inappropriate for testing the difference in the two variances. The sample variances for Boston and Vermont shingles are 0.0203 and 0.015, respectively. Because $t_{STAT} = 3.015 > 1.967$ or p-value $= 0.0028 < \alpha = 0.05$, reject H_0. There is sufficient evidence to conclude that there is a difference in the mean granule loss of Boston and Vermont shingles.

13.38 Population 1 = short term 2 = long term, 3 = world; One-year return: Levene test: Since the p-value $0.4621 > 0.05$ do not reject H_0. There is insufficient evidence to show a difference in the variance of the return among the three different types of bond funds at a 5% level of significance. Since the p-value is $0.4202 > 0.05$, do not, reject H_0. There is insufficient evidence to show a difference in the mean one-year returns among the three different types of bond funds at a 5% level of significance.

CHAPTER 14

Section 14.1

14.5 (a) For $df = 1$ and $\alpha = 0.05$, $\chi^2_\alpha = 3.841$. **(b)** For $df = 1$ and $\alpha = 0.025$, $\chi^2 = 5.024$. **(c)** For $df = 1$ and $\alpha = 0.01$, $\chi^2_\alpha = 6.635$.

14.7 (a) All $f_e = 25$. **(b)** Because $\chi^2_{STAT} = 4.00 > 3.841$, reject H_0.

14.9 (a) H_0: $\pi_1 = \pi_2$. H_1: $\pi_1 \neq \pi_2$. **(b)** Because $\chi^2_{STAT} = 2.4045 < 3.841$, do not reject H_0. There is insufficient evidence to conclude that the population proportion of those who recalled the brand is different for those who had a social media recommendation than for those who did web browsing. p-value $= 0.1210$. The probability of obtaining a test statistic of 2.4045 or larger when the null hypothesis is true is 0.1210. **(c)** You should not compare the results in (a) to those of Problem 10.30 (b) because that was a one-tail test.

14.11 (a) H_0: $\pi_1 = \pi_2$. H_1: $\pi_1 \neq \pi_2$. Because $\chi^2_{STAT} = (930 - 580)^2/580 + (70 - 420)^2/420 + (230 - 580)^2/580 + (770 - 420)^2 = 1{,}005.7471 > 6.635$, reject H_0. There is evidence of a difference in the proportion of Superbanked and Unbanked with respect to the proportion that use credit cards. **(b)** p-value $= 0.0000$. The probability of obtaining a difference in proportions that gives rise to a test statistic above 1,005.7471 is 0.0000 if there is no difference in the proportion of Superbanked and Unbanked who use credit cards. **(c)** The results of (a) and (b) are exactly the same as those of Problem 10.32. The χ^2 in (a) and the Z in Problem 10.32 (a) satisfy the relationship that $\chi^2 = 1{,}005.7471 = Z^2 = (31.7135)^2$, and the p-value in (b) is exactly the same as the p-value computed in Problem 10.32 (b).

14.13 (b) Since $\chi^2_{STAT} = 19.9467 > 3.841$, reject H_0. There is evidence that there is a significant difference between the proportion of co-browsing organizations and non-co-browsing organizations that use skills-based routing to match the caller with the *right* agent. **(c)** p-value is virtually zero. The probability of obtaining a test statistic of 19.9467 or larger when the null hypothesis is true is 0.0000. **(d)** The results are identical since $(4.4662)^2 = 19.9467$.

Section 14.2

14.15 (a) The expected frequencies for the first row are 20, 30, and 40. The expected frequencies for the second row are 30, 45, and 60. **(b)** Because $\chi^2_{STAT} = 12.5 > 5.991$, reject H_0.

14.17 (a) Since the calculated test statistic 5.3863 is less than the critical value of 7.8147, you do not reject H_0 and conclude that there is no evidence of a difference among the age groups in the proportion who have had important personal information stolen. (b) p-value = 0.1456. The probability of obtaining a data set that gives rise to a test statistic of 5.3863 or more is 0.1456 if there is no difference in the proportion who have had important personal information stolen.

14.19 (a) H_0: $\pi_1 = \pi_2 = \pi_3$. H_1: At least one proportion differs where population 1 = small, 2 = medium, 3 = large.

PHStat output:

Observed Frequencies

Deployed	Column Variable			
	Small	Medium	Large	Total
Yes	18	74	52	144
No	182	126	148	456
Total	200	200	200	600

Expected Frequencies

Deployed	Column Variable			
	Small	Medium	Large	Total
Yes	48	48	48	144
No	152	152	152	456
Total	200	200	200	600

Data

Level of Significance	0.05
Number of Rows	2
Number of Columns	3
Degrees of Freedom	2

Results

Critical Value	5.991465
Chi-Square Test Statistic	43.64035
p-Value	3.34E-10
Reject the Null Hypothesis	

Decision rule: $df = (c - 1) = (3 - 1) = 2$. If $\chi^2_{STAT} > 5.9915$, reject H_0.

Test statistic: $\chi^2_{STAT} \sum_{all\ cells} \frac{(f_o - f_e)^2}{f_e} = 43.64035$

Decision: Since $\chi^2_{STAT} = 43.64035$ is greater than the upper critical value of 5.9915, reject H_0. There is evidence of a difference among the groups with respect to the proportion of companies that have already deployed Big Data projects. (b) p-value = 0.0000. The probability of obtaining a sample that gives rise to a test statistic that is equal to or more than 43.64035 is 0.0000 if there is no difference among the groups with respect to the proportion of companies that have already deployed Big Data projects.

14.21 (a) Since the calculated test statistic 28.0506 is greater than the critical value of 7.8147, you reject H_0 and conclude that there is evidence of a significant difference among the companies of different sizes with respect to the proportion that are working simultaneously with five or more vendors. **(b)** p-value = 0.0000. The probability of obtaining a data set that gives rise to a test statistic of 28.0506 or more is 0.0000 if there is no difference among the companies of different sizes with respect to the proportion that are working simultaneously with five or more vendors.

Section 14.3

14.23 $df = (r - 1)(c - 1) = (3 - 1)(4 - 1) = 6$.

14.25 $\chi^2_{STAT} = 92.1028 > 16.919$, reject H_0 and conclude that there is evidence of a relationship between the type of dessert ordered and the type of entrée ordered.

14.27 H_0: There is no relationship between number of airline loyalty programs and age.
H_1: There is a relationship between number of airline loyalty programs and age.
PHStat output:

Observed Frequencies

Number of Loyalty Programs	Age						
	18–22	23–29	30–39	40–49	50–64	65+	Total
0	78	113	79	74	88	88	520
1	36	50	41	48	69	82	326
3-Feb	12	34	36	48	52	85	267
5-Apr	4	4	6	7	13	25	59
6	0	0	3	0	2	3	8
Total	130	201	165	177	224	283	1,180

Expected Frequencies

Number of Loyalty Programs	Age						
	18–22	23–29	30–39	40–49	50–64	65+	Total
0	57.28814	88.57627	72.71186	78	98.71186	124.7119	520
1	35.91525	55.53051	45.58475	48.9	61.88475	78.18475	326
41,673	29.41525	45.48051	37.33475	40.05	50.68475	64.03475	267
41,734	6.5	10.05	8.25	8.85	11.2	14.15	59
6	0.881356	1.362712	1.118644	1.2	1.518644	1.918644	8
Total	130	201	165	177	224	283	1,180

Calculations

		$f_o - f_e$			
20.71186	24.42373	6.288136	-4	-10.7119	-36.7119
0.084746	-5.53051	-4.58475	-0.9	7.115254	3.815254
-17.4153	-11.4805	-1.33475	7.95	1.315254	20.96525
-2.5	-6.05	-2.25	-1.85	1.8	10.85
-0.88136	-1.36271	1.881356	-1.2	0.481356	1.081356

		$(f_o - f_e)^2/f_e$			
7.488136	6.734518	0.543799	0.205128	1.162414	10.807
0.0002	0.550806	0.461117	0.016564	0.818083	0.186177
10.31067	2.89799	0.047718	1.57809	0.03413	6.864115
0.961538	3.64204	0.613636	0.386723	0.289286	8.319611
0.881356	1.362712	3.164099	1.2	0.152573	0.609457

Data

Level of Significance	0.01
Number of Rows	5
Number of Columns	6
Degrees of Freedom	20

Results

Critical Value	37.56623
Chi-Square Test Statistic	72.28969
p-Value	7.67E-08
Reject the Null Hypothesis	

Decision rule: If $\chi^2_{STAT} >$, reject H_0.

Test statistic: $\chi^2_{STAT} \sum\limits_{all\ cells} \dfrac{(f_o - f_e)^2}{f_e} = 72.2897$

Decision: Since $\chi^2_{STAT} = 72.2897 > 37.5662$, reject H_0. There is evidence to conclude there is a relationship between number of airline loyalty programs and age.

14.29 Because $\chi^2_{STAT} = 38.021 > 21.0261$ reject H_0. There is evidence of a relationship between identified main opportunity and geographic region.

Review

14.30 (a) Because $\chi^2_{STAT} = 0.412 < 3.841$, do not reject H_0. There is insufficient evidence to conclude that there is a relationship between a student's gender and pizzeria selection. **(b)** Because $\chi^2_{STAT} = 2.624 < 3.841$, do not reject H_0. There is insufficient evidence to conclude that there is a relationship between a student's gender and pizzeria selection. **(c)** Because $\chi^2_{STAT} = 4.956 < 5.991$, do not reject H_0. There is insufficient evidence to conclude that there is a relationship between price and pizzeria selection. **(d)** p-value $= 0.0839$. The probability of a sample that gives a test statistic equal to or greater than 4.956 is 8.39% if the null hypothesis of no relationship between price and pizzeria selection is true.

14.32 (a) Because $\chi^2_{STAT} = 11.895 < 12.592$, do not reject H_0. There is not enough evidence to conclude that there is a relationship between the attitudes of employees toward the use of self-managed work teams and employee job classification. **(b)** Because $\chi^2_{STAT} = 3.294 < 12.592$, do not reject H_0. There is insufficient evidence to conclude that there is a relationship between the attitudes of employees toward vacation time without pay and employee job classification.

CHAPTER 15

Section 15.2

15.11 (a) Yes. **(b)** No. **(c)** No. **(d)** Yes.

15.13 (a) The scatter plot shows a positive linear relationship. **(b)** For each increase in alcohol percentage of 1.0, mean predicted mean wine quality is estimated to increase by 0.5624. **(c)** $\hat{Y} = -0.3529 + 0.5624X = -0.3529 + 0.5624(10) = 5.2715$. **(d)** Wine quality appears to be affected by the alcohol percentage. Each increase of 1% in alcohol leads to a mean increase in wine quality of a little more than half a unit.

15.15 (b) $b_0 = -2.37$, $b_1 = 0.0501$. **(c)** For every cubic foot increase in the amount moved, predicted mean labor hours are estimated to increase by 0.0501. **(d)** 22.67 labor hours. **(e)** That as expected, the labor hours are affected by the amount to be moved.

15.17 (b) $b_0 = -748.1752$, $b_1 = 6.5988$. **(c)** For each additional million-dollar increase in revenue, the mean value is predicted to increase by an estimated \$6.5988 million. Literal interpretation of b_0 is not meaningful because an operating franchise cannot have zero revenue. **(d)** \$901.5234 million. **(e)** That the value of the franchise can be expected to increase as revenue increases.

15.19 (b) $b_0 = 11.9081$, $b_1 = 0.1303$. **(c)** For each increase of \$1 million of box office gross, the predicted DVD revenue is estimated to increase by \$0.1303 million. **(d)** \$24.937 million. **(e)** You can conclude that the mean predicted increase in DVD sales is \$130,300 for each million-dollar increase in movie gross.

Section 15.3

15.21 $r^2 = 0.90$. 90% of the variation in the dependent variable can be explained by the variation in the independent variable.

15.23 $r^2 = 0.75$. 75% of the variation in the dependent variable can be explained by the variation in the independent variable.

15.25 (a) $r^2 = \dfrac{SSR}{SST} = \dfrac{21.8677}{64.0000} = 0.3417$, 34.17% of the variation in wine quality can be explained by the variation in the percentage of alcohol.

(b) $S_{YX} = \sqrt{\dfrac{SSE}{n-2}} = \sqrt{\dfrac{\sum\limits_{i=1}^{n}(Y_i - \hat{Y}_i)^2}{n-2}} = \sqrt{\dfrac{42.1323}{48}} = 0.9369$.

(c) Based on (a) and (b), the model should be somewhat useful for predicting wine quality.

15.27 (a) $r^2 = 0.8892$. 88.92% of the variation in labor hours can be explained by the variation in cubic feet moved. **(b)** $S_{YX} = 5.0314$. **(c)** Based on (a) and (b), the model should be very useful for predicting the labor hours.

15.29 (a) $r^2 = 0.7997$, 79.97% of the variation in the value of a baseball franchise can be explained by the variation in its annual revenue. **(b)** $S_{YX} = 206.9141$. **(c)** Based on (a) and (b), the model should be useful for predicting the value of a baseball franchise.

15.31 (a) $r^2 = 0.4524$, 45.24% of the variation in DVD revenue can be explained by the variation in box office gross. **(b)** $S_{YX} = 12.1366$. The variation of DVD revenue around the prediction line is \$12.1366 million. The typical difference between actual DVD revenue and the predicted DVD revenue using the regression equation is approximately \$12.1366 million. **(c)** Based on (a) and (b), the model may only be somewhat useful for predicting DVD revenue. **(d)** Other variables that might explain the variation in DVD revenue could be the amount spent on advertising, the timing of the release of the DVDs, and the type of movie.

Section 15.5

15.33 A residual analysis of the data indicates a pattern, with sizable clusters of consecutive residuals that are either all positive or all negative. This pattern indicates a violation of the assumption of linearity. A curvilinear model should be investigated.

15.35 There does not appear to be a pattern in the residual plot. The assumptions of regression do not appear to be seriously violated.

15.37 Based on the residual plot, there does not appear to be a curvilinear pattern in the residuals. The assumptions of normality and equal variance do not appear to be seriously violated.

15.39 Based on the residual plot, there appears to be an outlier in the residuals, but no evidence of a pattern. The outlier is the Los Angeles Dodgers whose value has increased drastically due to a recent long term cable TV deal.

Section 15.6

15.41 (a) An increasing linear relationship exists. (b) There is evidence of a strong positive autocorrelation among the residuals.

15.43 (a) No, because the data were not collected over time. (b) If data were collected at a single store had been selected and studied over a period of time, you would compute the Durbin-Watson statistic.

15.45 (a)
$$b_1 = \frac{SSXY}{SSX} = \frac{201,399.05}{12,495,626} = 0.0161$$
$$b_0 = \bar{Y} - b_1\bar{X} = 71.2621 - 0.0161\,(4,393) = 0.458.$$

(b) $\hat{Y} = 0.458 + 0.0161X = 0.458 + 0.0161(4,500) = 72.908$, or \$72,908. (c) There is no evidence of a pattern in the residuals over time.

(d) $D = \dfrac{\sum\limits_{i=2}^{n} (e_i - e_{i-1})^2}{\sum\limits_{i=1}^{n} e_i^2} = \dfrac{1,243.2244}{599.0683} = 2.08 > 1.45$. There is no evidence of positive autocorrelation among the residuals. (e) Based on a residual analysis, the model appears to be adequate.

15.47 (a) $b_0 = -2.535$, $b_1 = 0.06073$. (b) \$2,505.40. (d) $D = 1.64 > d_U = 1.42$, so there is no evidence of positive autocorrelation among the residuals. (e) The plot shows some nonlinear pattern, suggesting that a nonlinear model might be better. Otherwise, the model appears to be adequate.

Section 15.7

15.49 (a) 3.00. (b) ± 2.1199. (c) Reject H_0. There is evidence that the fitted linear regression model is useful. (d) $1.32 \le \beta_1 \le 7.68$.

15.51 (a) $t_{STAT} = \dfrac{b_1 - \beta_1}{S_{b_1}} = \dfrac{0.5624}{0.1127} = 4.9913 > 2.0106$. Reject H_0. There is evidence of a linear relationship between the percentage of alcohol and wine quality.
(b) $b_1 \pm t_{\alpha/2}S_{b_1} = 0.5624 \pm 2.0106(0.1127)\ 0.3359 \le \beta_1 \le 0.7890$.

15.53 (a) $t_{STAT} = 16.52 > 2.0322$; reject H_0. There is evidence of a linear relationship between the number of cubic feet moved and labor hours. (b) $0.0439 \le \beta_1 \le 0.0562$.

15.55 (a) $t_{STAT} = 10.5744 > 2.0484$ or because the p-value is 0.0000, reject H_0 at the 5% level of significance. There is evidence of a linear relationship between annual revenue and franchise value. (b) $5.3205 \le \beta_1 \le 7.8771$.

15.57 (a) $t_{STAT} = 4.4532 > 2.0639$ or because the p-value $= 0.0002 < 0.05$; reject H_0. There is evidence of a linear relationship between box office gross and sales of DVDs. (b) $0.0699 \le \beta_1 \le 0.1907$.

15.59 (a) (% daily change in SPXL) $= b_0 + 3.0$ (% daily change in S&P 500 index). (b) If the S&P 500 gains 10% in a year, SPXL is expected to gain an estimated 30%. (c) If the S&P 500 loses 20% in a year, SPXL is expected to lose an estimated 60%. (d) Risk takers will be attracted to leveraged funds, and risk-averse investors will stay away.

15.61 (a), (b) First weekend and U.S. gross: $r = 0.7264$, $t_{STAT} = 2.5893 > 2.4469$, p-value $= 0.0413 < 0.05$. reject H_0. At the 0.05 level of significance, there is evidence of a linear relationship between first weekend sales and U.S. gross. First weekend and worldwide gross: $r = 0.8234$, $t_{STAT} = 3.5549 > 2.4469$, p-value $= 0.0120 < 0.05$. reject H_0. At the 0.05 level of significance, there is evidence of a linear relationship between first weekend sales and worldwide gross. U.S. gross and worldwide gross: $r = 0.9629$, $t_{STAT} = 8.7456 > 2.4469$, p-value $= 0.0001 < 0.05$. Reject H_0. At the 0.05 level of significance, there is evidence of a linear relationship between U.S. gross and worldwide gross.

15.63 (a) $r = 0.8009$. There appears to be a strong positive linear relationship between social media networking and the GDP per capita. (b) $t_{STAT} = 6.2744$, p-value $= 0.0000 < 0.05$. Reject H_0. At the 0.05 level of significance, there is a significant linear relationship between social media networking and the GDP per capita. (c) There appears to be a strong relationship.

Section 15.8

15.65 (a) $15.95 \le \mu_{Y|X=4} \le 18.05$. (b) $14.651 \le Y_{X=4} \le 19.349$.

15.67 (a) $\hat{Y} = -0.3529 + (0.5624)(10) = 5.2715\ \hat{Y} \pm t_{\alpha/2}S_{YX}\sqrt{h_i}$
$$= 5.2715 \pm 2.0106(0.9369)\sqrt{0.0249}$$
$$4.9741 \le \mu_{Y|X=10} \le 5.5690.$$

(b) $\hat{Y} \pm t_{\alpha/2}S_{YX}\sqrt{1 + h_i}$
$$= 5.2715 \pm 2.0106(9,369)\sqrt{1 + 0.0249}$$
$$3.3645 \le Y_{X=10} \le 7.1786.$$

(c) Part (b) provides a prediction interval for the individual response given a specific value of the independent variable, and part (a) provides an interval estimate for the mean value, given a specific value of the independent variable. Because there is much more variation in predicting an individual value than in estimating a mean value, a prediction interval is wider than a confidence interval estimate.

15.69 (a) $20.799 \le \mu_{Y|X=500} \le 24.542$. (b) $12.276 \le Y_{X=500} \le 33.065$. (c) You can estimate a mean more precisely than you can predict a single observation.

15.71 (a) $822.1742 \le \mu_{Y|X=250} \le 980.8727$. (b) $470.3155 \le Y_{X=250} \le 1,332.731$. (c) Part (b) provides a prediction interval for an individual response given a specific value of X, and part (a) provides a confidence interval estimate for the mean value, given a specific value of X. Because there is much more variation in predicting an individual value than in estimating a mean, the prediction interval is wider than the confidence interval.

Review

15.74 (a) $b_0 = 24.84, b_1 = 0.14.$ **(b)** For each additional case, the predicted delivery time is estimated to increase by 0.14 minute. **(c)** 45.84. **(d)** No, 500 is outside the relevant range of the data used to fit the regression equation. **(e)** $r^2 = 0.972.$ **(f)** There is no obvious pattern in the residuals, so the assumptions of regression are met. The model appears to be adequate. **(g)** $t_{STAT} = 24.88 > 2.1009$; reject H_0. **(h)** $44.88 \leq \mu_{Y|X=150} \leq 46.80. \ 41.56 \leq Y_{X=150} \leq 50.12.$ **(i)** The number of cases explains almost all of the variation in delivery time.

15.76 (a) $b_0 = 276.848, b_1 = 50.8031.$ **(b)** For each additional 1,000 square feet in the size of the house, the mean assessed value is predicted to increase by $50,803.10. The estimated selling price of a house with a 0 size is $276,848 thousand. However, this interpretation is not meaningful because the size of the house cannot be 0. **(c)** $\hat{Y} = 276.848 + 50.8031(2) = 378.4542$ thousand dollars. **(d)** $r^2 = 0.3273.$ So 32.73% of the variation in assessed value be explained by the variation in size. **(e)** Neither the residual plot nor the normal probability plot reveals any potential violation of the linearity, equal variance, and normality assumptions. **(f)** $t_{STAT} = 3.6913 > 2.0484$, p-value is 0.0009. Because p-value < 0.05, reject H_0. There is evidence of a linear relationship between assessed value and size. **(g)** $22.6113 \leq \beta_1 \leq 78.9949.$ **(h)** The size of the house is somewhat useful in predicting the assessed value, but since only 32.73% of the variation in assessed value is explained by variation in size, other variables should be considered.

15.78 (a) $b_0 = 0.30, b_1 = 0.00487.$ **(b)** For each additional point on the GMAT score, the predicted GPA is estimated to increase by 0.00487. Because a GMAT score of 0 is not possible, the Y intercept does not have a practical interpretation. **(c)** 3.222. **(d)** $r^2 = 0.798.$ **(e)** There is no obvious pattern in the residuals, so the assumptions of regression are met. The model appears to be adequate. **(f)** $t_{STAT} = 8.43 > 2.1009$; reject H_0. **(g)** $3.144 \leq \mu_{Y|X=600} \leq 3.301, 2.866 \leq Y_{X=600} \leq 3.559.$ **(h)** $.00366 \leq \beta_1 \leq .00608.$ **(i)** Most of the variation in GPA can be explained by variation in the GMAT score.

15.80 (a) There is no clear relationship shown on the scatter plot. **(c)** Looking at all 23 flights, when the temperature is lower, there is likely to be some O-ring damage, particularly if the temperature is below 60 degrees. **(d)** 31 degrees is outside the relevant range, so a prediction should not be made. **(e)** Predicted $Y = 18.036 - 0.240X$, where X = temperature and Y = O-ring damage. **(g)** A nonlinear model would be more appropriate. **(h)** The appearance on the residual plot of a non-linear pattern indicates that a nonlinear model would be better. It also appears that the normality assumption is invalid.

15.82 (a) $b_0 = -177.4298, b_1 = 5.3450.$ **(b)** For each additional million-dollar increase in revenue, the franchise value will increase by an estimated $5.3450 million. Literal interpretation of b_0 is not meaningful because an operating franchise cannot have zero revenue. **(c)** $624.3226 million. **(d)** $r^2 = 0.9331.$ 93.31% of the variation in the value of an NBA franchise can be explained by the variation in its annual revenue. **(e)** There does not appear to be a pattern in the residual plot. The assumptions of regression do not appear to be seriously violated. **(f)** $t_{STAT} = 19.764 > 2.0484$ or because the p-value is 0.0000, reject H_0 at the 5% level of significance. There is evidence of a linear relationship between annual revenue and franchise value. **(g)** $599.5015 \leq \mu_{Y|X=150} \leq 649.1438.$ **(h)** $486.2403 \leq Y_{X=150} \leq 762.405.$ **(i)** The strength of the relationship between revenue and value is higher for NBA franchises than for European soccer teams and Major League Baseball teams.

15.84 (a) $b_0 = -2,629.222, b_1 = 82.472.$ **(b)** For each additional centimeter in circumference, the weight is estimated to increase by

82.472 grams. **(c)** 2,319.08 grams. **(d)** Yes, since circumference is a very strong predictor of weight. **(e)** $r^2 = 0.937.$ **(f)** There appears to be a nonlinear relationship between circumference and weight. **(g)** p-value is virtually $0 < 0.05$; reject H_0. **(h)** $72.7875 \leq \beta_1 \leq 92.156.$

15.86 (a) The correlation between compensation and stock performance is 0.1854. **(b)** $t_{STAT} = 2.6543$; p-value $= 0.0086 < 0.05$. The correlation between compensation and stock performance is significant, but only 3.44% of the variation in compensation can be explained by return. **(c)** The small correlation between compensation and stock performance was surprising (or maybe it shouldn't have been!).

CHAPTER 16

Section 16.1

16.8 (a) For each one-unit increase in X_1, you estimate that the mean of Y will decrease 2 units, holding X_2 constant. For each one-unit increase in X_2, you estimate that the mean of Y will increase 7 units, holding X_1 constant. **(b)** The Y intercept, equal to 50, estimates the value of Y when both X_1 and X_2 are 0.

16.10 (a) $\hat{Y} = -0.2245 + 0.0111X_1 + 0.0445X_2.$ **(b)** For a given total risk-based capital (%), each increase of 1% in the efficiency ratio is estimated to result in a mean increase in ROA of 0.0111%. For a given efficiency ratio, each increase of 1% in the total risk-based capital (%) is estimated to result in a mean increase in ROA of 0.0445%. **(c)** The interpretation of b_0 has no practical meaning here because it would have been the estimated mean ROA when the efficiency ratio and the total risk-based capital are each zero. **(d)** $\hat{Y}_i = -0.2245 + 0.0111(60) + 0.0445(15) = 1.1123$ or $69,878. **(e)** $0.9888 \leq \mu_{Y|X} \leq 1.2357.$ **(f)** $-0.4268 \leq Y_X \leq 2.6513.$ **(g)** Since there is much more variation in predicting an individual value than in estimating a mean value, a prediction interval is wider than a confidence interval estimate holding everything else fixed.

16.12 (a) $\hat{Y} = -186.5501 + 0.0333X_1 + 50.8778X_2.$ **(b)** For a given amount of voluntary turnover, each increase of $1 million in total world-wide revenue is estimated to result in a mean increase in the number of full-time jobs added in a year by 0.0333. For a given amount of total worldwide revenue, each increase of 1% in voluntary turnover is estimated to result in the mean increase in the number of full-time jobs added in a year of 50.8778. **(c)** The Y intercept of -186.5501 has no direct interpre-tation since it represents the value of the mean increase in the number of full-time jobs added in a year when there is no worldwide revenue and no voluntary turnover. **(d)** The number of full-time jobs added seems to be affected by the amount of worldwide revenue and the voluntary turnover.

16.14 (a) $\hat{Y} = 532.2883 + 407.1346X_1 - 2.8257X_2$, where X_1 = land area, X_2 = age. **(b)** For a given age, each increase by one acre in land area is estimated to result in an increase in the mean fair market value by $407.1346 thousands. For a given land area, each increase of one year in age is estimated to result in a decrease in the mean fair market value by $2.8257 thousands. **(c)** The interpretation of b_0 has no practical meaning here because it would represent the estimated fair market value of a new house that has no land area. **(d)** $\hat{Y} = 5,332.2883 + 407.1346(0.25) - 2.8257(55) = 478.6577 thousands. **(e)** $446.8367 \leq \mu_{Y|X} \leq 510.4788.$ **(f)** $307.2577 \leq Y_X \leq 650.0577.$

Section 16.2

16.16 (a) $MSR = 15, MSE = 12.$ **(b)** 1.25. **(c)** $F_{STAT} = 1.25 < 4.10$; do not reject H_0. **(d)** 0.20. **(e)** 0.04.

16.18 (a) $F_{STAT} = 0.6531 < 3.44$. Do not reject H_0. There is insufficient evidence of a significant linear relationship with at least one of the independent variables. **(b)** p-value $= 0.5302$. The probability of obtaining an F test statistic of 0.6531 or larger is 0.5302 if H_0 is true. **(c)** $r^2_{Y.12} = SSR/SST = 96,655.1/1,724,596.2 = 0.056$. So, 5.6% of the variation in the mean annual revenue can be explained by variation in the mean age and mean BizAnalyzer score.

16.20 (a) $MSR = SSR/k = 7.5929/2 = 3.7964$
$MSE = SSE/(n - k - 1) = 119.2044/197 = 0.6051$
$F_{STAT} = MSR/MSE = 3.7964/0.6051 = 6.2741$
$F_{STAT} = 6.2741 > 3.0$. Reject H_0. There is evidence of a significant linear relationship. **(b)** p-value $= 0.0023$. The probability of obtaining an F test statistic of 6.2741 or larger is 0.0023 if H_0 is true. **(c)** $r^2_{Y.12} = SSR/SST = 7.5929/126.7973 = 0.0599$. So, 5.99% of the variation in ROA can be explained by variation in used efficiency ratio and total risk-based capital.

(d) $r^2_{adj} = 1 - \left[(1 - r^2_{Y.12}) \dfrac{n - 1}{n - k - 1} \right] =$

$1 - \left[(1 - 0.0599) \dfrac{200 - 1}{200 - 2 - 1} \right] = 0.0503$

16.22 (a) $MSR = SSR/k = 19,534,514.2835/2 = 9,767,257.1417$
$MSE = SSE/(n - k - 1) = 115,096,077.0499/93 = 1,237,592.2263$
$F_{STAT} = MSR/MSE = 9,767,257.1417/1,237,592.2263 = 7.8921$
$F_{STAT} = 7.8921 > 3.0943$. Reject H_0. There is evidence of a significant linear relationship. **(b)** p-value <0.0007. The probability of obtaining an F test statistic of 7.8921 or larger is less than 0.0007 if H_0 is true. **(c)** $r^2_{Y.12} = SSR/SST = 19,534,514.2835/134,630,591.3333 = 0.1451$. So, 14.51% of the variation in the number of full-time jobs added can be explained by variation in the total worldwide revenue ($millions), and full-time voluntary turnover (%). **(d)** $r^2_{adj} = 0.1267$

Section 16.3

16.24 Since the data were not collected over time, there is no reason to plot the residuals over time. **(c)** There appears to be a departure in the equal variance assumption in the plot of the residuals versus the efficiency ratio. Therefore, a data transformation should be considered.

16.26 Based on a residual analysis, there is evidence of a violation of the assumptions of equal variance and normality. **(b)** Since the data were not collected over time, the Durbin-Watson test is not appropriate. **(c)** No.

16.28 (a) The residual analysis reveals no patterns. **(b)** Since the data are not collected over time, the Durbin-Watson test is not appropriate. **(c)** There are no apparent violations in the assumptions.

Section 16.4

16.30 (a) Variable X_2 has a larger slope in terms of the t statistic of 3.75 than variable X_1, which has a smaller slope in terms of the t statistic of 3.33. **(b)** $1.46824 \leq \beta_1 \leq 6.53176$. **(c)** For X_1: $t_{STAT} = 4/1.2 = 3.33 > 2.1098$, with 17 degrees of freedom for $\alpha = 0.05$. Reject H_0. There is evidence that X_1 contributes to a model already containing X_2. For X_2: $t_{STAT} = 3/0.8 = 3.75 > 2.1098$, with 17 degrees of freedom for $\alpha = 0.05$. Reject H_0. There is evidence that X_2 contributes to a model already containing X_1. Both X_1 and X_2 should be included in the model.

16.32 (a) 95% confidence interval on β_1: $b_1 \pm t_{n-k-1}s_{b_1}$,
$0.0111 \pm 1.9721(0.0051)$ $0.0011 \leq \beta_1 \leq 0.0212$.
(b) For X_1: $t_{STAT} = b_1/s_{b_1} = 0.0111/0.0051 = 2.1881 > 1.9721$ with 197 degrees of freedom for $\alpha = 0.05$. Reject H_0. There is evidence that the variable X_1 contributes to a model already containing X_2.

For X_2: $t_{STAT} = b_2/s_{b_2} = 0.0445/0.0145 = 3.065 > 1.9721$ with 197 degrees of freedom for $\alpha = 0.05$. Reject H_0. There is evidence that the variable X_2 contributes to a model already containing X_1. Both variables X_1 and X_2 should be included in the model.

16.34 (a) $0.0333 \pm 1.9858(0.0092)$ $0.0151 \leq \beta_1 \leq 0.0515$.
(b) For X_1: $t_{STAT} = b_1/s_{b_1} = 0.0333/0.0092 = 3.639 > 1.9858$ with 93 degrees of freedom for $\alpha = 0.05$. Reject H_0. There is evidence that the variable X_1 contributes to a model already containing X_2. For X_2: $t_{STAT} = b_2/s_{b_2} = 50.8778/23.7425 = 2.1429 > 1.9858$ with 93 degrees of freedom for $\alpha = 0.05$. Reject H_0. There is evidence that the variable X_2 contributes to a model already containing X_1. Both variables X_1 and X_2 should be included in the model.

16.36 (a) $274.1702 \leq \beta_1 \leq 540.0990$. **(b)** For X_1: $t_{STAT} = 6.2827$ and p-value $= 0.0000$. Because p-value < 0.05, reject H_0. There is evidence that X_1 contributes to a model already containing X_2. For X_2: $t_{STAT} = -4.1475$ and p-value $= 0.0003$. Because p-value < 0.05 reject H_0. There is evidence that X_2 contributes to a model already containing X_1: $F_{STAT} = 30.4533$ p-value $= 0.0000$. Both X_1 (land area) and X_2 (age) should be included in the model.

Section 16.5

16.38 Because $t_{STAT} = 3.27 > 2.1098$, reject H_0. X_2 makes a significant contribution to the model.

16.40 (a) $\hat{Y} = 243.7371 + 9.2189X_1 + 12.6967X_2$, where $X_1 =$ number of rooms and $X_2 =$ neighborhood (east $= 0$). **(b)** Holding constant the effect of neighborhood, for each additional room, the mean selling price is estimated to increase by 9.2189 thousands of dollars, or $9,218.9. For a given number of rooms, a west neighborhood is estimated to increase the mean selling price over an east neighborhood by 12.6967 thousands of dollars, or $12,696.7. **(c)** $\hat{Y} = 243.7371 + 9.2189(9) + 12.6967(0) = 326.7076$, or $326,707.6. $309,560.04 \leq Y_X \leq 343,855.1$. $321,471.44 \leq \mu_{Y|X} \leq 331,943.71$. **(d)** Based on a residual analysis, the model appears to be adequate. **(e)** $F_{STAT} = 55.39$, the p-value is virtually 0. Because p-value < 0.05, reject H_0. There is evidence of a significant relationship between selling price and the two independent variables (rooms and neighborhood). **(f)** For X_1: $t_{STAT} = 8.9537$, the p-value is virtually 0. Reject H_0. Number of rooms makes a significant contribution and should be included in the model. For X_2: $t_{STAT} = 3.5913$, p-value $= 0.0023 < 0.05$. Reject H_0. Neighborhood makes a significant contribution and should be included in the model. Based on these results, the regression model with the two independent variables should be used. **(g)** $7.0466 \leq \beta_1 \leq 11.3913$. **(h)** $5.2378 \leq \beta_2 \leq 20.1557$. **(i)** $r^2_{adj} = 0.851$. **(j)** The slope of selling price with number of rooms is the same, regardless of whether the house is located in an east or west neighborhood. **(k)** $\hat{Y} = 253.95 + 8.032X_1 - 5.90X_2 + 2.089X_1X_2$. For X_1X_2, p-value $= 0.330$. Do not reject H_0. There is no evidence that the interaction term makes a contribution to the model. **(l)** The model in (b) should be used. **(m)** The number of rooms and the neighborhood both significantly affect the selling price, but the number of rooms has a greater effect.

16.42 (a) Predicted time $= 8.01 + 0.00523$ Depth $- 2.105$ Dry. **(b)** Holding constant the effect of type of drilling, for each foot increase in depth of the hole, the mean drilling time is estimated to increase by 0.00523 minutes. For a given depth, a dry drilling hole is estimated to reduce the drilling time over wet drilling by a mean of 2.1052 minutes. **(c)** 6.428 minutes, $6.210 \leq \mu_{Y|X} \leq 6.646$, $4.923 \leq Y_X \leq 7.932$.

(d) The model appears to be adequate. **(e)** $F_{STAT} = 111.11 > 3.09$; reject H_0. **(f)** $t_{STAT} = 5.03 > 1.9847$; reject H_0. $t_{STAT} = -14.03 < -1.9847$; reject H_0. Include both variables. **(g)** $0.0032 \leq \beta_1 \leq 0.0073$. **(h)** $-2.403 \leq \beta_2 \leq -1.808$. **(i)** 69.0%. **(j)** The slope of the additional drilling time with the depth of the hole is the same, regardless of the type of drilling method used. **(k)** The p-value of the interaction term $= 0.462 > 0.05$, so the term is not significant and should not be included in the model. **(l)** The model in part (b) should be used. Both variables affect the drilling time. Dry drilling holes should be used to reduce the drilling time.

16.44 (a) $\hat{Y} = 2.5213 - 0.0313X_1 - 0.1131X_2 + 0.0024X_3$, where $X_1 = $ efficiency ratio, $X_2 = $ total risk-based capital, $X_3 = X_1 X_2$. For $X_1 X_2$: the p-value is $0.0297 < 0.05$. Reject H_0. There is evidence that the interaction term makes a contribution to the model. **(b)** Since there is evidence of an interaction effect between efficiency ratio and total risk-based capital, the model in **(a)** should be used.

16.46 (a) $\hat{Y} = 85.1106 + 0.0033X_1 + 15.8856X_2 + 0.0045X_3$, where $X_1 = $ total worldwide revenue ($millions), $X_2 = $ full-time voluntary turnover (%), $X_3 = X_1 X_2$. For $X_1 X_2$: the p-value is $0.0396 < 0.05$. Reject H_0. There is evidence that the interaction term makes a contribution to the model. **(b)** Since there is evidence of an interaction effect between total worldwide revenue ($millions) and full-time voluntary turnover, the model in (a) should be used.

16.48 (a) For $X_1 X_2$, p-value $= 0.2353 > 0.05$. Do not reject H_0. There is insufficient evidence that the interaction term makes a contribution to the model. **(b)** Because there is not enough evidence of an interaction effect between total staff present and remote hours, the model in Problem 16.7 should be used.

Review

16.50 (a) $\hat{Y} = -3.9152 + 0.0319X_1 + 4.2228X_2$, where $X_1 = $ number cubic feet moved and $X_2 = $ number of pieces of large furniture. **(b)** Holding constant the number of pieces of large furniture, for each additional cubic foot moved, the mean labor hours are estimated to increase by 0.0319. Holding constant the amount of cubic feet moved, for each additional piece of large furniture, the mean labor hours are estimated to increase by 4.2228. **(c)** $\hat{Y} = -3.9152 + 0.0319$ $(500) + 4.2228 (2) = 20.4926$. **(d)** Based on a residual analysis, the errors appear to be normally distributed. The equal-variance assumption might be violated because the variances appear to be larger around the center region of both independent variables. There might also be violation of the linearity assumption. A model with quadratic terms for both independent variables might be fitted. **(e)** $F_{STAT} = 228.80$, p-value is virtually 0. Because p-value < 0.05, reject H_0. There is evidence of a significant relationship between labor hours and the two independent variables (the amount of cubic feet moved and the number of pieces of large furniture). **(f)** The p-value is virtually 0. The probability of obtaining a test statistic of 228.80 or greater is virtually 0 if there is no significant relationship between labor hours and the two independent variables (the amount of cubic feet moved and the number of pieces of large furniture). **(g)** $r^2 = 0.9327$. 93.27% of the variation in labor hours can be explained by variation in the number of cubic feet moved and the number of pieces of large furniture. **(h)** $r^2_{adj} = 0.9287$. **(i)** For X_1: $t_{STAT} = 6.9339$, the p-value is virtually 0. Reject H_0. The number of cubic feet moved makes a significant contribution and should be included in the model. For X_2: $t_{STAT} = 4.6192$, the p-value is virtually 0. Reject H_0. The number of pieces of large furniture makes a significant contribution and should be included in the model. Based on these results, the regression model with the two independent variables should be used. **(j)** For X_1: $t_{STAT} = 6.9339$, the p-value is virtually 0. The probability of obtaining a sample that will yield a test statistic farther away than 6.9339 is virtually 0 if the number of cubic feet moved does not make a significant contribution,

holding the effect of the number of pieces of large furniture constant. For X_2: $t_{STAT} = 4.6192$, the p-value is virtually 0. The probability of obtaining a sample that will yield a test statistic farther away than 4.6192 is virtually 0 if the number of pieces of large furniture does not make a significant contribution, holding the effect of the amount of cubic feet moved constant. **(k)** $0.0226 \leq \beta_1 \leq 0.0413$. You are 95% confident that the mean labor hours will increase by between 0.0226 and 0.0413 for each additional cubic foot moved, holding constant the number of pieces of large furniture. In Problem 12.44, you are 95% confident that the labor hours will increase by between 0.0439 and 0.0562 for each additional cubic foot moved, regardless of the number of pieces of large furniture. **(l)** Both the number of cubic feet moved and the number of large pieces of furniture are useful in predicting the labor hours, but the cubic feet removed is more important.

16.52 (a) $\hat{Y} = 257.9033 + 53.3606X_1 + 0.2521X_2$, where $X_1 = $ house size and $X_2 = $ age. **(b)** Holding constant the age, for each additional thousand square feet in the size of the house, the mean assessed value is estimated to increase by 53.3606 thousand dollars. Holding constant the size of the house, for each additional year in age, the assessed value is estimated to increase by 0.2521 thousand dollars. **(c)** $\hat{Y} = 257.9033 + 53.3606(2) + 0.2521(55) = 378.4093$ thousand dollars. **(d)** Based on a residual analysis, the model appears to be adequate. **(e)** $F_{STAT} = 6.6459$, the p-value $= 0.0045$. Because p-value < 0.05, reject H_0. There is evidence of a significant relationship between assessed value and the two independent variables (size of the house and age). **(f)** The p-value is 0.0045. The probability of obtaining a test statistic of 6.6459 or greater is virtually 0 if there is no significant relationship between assessed value and the two independent variables (size of the house and age). **(g)** $r^2 = 0.3299$. 32.99% of the variation in assessed value can be explained by variation in the size of the house and age. **(h)** $r^2_{adj} = 0.2803$. **(i)** For X_1: $t_{STAT} = 3.3128$, the p-value is 0.0026. Reject H_0. The size of the house makes a significant contribution and should be included in the model. For X_2: $t_{STAT} = 0.3203$, p-value $= 0.7512 > 0.05$. Do not reject H_0. Age does not make a significant contribution and should not be included in the model. Based on these results, the regression model with only the size of the house should be used. **(j)** For X_1: $t_{STAT} = 3.3128$, the p-value is virtually 0. The probability of obtaining a sample that will yield a test statistic farther away than 3.3128 is 0.0026 if the house size does not make a significant contribution, holding age constant. For X_2: $t_{STAT} = 0.3203$, the p-value is 0.7512. The probability of obtaining a sample that will yield a test statistic farther away than 0.3203 is 0.7512 if the age does not make a significant contribution holding the effect of the house size constant. **(k)** $20.3109 \leq \beta_1 \leq 86.4104$. You are 95% confident that the assessed value will increase by an amount somewhere between $20.3109 thousand and $86.4104 thousand for each additional thousand square foot increase in house size, holding constant the age of the house. In Problem 12.76, you are 95% confident that the assessed value will increase by an amount somewhere between $22.6113 thousand and $78.9949 thousand for each additional 1,000 square foot increase in house size, regardless of the age of the house. **(l)** Only size of the house should be included in the model.

16.54 (a) $\hat{Y} = 694.9557 + 8.6059X_1 + 2069X_2$, where $X_1 = $ assessed value and $X_2 = $ age. **(b)** Holding age constant, for each additional $1,000, the taxes are estimated to increase by a mean of $8.61 thousand. Holding assessed value constant, for each additional year, the taxes are estimated to increase by $2.069 **(c)** $\hat{Y} = 694.9557 + 8.6059(400) + 2.069(50) = 4,240.542$ dollars. **(d)** Based on a residual analysis, the errors appear to be normally distributed. The equal-variance assumption appears to be valid. **(e)** $F_{STAT} = 22.0699$, p-value $= 0.0000$. Because p-value $= 0.0000 < 0.05$, reject H_0. There is evidence of a significant relationship between taxes and the two independent variables (assessed value and age). **(f)** p-value $= 0.0000$. The probability of obtaining an F_{STAT} test statistic of 22.0699 or greater is virtually 0 if there is no significant relationship between taxes and the two independent variables (assessed value and age). **(g)** $r^2 = 0.6205$. 62.05% of the variation in taxes can be explained by variation in assessed value and age. **(h)** $r_{adj}^2 = 0.5924$. **(i)** For X_1: $t_{STAT} = 6.5271$, p-value $= 0.0000 < 0.05$. Reject H_0. The assessed value makes a significant contribution and should be included in the model. For X_2: $t_{STAT} = 0.3617$, p-value $= 0.7204 > 0.05$. Do not reject H_0. The age of a house does not make a significant contribution and should not be included in the model. Based on these results, the regression model with only assessed value should be used. **(j)** For X_1: p-value $= 0.0000$. The probability of obtaining a sample that will yield a test statistic farther away than 6.5271 is 0.0000 if the assessed value does not make a significant contribution, holding age constant. For X_2: p-value $= 0.7204$. The probability of obtaining a sample that will yield a test statistic farther away than 0.3617 is 0.7204 if the age of a house does not make a significant contribution, holding the effect of the assessed value constant. **(k)** $5.9005 \leq \beta_1 \leq 11.3112$. You are 95% confident that the mean taxes will increase by an amount somewhere between \$5.90 and \$11.31 for each additional \$1,000 increase in the assessed value, holding constant the age. In Problem 12.77, you are 95% confident that the mean taxes will increase by an amount somewhere between \$5.91 and \$11.07 for each additional \$thousand increase in assessed value, regardless of the age. **(l)** Based on your answers to (b) through (k), the age of a house does not have an effect on its taxes.

16.56 (a) $\hat{Y} = 183.1738 - 25.5406X_1 - 6.9866X_2$, where $X_1 = $ ERA and $X_2 = $ League (American $= 0$, National $= 1$). **(b)** Holding constant the effect of the league, for each additional ERA, the number of wins is estimated to decrease by a mean of 25.5406. For a given ERA, a team in the National League is estimated to have a mean of 6.9866 fewer wins than a team in the American League. **(c)** $\hat{Y} = 183.1738 - 25.5406(4.0) - 6.9866(0) = 81.0113$ wins $= 81$ wins. **(d)** Based on a residual analysis, there is no pattern in the errors. There is no apparent violation of other assumptions. **(e)** $F_{STAT} = 23.4629$, p-value $= 0.0000$. Since p-value < 0.05, reject H_0. There is evidence of a significant relationship between wins and the two independent variables (ERA and league). **(f)** For X_1: $t_{STAT} = -6.8476$, p-value $= 0.0000 < 0.05$. Reject H_0. ERA makes a significant contribution and should be included in the model. For X_2: $t_{STAT} = -2.368$, p-value $= 0.0253 < 0.05$. Reject H_0. The league makes a significant contribution and should be included in the model. Based on these results, the regression model with ERA and league as the independent variables should be used. **(g)** $-33.1937 \leq \beta_1 \leq -17.8876$ **(h)** $-13.0404 \leq \beta_2 \leq -0.9328$ **(i)** $r_{adj}^2 = 0.6077$. So 60.77% of the

variation in wins can be explained by the variation in ERA and league after adjusting for number of independent variables and sample size. **(j)** The slope of the number of wins with ERA is the same regardless of whether the team belongs to the American or the National League. **(k)** For X_1X_2: the p-value is $0.3024 > 0.05$. Do not reject H_0. There is no evidence that the interaction term makes a contribution to the model. **(l)** The regression model with ERA and league as the independent variables should be used.

16.58 The r^2 of the multiple regression is 0.1996. 19.96% of the variation in earnings per share growth can be explained by the variation of sales growth (%) and return on equity (%). The F test statistic for the combined significance of sales growth (%) and return on equity (%) is 12.0965 with a p-value of 0.0000. Hence, at a 5% level of significance, there is evidence to conclude sales growth (%) and/or return on equity (%) affect earnings per share growth. The p-value of the t test for the significance of sales growth is $0.0002 < 0.05$. Hence, there is sufficient evidence to conclude that sales growth affects earnings per share growth holding constant the effect of return on equity. The p-value of the t test for the significance of return on equity is $0.0037 < 0.05$. There is evidence to conclude that return on equity affects earnings per share growth holding constant the effect of sales growth. There do not appear to be any obvious patterns in the residual plots. Hence, both sales growth (%) and return on equity (%) should be used in a regression model to predict earnings per share growth.

16.60 $b_0 = 18.2892$ (die temperature), $b_1 = 0.5976$, (die diameter), $b_2 = -13.5108$. The r^2 of the multiple regression is 0.3257 so 32.57% of the variation in unit density can be explained by the variation of die temperature and die diameter. The F test statistic for the combined significance of die temperature and die diameter is 5.0718 with a p-value of 0.0160. Hence, at a 5% level of significance, there is enough evidence to conclude that die temperature and die diameter affect unit density. The p-value of the t test for the significance of die temperature is 0.2117, which is greater than 5%. Hence, there is insufficient evidence to conclude that die temperature affects unit density holding constant the effect of die diameter. The p-value of the t test for the significance of die diameter is 0.0083, which is less than 5%. There is enough evidence to conclude that die diameter affects unit density at the 5% level of significance holding constant the effect of die temperature. After removing die temperature from the model, $b_0 = 107.9267$ (die diameter), $b_1 = -13.5108$. The r^2 of the multiple regression is 0.2724. So 27.24% of the variation in unit density can be explained by the variation of die diameter. The p-value of the t test for the significance of die diameter is 0.0087, which is less than 5%. There is enough evidence to conclude that die diameter affects unit density at the 5% level of significance. There is some lack of equality in the residuals and some departure from normality.